W9-CGU-495

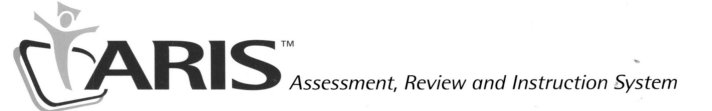
ARIS™ *Assessment, Review and Instruction System*

ONLINE STUDY & HOMEWORK MATERIALS

I M P O R T A N T : Following are instructions to access online resources to support your McGraw-Hill textbook

The URL associated with your text is:
http://www.mhhe.com/grr

Option 1: **ARIS LOGIN.** Your instructor may use **ARIS** as a homework and assessment tool. If so, you must register in order to ensure your assignments are recorded into your instructor's gradebook.

Option 2: If your instructor is **NOT** using **ARIS** as a homework and assessment tool, you are welcome to access the material on the site without registering. Simply go to the URL listed above. You are free to access these materials for your own self-study.

ARIS LOGIN. *To Register you need:*

1. **Section Code:** Provided by your instructor.

2. **Registration Code:** Provided in the gray scratch-off area below.

3. **URL:** Go to the URL listed at the top of this card and follow the directions for creating an ARIS account.

Scratch off for registration code

McGraw Hill Higher Education

Giambattista: College Physics, 2E
ISBN-13: 978-0-07-326274-1
ISBN-10: 0-07-326274-9

COLLEGE PHYSICS

second edition • VOLUME 2

Alan Giambattista
Cornell University

Betty McCarthy Richardson
Cornell University

Robert C. Richardson
Cornell University

Customized for Youngstown State University

McGraw Hill **Custom Publishing**

Boston   Burr Ridge, IL   Dubuque, IA   New York   San Francisco   St. Louis
Bangkok   Bogotá   Caracas   Lisbon   London   Madrid
Mexico City   Milan   New Delhi   Seoul   Singapore   Sydney   Taipei   Toronto

The McGraw-Hill Companies

COLLEGE PHYSICS
VOLUME 2
Customized for Youngstown State University

This book is a McGraw-Hill Custom Publishing textbook and contains select material from *College Physics*, Second Edition by Alan Giambattista, Betty McCarthy Richardson, and Robert C. Richardson. Copyright © 2007 by The McGraw-Hill Companies, Inc. Reprinted with permission of the publisher. Many custom published texts are modified versions or adaptations of our best-selling textbooks. Some adaptations are printed in black and white to keep prices at a minimum, while others are in color.

1 2 3 4 5 6 7 8 9 0 CDC CDC 0 9 8 7 6 5

ISBN-13: 978-0-07-327644-1
ISBN-10: 0-07-327644-8

Editor: Elaine Manke
Production Editor: Susan Culbertson
Cover Design: Fairfax Hutter
Printer/Binder: C-Doc Services, Inc.

About the Authors

Alan Giambattista grew up in Nutley, New Jersey. In his junior year at Brigham Young University he decided to pursue a physics major, after having explored math, music, and psychology. He did his graduate studies at Cornell University and has taught introductory college physics for over twenty years. When not found at the computer keyboard working on *College Physics*, he can often be found at the keyboard of a harpsichord or piano. He is a member of the Cayuga Chamber Orchestra and has given performances of the Bach harpsichord concerti at several regional Bach festivals. He met his wife Marion in a singing group and presently they live in an 1824 former parsonage surrounded by a dairy farm. Besides making music and taking care of the house, gardens, and fruit trees, they love to travel together.

Betty McCarthy Richardson was born and grew up in Marblehead, Massachusetts, and tried to avoid taking any science classes after eighth grade but managed to avoid only ninth grade science. After discovering that physics tells how things work, she decided to become a physicist. She attended Wellesley College and did graduate work at Duke University. While at Duke, Betty met and married fellow graduate student Bob Richardson and had two daughters, Jennifer and Pamela. Betty began teaching physics at Cornell in 1977. Many years later, she is still teaching the same course, Physics 101/102, an algebra-based course with all teaching done one-on-one in a Learning Center. From her own early experience of math and science avoidance, Betty has empathy with students who are apprehensive about learning physics. Betty's hobbies include collecting old children's books, reading, enjoying music, travel, and dining with royalty. A highlight for Betty during the Nobel Prize festivities in 1996 was being escorted to dinner at the Stockholm Royal Palace on the arm of King Carl XVI Gustav of Sweden and sitting between the king and the prime minister. Currently she is spending spare time enjoying grandsons Jasper (the 1-m child in Chapter 1), and Dashiell and Oliver, the twins of Chapter 12.

Robert C. Richardson was born in Washington, D.C., attended Virginia Polytechnic Institute, spent time in the United States Army, and then returned to graduate school in physics at Duke University where his thesis work involved NMR studies of solid helium-3. In the fall of 1966 Bob began work at Cornell University in the laboratory of David M. Lee. Their research goal was to observe the nuclear magnetic phase transition in solid ^{3}He that could be predicted from Richardson's thesis work with Professor Horst Meyer at Duke. In collaboration with graduate student Douglas D. Osheroff, they worked on cooling techniques and NMR instrumentation for studying low-temperature helium liquids and solids. In the fall of 1971, they made the accidental discovery that liquid ^{3}He undergoes a pairing transition similar to that of superconductors. The three were awarded the Nobel Prize for that work in 1996. Bob is currently the F. R. Newman Professor of Physics and the Vice Provost for Research. He has been active in teaching various introductory physics courses throughout his time at Cornell. In his spare time he enjoys gardening and photography.

In memory of Vada S. Giudice

Alan

In memory of our daughter Pamela,
and for Oliver, Dashiell, Jasper, Jennifer,
and Jim Merlis

Bob and Betty

Brief Contents

Contents

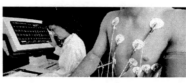

PART THREE
Electromagnetism

PART FOUR
Electromagnetic Waves and Optics

List of Selected Applications

Transportation

Sports

Everyday Life

Preface

College Physics is intended for a two-semester college course in introductory physics using algebra and trigonometry. Our main goals in writing this book are

- to present the basic concepts of physics that students need to know for later courses and future careers,
- to emphasize that physics is a tool for understanding the real world, and
- to teach transferable problem-solving skills that students can use throughout their lives.

We have kept these goals in mind while developing the main themes of the book.

NEW TO THIS EDITION

Although the fundamental philosophy of the book has not changed, detailed feedback from over 170 reviewers (many of whom used the first edition in the classroom) and 10 class tests have enabled us to fine-tune our approach to make the text even more user-friendly, conceptually based, and relevant for students. The second edition also has some added features to further facilitate student learning.

Review and Synthesis with MCAT Review®

Eight **Review and Synthesis** sections now appear throughout the text, following groups of related chapters. The *MCAT® Review* includes actual reading passages and questions written for the **Medical College Admission Test (MCAT)**. The *Review Exercises* are intended to serve as a bridge between textbook problems that are linked to a particular chapter and exam problems that are not. These exercises give students practice in formulating a problem-solving strategy without an external clue (section or chapter number) that indicates which concepts are involved. Many of the problems draw on material from more than one chapter to help the student integrate new concepts and skills with what has been learned previously.

Improved Organization of Chapters 2 through 4

There are some areas of innovative organization in *College Physics* (see pp. xv–xvi). Chapters 2–4 have been further improved for the second edition:

- Based on reviewer feedback, the introduction of forces in Chapter 2 was simplified. All material involving surface tension, buoyant forces, Coulomb's law, and electric fields was removed.
- Chapter 2 now has a larger number of quantitative examples and problems and has more examples that involve drawing free-body diagrams.
- Some reviewers felt that the treatment of vector addition was "too spread out" in the first edition. Sections 2.2–2.5 now provide a complete treatment of vector addition. The examples start with one-dimensional problems and then progress to two dimensions.
- *General* definitions of position, displacement, velocity, and acceleration—using vector diagrams—are now presented in Chapter 3. Reinforcing the vector nature of these quantities helps students avoid the common misconceptions that can arise when they are defined first in one dimension and then redefined with different notation in two dimensions. Once again, the examples that illustrate each concept start with the simplest one dimensional applications and then progress to two dimensions within each section.

"The new chapters 2–4 are an improvement over their versions in the 1ˢᵗ edition of G/R/R. . . . My bottom line evaluation . . . is that a good book has been made even better."

Dr. Carl Covatto, Arizona State University

Revision of Chapter 6

Chapter 6 was streamlined to give a clearer picture of the idea of energy conservation. Potential energy is introduced earlier in the chapter, using a simplified discussion of the connection between the work done by a conservative force and the change in potential energy associated with that force.

Revision of Chapter 15

Chapter 15 was revised to simplify the presentation of entropy and to eliminate nonstandard terminology. The first law of thermodynamics is now written $\Delta U = Q + W$, consistent with the use of W in Chapter 6 to represent the work done *on* a system. This is the same sign convention used in most chemistry classes and is increasingly common in high school physics classes now that the Advanced Placement Physics B exam uses it.

Revisions to Problem Sets

Great care was taken by both the authors and the contributors to the second edition to revise the end-of-chapter problems. About 25% are completely new. The problems now have more variety in level: in particular, we increased the number of easier problems that help students gain confidence and reinforce new skills before they tackle more challenging problems.

Revised Art Program

The majority of reviewers of the first edition praised its innovative art program. However, reviewers also commented that some of the showcase illustrations were "distracting" and "too large." In response, we assembled a panel of experienced instructors to advise us on the illustrations and photos. The panel helped us identify the most useful showcase illustrations to retain for the second edition. They advised us on how to revise illustrations to make them clearer and more useful and on where to add graphs, diagrams, simpler sketches, and free-body diagrams to enhance the text discussions and examples. The second edition increases the emphasis on simpler sketches and free-body diagrams similar to those that students should draw on their own homework or exams.

COMPREHENSIVE COVERAGE

Students should be able to get the whole story from the book. The first edition text was tested in our self-paced course, where students must rely on the textbook as their primary learning resource. Nonetheless, completeness and clarity are equally advantageous when the book is used in a more traditional classroom setting. *College Physics* frees the instructor from having to try to "cover" everything. The instructor can then tailor class time to more important student needs—reinforcing difficult concepts, working through example problems, engaging the students in cooperative learning activities, describing applications, or presenting demonstrations.

INTEGRATING CONCEPTUAL PHYSICS INTO A QUANTITATIVE COURSE

"Conceptual ideas are important, ideas must be motivated, physics should be integrated, a coherent problem-solving approach should be developed. I'm not sure other books are as explicit in these goals, or achieve them as well as Giambattista, Richardson, and Richardson."

Dr. Michael G. Strauss,
University of Oklahoma

Some students approach introductory physics with the idea that physics is just the memorization of a long list of equations and the ability to plug numbers into those equations. We want to help students see that a relatively small number of basic physics concepts are applied to a wide variety of situations. Physics education research has shown that students do not automatically acquire conceptual understanding; the concepts must be explained and the students given a chance to grapple with them. Our presentation, based on years of teaching this course, blends conceptual understanding with analytical skills. The **Conceptual Examples** and **Conceptual Practice Problems** in the text and a variety of Conceptual and Multiple-Choice Questions at the end of each chapter give students a chance to check and to enhance their conceptual understanding.

INTRODUCING CONCEPTS INTUITIVELY

We introduce key concepts and quantities in an informal way by establishing why the quantity is needed, why it is useful, and why it needs a precise definition. Then we make a transition from the informal, intuitive idea to a formal definition and name. Concepts motivated in this way are easier for students to grasp and remember than are concepts introduced by seemingly arbitrary, formal definitions.

For example, in Chapter 8, the idea of rotational inertia emerges in a natural way from the concept of rotational kinetic energy. Students can understand that a rotating rigid body has kinetic energy due to the motion of its particles. We discuss why it is useful to be able to write this kinetic energy in terms of a single quantity common to all the particles (the angular speed), rather than as a sum involving particles with many different speeds. When students understand why rotational inertia is defined the way it is, they are better prepared to move on to the concepts of torque and angular momentum.

We avoid presenting definitions or formulas without any motivation. When an equation is not derived in the text, we at least describe where the equation comes from or give a plausibility argument. For example, Section 9.9 introduces Poiseuille's law with two identical pipes in series to show why the volume flow rate must be proportional to the pressure drop per unit length. Then we discuss why $\Delta V/\Delta t$ is proportional to the fourth power of the radius (rather than to r^2, as it would be for an ideal fluid).

Similarly, we have found that the definitions of the displacement and velocity vectors seem arbitrary and counterintuitive to students if introduced without any motivation. Therefore, we precede any discussion of kinematic quantities with an introduction to Newton's laws, so students know that forces determine how the state of motion of an object changes. Then, when we define the kinematic quantities to give a precise definition of acceleration, we can apply Newton's second law quantitatively to see how forces affect the motion. We give particular attention to laying the groundwork for a concept when its name is a common English word such as *velocity* or *work*.

WRITTEN IN CLEAR AND FRIENDLY STYLE

We have kept the writing down-to-earth and conversational in tone—the kind of language an experienced teacher uses when sitting at a table working one-on-one with a student. We hope students will find the book pleasant to read, informative, and accurate without seeming threatening, and filled with analogies that make abstract concepts easier to grasp. We want students to feel confident that they can learn by studying the textbook.

While learning correct physics terminology is essential, we avoid all *unnecessary* jargon—terminology that just gets in the way of the student's understanding. For example, we never use the term *centripetal force*, since its use sometimes leads students to add a spurious "centripetal force" to their free-body diagrams. Likewise, we use *radial component of acceleration* because it is less likely to introduce or reinforce misconceptions than *centripetal acceleration*.

INNOVATIVE ORGANIZATION

There are a few places where, for pedagogical reasons, the organization of our text differs from that of most textbooks. The most significant reorganization is in the treatment of forces and motion. In *College Physics*, the central theme of Chapters 2–4 is *force*. Kinematics is introduced as a tool to understand how forces affect motion. Overall, we spend less time on kinematics and more time on forces than other texts do. This approach has the following advantages:

- The first few chapters in any text set up student expectations that are hard to change later. If the course starts with a series of definitions of the kinematic quantities, with no explanation of *why* we are interested in those quantities, students may see physics as a series of equations to memorize and manipulate.

"I think chapter 8 is particularly well-written. Rotational motion, magnetism, and ac circuits spring to mind as the most notoriously difficult subjects to teach in this course. The authors have chosen a number of excellent biomechanical examples in chapter 8 and this chapter's presentation alone might persuade some lecturers to switch texts."

Dr. Nelson E. Bickers,
University of Southern
California

"I strongly support the idea of having the chapter on Newton's law before the chapter on kinematics. Some other books have the kinematics chapter before the Newton's law chapter. Newton's law is the highlight of my course, and it makes more sense to me to teach that a net external force causes acceleration before explaining that acceleration changes the velocity. From this viewpoint this book works better than other physics textbooks that I used previously."

Dr. Sanichiro Yoshida,
Southeastern Louisiana
University

"At this point, I have had students for both semesters of college physics. I have commented to them that G/R/R uses a nonstandard approach to physics by doing forces first. Some of them are puzzled by the standard approach of kinematics first; one even said 'how can you do anything without forces?' I agree, the authors and McGraw-Hill should be commended for their willingness to do something different."

Dr. Carl Covatto,
Arizona State University

- We explain to students that the kinematic concepts help us understand the effect that a net force has on the motion of an object. Newton's second law is presented as the key reason why we need a precise definition of acceleration. Defining acceleration requires precise definitions of displacement and velocity. If the definitions of these quantities are imprecise, we cannot hope to understand how forces affect the motion of an object.

- Learning constant-acceleration kinematics before forces may suggest to students that physics is not connected to the real world. If they are told that objects all fall with the same acceleration—which they know from experience to be false—they learn not to trust the principles they're learning. With an understanding of forces and Newton's laws, *College Physics* shows that constant acceleration is an approximation and explains how to judge when that approximation is reasonable.

- We use correct vector notation, terminology, and methods from the very beginning. Even in a one-dimensional problem, displacements, velocities, and accelerations are always treated as vector quantities. For example, we carefully distinguish components from magnitudes by writing "$v_x = -5$ m/s" and never "$v = -5$ m/s," even if the object moves only along the x-axis. Several professors, who used our first edition in place of a previous textbook, reported a reduction in the number of students struggling with vector components.

- We begin in Chapter 2 with Newton's laws of motion so the students can build a solid conceptual framework in simpler situations before the mathematics gets more complex. If forces were not introduced until Chapter 4, the students would have much less time to overcome conceptual difficulties associated with Newton's laws and would have much less practice applying them.

ACCURACY ASSURANCE

The authors and the publisher acknowledge the fact that inaccuracies can be a source of frustration for both the instructor and students. Therefore, throughout the writing and production of this edition, we have worked diligently to eliminate errors and inaccuracies. Ten professors performed independent accuracy checks of textual examples, practice problems, and solutions and worked the new and revised end-of-chapter questions and problems. Bill Fellers of Fellers Math & Science also conducted an independent accuracy check and worked all end-of-chapter questions and problems in the final draft of the manuscript. He then coordinated the resolution of discrepancies between accuracy checks, ensuring the accuracy of the text, the end-of-book answers, and the solutions manuals. Corrections were then made to the manuscript before it was typeset.

The page proofs of the text were double-proofread against the manuscript to ensure the correction of any errors introduced when the manuscript was typeset. The textual examples, practice problems and solutions, end-of-chapter questions and problems, and problem answers were accuracy checked by Fellers Math & Science again at the page proof stage after the manuscript was typeset. This last round of corrections was then cross-checked against the solutions manuals.

PROVIDING STUDENTS WITH THE TOOLS THEY NEED

Problem-Solving Approach

Problem-solving skills are central to an introductory physics course. We illustrate these skills in the example problems. Lists of problem-solving strategies are sometimes useful; we provide such strategies when appropriate. However, the most elusive skills—perhaps the most important ones—are subtle points that defy being put into a neat list. To develop real problem-solving expertise, students must learn how to think critically and analytically. Problem solving is a multidimensional, complex process; an algorithmic approach is not adequate to instill real problem-solving skills.

Strategy   We begin each example with a discussion—in language that the students can understand—of the *strategy* to be used in solving the problem. The strategy illustrates the kind of analytical thinking students must do when attacking a problem: How do I decide what approach to use? What laws of physics apply to the problem and which of them are *useful* in this solution? What clues are given in the statement of the question? What information is implied rather than stated outright? If there are several valid approaches, how do I determine which is the most efficient? What assumptions can I make? What kind of sketch or graph might help me solve the problem? Is a simplification or approximation called for? If so, how can I tell if the simplification is valid? Can I make a preliminary estimate of the answer? Only after considering these questions can the student effectively solve the problem.

Solution   Next comes the detailed *solution* to the problem. Explanations are intermingled with equations and step-by-step calculations to help the student understand the approach used to solve the problem. We want the student to be able to follow the mathematics without wondering, "Where did that come from?"

Discussion   The numerical or algebraic answer is not the end of the problem; our examples end with a *discussion*. Students must learn how to determine whether their answer is consistent and reasonable by checking the order of magnitude of the answer, comparing the answer to a preliminary estimate, verifying the units, and doing an independent calculation when more than one approach is feasible. When there are several different approaches, the discussion looks at the advantages and disadvantages of each approach. We also discuss the implications of the answer—what can we learn from it? We look at special cases and look at "what if" scenarios. The discussion sometimes generalizes the problem-solving techniques used in the solution.

Practice Problem   After each Example, a Practice Problem gives students a chance to gain experience using the same physics principles and problem-solving tools. By comparing their answers to those provided at the end of each chapter, they can gauge their understanding and decide whether to move on to the next section.

Our many years of experience in teaching the college physics course in a one-on-one setting has enabled us to anticipate where we can expect students to have difficulty. In addition to the consistent problem-solving approach, we offer several other means of assistance to the student throughout the text. A boxed problem-solving strategy gives detailed information on solving a particular type of problem, while an icon 🔲 for problem-solving tips draws attention to techniques that can be used in a variety of contexts. A hint in a worked example or end-of-chapter problem provides a clue on what approach to use or what simplification to make. A warning icon 🔳 emphasizes an explanation that clarifies a possible point of confusion or a common student misconception.

An important problem-solving skill that many students lack is the ability to extract information from a graph or to sketch a graph without plotting individual data points. Graphs often help students visualize physical relationships more clearly than they can do with algebra alone. We emphasize the use of graphs and sketches in the text, in worked examples, and in the problems.

Using Approximation, Estimation, and Proportional Reasoning

College Physics is forthright about the constant use of simplified models and approximations in solving physics problems. One of the most difficult aspects of problem solving that students need to learn is that some kind of simplified model or approximation is usually required. We discuss how to know when it is reasonable to ignore friction or air resistance, treat *g* as constant, ignore viscosity, treat a charged object as a point charge, or ignore diffraction. A brief discussion of air resistance and terminal velocity in Chapter 4 enables us to discuss when it is reasonable to ignore air resistance—and also to show students that physics can account for these other effects.

Some Examples and Problems require the student to make an estimate—a useful skill both in physics problem solving and in many other fields. Similarly, we teach proportional reasoning as not only an elegant shortcut but also as a means to understanding

"The major strength of this text is its approach, which makes students think out the problems, rather than always relying on a formula to get an answer. The way the authors encourage students to investigate whether the answer makes sense, and compare the magnitude of the answer with common sense is good also."

Dr. Jose D'Arruda, University of North Carolina, Pembroke

"I understood the math, mostly because it was worked out step-by-step, which I like."

Student, Bradley University

"The math was really clear. I was impressed with how easy the math and steps involved were to understand."

Student, Bradley University

"The 'Strategy & Discussion' in each example were extremely helpful in understanding the ideas."

Student, Houston Community College

"The warning signs about many of the misconceptions, traps, and common mistakes is a very helpful and novel idea. Those of us who have taught undergraduate students in service courses have spent considerable time on these. It is good to see them in a book."

Dr. H.R. Chandrasekhar, University of Missouri, Columbia

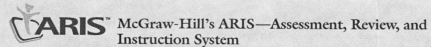

patterns. We frequently use percentages and ratios to give students practice in using and understanding them.

Showcasing an Innovative Art Program

To help show that physics is more than a collection of principles that explain a set of contrived problems, in every chapter we have developed several innovative **Showcase Illustrations** to bring to life the connections between physics concepts and the complex ways in which they are applied. We believe these illustrations, with subjects ranging from three-dimensional views of electric field lines to the biomechanics of the human body and from representations of waves to the distribution of electricity in the home, will help students see the power and beauty of physics.

Helping Students See the Relevance of Physics in Their Lives

Students in an introductory college physics course have a wide range of backgrounds and interests. We stimulate interest in physics by relating the principles to applications relevant to students' lives and in line with their interests. The text, examples, and end-of-chapter problems draw from the everyday world; from familiar technological applications; and from other fields such as biology, medicine, archaeology, astronomy, sports, environmental science, and geophysics. (Applications in the text are marked with an icon in the margin 🔬 for applications in the biological or medical sciences and 📞 for other applications).

The **Physics at Home** experiments give students an opportunity to explore and see physics principles operate in their everyday lives. These activities are chosen for their simplicity and for the effective demonstration of physics principles.

Each **Chapter Opener** includes a photo and vignette, designed to capture student interest and maintain it through the chapter. The vignette describes the situation shown in the photo and asks the student to consider the relevant physics. A reduced version of the chapter opener photo marks where the question from the vignette is answered within the chapter.

ADDITIONAL RESOURCES FOR INSTRUCTORS AND STUDENTS

🎓ARIS™ McGraw-Hill's ARIS—Assessment, Review, and Instruction System

McGraw-Hill's ARIS for *College Physics* is a complete, online electronic homework and course management system, designed for greater ease of use than any other system available. Free for instructor use upon the adoption of any

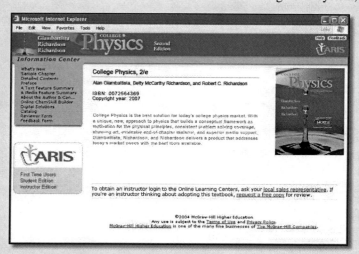

McGraw-Hill physics text, instructors can create course materials and assignments and share them with colleagues with a few clicks of the mouse. (ARIS is also free for students with the purchase of a new *College Physics* textbook from McGraw-Hill.) All PowerPoint lectures, assignments, quizzes, and interactives are directly tied to text-specific materials in *College Physics*, but instructors can also edit questions and algorithms, import their own content, and create announcements and due dates for assignments. ARIS has automatic grading and reporting of easy-to-assign algorithmically generated homework, quizzing, and testing. All student activity within McGraw-Hill's ARIS is automatically recorded and available to the instructor through a fully integrated grade book that can be downloaded to Excel.

Physics Interactives

McGraw-Hill is proud to bring you an assortment of outstanding Interactives like no other. These Interactives offer a fresh and dynamic method to teach the physics basics by providing students with activities that are completely accurate and work with real data. The Interactives allow students to manipulate parameters and gain a better understanding of the more difficult physics concepts by watching the effect of these manipulations. Each interactive includes:

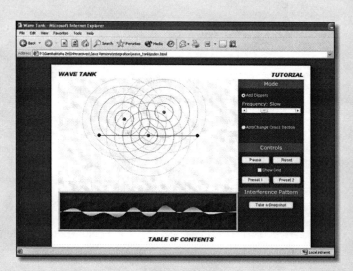

- Analysis tool (interactive model)
- Tutorial describing its function
- Content describing its principle themes

Students can easily jump between the Tutorial and the Analysis Tool with just the click of the mouse. Instructor's can assign the Interactives along with accompanying quizzes within ARIS. An instructor's guide for each Interactive with a complete overview of the content and navigational tools, a quick demonstration description, further study with the textbook, and suggested end-of-chapter follow-up questions is also provided as an instructor's resource in ARIS.

Digital Content Manager CD

Electronic art at your fingertips! This cross-platform DVD/CD ROM provides you with visuals from the text in multiple formats. You can easily create customized classroom presentations, visually based tests and quizzes, dynamic content for a course website, or attractive printed support materials. Available on the DVD or CD are the following resources in digital formats. The jpeg items have also been placed into PowerPoint files for ease of use.

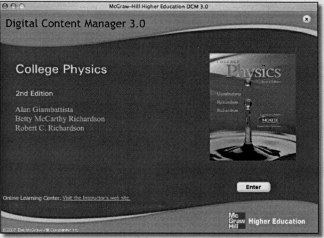

- **Active Art Library**: These key art pieces—formatted as PowerPoint slides—allow you to illustrate difficult concepts in a step-by-step manner. The artwork is broken into small, incremental pieces, so you can incorporate the illustrations into your lecture in whatever sequence or format you desire.
- **Art and Photo Library**: Full-color digital files of all of the illustrations and many of the photos in the text can be readily incorporated into lecture presentations, exams, or custom-made classroom materials.
- **Worked Example Library, Table Library, and Numbered Equations Library**: Access the worked examples, tables, and equations from the text in electronic format for inclusion in your classroom resources.
- **Interactive Animations Library**: Flash files of the Physics Interactives described above are included so that you can easily make use of the Interactives in a lecture or classroom setting.
- **Lecture Outlines**: Lecture notes, incorporating illustrations and animated images, have been written to the second edition text. They are provided in PowerPoint format so that you may use these lectures as written or customize them to fit your lecture.

Classroom Performance System

The Classroom Performance System (CPS) by eInstruction brings interactivity into the classroom or lecture hall. It is a wireless response system that gives the instructor and students immediate feedback from the entire class. The wireless response pads are essentially remotes that are easy to use and engage students. CPS allows instructors to motivate student preparation, interactivity and active learning. Instructors receive immediate feedback to gauge which concepts students understand. Questions covering the content of the *College Physics* text (formatted in both CPS eInstruction and PowerPoint) are available on ARIS and the Instructor's Testing and Resource CD-ROM for *College Physics*.

ALEKS®

Help students master the math skills needed to understand difficult physics problems. ALEKS® [Assessment and LEarning in Knowledge Spaces] is an artificial intelligence–based system for individualized math learning available via the World Wide Web.

ALEKS® is

- A robust course management system. It tells you exactly what your students know and don't know.
- Focused and efficient. It enables students to quickly master the math needed for college physics.
- Artificial intelligence. It totally individualizes assessment and learning.
- Customizable. Click on or off each course topic.
- Web based. Use a standard browser for easy Internet access.
- Inexpensive. There are no setup fees or site license fees.

ALEKS® is a registered trademark of ALEKS Corporation.

Instructor's Testing and Resource CD-ROM

This cross-platform CD-ROM contains the *Test Bank* and *The Instructor's Resource Guide* (with Solutions manual, demonstrations, physics education research ideas, and just-in-time-teaching suggestions), the end-of-chapter problems from the text, and multiple-choice quizzes from ARIS, in both Word and PDF formats. The Test Bank questions are also found in the included test-generating software. The Word files for problems and quizzes can be used in combination with the testing software or independently. The CD-ROM also includes questions for use with personal response systems (in CPS or PowerPoint formats) and Instructor's Guides for the physics interactives.

Instructor's Resource Guide

The *Instructor's Resource Guide* includes many unique assets for instructors, such as demonstrations, suggested reform ideas from physics education research, and ideas for incorporating just-in-time teaching techniques. It also includes answers to the end-of-chapter conceptual questions and complete, worked-out solutions for all the end-of-chapter problems from the text.

Transparencies

This boxed set includes nearly 300 full-color acetates featuring images from the text. The images have been modified to ensure maximum readability in both small and large classroom settings.

Test Bank

The *College Physics* Test Bank is also available in a printed version. The Test Bank includes over 2000 test questions in multiple-choice format at a variety of difficulty levels.

Student Solutions Manual

The *Student Solutions Manual* contains complete worked-out solutions to selected end-of-chapter problems, selected Review and Synthesis problems, and the MCAT Review Exercises from the text. The solutions in this manual follow the problem-solving strategy outlined in the text's examples and also guide students in creating diagrams for their own solutions.

For more information, contact a McGraw-Hill customer service representative at (800) 338–3987, or by email at www.mhhe.com. To locate your sales representative, go to www.mhhe.com for Find My Sales Rep.

To the Student

HOW TO SUCCEED IN YOUR PHYSICS CLASS

It's true—how much you get out of your studies depends on how much you put in. Success in a physics class requires:

- Commitment of time and perseverance
- Knowing and motivating yourself
- Getting organized
- Managing your time

This section will help you learn how to be effective in these areas, as well as offer guidance in:

- Getting the most out of your lecture
- Finding extra help when you need it
- Getting the most out of your textbook
- How to study for an exam

Commitment of Time and Perseverance

Learning and mastering takes time and patience. Nothing worthwhile comes easily. Be committed to your studies and you will reap the benefits in the long run. A regular, sustained effort is much more effective than sporadic bouts of cramming.

Knowing and Motivating Yourself

What kind of learner are you? When are you most productive? Know yourself and your limits, and work within them. Know how to motivate yourself to give your all to your studies and achieve your goals.

There are many types of learners, and no right or wrong way of learning. Which category do you fall into?

- **Visual learner** You respond best to "seeing" processes and information. Focus on text illustrations and graphs. Use course handouts and the animations on the course and text websites to help you. Draw diagrams in your notes to illustrate concepts.
- **Auditory learner** You work best by listening to—and possibly recording—the lecture and by talking information through with a study partner.
- **Tactile/Kinesthetic Learner** You learn best by being "hands on." You'll benefit by applying what you've learned during lab time. Writing and drawing are physical activities, so don't neglect taking notes on your reading and the lecture to explain the content in your own words. Try pacing while you read the text. Stand up and write on a chalkboard during discussions in your study group.

Identify your own personal preferences for learning and seek out the resources that will best help you with your studies. Also remember, even though you have a preferred style of learning, most learners benefit when they engage in all styles of learning.

Getting Organized

It's simple, yet it's fundamental. It seems the more organized you are, the easier things come. Take the time before your course begins to analyze your life and your study habits. Get organized now and you'll find you have a little more time—and a lot less stress.

- **Find a calendar system that works for you**. The best kind is one that you can take with you everywhere. To be truly organized, you should integrate all aspects of your life into this one calendar—school, work, and leisure. Some people also find it helpful to have an additional monthly calendar posted by their desk for "at a

A good rule of thumb is to allow 2 hours of study time for every hour you spend in lecture. For instance, a 3-hour lecture deserves 6 hours of study time per week. If you commit to studying for this course daily, you're investing a little less than one hour per day, including the weekend.

Begin each of the tasks assigned in your course with the goal of understanding the material. Simply completing the assignment does not mean that learning has taken place. Your fellow students, your instructor, and this textbook can all be important resources in broadening your knowledge.

Add extra "padding" into your personal deadlines. If you have a report due on Friday, set a goal for yourself to have it done on Wednesday. Then, take time on Thursday to look over your project with a fresh eye. Make any corrections or enhancements and have it ready to turn in on Friday.

glance" dates and to have a visual planner. If you do this, be sure you are consistently synchronizing both calendars so as not to miss anything. *More tips for organizing your calendar can be found in the time management discussion below.*

- By the same token, **keep everything for your course or courses in one place—** and at your fingertips. A three-ring binder works well because it allows you to add or organize handouts and notes from class in any order you prefer. Incorporating your own custom tabs helps you flip to exactly what you need at a moment's notice.
- **Find your space**. Find a place that helps you be organized and focused. If it's your desk in your dorm room or in your home, keep it clean. Clutter adds confusion and stress and wastes time. Perhaps your "space" is at the library. If that's the case, keep a backpack or bag that's fully stocked with what you might need—your text, binder or notes, pens, highlighters, Post-its, phone numbers of study partners. [*Hint:* A good place to keep phone numbers is in your "one place for everything calendar."]

Managing Your Time

Managing your time is the single most important thing you can do to help yourself, but it's probably one of the most difficult tasks to successfully master.

In college, you are expected to work much harder and to learn much more than you ever have before. To be successful you need to invest in your education with a commitment of time. We all lead busy lives, but we all make choices as to how we spend our time. Choose wisely.

- **Know yourself and when you'll be able to study most efficiently**. When are you most productive? Are you a night owl? Or an early bird? Plan to study when you are most alert and can have uninterrupted segments. This could include a quick 5-minute review before class or a one-hour problem-solving study session with a friend.
- **Create a set daily study time for yourself**. Having a set schedule helps you commit to studying and helps you plan instead of cram. Find—and use—a planner that is small enough that you can take it with you everywhere. This may be a simple paper calendar or an electronic version. They all work on the same premise: **organize *all* of your activities in one place**.
- **Schedule study time using shorter, focused blocks with small breaks**. Doing this offers two benefits: (1) You will be less fatigued and gain more from your effort and (2) Studying will seem less overwhelming, and you will be less likely to procrastinate.
- **Plan time for leisure, friends, exercise, and sleep**. Studying should be your main focus, but you need to balance your time—and your life.
- **Log your homework deadlines and exam dates** in your personal calendar.
- Try to **complete tasks ahead of schedule**. This will give you a chance to carefully review your work before it is due. You'll feel less stressed in the end.
- **Know where help can be found**. At the beginning of the semester, find your instructor's office hours, your lab partner's contact information, and the "Help Desk" or Learning Resource Center if your course offers one. Make use of all of the support systems that your college or university has to offer. Ask questions both in class and during your instructor's office hours. Don't be shy—your instructor is there to help you learn.
- **Prioritize!** In your calendar or planner, highlight or number key projects; do them first, and then cross them off when you've completed them. Give yourself a pat on the back for getting them done!
- **Review your calendar and reprioritize *daily***.
- **Resist distractions by setting and sticking to a designated study time**.
- **Multitask when possible**. You may find a lot of extra time you didn't think you had. Review material in your head or think about how to tackle a tough problem while walking to class or doing laundry.

Plan to study and plan for leisure. Being well balanced will help you focus when it is time to study.

Try combining social time with studying in a group, or social time with mealtime or exercise. Being a good student doesn't mean you have to be a hermit. It does mean you need to know how to smartly budget your time.

Getting the Most Out of Lectures

Your instructors want you to succeed. They put a lot of effort into preparing their lectures and other materials designed to help you learn. Attending class is one of the simplest, most valuable things you can do to help yourself. But it doesn't end there—getting the most out of your lectures means being organized. Here's how:

Prepare Before You Go to Class Study the text on the lecture topic *before* attending class. Familiarizing yourself with the material gives you the ability to take notes selectively rather than scrambling to write everything down. You'll be able to absorb more of the subtleties and difficult points from the lecture. You may also develop some good questions to ask your instructor.

Don't feel overwhelmed by this task. Spend time the night before class gaining a general overview of the topics for the next lecture using your syllabus. If your schedule does not allow this, plan to arrive at class 5–15 minutes before lecture. Bring your text with you and skim the chapter before lecture begins.

Don't try to read an entire chapter in one sitting; study one or two sections at a time. It's difficult to maintain your concentration in a long session with so many new concepts and skills to learn.

Be a Good Listener Most people think they are good listeners, but few really are. Are you?

Obvious, but important points to remember:

- You can't listen if you are talking.
- You aren't listening if you are daydreaming or constantly distracted by other concerns.
- Listening and comprehending are two different things. Listen carefully in class. The language of science is precise; be sure you understand your instructor. If you don't understand something your instructor is saying, ask a question or jot a note and visit the instructor during office hours. You are likely doing others a favor when you ask questions because there are probably others in the class who have the same questions.

Take Good Notes

- Use a standard size notebook, or better yet, a three-ring binder with loose leaf notepaper. The binder will allow you to organize and integrate your notes and handouts, integrate easy-to-reference tabs, and the like.
- Color-code your notes. Use one color of ink pen to take your initial notes. You can annotate later using a pencil, which can be erased if need be.
- Start a new page with each lecture or note-taking session.
- Label each page with the date and a heading for each day.
- Focus on main points and try to use an outline format to take notes to capture key ideas and organize sub-points.

- Take your text to lecture, and keep it open to the topics being discussed. You can also take brief notes in your textbook margin or reference textbook pages in your notebook to help you study later.
- Review and edit your notes shortly after class—within 24 hours—to make sure they make sense and that you've recorded core thoughts. You may also want to compare your notes with a study partner later to make sure neither of you have missed anything.
- This is a very IMPORTANT point: *You can and should also add notes from your reading of the textbook.*

Get a Study Partner Find a few study partners and get together regularly. Four or five study partners to a group is a good number. Too many students make the group unwieldy, but you want enough students to ensure the group can meet even if one or two people can't make it. Having study partners has many benefits. First, they can help you keep your commitment to this class. By having set study dates, you can combine study and social time, and maybe even make it fun! In addition, you now have several minds to help digest the information from the lecture and the text:

- Talk through concepts and go over the difficulties you may be having. Take turns explaining things to each other. You learn a tremendous amount when you teach someone else.
- Compare your notes and solutions to the Practice Problems.
- Try a new approach to a problem or look at the problem from the perspective of your partner. There are often many ways to do the same problem. You can benefit from the insights of others—and they from you—but resist the temptation to simply copy solutions. You need to learn how to solve the problem yourself.
- Quiz each other and discuss some of the Conceptual Questions from the end of the chapter.
- Don't take advantage of your study partner by skipping class or skipping study dates. You obviously won't have a study partner—or a friend—much longer if it's not a mutually beneficial arrangement!

Getting the Most Out of Your Textbook

We hope that you enjoy your physics course using this text. While studying physics does require hard work, we have tried to remove the obstacles that sometimes make introductory physics unnecessarily difficult. We have also tried to reveal the beauty inherent in the principles of physics and how these principles are manifest all around you.

In our years of teaching experience, we have found that studying physics is a skill that must be learned. It's much more effective to *study* a physics textbook, which involves active participation on your part, than to read through passively. Even though active study takes more time initially, in the long run it will save you time; you learn more in one active study session than in three or four superficial readings.

As you study, take particular note of the following elements:

Consider the **chapter opener**. It will help you make the connection between the physics you are about to study and how it affects the world around you. Each chapter opener includes a photo and vignette designed to pique your interest in the chapter. The vignette describes the situation shown in the photo and asks you to consider the relevant physics. The question is then answered within the chapter. Look for the reduced opener photo on the referenced page.

Evaluate the **Concepts and Skills to Review** on the first page of each chapter. It lists important material from previous chapters that you should understand before you start reading. If you have problems recalling any of the concepts, you can revisit the sections referenced in the list.

Study the figures and graphs carefully. **Showcase illustrations** and more straightforward **diagrammatic illustrations** are used in combination throughout the text to help you grasp concepts. Showcase illustrations help you visualize the most difficult concepts. When looking at graphs, try to see the wealth of information displayed. Ask yourself about the physical meaning of the slope, the area under the curve, the overall shape of the graph, the vertical and horizontal intercepts, and any maxima and minima.

Chapter
24
Optical Instruments

he Hubble Space Telescope, orbiting the Earth at an altitude of about 600 km, was launched in 1990 by the crew of the space shuttle *Discovery*. What is the advantage of having a telescope in space when there are telescopes on Earth with larger light-gathering capabilities? What justifies the cost of two billion dollars to place this 12.5-ton instrument into orbit? (See p. 898 for the answer.)

Concepts & Skills to Review

- translational equilibrium (Section 2.3)
- uniform circular motion and circular orbits (Sections 5.1 and 5.4)
- angular acceleration (Section 5.6)
- conservation of energy (Section 6.1)
- center of mass and its motion (Sections 7.5 and 7.6)

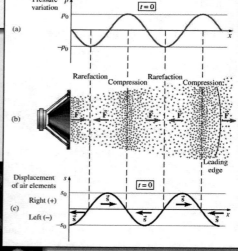

Various **Reinforcement Notes** appear in the margin to emphasize the important points in the text.

Displacement: final position vector minus initial position vector

⬤ Reminder: the symbol Δ stands for *the change in*. If the initial value of a quantity Q is Q_i and the final value is Q_f, then $\Delta Q = Q_f - Q_i$. ΔQ is read "delta Q."

Once the train's engine is repaired and it goes on its way, we might want to describe its motion. At 3:14 P.M., it leaves its initial position, 3 km east of the origin (Fig. 3.2a). At 3:56 P.M., the train is 26 km west of the origin, which is 29 km to the west of its initial position. **Displacement** is defined as the change of the position vector—the final position vector minus the initial position vector. Displacement is written $\Delta\vec{r}$ where the symbol Δ (the uppercase Greek letter delta) means *the change in* the quantity that follows. If the initial and final position vectors are $\vec{r}_i$ and $\vec{r}_f$, then

Definition of displacement:

$$\Delta\vec{r} = \vec{r}_f - \vec{r}_i \qquad (3\text{-}1)$$

Important **Equations** are numbered for easier reference. Equations that correspond to important laws are boxed for quick identification.

Statements of important physics **Rules and Laws** are boxed to highlight the most important and central concepts.

Newton's First Law of Motion

An object's velocity does not change if and only if the net force acting on the object is zero.

Problem-Solving Strategy for Newton's Second Law

- Decide what objects will have Newton's second law applied to them.
- Identify all the *external* forces acting on that object.
- Draw a free-body diagram to show all the forces acting on the object.
- Choose a coordinate system. If the direction of the net force is known, choose axes so that the net force (and the acceleration) are along one of the axes.
- Find the net force by adding the forces as vectors.
- Use Newton's second law to relate the net force to the acceleration.
- Relate the acceleration to the change in the velocity vector during a time interval of interest.

Boxed **Problem-Solving Strategies** give detailed information on solving a particular type of problem. These are supplied for the most fundamental physical rules and laws.

A **warning note** describes possible points of confusion or any common misconceptions that may apply to a particular concept.

A **problem-solving tip** will guide you in applying problem-solving techniques.

Chapter 1   Introduction

Therefore $C \propto r$. If the radius doubles, the circumference also doubles. The area of a circle is proportional to the *square* of the radius ($A = \pi r^2$, so $A \propto r^2$). The area must increase by the same factor as the radius *squared*, so if the radius doubles, the area increases by a factor of $2^2 = 4$.

... 1.1

... of Increasing Radius on the Volume of a Sphere

... sphere is given by the equation
$$V = \tfrac{4}{3}\pi r^3$$
where V is the volume and r is the radius of the sphere. If the radius of the sphere is increased by a factor of 3, by what factor does the volume of the sphere change?

Strategy   The problem gives us the ratio of the new radius and the old radius:
$$\frac{r_2}{r_1} = 3$$
The subscripts help us keep track of which sphere's volume and radius we mean; the radius of the original sphere is r_1 and the radius of the new sphere is r_2. Since $\tfrac{4}{3}$ and π are constants, we can work in terms of proportions.

Solution   The volume of a sphere is proportional to the cube of its radius:
$$V \propto r^3$$
Since the radius increased by a factor of three, and volume is proportional to the cube of the radius, the new volume should be bigger by a factor of $3^3 = 27$.

Discussion   A slight variation on the solution is to write out the proportionality in terms of ratios of the corresponding sides of the two equations:
$$\frac{V_2}{V_1} = \frac{\tfrac{4}{3}\pi r_2^3}{\tfrac{4}{3}\pi r_1^3} = \left(\frac{r_2}{r_1}\right)^3$$
Substituting the ratio of r_2 to r_1 yields
$$\frac{V_2}{V_1} = 3^3 = 27$$
which says that V_2 is 27 times V_1.

Practice Problem 1.1   **Power Dissipated by a Lightbulb**

The electrical power P dissipated by a lightbulb of resistance R is $P = V^2/R$, where V represents the line voltage. During a brownout, the line voltage is 10.0% less than its normal value. How much power is drawn by a lightbulb during the brownout if it normally draws 100.0 watts? Assume that the resistance does not change.

There are not enough letters in the alphabet to assign a unique letter to each quantity. The same letter V can represent volume in one context and voltage in another. Avoid attempting to solve problems by picking equations that seem to have the correct letters. A skilled problem-solver understands *specifically* what quantity each symbol in a particular equation represents, can specify correct units for each quantity, and understands the situations to which the equation applies.

Learn how to use the button on your calculator (usually labeled EE) to enter a number in scientific notation. To enter 1.2×10^8, press 1.2, EE, 8.

1.4   SCIENTIFIC NOTATION AND SIGNIFICANT FIGURES

In physics, we deal with some numbers that are very small and others that are very large. It can get cumbersome to write numbers in conventional decimal notation. In **scientific notation**, any number is written as the product of a number between 1 and 10 and an integer power of ten. Thus the radius of Earth, approximately 6,380,000 m at the equator, can be written 6.38×10^6 m; the radius of a hydrogen atom, 0.000 000 000 053 m, can be written 5.3×10^{-11} m. Scientific notation eliminates the need to write zeros to locate the decimal point correctly.

In science, a measurement or the result of a calculation must indicate the **precision** to which the number is known. The precision of a device used to make a measurement is limited by the finest division on the scale. Using a meterstick with millimeter divisions

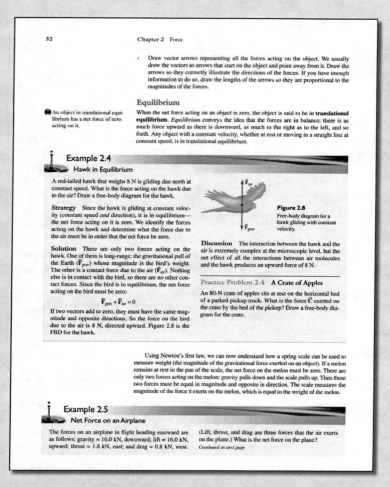

When you come to an **Example**, pause after you've read the problem. Think about the strategy you would use to solve the problem. See if you can work through the problem on your own. Now study the *Strategy, Solution,* and *Discussion* in the textbook. Sometimes you will find that your own solution is right on the mark; if not, you can focus your attention on the areas of misunderstanding or any mistakes you may have made.

Work the *Practice Problem* after each Example to practice applying the physics concepts and problem-solving skills you've just learned. Check your answer with the one given at the end of the chapter. If your answer isn't correct, review the previous section in the textbook to try to find your mistake.

Making the Connection identifies places in the text where physics can be applied to other areas of your life. Familiar topics and interests are discussed in the accompanying text, including examples from biology, archaeology, astronomy, sports, and the everyday world. The biology/life science examples have a special icon. ⟶

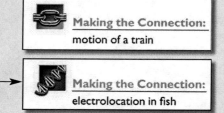

Making the Connection:
motion of a train

Making the Connection:
electrolocation in fish

Try the *Physics at Home* experiments in your dorm room or at home. They reinforce key physics concepts and help you see how these concepts operate in the world around you.

PHYSICS AT HOME

For an easy demonstration of inertia, place a quarter on top of an index card, or a credit card, balanced on top of a drinking glass (Fig. 2.7a). With your thumb and forefinger, flick the card so it flies out horizontally from under the quarter. What happens to the quarter? The horizontal force on the coin due to friction is small. With a negligibly small horizontal force, the coin tends to remain motionless while the card slides out from under it (Fig. 2.7b). Once the card is gone, gravity pulls the coin down into the glass (Fig. 2.7c).

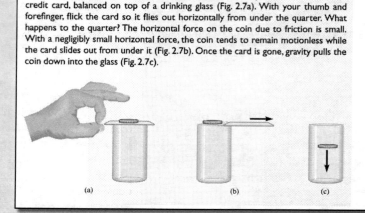

(a)   (b)   (c)

Figure 2.7 A demonstration of inertia.

MASTER THE CONCEPTS

- The angular displacement $\Delta\theta$ is the angle through which an object has turned. Positive and negative angular displacements indicate rotation in different directions. Conventionally, positive represents counterclockwise motion.

- Average angular velocity:

$$\omega_{av} = \frac{\theta_2 - \theta_1}{t_2 - t_1} = \frac{\Delta\theta}{\Delta t} \qquad (5\text{-}2)$$

- Average angular acceleration:

$$\alpha_{av} = \frac{\omega_2 - \omega_1}{t_2 - t_1} = \frac{\Delta\omega}{\Delta t} \qquad (5\text{-}15)$$

- The instantaneous angular velocity and acceleration are the limits of the average quantities as $\Delta t \to 0$.

- A useful measure of angle is the radian:

$$2\pi \text{ radians} = 360°$$

Using radian measure for θ, the arc length s of a circle of radius r subtended by an angle θ is

$$s = \theta r \quad (\theta \text{ in radian measure}) \qquad (5\text{-}4)$$

Using radian measure for ω, the speed of an object in circular motion (including a point on a rotating object) is

$$v = r|\omega| \quad (\omega \text{ in radians per unit time}) \quad (5\text{-}7)$$

- Using radian measure for α, the tangential acceleration component is related to the angular acceleration by

$$a_t = r|\alpha| \quad (\alpha \text{ in radians per ti}$$

- An object moving in a circle has a radia component given by

$$a_r = \frac{v^2}{r} = \omega^2 r \quad (\omega \text{ in radians per unit t}$$

- The tangential and radial acceleration components are two perpendicular components of the acceleration vector. The radial acceleration component changes the direction of the velocity and the tangential acceleration component changes the speed.

- Uniform circular motion means that v and ω are constant. In uniform circular motion, the time to complete one revolution is constant and is called the period T. The frequency f is the number of revolutions completed per second.

$$f = 1/T \qquad (5\text{-}8)$$

$$|\omega| = v/r = 2\pi f \qquad (5\text{-}9)$$

where the SI unit of angular velocity is rad/s and that of frequency is rev/s = Hz.

- A rolling object is both rotating and translating. If the object rolls without skidding or slipping, then

$$v_{axle} = r|\omega| \qquad (5\text{-}10)$$

- Kepler's third law says that the square of the period of a planetary orbit is proportional to the cube of the orbital radius:

$$T^2 = \text{constant} \times r^3 \qquad (5\text{-}14)$$

- For constant angular acceleration, we can use equations analogous to those we developed for constant acceleration a_x:

23.3 The Refraction of Light: Snell's Law

10. Sunlight strikes the surface of a lake at an angle of incidence of 30.0°. At what angle with respect to the normal would a fish see the Sun?

11. Sunlight strikes the surface of a lake. A diver sees the Sun at an angle of 42.0° with respect to the vertical. What angle do the Sun's rays in air make with the vertical?

12. A beam of light in air is incident upon a stack of four flat transparent materials with indices of refraction 1.20, 1.40, ... f incidence for the beam on ... s 60.0°, what angle does the

Problems

- Ⓒ   Combination conceptual/quantitative problem
- 🖳   Biological or medical application
- No ✦   Easy to moderate difficulty level
- ✦   More challenging
- ✦✦   Most challenging
- Blue #   Detailed solution in the Student Solutions Manual
- ⬚1 2⬚   Problems paired by concept

2.1 Force

1. A person is standin... following is *no* a... force due to the floo... feet, the weight of t...

2. Which item/s in th...

the ground when the brick starts to slide? (b) What is the acceleration of the brick as it slides down the board?

95. In the human nervous system, signals are transmitted along neurons as *action potentials* that travel at speeds of up to 100 m/s. (An action potential is a traveling influx of sodium ions through the membrane of a neuron.) The signal is passed from one neuron to another by the release of neurotransmitters in the synapse. Suppose someone steps on your toe. The pain signal

Write your *own* chapter summary or outline, adding notes from class where appropriate, and then compare it with the *Master the Concepts* provided at the end of the chapter. This will help you identify the most important and fundamental concepts in each chapter.

Along with working the problems assigned by your instructor, try quizzing yourself on the **Multiple-Choice Questions**. Check your answers against the answers at the end of the book. Consider the **Conceptual Questions** to check your qualitative understanding of the key ideas from the chapter. Try writing some responses to practice your writing skills and to help prepare for any essay problems on the exam.

When working the **Problems** and **Comprehensive Problems** assigned by your instructor, pay special attention to the explanatory paragraph below the Problem heading and the keys accompanying each problem.

- *Paired Problems* are connected with a box. Your instructor may assign the even-numbered problem, which has no answer at the end of the book. However, working the connected odd-numbered problem will allow you to check your answer at the back of the book and apply what you have learned to working the even-numbered problem.

- Problem numbers highlighted in blue have a solution available in the *Student Solutions Manual* if you need additional help or would like to double-check your work.

- The *difficulty level* for each problem is indicated using a ✦. The least difficult problems have no diamond. Problems of intermediate difficulty have one diamond, and the most difficult problems have two diamonds. Read through all of the assigned problems and budget your time accordingly.

- A Ⓒ indicates a combination **Conceptual and Quantitative** problem.

While working your solutions to problems, try to **keep your work in symbolic form** until the very end. Symbolic solutions will allow you to view which factors affect the results and how the answer would change should any one of the variables in the problem change their value. In this fashion, your solution to any one problem becomes a solution to a whole series of similar problems.

Substituting values into your final symbolic solution will then enable you to judge if your answer is reasonable and provide greater ease in troubleshooting your error if it is not. Always perform a "reality check" at the end of each problem. Did you obtain a reasonable answer given the question being asked?

REVIEW AND SYNTHESIS: CHAPTERS 1–5

Review Exercises

1. From your knowledge of Newton's second law and dimensional analysis, find the units (in SI base units) of the spring constant k in the equation $F = kx$, where F is a force and x is a distance.

2. Harrison traveled 2.00 km west, then 5.00 km in a direction 53.0° south of west, then 1.00 km in a direction 60.0° north of west. (a) In what direction, and for how far, should Harrison travel to return to his starting point? (b) If Harrison returns directly to his starting point with a speed of 5.00 m/s, how long will the return trip take?

3. Mike swims 50.0 m with a speed of 1.84 m/s, then turns around and swims 34.0 m in the opposite direction with a speed of 1.62 m/s. (a) What is his average speed? (b) What is his average velocity?

4. You are watching a television show about Navy pilots. The narrator says that when a Navy jet takes off, it

forces are negligible. (a) How far apart are the astronaut and the asteroid 5.00 s after the astronaut stops pushing? (b) What is their relative speed at this time?

9. In the fairy tale, Rapunzel, the beautiful maiden let her long golden hair hang down from the tower in which she was held prisoner so that her prince could use her hair as a climbing rope to climb the tower and rescue her. (a) Estimate how much force is required to pull a strand of hair out of your head. (b) There are about 10^5 hairs growing out of Rapunzel's head. If the prince has a mass of 60 kg, estimate the average force pulling on each strand of hair. Will Rapunzel be bald by the time the prince reaches the top of the 30-m tower?

10. Marie slides a paper plate with a slice of pizza across a horizontal table to her friend Jaden. The coefficient of friction between the table and plate is 0.32. If the pizza must travel 44 cm to get from Marie to Jaden, what ini-

After a group of related chapters, you will find a **Review and Synthesis** section. This section will provide *Review Exercises* that require you to combine two or more concepts learned in the previous chapters. Working these problems will help you to prepare for cumulative exams. This section also contains *MCAT Review* exercises. These problems were written for the actual MCAT exam and will provide additional practice if this exam is part of your future plans.

How to Study for an Exam

- Be an active learner:
  - read
  - be an active participant in class; ask questions
  - apply what you've learned; think through scenarios rather than memorizing your notes
- Finish reading all material—text, notes, handouts—at least three days prior to the exam.
- Three days prior to the exam, set aside time each day to do self-testing, work practice problems, and review your notes. Useful tools to help:
  - end-of-chapter summaries
  - questions and practice problems
  - text website
  - your professor's course website
  - the Student Solutions Manual
  - your study partner
- Analyze your weaknesses, and create an "I don't know this yet" list. Focus on strengthening these areas and narrow your list as you study.
- If you find that you were unable to allow the full three days to study for the exam, the most important thing you can do is try some practice problems that are similar to those your instructor assigned for homework. Choose odd-numbered problems so that you can check your answer. The Review and Synthesis problems are designed to help you prepare for exams. Try to solve each problem under exam conditions—use a formula sheet, if your instructor provides one with the exam, but don't look at the book or your notes. If you can't solve the problem, then you have found an area of weakness. Study the material needed to solve that problem and closely related material. Then try another similar problem.
- VERY IMPORTANT—Be sure to sleep and eat well before the exam. Staying up late and memorizing the night before an exam doesn't help much in physics. On a physics exam, you will be asked to demonstrate reasoning and analytical skills acquired by much practice. If you are fatigued or hungry, you won't perform at your highest level.

We hope that these suggestions will help you get the most out of your physics course. After many years working with students, both in the classroom and one-on-one in a self-paced course, we wrote this book so you could benefit from our experience. In *College Physics*, we have tried to address the points that have caused difficulties for our students in the past. We also wish to share with you some of the pleasure and excitement we have found in learning about the physical laws that govern our world.

Alan Giambattista
Betty Richardson
Bob Richardson

Acknowledgments

We are grateful to the faculty, staff, and students at Cornell University, who helped us in a myriad of ways. We especially thank our friend and colleague Bob Lieberman who shepherded us through the process as our literary agent and who inspired us as an exemplary physics teacher. Donald F. Holcomb, Persis Drell, Peter Lepage, and Phil Krasicky read portions of the manuscript and provided us with many helpful suggestions. Raphael Littauer contributed many innovative ideas and served as a model of a highly creative, energetic teacher.

We are indebted to all those who helped us class test the manuscript at Cornell: Jeevak Parpia, David G. Cassel, Robert M. Cotts, Richard Galik, Douglas B. Fitchen, Robin Hughes, Joseph Rogers, and Janet Scheel. We also appreciate the assistance of Leonard J. Freelove and Rosemary French. We thank our enthusiastic and capable graduate teaching assistants and, above all, the students in Physics 101-102, who patiently taught us how to teach physics.

We are grateful for the guidance and enthusiasm of Daryl Bruflodt and Mary Hurley at McGraw-Hill, whose tireless efforts were invaluable in bringing this project to fruition. We would like to thank the entire team of talented professionals assembled by McGraw-Hill to publish this book, including Traci Andre, Linda Avenarius, Carrie Burger, Judi David, Bill Fellers, Laura Fuller, David Hash, Nikki Koeller, Melissa Leick, Ellen Osterhaus, Emily Osterholz, Kent Peterson, Mary Reeg, Gloria Schiesl, Pat Steele, Todd Turner, Dan Wallace, and many others whose hard work has contributed to making the book a reality.

We are grateful to Bill Fellers, David Besson, Lloyd Bumm, Stephane Coutu, David Gerdes, Richard Heinz, Kwong Lau, Joe Perez, V. K. Saxena, Doug Tussey, and Arthur Wiggins for accuracy-checking the manuscript and for their many helpful suggestions.

Our thanks also go to Susanne Lee and Tim Stelzer for their suggestions on the reorganization of Chapters 2 through 4; to Janet Scheel, Warren Zipfel, Rebecca Williams, and Mike Nichols for contributing some of the medical and biological applications; to Anita Corn and Mike Strauss for contributing to the end-of-chapter and Review and Synthesis problems; and to Nick Taylor and Jason Marshall for writing answers to the Conceptual Questions.

From Alan: Above all, I am deeply grateful to my family. Marion, Katie, Charlotte, Julia, and Denisha, without your love, support, encouragement, and patience, this book could never have been written.

From Bob and Betty: We thank our daughter Pamela's classmates and friends at Cornell and in the Vanderbilt Master's in Nursing program who were an early inspiration for the book, and we thank Dr. Philip Massey who was very special to Pamela and is dear to us. We thank our friends at *blur*, Alex, Damon, Dave, and Graham, who love physics and are inspiring young people of Europe to explore the wonders of physics through their work with the European Space Agency's Mars mission. Finally we thank our daughter Jennifer, our grandsons Jasper, Dashiell, and Oliver, and son-in-law Jim who endured our protracted hours of distraction while this book was being written.

Reviewers, Class Testers, and Advisors

This text reflects an extensive effort to evaluate the needs of college physics instructors and students, to learn how well we met those needs, and to make improvements where we fell short. We gathered information from numerous reviews, class tests, focus groups, and from an art review panel.

The primary stage of our research began with commissioning reviews from instructors across the United States and Canada. We asked them to submit suggestions for improvement on areas such as content, organization, illustrations, and ancillaries. The detailed comments of these reviewers constituted the basis for the revision plan.

We organized focus groups across the United States in 2003, 2004, and 2005. Participants reviewed our text in comparison to other books and suggested improvements to *College Physics* and ways in which we as publishers could help to improve the content of the college physics course.

We also formed an art review panel led by Matt Evans, who coordinated detailed reviews of the first edition art program from Valentina Gutierrez, Leo Piilonen, Carlos Wexler, and Sanichiro Yoshida. These instructors provided invaluable feedback on the instructional design and quality of the photo and illustration program. The beautiful and exceptionally accurate art program of the second edition is the result of their efforts.

We would like to thank our diary reviewers, Rhett Allain, Joe Collins, Richard Heinz, and Alberto Sadun. We relied on these seasoned instructors to supply opinions continuously during their use of the text through the 2003–2004 school year.

Finally, we received extremely useful advice on the instructional design, quality, and content of the print and media ancillary packages from Rhett Allain, Joe Collins, Richard Heinz, Marllin Simon, and Michael Thoenessen.

Considering the sum of these opinions, this text now embodies the collective knowledge, insight, and experience of hundreds of college physics instructors. Their influence can be seen in everything from the content, accuracy, and organization of the text to the quality of the illustrations.

We are grateful to the following instructors for their thoughtful comments and advice:

Reviewers and Focus Group Attendees

Wathiq Abdul-Razzaq   *West Virginia University*

Yildirim Aktas   *University of North Carolina, Charlotte*

Dr. Murty A. Akundi   *Xavier University of Louisiana*

Ricardo Alarcon   *Arizona State University*

Naushad Ali   *Southern Illinois University, Carbondale*

Rhett Allain   *Southeastern Louisiana University*

Dan Amidei   *University of Michigan*

Farhang Amiri   *Weber State University*

Peter Anderson   *Oakland Community College*

Jim Andrews   *Youngstown State University*

Sanjeev Arora   *Fort Valley State University*

Karamjeet Arya   *San Jose State University*

David T. Bannon   *Oregon State University*

David Baxter   *Indiana University*

Paul Beale   *University of Colorado–Boulder*

James R. Benbrook   *University of Houston*

David Bennum   *University of Nevada, Reno*

Mike Berger   *Indiana University*

Gene Bickers   *University of Southern California*

Ignacio Birriel   *Moorehead State University*

Jennifer Birriel   *Moorehead State University*

Julio Blanco   *California State University–Northridge*

Luca Bombelli   *University of Mississippi*

Richard Bone   *Florida International University*

Bob Boughton   *Bowling Green State University*

Jeffrey M. Bowen   *Bucknell University*

Eric Brewe   *Hawaii Pacific University*

William J. Briscoe   *The George Washington University*

Meade Brooks   *Collin County Community College*

Michael Broyles   *Collin County Community College*

Lloyd A. Bumm   *The University of Oklahoma, Department of Physics and Astronomy*

H. R. Chandrasekhar   *University of Missouri, Columbia*

Don Chodrow   *James Madison University*

Anastasia Chopelas   *University of Washington*

Lee Chow   *University of Central Florida*

Krishna M. Chowdary   *Bucknell University*

Gerald B. Cleaver   *Baylor University*

John Cockman, Jr.   *Appalachian State University*

J. M. Collins   *Marquette University Physics Department*

Anita B. Corn   *Colorado School of Mines*

Stephen R. Cotanch   *North Carolina State University*

Stephane Coutu   *The Pennsylvania State University*

Carl Covatto   *Arizona State University, Tempe*

Kevin Crosby   *Carthage College*

Yesim Darici   *Florida International University*

Edward Derringh   *Wentworth Institute of Technology*

D. J. De Smet   *University of Alabama*

T. S. Dhillon   *University of Texas–Pan American*

Renee D. Diehl   *The Pennsylvania State University*

Joseph N. D. Dodoo   *University of Maryland Eastern Shore*

A. J. Abu El-Haija   *Indiana University of Pennsylvania*

Matt Evans   *University of Wisconsin, Eau Claire*

John W. Farley   *UNLV*

Jerry Feldman   *George Washington University*

Herbert A. Fertig   *University of Kentucky*

Carlos E. Figueroa   *Cabrillo College*

Lyle Ford   *University of Wisconsin, Eau Claire*

Donald Franceschetti   *University of Memphis*

Carl Frederickson   *University of Central Arkansas*

Robert G. Fuller   *University of Nebraska–Lincoln*

Frank Gaitan   *Southern Illinois University, Carbondale*

Richard Gass   *University of Cincinnati*

Michael R. Geller   *University of Georgia*

David Gerdes   *University of Michigan*

Michael Giangrande   *Oakland Community College*

Mike Gorman   *University of Houston*

Ilia Gulkarov   *Northeastern Illinois University*

Martin Guthold   *Wake Forest University*

Valentina Gutierrez   *Austin Peay State University*

Robert Hagood   *Washtenaw Community College*

Paul Halpern   *University of the Sciences in Philadelphia*

Ann Hanks   *American River College*

Jason Harlow   *University of the Pacific*

Gary Hastings   *Georgia State University*

Richard M. Heinz   *Indiana University*

Erik Hendrickson   *University of Wisconsin, Eau Claire*

Donald L. Henry   *Shepherd University*

Allen M. Hermann   *University of Colorado, Boulder*

John Hill   *Iowa State University*

Laurent Hodges   *Iowa State University*

Brian W. Holmes   *San Jose State University*

C. Gregory Hood   *Tidewater Community College*

John D. Hopkins   *The Pennsylvania State University*

Wendell Horton   *University of Texas at Austin*

Huan Z. Huang   *UCLA*

Charles Hughes   *University of Central Oklahoma*

Christopher Hunt   *Prince George's Community College*

Joey Huston   *Michigan State University*

Diane A. Jacobs   *Eastern Michigan University*

Bob Jacobsen   *University of California, Berkeley*

Mohsen Janatpour   *College of San Mateo*

Yong S. Joe   *Ball State University*

J. Bruce Johnson   *Arkansas State University*

Edson Justinianio   *East Carolina University*

Joseph Kapusta   *University of Minnesota*

Illka Koskelo   *San Francisco State University*

Dorina Kosztin   *University of Missouri, Columbia*

Fred Kuttner   *University of California, Santa Cruz*

Gregory P. Lafyatis   *The Ohio State University*

Allen Landers   *Auburn University*

Kwong Lau   *University of Houston*

Kevin Lee   *University of Nebraska–Lincoln*

Susanne M. Lee   *University at Albany, State University of New York*

Jon Levin   *University of Tennessee*

Say-Peng Lim   *California State University–Northridge*

Varavut Limpasuvan   *Coastal Carolina University*

Jingyu Lin   *Kansas State University*

T. Y. Ling   *The Ohio State University*

Dean Livelybrooks   *University of Oregon*

M. A. K. Lodhi   *Texas Tech University*

Mark Lucas   *The Ohio State University*

Kingshuk Majumdar   *Berea College*

Pete Markowitz   *Florida International University*

Mark E. Mattson   *James Madison University*

Richard A. Matzner   *University of Texas at Austin*

Joseph McCullough   *Cabrillo College*

Arthur R. McGurn   *Western Michigan University*

Roger McNeil   *Louisiana State University*

Rahul Mehta   *University of Central Arkansas*

David H. Miller   *Purdue University*

John A. Milsom   *University of Arizona*

T. Ted Morishige   *University of Central Oklahoma*

Pat Moyer   *The University of North Carolina at Charlotte*

Orland David Mylander   *California State Polytechnic, Pomona*

David Norwood   *Southeastern Louisiana University*

Tom Oder   *Youngstown State University*

Halina Opyrchal   *New Jersey Institute of Technology*

Brad Orr   *The University of Michigan*

Michael J. Panunto   *California Polytechnic State University*

Patrick Papin   *San Diego State University*

Philip Edward Patterson   *Southern Polytechnic State University*

J. Scott Payson   *Wayne State University, Detroit*

J. D. Perez   *Auburn University*

Vladimir Petricevic   *City College of the City University of New York*

Leo Piilonen   *Virginia Polytechnic Institute and State University*

T. A. K. Pillai   *University of Wisconsin, LaCrosse*

Russell A. Poch   *Howard Community College*

Amy L. Pope   *Clemson University*

Wendell Potter   *University of California–Davis*

Michael Pravica   *University of Nevada, Las Vegas*

E. W. Prohofsky   *Purdue University*

Michael Ram   *University of Buffalo*

Bruce C. Reed   *Alma College*

David D. Reid   *University of Chicago*

Timothy M. Ritter   *The University of North Carolina at Pembroke*

Patricia Robbert   *University of New Orleans*

Melodi Rodrigue   *University of Nevada, Reno*

Alberto C. Sadun   *University of Colorado at Denver*

Hassan Sayyar   *University of Arkansas at Monticello*

Earl Scime   *West Virginia University*

C. Gregory Seab   *University of New Orleans*

Shahin Shabanian   *Pennsylvania College of Technology*

Neil Shafer-Ray   *The University of Oklahoma*

Bart M. Sheinberg   *Houston Community College System Northwest College*

Carmen K. Shepard   *Southwestern Illinois College*

Paul Sokol   *The Pennsylvania State University*

David Sokoloff   *University of Oregon*

Gene D. Sprouse   *SUNY, Stony Brook*

Tim Stelzer   *University of Illinois at Urbana-Champaign*

Michael G. Strauss   *The University of Oklahoma*

Carey E. Stronach   *Virginia State University*

W. M. Stuckey   *Elizabethtown College*

Chun Fu Su   *Mississippi State University*

Bridget M. Tartick   *SUNY Geneseo*

Salam Tawfiq   *University of Toronto (UTSC)*

Marshall Thomsen   *Eastern Michigan University*

Dominique Toublan   *University of Illinois at Urbana-Champaign*

Douglas C. Tussey   *The Pennsylvania State University*

Bruno Ullrich   *Bowling Green State University*

John A. Underwood   *Austin Community College*

Melissa Vigil   *Marquette University*

Giovanni Vignale   *University of Missouri*

Denise M. Wetli   *Wake Tech Community College*

Carlos Wexler   *University of Missouri, Columbia*

Arthur W. Wiggins   *Oakland Community College*

Walter Wimbush   *Northern Virginia Community College*

Capp Yess   *Morehead State University*

Sanichiro Yoshida   *Southeastern Louisiana University*

David Young   *Louisiana State University*

Ben Yu-Kuang Hu   *University of Akron*

Michael G. Ziegler   *The Ohio State University*

Class Testers

We'd like to thank the students and faculty at the following schools for class testing our book:

Bradley University

Cabrillo College

Louisiana State University

University of Missouri

Contributors

We are deeply indebted to:

Professor Suzanne Willis of Northern Illinois University and Professor Susanne M. Lee of University at Albany, SUNY for creating the instructor resources and demonstrations in the *College Physics Instructors' Resource Guide*.

Professor Jack Cuthbert of Holmes Community College, Ridgeland for the Test Bank to accompany *College Physics* .

Professor Lorin Swint Matthews of Baylor University for the CPS eInstruction Questions to accompany *College Physics*.

Professor Edson Justiniano of East Carolina University for the PowerPoint Lectures to accompany *College Physics*.

Professor Allen Landers of Auburn University for his work on the *College Physics* collection of Active Art on the Digital Content Manager CD-ROM.

Professors Joe Collins of Marquette University, Meade Brooks of Collin County Community College, Anita Corn of Colorado School of Mines, Carl Covatto of Arizona State University, and John Hopkins of The Pennsylvania State University for their reviews of and input on the new Flash versions of the Physics Interactives.

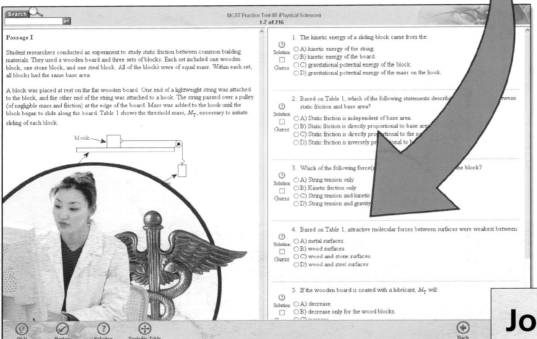

Electric Forces and Fields

The elegant fish in the photograph is the *Gymnarchus niloticus*, a native of Africa found in the Nile River. *Gymnarchus* has some interesting traits. It swims gracefully with equal facility either forward or backward. Instead of propelling itself by lashing its tail sideways, as most fish do, it keeps its spine straight—not only when swimming straight ahead, but even when turning. Its propulsion is accomplished by means of the undulations of the fin along its back.

    Gymnarchus navigates with great precision, darting after its prey and evading obstacles in its path. What is surprising is that it does so just as precisely when swimming backward. Furthermore, *Gymnarchus* is nearly blind; its eyes respond only to extremely bright light. How then, is it able to locate its prey in the dim light of a muddy river? (See p. 579 for the answer.)

**Concepts &
Skills to
Review**

- gravitational forces, fundamental forces (Sections 2.6 and 2.9)
- free-body diagrams (Section 2.3)
- Newton's second law: force and acceleration (Section 3.3)
- motion with constant acceleration (Sections 4.1–4.4)
- equilibrium (Section 2.3)
- adding vectors; resolving a vector into components (Sections 2.2 and 2.4)

16.1   ELECTRIC CHARGE

In Part Three of this book, we study electric and magnetic fields in detail. Recall from Chapter 2 that all interactions in the universe fall into one of four categories: gravitational, electromagnetic, strong, and weak. All of the familiar, everyday forces other than gravity—contact forces, tension in cables, and the like—are fundamentally electromagnetic. What we think of as a single interaction is really the net effect of huge numbers of microscopic interactions between electrons and atoms. Electromagnetic forces bind electrons to nuclei to form atoms and molecules. They hold atoms together to form liquids and solids, from skyscrapers to trees to human bodies. Technological applications of electromagnetism abound, especially once we realize that radio waves, microwaves, light, and other forms of electromagnetic radiation consist of oscillating electric and magnetic fields.

Many everyday manifestations of electromagnetism are complex; hence we study simpler situations in order to gain some insight into how electromagnetism works. The hybrid word *electromagnetism* itself shows that electricity and magnetism, which were once thought to be completely separate forces, are really aspects of the same fundamental interaction. This unification of the studies of electricity and magnetism occurred in the late nineteenth century. However, understanding comes more easily if we first tackle electricity (Chapters 16–18), then magnetism (Chapter 19), and finally see how they are closely related (Chapters 20–22).

The existence of electrical forces has been familiar to humans for at least 3000 years. The ancient Greeks used pieces of amber—a hard, fossilized form of the sap from pine trees—to make jewelry. When a piece of amber was polished by rubbing it with a piece of fabric, it was observed that the amber would subsequently attract small objects, such as bits of string or hair. Using modern knowledge, we say that the amber is *charged* by rubbing: some electric charge is transferred between the amber and the cloth. Our word *electric* comes from the Greek word for amber (*elektron*).

A similar phenomenon occurs on a dry day when you walk across a carpeted room wearing socks. Charge is transferred between the carpet and your socks and between your socks and your body. Some of the charge you have accumulated may be unintentionally transferred from your fingertips to a doorknob or to a friend—accompanied by the sensation of a shock.

Types of Charge

Electric charge is not *created* by these processes; it is just transferred from one object to another. The law of **conservation of charge** is one of the fundamental laws of physics; no exceptions to it have ever been found.

Conservation of charge:

The net charge of a closed system never changes.

Experiments with amber and other materials that can be charged show that there are two types of charge; Benjamin Franklin (1706–1790) was the first to call them *positive* (+) and *negative* (–). The **net charge** of a system is the algebraic sum—taking care

Net charge: the algebraic sum of all the charges in a system to include the positive and negative signs—of the charges of the constituent particles in the system. When a piece of glass is rubbed by silk, the glass acquires a positive charge and the silk a negative charge; the net charge of the system of glass and silk does not change. An object that is **electrically neutral** has equal amounts of positive and negative charge and thus a net charge of zero. The symbols used for quantity of charge are q or Q.

Ordinary matter consists of atoms, which in turn consist of electrons, protons, and neutrons. The protons and neutrons are called *nucleons* because they are found in the nucleus. The neutron is electrically neutral (thus the name *neutron*). The charges on the proton and the electron are of *equal magnitude* but of opposite sign. The charge on the proton is arbitrarily chosen to be positive; that on the electron is therefore negative. A neutral atom has equal numbers of protons and electrons, a balance of positive and negative charge. If the number of electrons and protons is not equal, then the atom is called an *ion* and has a nonzero net charge. If the ion has more electrons than protons, its net charge is negative; if the atom has fewer electrons than protons, its net charge is positive.

Elementary Charge

The *magnitude* of charge on the proton and electron is the same (see Table 16.1). That amount of charge is called the **elementary charge** (symbol e). In terms of the SI unit of charge, the coulomb (C), the value of e is

$$e = 1.602 \times 10^{-19}\ \text{C} \tag{16-1}$$

Since ordinary objects have only slight imbalances between positive and negative charge, the coulomb is often an inconveniently large unit. For this reason, charges are often given in millicoulombs (mC), microcoulombs (μC), nanocoulombs (nC), or picocoulombs (pC). The coulomb is named after the French physicist Charles Coulomb (1736–1806), who developed the expression for the electric force between two charged particles.

The net charge of any object is an integral multiple of the elementary charge. Even in the extraordinary matter found in exotic places like the interior of stars, the upper atmosphere, or in particle accelerators, the observable charge is always an integer times e.

Table 16.1

Masses and Electrical Charges of the Proton, Electron, and Neutron

Particle	Mass	Electrical Charge
Proton	$m_\text{p} = 1.673 \times 10^{-27}\ \text{kg}$	$q_\text{p} = +e = +1.602 \times 10^{-19}\ \text{C}$
Electron	$m_\text{e} = 9.109 \times 10^{-31}\ \text{kg}$	$q_\text{e} = -e = -1.602 \times 10^{-19}\ \text{C}$
Neutron	$m_\text{n} = 1.675 \times 10^{-27}\ \text{kg}$	$q_\text{n} = 0$

Example 16.1

An Unintentional Shock

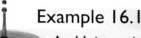

The magnitude of charge transferred when you walk across a carpet, reach out to shake hands, and unintentionally give a shock to a friend might be typically about 1 nC. (a) If the charge is transferred by electrons only, how many electrons are transferred? (b) If your body has a net charge of –1 nC, estimate the percentage of excess electrons. [*Hint:* The mass of the electron is only about 1/2000 that of a nucleon, so most of the mass of the body is in the nucleons. For an order-of-

magnitude calculation, we can just assume that $\frac{1}{2}$ of the nucleons are protons.]

Strategy Since the coulomb (C) is the SI unit of charge, the "n" must be the prefix "nano-" (= 10^{-9}). We know the size of the elementary charge in coulombs. For part (b), we first make an order-of-magnitude estimate of the number of electrons in the human body.

Continued on next page

Example 16.1 Continued

Solution (a) The number of electrons transferred is the quantity of charge transferred divided by the charge of each electron:

$$\frac{-1 \times 10^{-9} \text{ C}}{-1.6 \times 10^{-19} \text{ C per electron}} = 6 \times 10^{9} \text{ electrons}$$

Notice that the magnitude of the charge transferred is 1 nC, but since it is transferred by electrons, the sign of the charge transferred is negative.

(b) We estimate a typical body mass of around 70 kg. Most of the mass of the body is in the nucleons, so

$$\text{number of nucleons} = \frac{\text{mass of body}}{\text{mass per nucleon}} = \frac{70 \text{ kg}}{1.7 \times 10^{-27} \text{ kg}}$$

$$= 4 \times 10^{28} \text{ nucleons}$$

Assuming that roughly $\frac{1}{2}$ of the nucleons are protons,

$$\text{number of protons} = \frac{1}{2} \times 4 \times 10^{28} = 2 \times 10^{28} \text{ protons}$$

In an electrically neutral object, the number of electrons is equal to the number of protons. With a net charge of −1 nC, the body has 6×10^{9} extra electrons. The percentage of excess electrons is then

$$\frac{6 \times 10^{9}}{2 \times 10^{28}} \times 100\% = (3 \times 10^{-17})\%$$

Discussion As shown in this example, charged macroscopic objects have *tiny* differences between the magnitude of the positive charge and the magnitude of the negative charge. For this reason, electrical forces between macroscopic bodies are often negligible.

Practice Problem 16.1   Excess Electrons on a Balloon

How many excess electrons are found on a balloon with a net charge of −12 nC?

One of the important differences between the gravitational force and the electrical force comes about because charge has either a positive or a negative sign, while mass is always a positive quantity. The gravitational force between two massive bodies is always an attractive force, while the electrical force between two charged particles can be attractive or repulsive depending on the signs of the charges. Two particles with charges of the same sign repel one another, while two particles with charges of opposite sign attract one another. More briefly,

Like charges repel one another; unlike charges attract one another.

A common shorthand is to say "a charge" instead of saying "a particle with charge."

Polarization

Polarization: charge separation within an object

An electrically neutral object may have regions of positive and negative charge within it, separated from one another. Such an object is **polarized**. A polarized object can experience an electric force even though its net charge is zero. A rubber rod charged negatively after being rubbed with fur attracts small bits of paper. So does a glass rod that is *positively* charged after being rubbed with silk (Fig. 16.1a,b). The bits of paper are electrically neutral, but a charged rod polarizes the paper—it attracts the unlike charge in the paper a bit closer and pushes the like charge in the paper a bit farther away (Fig. 16.1c).

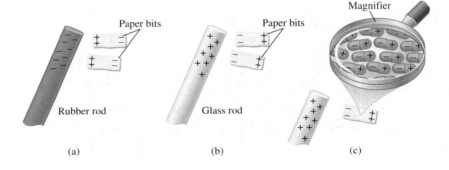

Figure 16.1 (a) Negatively charged rubber rod attracting bits of paper. (b) Positively charged glass rod attracting bits of paper. (c) Magnified view of polarized molecules within a bit of paper.

The attraction between the rod and the unlike charge then becomes a little stronger than the repulsion between the rod and the like charge, since the electrical force gets weaker as the separation increases and the like charge is farther away. Thus, the net force on the paper is always attractive, regardless of the sign of charge on the rod.

In this case, we say that the paper is *polarized by induction;* the polarization of the paper is induced by the charge on the nearby rod. When the rod is moved away, the paper is no longer polarized. Some objects, including some molecules, are intrinsically polarized. An electrically neutral water molecule, for example, has equal amounts of positive and negative charge (10 protons and 10 electrons), but the center of positive charge and the center of negative charge do not coincide. The electrons in the molecule are shared in such a way that the oxygen end of the molecule has a negative charge, while the hydrogen atoms are positive.

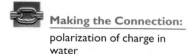

Making the Connection:

polarization of charge in water

PHYSICS AT HOME

On a dry day, run a comb through your hair (this works best if your hair is clean and dry and you have not used conditioner) or rub the comb on a wool sweater. When you are sure the comb is charged (by observing the behavior of your hair, listening for crackling sounds, etc.), go to a sink and turn the water on so that a *thin* stream of water comes out. It does not matter if the stream breaks up into droplets near the bottom. Hold the charged comb near the stream of water. You should see that the water experiences a force due to the charge on the comb (Fig. 16.2). Is the force attractive or repulsive? Does this mean that the water coming from the tap has a net charge? Explain why holding the comb near the top of the stream is more effective than holding it farther down (at the same horizontal distance from the stream).

16.2   ELECTRICAL CONDUCTORS AND INSULATORS

Ordinary matter consists of atoms containing electrons and nuclei. The electrons differ greatly in how tightly they are bound to the nucleus. In atoms with many electrons, most of the electrons are tightly bound—under ordinary circumstances nothing can tear them away from the nucleus. Some of the electrons are much more weakly bound and can be removed from the nucleus in one way or another.

Materials vary dramatically in how easy or difficult it is for charge to move within them. Materials in which some charge can move easily are called electrical **conductors**, while materials in which charge does not move easily are called electrical **insulators**.

Metals are materials in which *some* of the electrons are so weakly bound that they are not tied to any one particular nucleus; they are free to wander about within the metal. The *free electrons* in metals make them good conductors. Some metals are better conductors than others, with copper being one of the best. Glass, plastics, rubber, wood, paper, and many other familiar materials are insulators. Insulators do not have free electrons; each electron is bound to a particular nucleus.

The terms *conductor* and *insulator* are applied frequently to electrical wires, which are omnipresent in today's society (Fig. 16.3). The copper wires allow free electrons to

Figure 16.2 A stream of water is deflected by a charged comb.

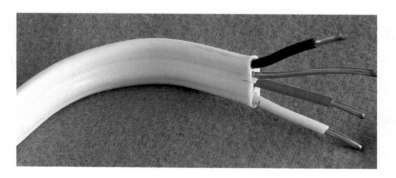

Figure 16.3 Some electrical wires. The metallic conductors are surrounded by insulating material. The insulation must be stripped away where the wire makes an electrical connection with something else.

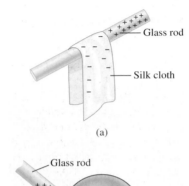

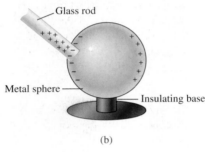

Figure 16.4 Charging a conductor. (a) After rubbing a glass rod with a silk cloth, the glass rod is left with a net positive charge and the silk is left with a net negative charge. (b) Touching the glass rod to a metal sphere. The positively charged glass attracts some of the free electrons from the metal onto the glass. (c) The glass rod is removed. The metal sphere now has fewer electrons than protons, so it has a net positive charge. Even though negative charge is actually transferred (electrons), it is often said that "positive charge is transferred to the metal" since the net effect is the same.

flow. The plastic or rubber insulator surrounding the wires keeps the electrical current—the flow of charge—from leaving the wires (and entering your hand, for instance).

Water is usually thought of as an electrical conductor. It is wise to assume so and take precautions such as not handling electrical devices with wet hands. Actually, *pure* water is an electrical insulator. Pure water consists mostly of complete water molecules (H_2O), which carry no net charge as they move about; there is only a tiny concentration of ions (H^+ and OH^-). But tap water is by no means pure—it contains dissolved minerals. The mineral ions make tap water an electrical conductor. The human body contains many ions and therefore is a conductor.

Similarly, air is a good insulator, because most of the molecules in air are electrically neutral, carrying no charge as they move about. However, air does contain some ions; air molecules are ionized by radioactive decays or by cosmic rays.

Intermediate between conductors and insulators are the **semiconductors**. The part of the computer industry clustered in northern California is referred to as "Silicon Valley" because silicon is a common semiconductor used in making computer chips and other electronic devices. *Pure* semiconductors are good insulators, but by *doping* them—adding tiny amounts of impurities in a controlled way—their electrical properties can be fine-tuned.

Charging by Rubbing

When objects are given net charges by rubbing them against one another, both electrons and ions (charged atoms) can be transferred from one object to the other. Charging works best in dry air. When the humidity is high, a film of moisture condenses on the surfaces of objects; charge can then leak off more easily, so it is difficult to build up charge.

Notice that we rub two *insulators* together to separate charge. A piece of metal can be rubbed all day with fur or silk without charging the metal; it is too easy for the charge in the metal to move around and avoid getting scraped off. Once an insulator is charged, the charge remains where it is.

How can a conductor be charged? First rub two insulators together to separate charge; then touch one of the charged insulators to the conductor (Fig. 16.4). Since the charge transferred to the conductor spreads out, the process can be repeated to build up more and more charge on the conductor.

Grounding

How can a conductor be discharged? One way is to *ground* it. The Earth is a conductor because of the presence of ions and moisture and is large enough that for many purposes it can be thought of as a limitless reservoir of charge. (The word *reservoir* is used deliberately to call to mind heat reservoirs. A heat reservoir has such a large heat capacity that it is possible to exchange heat with it without changing its temperature appreciably.) To *ground* a conductor means to provide a conducting path between it and the Earth (or to another charge reservoir). A charged conductor that is grounded discharges because the charge spreads out by moving off the conductor and onto the Earth.

A buildup of even a relatively small amount of charge on a truck that delivers gasoline could be dangerous—a spark could trigger an explosion. To prevent such a charge buildup, the truck grounds its tank before starting to deliver gasoline to the service station.

The round opening of modern electrical outlets is called *ground*. It is literally connected by a conducting wire to the ground, either through a metal rod driven into the Earth or through underground metal water pipes. The purpose of the ground connection is more fully discussed in the next chapter, but you can understand one purpose already: it prevents static charges from building up on the conductor that is grounded.

Charging by Induction

A conductor is not necessarily discharged when it is grounded if there are other charges nearby. It is even possible to charge an initially neutral conductor by grounding it. In the process shown in Fig. 16.5, the charged insulator never touches the conducting sphere.

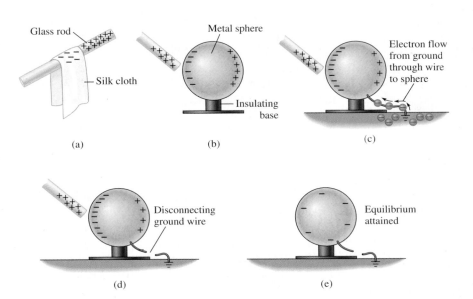

(a)

(b)

(c)

(d)

(e)

Glass rod

Silk cloth

Metal sphere

Insulating base

Electron flow from ground through wire to sphere

Disconnecting ground wire

Equilibrium attained

Figure 16.5 Charging by induction. (a) A glass rod is charged by rubbing it with silk. (b) The positively charged glass rod is held near a metal sphere, but does not touch it. The sphere is polarized as free electrons within the sphere are attracted toward the glass rod. (c) When the sphere is grounded, electrons from the ground move onto the sphere, attracted there by positive charges on the sphere. (d) The ground connection is broken without moving the glass rod. (e) Now the glass rod is removed with the ground wire still disconnected. Charge spreads over the metal surface as the like charges repel each other. The sphere is left with a net negative charge because of the excess electrons.

The positively charged rod first polarizes the sphere, attracting the negative charges on the sphere while repelling the positive charges. Then the sphere is grounded. The resulting separation of charge on the conducting sphere causes negative charges from the Earth to be attracted along the grounding wire and onto the sphere by the nearby positive charges.

● The symbol $\perp$ represents a connection to ground.

Conceptual Example 16.2

The Electroscope

An electroscope is charged negatively and the gold foil leaves hang apart as in Fig. 16.6. What happens to the leaves as the following operations are carried out in the order listed? Explain what you see after each step. (a) You touch the metal bulb at the top of the electroscope with your hand. (b) You bring a glass rod that has been rubbed with silk *near* the bulb without touching it. [*Hint:* A glass rod rubbed with silk is positively charged.] (c) The glass rod touches the metal bulb.

Solution and Discussion (a) By touching the electroscope bulb with your hand, you ground it. Charge is transferred between your hand and the bulb until the bulb's net charge is zero. Since the electroscope is now discharged, the foil leaves hang down as in Fig. 16.7. (b) When the positively charged rod is held near the bulb, the electroscope becomes polarized by induction. Negatively charged free electrons are drawn toward the bulb, leaving the foil leaves with a positive net charge (Fig. 16.8). The leaves hang apart due to the mutual repulsion of the net positive charges on them. (c) When the positively charged rod touches the bulb, some negative charge is transferred from the bulb

Figure 16.6

An electroscope is a device used to demonstrate the presence of charge. A conducting pole has a metallic bulb at the top and a pair of flexible leaves of gold foil at the bottom. The leaves are pushed apart due to the repulsion of the negative charges.

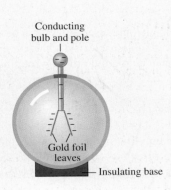

Conducting bulb and pole

Gold foil leaves

Insulating base

Figure 16.7

With no net charge, the leaves hang straight down.

Continued on next page

Conceptual Example 16.2 Continued

Positively charged rod

Figure 16.8
With a positively charged rod near the bulb, the electroscope has no net charge but it is polarized: the bulb is negative and the leaves are positive. Repulsion between the positive charges on the leaves pushes them apart.

to the rod. The electroscope now has a positive net charge. The glass rod still has a positive net charge that repels the positive charge on the electroscope, pushing it as far away as possible—toward the foil leaves. The leaves hang farther apart, since they now have *more* positive charge on them than before.

Conceptual Practice Problem 16.2
Removing the Glass Rod

What happens to the leaves as the glass rod is moved away?

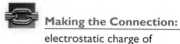

Making the Connection:
electrostatic charge of adhesive tape

PHYSICS AT HOME

Ordinary transparent tape has an adhesive that allows it to stick to paper and many other materials. Since the sticking force is electrical in nature, it is not too surprising that adhesive can be used to separate charge. If you have ever peeled a roll of tape too quickly and noticed that the strip of tape curls around and behaves strangely, you have seen effects of this charge separation—the strip of tape has a net charge (and so does the tape left behind, but of opposite sign). Tape pulled *slowly* off a surface does not tend to have a net charge. There are some instructive experiments you can perform:

- Pull a strip of tape quickly from the roll. How can you tell if the tape has a net charge?

- Take the roll of tape into a dark closet. What do you see when you pull a strip quickly from the roll?

- See if the strip is attracted or repelled when you hold it near a paper clip. Explain what you see.

- Rub the tape on both sides between your thumb and forefinger. Now try the paper clip again. What has happened? Explain.

- Pull a second strip of tape *slowly* from the roll. Is the force between the two strips attractive or repulsive? What does that tell you?

- Hold the second strip near the paper clip. Is there a net force? What can you conclude?

- Can you think of a way of reliably making two strips of tape with like charges? With unlike charges?

- Enough suggestions—have some fun and see what you can discover!

Making the Connection:
photocopier

The Photocopier

The operation of photocopiers (and laser printers) is based on the separation of charge and the attraction between unlike electric charges (Fig. 16.9). Positive charge is applied to a selenium-coated aluminum drum by rotating the drum under an electrode. The drum is then illuminated with a projected image of the document to be copied (or by a laser).

Selenium is a *photoconductor*—a light-sensitive semiconductor. When no light shines on the selenium, it is a good insulator; but when light shines on it, it becomes a good conductor. The selenium coating on the drum is initially in the dark. Behaving as an insulator, it can be electrically charged. When the selenium is illuminated, it becomes conducting wherever light falls on it. Electrons from the aluminum—a good

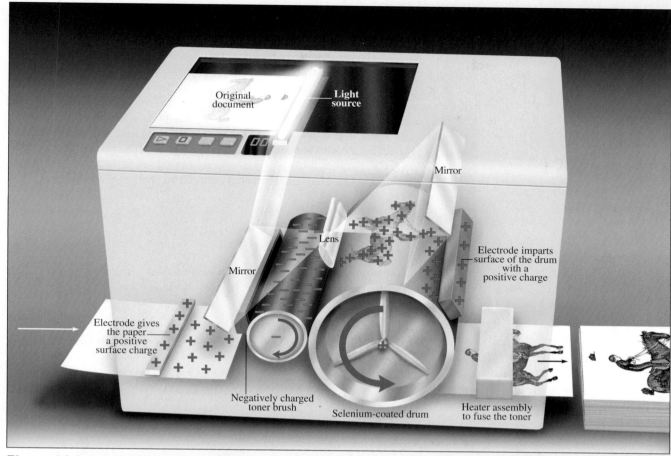

Figure 16.9 The operation of a photocopier is based on the attraction of negatively charged toner particles to regions on the drum that are positively charged.

conductor—pass into the illuminated regions of selenium and neutralize the positive charge. Regions of the selenium coating that remain dark do not allow electrons from the aluminum to flow in, so those regions remain positively charged.

Next, the drum is allowed to come into contact with a black powder called *toner*. The toner particles have been given a negative charge so they will be attracted to positively charged regions of the drum. Toner adheres to the drum where there is positive charge, but no toner adheres to the uncharged regions. A sheet of paper is now rotated onto the drum and positive charge is applied to the back surface of the paper. The charge on the paper is larger than that on the drum, so the paper attracts the negatively charged toner away from the drum, forming an image of the original document on the paper. The final step is to fuse the toner to the paper by passing the paper between hot rollers. With the ink sealed into the fibers of the paper, the copy is finished.

16.3   COULOMB'S LAW

Let's now begin a quantitative treatment of electrical forces among charged objects. Coulomb's law gives the electric force acting between two *point charges*. A **point charge** is a point-like object with a nonzero electric charge. Recall that a point-like object is small enough that its internal structure is of no importance. The electron can be treated as a point charge, since there is no experimental evidence for any internal structure.

The proton *does* have internal structure—it contains three particles called *quarks* bound together—but, since its size is only about 10^{-15} m, it too can be treated as a point charge for most purposes. A charged metal sphere of radius 10 cm can be treated as a point charge if it interacts with another such sphere 100 m away, but not if the two spheres are only a few centimeters apart. Context is everything!

Like gravity, the electric force is an *inverse square law* force. That is, the strength of the force decreases as the separation increases such that the force is proportional to the inverse square of the separation r between the two point charges ($F \propto 1/r^2$). The strength of the force is also proportional to the *magnitude* of each of the two charges ($|q_1|$ and $|q_2|$) just as the gravitational force is proportional to the *mass* of each of two interacting objects.

The magnitude of the electrical force that each of two charges exerts on the other is given by

$$F = \frac{k\,|q_1|\,|q_2|}{r^2} \qquad (16\text{-}2)$$

Since we use the *magnitudes* of q_1 and q_2, F—the magnitude of a vector—is always a positive quantity. The proportionality constant k is experimentally found to have the value

$$k = 8.99 \times 10^9\ \frac{\text{N}\cdot\text{m}^2}{\text{C}^2} \qquad (16\text{-}3\text{a})$$

The constant k, which we call the *Coulomb constant*, can be written in terms of another constant ϵ_0, the *permittivity of free space*:

$$\epsilon_0 = \frac{1}{4\pi k} = 8.85 \times 10^{-12}\ \frac{\text{C}^2}{\text{N}\cdot\text{m}^2} \qquad (16\text{-}3\text{b})$$

Using ϵ_0, the magnitude of the force is

$$F = \frac{|q_1||q_2|}{4\pi\epsilon_0 r^2}$$

The direction of the electrical force exerted on one point charge due to another point charge is always along the line that joins the two point charges. Remember that, unlike the gravitational force, the electric force can either be attractive or repulsive, depending on the signs of the charges. Coulomb's law is in agreement with Newton's third law: the forces on the two charges are equal in magnitude and opposite in direction (Fig. 16.10).

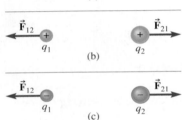

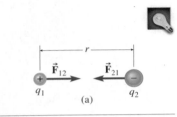

Figure 16.10 The electric force on (a) two opposite charges; (b) and (c) two like charges. Vectors are drawn showing the force on each of the two interacting charges.

Problem-Solving Tips for Coulomb's Law

1. Use consistent units; since we know k in standard SI units (N·m²/C²), distances should be in meters and charges in coulombs. When the charge is given in μC or nC, be sure to change the units to coulombs: 1 μC = 10^{-6} C and 1 nC = 10^{-9} C.

2. When finding the electric force on a single charge due to two or more other charges, find the force due to each of the other charges separately. The net force on a particular charge is the vector sum of the forces acting on that charge due to each of the other charges. Often it helps to separate the forces into x- and y-components, add the components separately, then find the magnitude and direction of the net force from its x- and y-components.

3. If several charges lie along the same line, do not worry about an intermediate charge "shielding" the charge located on one side from the charge on the other side. The electric force is long-range just as is gravity; the gravitational force on the Earth due to the Sun does not stop when the Moon passes between the two.

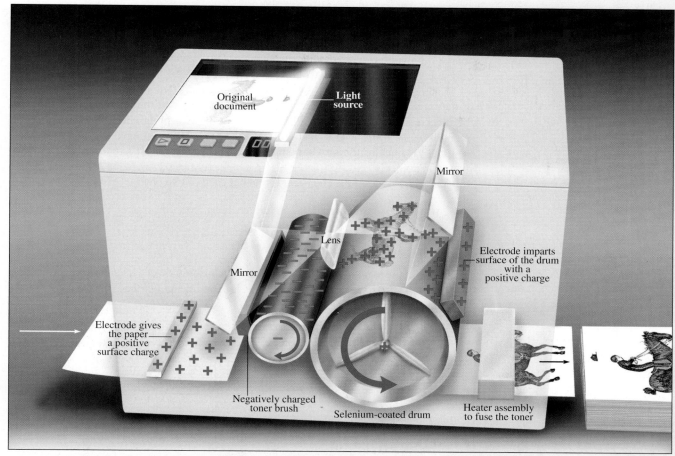

Figure 16.9 The operation of a photocopier is based on the attraction of negatively charged toner particles to regions on the drum that are positively charged.

conductor—pass into the illuminated regions of selenium and neutralize the positive charge. Regions of the selenium coating that remain dark do not allow electrons from the aluminum to flow in, so those regions remain positively charged.

Next, the drum is allowed to come into contact with a black powder called *toner*. The toner particles have been given a negative charge so they will be attracted to positively charged regions of the drum. Toner adheres to the drum where there is positive charge, but no toner adheres to the uncharged regions. A sheet of paper is now rotated onto the drum and positive charge is applied to the back surface of the paper. The charge on the paper is larger than that on the drum, so the paper attracts the negatively charged toner away from the drum, forming an image of the original document on the paper. The final step is to fuse the toner to the paper by passing the paper between hot rollers. With the ink sealed into the fibers of the paper, the copy is finished.

16.3 COULOMB'S LAW

Let's now begin a quantitative treatment of electrical forces among charged objects. Coulomb's law gives the electric force acting between two *point charges*. A **point charge** is a point-like object with a nonzero electric charge. Recall that a point-like object is small enough that its internal structure is of no importance. The electron can be treated as a point charge, since there is no experimental evidence for any internal structure.

The proton *does* have internal structure—it contains three particles called *quarks* bound together—but, since its size is only about 10^{-15} m, it too can be treated as a point charge for most purposes. A charged metal sphere of radius 10 cm can be treated as a point charge if it interacts with another such sphere 100 m away, but not if the two spheres are only a few centimeters apart. Context is everything!

Like gravity, the electric force is an *inverse square law* force. That is, the strength of the force decreases as the separation increases such that the force is proportional to the inverse square of the separation r between the two point charges ($F \propto 1/r^2$). The strength of the force is also proportional to the *magnitude* of each of the two charges ($|q_1|$ and $|q_2|$) just as the gravitational force is proportional to the *mass* of each of two interacting objects.

The magnitude of the electrical force that each of two charges exerts on the other is given by

$$F = \frac{k\,|q_1|\,|q_2|}{r^2} \qquad (16\text{-}2)$$

Since we use the *magnitudes* of q_1 and q_2, F—the magnitude of a vector—is always a positive quantity. The proportionality constant k is experimentally found to have the value

$$k = 8.99 \times 10^9 \; \frac{\text{N}\cdot\text{m}^2}{\text{C}^2} \qquad (16\text{-}3\text{a})$$

The constant k, which we call the *Coulomb constant*, can be written in terms of another constant ϵ_0, the *permittivity of free space*:

$$\epsilon_0 = \frac{1}{4\pi k} = 8.85 \times 10^{-12} \; \frac{\text{C}^2}{\text{N}\cdot\text{m}^2} \qquad (16\text{-}3\text{b})$$

Using ϵ_0, the magnitude of the force is

$$F = \frac{|q_1||q_2|}{4\pi\epsilon_0 r^2}$$

The direction of the electrical force exerted on one point charge due to another point charge is always along the line that joins the two point charges. Remember that, unlike the gravitational force, the electric force can either be attractive or repulsive, depending on the signs of the charges. Coulomb's law is in agreement with Newton's third law: the forces on the two charges are equal in magnitude and opposite in direction (Fig. 16.10).

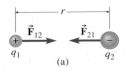

(a)

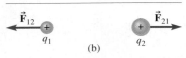

(b)

(c)

Figure 16.10 The electric force on (a) two opposite charges; (b) and (c) two like charges. Vectors are drawn showing the force on each of the two interacting charges.

Problem-Solving Tips for Coulomb's Law

1. Use consistent units; since we know k in standard SI units (N·m²/C²), distances should be in meters and charges in coulombs. When the charge is given in μC or nC, be sure to change the units to coulombs: 1 μC = 10^{-6} C and 1 nC = 10^{-9} C.

2. When finding the electric force on a single charge due to two or more other charges, find the force due to each of the other charges separately. The net force on a particular charge is the vector sum of the forces acting on that charge due to each of the other charges. Often it helps to separate the forces into x- and y-components, add the components separately, then find the magnitude and direction of the net force from its x- and y-components.

3. If several charges lie along the same line, do not worry about an intermediate charge "shielding" the charge located on one side from the charge on the other side. The electric force is long-range just as is gravity; the gravitational force on the Earth due to the Sun does not stop when the Moon passes between the two.

Example 16.3

Electric Force on a Point Charge

Suppose three point charges are arranged as shown in Fig. 16.11. A charge $q_1 = +1.2$ μC is located at the origin of an (x, y) coordinate system; a second charge $q_2 = -0.60$ μC is located at (1.20 m, 0.50 m) and the third charge $q_3 = +0.20$ μC is located at (1.20 m, 0). What is the force on q_3 due to the other two charges?

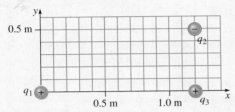

Figure 16.11

Location of point charges in Example 16.3.

Strategy The force on q_3 due to q_1 and the force on q_3 due to q_2 are determined separately. After sketching a free-body diagram, we add the two forces. Adding the repulsive force due to q_1 and the attractive force due to q_2 gives a net force with components upward and to the right. Charge q_1 is more than twice as far away as q_2; even though $|q_1| = 2|q_2|$, the electric force is inversely proportional to distance *squared*, so the force due to q_2 is stronger than the force due to q_1. Let the distance between charges 1 and 3 be $r_{13} = 1.20$ m and the distance between charges 2 and 3 be $r_{23} = 0.50$ m.

Solution Charges 1 and 3 are both positive. The force $\vec{F}_{31}$ on q_3 due to q_1 is repulsive; it can be represented by a vector pointing in the positive x-direction (Fig. 16.12a). Charge q_2 is negative, so it attracts q_3 along the line joining those two charges; $\vec{F}_{32}$ points in the positive y-direction.

The magnitudes of the charges and the separations between the charges were given in the statement of the problem. We first find the magnitude of force $\vec{F}_{31}$ on q_3

due to q_1 from Coulomb's law and then repeat the same process to find the magnitude of force $\vec{F}_{32}$ on q_3 due to q_2.

From Coulomb's law and the given information

$$F_{31} = \frac{k|q_1||q_3|}{r_{13}^2}$$

$$= 8.99 \times 10^9 \frac{\text{N} \cdot \text{m}^2}{\text{C}^2} \times \frac{(1.2 \times 10^{-6} \text{ C}) \times (0.20 \times 10^{-6} \text{ C})}{(1.20 \text{ m})^2}$$

$$= 1.50 \times 10^{-3} \text{ N}$$

Now for the force due to charge 2.

$$F_{32} = \frac{k|q_2||q_3|}{r_{23}^2}$$

$$= 8.99 \times 10^9 \frac{\text{N} \cdot \text{m}^2}{\text{C}^2} \times \frac{(0.60 \times 10^{-6} \text{ C}) \times (0.20 \times 10^{-6} \text{ C})}{(0.50 \text{ m})^2}$$

$$= 4.32 \times 10^{-3} \text{ N}$$

As expected, $F_{32} > F_{31}$.

Adding the two force vectors gives the total force $\vec{F}_3$. *Since the vectors happen to be perpendicular*, we can use the Pythagorean theorem to find the magnitude of the sum (Fig. 16.12b).

The magnitude of F_3 is

$$F_3 = \sqrt{F_{31}^2 + F_{32}^2}$$

$$= \sqrt{(1.50 \times 10^{-3} \text{ N})^2 + (4.32 \times 10^{-3} \text{ N})^2}$$

$$= 4.6 \times 10^{-3} \text{ N}$$

where we have rounded to two significant figures. With the aid of Fig. 16.12b, we can find the direction of the force.

$$\tan \theta = \frac{F_{32}}{F_{31}} = \frac{4.32 \times 10^{-3} \text{ N}}{1.50 \times 10^{-3} \text{ N}} = 2.88$$

$$\theta = 71° \text{ above the } x\text{-axis}$$

Discussion The net force has a direction compatible with our expectation—it has components in the $+x$- and $+y$-directions. The force due to q_2 is stronger, so the y-component of the net force is larger than the x-component; the force makes a smaller angle with the y-axis (19°) than with the x-axis (71°).

Practice Problem 16.3 Electric Force on Charge 2

Find the magnitude and direction of the electric force on charge 2 due to charges 1 and 3 in Fig. 16.11. [*Hint:* $\vec{F}_{21}$ and $\vec{F}_{23}$ are *not* perpendicular.]

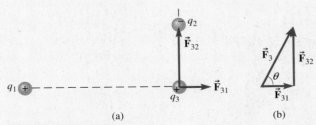

Figure 16.12

(a) The directions of forces $\vec{F}_{31}$ and $\vec{F}_{32}$. (b) Vectors $\vec{F}_{31}$ and $\vec{F}_{32}$ and their sum $\vec{F}_3$.

If we consider the forces acting on the microscopic building blocks of matter (such as atoms, molecules, ions, and electrons), we find that the electrical forces are much stronger than the gravitational forces between them. Only when we put a large number of atoms and molecules together to make a massive object can the gravitational force dominate. This domination occurs only because there is an almost perfect balance between positive and negative charges in a large object, leading to nearly zero net charge.

Example 16.4

Two Charged Balls, Hanging in Equilibrium

Two Styrofoam balls of mass 10.0 g are suspended by threads of length 25 cm. The balls are charged, after which they hang apart, each at $\theta = 15.0°$ to the vertical (Fig. 16.13). (a) Are the signs of the charges the same or opposite? (b) Are the magnitudes of the charges necessarily the same? Explain. (c) Find the net charge on each ball, *assuming* that the charges are equal.

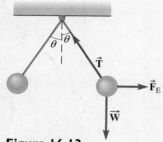

Figure 16.13

Sketch of the situation.

Strategy Each ball exerts an electric force on the other since both are charged. The *gravitational* forces that the balls exert on one another are negligibly small, but the gravitational forces that the Earth exerts on the balls are not negligible. The third force acting on each of the balls is due to the tension in a thread. We choose to analyze the forces acting on the ball using a free-body diagram. The sum of the three forces must be zero since the ball is in equilibrium.

Solution Each ball experiences three forces: the electrical force, the gravitational force, and the pull of the thread, which is under tension. Figure 16.14 shows a free-body diagram for one of the balls.

(a) The electric force is clearly repulsive—the balls are pushed apart—so the charges must have the same sign. There is no way to tell whether they are both positive or both negative.

(b) At first glance it *might* appear that the charges must be the same; the balls are hanging at the same angle, so there is no clue as to which charge is larger. But look again at Coulomb's law: the force on either of the balls is proportional to the product of the two charge magnitudes;

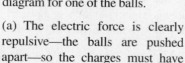

Figure 16.14

A free-body diagram for one ball.

$F \propto |q_1||q_2|$. In accordance with Newton's third law, Coulomb's law says that the two forces that make up the interaction are equal in magnitude and opposite in direction. The charges are not necessarily equal.

(c) Let us choose the x- and y-axes in the horizontal and vertical directions, respectively. Of the three forces acting on a ball, only one, that due to the tension in the thread, has both x- and y-components. From Fig. 16.14, the tension in the thread has a y-component equal in magnitude to the weight of the ball, and an x-component equal in magnitude to the electric force on the ball. By similar triangles (Fig. 16.15),

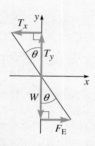

Figure 16.15

Similar triangles used in the solution.

$$\frac{F_E}{W} = \tan \theta \quad \text{or} \quad F_E = W \tan \theta$$

From Coulomb's law [Eq. (16-2)],

$$F_E = \frac{k|q|^2}{r^2} \tag{1}$$

where $|q|$ is the magnitude of the charge on each of the two balls (now assumed to be equal). The separation of the balls (Fig. 16.16) is

$$r = 2(d \sin \theta) \tag{2}$$

where $d = 25$ cm is the length of the thread.

Some algebra now enables us to solve for $|q|$. From Coulomb's law,

$$|q|^2 = \frac{F_E r^2}{k} \tag{3}$$

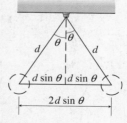

Figure 16.16

Finding the separation between the two balls.

Continued on next page

Example 16.4 Continued

We can substitute expressions (1) and (2) into Eq. (3) for F_E and r:

$$|q|^2 = \frac{(W \tan \theta)\,(2d \sin \theta)^2}{k}$$

$$= \frac{4d^2 mg \tan \theta \sin^2 \theta}{k}$$

$$|q| = \sqrt{\frac{4 \times (0.25\ \text{m})^2 \times 0.0100\ \text{kg} \times 9.8\ \text{N/kg} \times \tan 15.0° \times \sin^2 15.0°}{8.99 \times 10^9\ \text{N·m}^2/\text{C}^2}}$$

$$= 0.22\ \mu\text{C}$$

The charges can either be both positive or both negative, so the charges are either both $+0.22\ \mu$C or both $-0.22\ \mu$C.

Discussion   We can check the units in the final expression for q:

$$\sqrt{\frac{\text{m}^2 \times \text{kg} \times \text{N/kg}}{\text{N·m}^2/\text{C}^2}} = \sqrt{\frac{\text{N·m}^2}{\text{N·m}^2/\text{C}^2}} = \sqrt{\text{C}^2} = \text{C}\quad\text{(OK!)}$$

Another check: if the balls were uncharged, they would hang straight down ($\theta = 0$). Substituting $\theta = 0$ into the final algebraic expression does give $q = 0$.

How large a charge would make the threads horizontal? As the charge on the balls is increased, the angle of the thread *approaches* 90° but can never reach 90° because the tension in the thread must always have an upward component to balance gravity. In the algebraic answer, as $\theta \to 90°$, $\tan \theta \to \infty$ and $\sin \theta \to 1$, which would yield a charge q approaching ∞. The threads cannot be horizontal for any *finite* amount of charge.

Practice Problem 16.4   Three Point Charges

Three identical point charges $q = -2.0$ nC are at the vertices of an equilateral triangle with sides of length 1.0 cm. What is the magnitude of the electrical force acting on any one of them?

16.4   THE ELECTRIC FIELD

Recall that the gravitational field at a point is defined to be the gravitational force per unit mass on an object placed at that point. If the gravitational force on an apple of mass m due to the Earth is $\vec{F}_g$, then the Earth's gravitational field $\vec{g}$ at the location of the apple is given by

$$\vec{g} = \frac{\vec{F}_g}{m}$$

The directions of $\vec{F}_g$ and $\vec{g}$ are the same since m is positive. The gravitational field we encounter most often is that due to the Earth, but the gravitational field could be due to any astronomical body, or to more than one body. For instance, an astronaut may be concerned with the gravitational field at the location of her spacecraft due to the Sun, the Earth, and the Moon combined. Since gravitational forces add as vectors—as do all forces—the gravitational field at the location of the spacecraft is the vector sum of the separate gravitational fields due to the Sun, the Earth, and the Moon.

Similarly, if a point charge q is in the vicinity of other charges, it experiences an electric force $\vec{F}_E$. The **electric field** (symbol $\vec{E}$) at any point is defined to be the electric force per unit *charge* at that point (Fig. 16.17):

$$\vec{E} = \frac{\vec{F}_E}{q}\tag{16-4a}$$

The SI units of the electric field are N/C.

In contrast to the gravitational force, which is always in the same direction as the gravitational field, the electric force can either be parallel or antiparallel to the electric field depending on the sign of the charge q that is sampling the field. *If q is positive*, the direction of the electric force $\vec{F}_E$ is the same as the direction of the electric field $\vec{E}$; if q is negative, the two vectors have opposite directions. To probe the electric field in some region, imagine placing a point charge q at various points. At each point you calculate the electric force on this *test charge* and divide the force by q to find the electric field at that point. It is usually easiest to imagine a *positive* test charge so that the field direction is the same as the force direction, but the field comes out the same regardless of the sign or magnitude of q, unless its magnitude is large enough to disturb the other charges and thereby change the electric field.

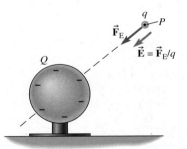

Figure 16.17 The electric field $\vec{E}$ that exists at a point P due to a charged object with charge Q is equal to the electric force $\vec{F}_E$ experienced by a small test charge q placed at that point divided by q.

Why is $\vec{\mathbf{E}}$ defined as the force per unit *charge* instead of per unit mass as done for gravitational field? The gravitational force on an object is proportional to its mass, so it makes sense to talk about the force per unit mass (the SI units of $\vec{\mathbf{g}}$ are N/kg). In contrast to the gravitational force, the electrical force on a point charge is instead proportional to its *charge*.

Why is the electric field a useful concept? For the same reason that the gravitational field is. Once we know that the electric field at some point is $\vec{\mathbf{E}}$, then it is easy to calculate the electric force $\vec{\mathbf{F}}_E$ on any point charge q placed at that point:

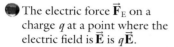 The electric force $\vec{\mathbf{F}}_E$ on a charge q at a point where the electric field is $\vec{\mathbf{E}}$ is $q\vec{\mathbf{E}}$.

$$\vec{\mathbf{F}}_E = q\vec{\mathbf{E}} \qquad (16\text{-}4b)$$

 Note that $\vec{\mathbf{E}}$ is the electric field at the location of point charge q due to all the *other* charges in the vicinity. Certainly the point charge produces a field of its own at nearby points; this field causes forces on *other* charges. In other words, a point charge exerts no force on itself.

Example 16.5

Charged Sphere Hanging in a Uniform $\vec{\mathbf{E}}$ Field

A small sphere of mass 5.10 g is hanging vertically from an insulating thread that is 12.0 cm long. By charging some nearby flat metal plates, the sphere is subjected to a horizontal electric field of magnitude 7.20×10^5 N/C. As a result, the sphere is displaced 6.00 cm horizontally in the direction of the electric field (Fig. 16.18). (a) What is the angle θ that the thread makes with the vertical? (b) What is the tension in the thread? (c) What is the charge on the sphere?

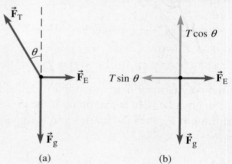

Figure 16.19

(a) A free-body diagram showing forces acting on the sphere. (b) Free-body diagram in which the force due to the cord is replaced by its vertical and horizontal components.

Strategy We assume that the sphere is small enough to be treated as a point charge. Then the electric force on the sphere is given by $\vec{\mathbf{F}}_E = q\vec{\mathbf{E}}$. Figure 16.18 shows that the sphere is pushed to the right by the field; therefore, $\vec{\mathbf{F}}_E$ is to the right. Since $\vec{\mathbf{F}}_E$ and $\vec{\mathbf{E}}$ have the same direction, the charge on the sphere is positive. After drawing a free-body diagram showing all the forces acting on the sphere, we set the net force on the sphere equal to zero since it hangs in equilibrium.

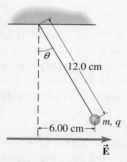

Figure 16.18

A charged sphere hanging in a uniform $\vec{\mathbf{E}}$ field.

electrical force must balance the horizontal component of the same force. In Fig. 16.19b, we show the components of $\vec{\mathbf{F}}_T$. The magnitude of $\vec{\mathbf{F}}_T$ is the tension in the thread T.

Looking at the free-body diagram and reviewing what we have in the given information, we cannot determine $\vec{\mathbf{F}}_E$ yet because the value of the charge q is unknown. There is also no information on the tension in the thread. The weight, however, can be determined since the mass is known:

$$F_g = mg$$

The weight must be equal to the upward component of $\vec{\mathbf{F}}_T$:

$$mg = T \cos \theta$$

Substituting known values,

$$5.10 \times 10^{-3} \text{ kg} \times 9.80 \text{ N/kg} = 0.0500 \text{ N} = T \cos 30.0°$$

$$T = \frac{0.0500 \text{ N}}{\cos 30.0°} = 5.77 \times 10^{-2} \text{ N}$$

Solution (a) The angle θ can be found from the geometry of Fig. 16.18. The thread's length (12.0 cm) is the hypotenuse of a right triangle. The side of the triangle opposite angle θ is the horizontal displacement (6.00 cm). Thus,

$$\sin \theta = \frac{6.00 \text{ cm}}{12.0 \text{ cm}} = 0.500 \quad \text{and} \quad \theta = 30.0°$$

(b) We start by drawing a free-body diagram (Fig. 16.19a). The gravitational force must balance the vertical component of the thread's pull on the sphere ($\vec{\mathbf{F}}_T$). The

Continued on next page

Example 16.5 Continued

This result gives the magnitude of $\vec{F}_T$. The direction is along the thread toward the support point, at an angle of 30.0° from the vertical.

(c) We set the horizontal component of the thread force equal to the magnitude of the electrical force.

$$T \sin \theta = F_E = |q|E$$

We can now solve for $|q|$.

$$|q| = \frac{T \sin \theta}{E} = \frac{(5.77 \times 10^{-2}\text{ N}) \sin 30.0°}{7.20 \times 10^5\text{ N/C}} = 40.1\text{ nC}$$

We have determined the magnitude of the charge. The sign of the charge is positive because the electric force on the sphere is in the direction of the electric field. Therefore,

$$q = 40.1\text{ nC}$$

Discussion   This problem has many steps, but, taken one by one, each step helps to solve for one of the unknowns and leads the way to find the next unknown. At first glance, it may appear that not enough information is given, but after a figure is drawn to aid in the visualization of the forces and their components, the steps to follow are more easily determined.

Practice Problem 16.5   Effect of Doubling the Charge on the Hanging Mass

If the charge on the sphere were doubled in Example 16.5, what angle would the thread make with the vertical?

Electric Field due to a Point Charge

The electric field due to a single point charge Q can be found using Coulomb's law. Imagine a positive test charge q placed at various locations. Coulomb's law says that the force acting on the test charge is

$$F = \frac{k|q||Q|}{r^2} \qquad (16\text{-}2)$$

The electric field strength is then

$$E = \frac{F}{|q|} = \frac{k|Q|}{r^2} \qquad (16\text{-}5)$$

The field falls off as $1/r^2$, following the same inverse square law as the electrical force.

What is the direction of the field? If Q is positive, then a positive test charge would be repelled, so the field vector points away from Q (or *radially outward*). If Q is negative, then the field vector points toward Q (*radially inward*).

The electric field due to more than one point charge can be found using the **principle of superposition**:

The electric field at any point is the vector sum of the field vectors at that point caused by each charge separately.

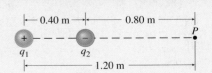

Example 16.6

Electric Field at a Point in Space

Two point charges are located on the *x*-axis (Fig. 16.20). Charge $q_1 = +0.60\ \mu\text{C}$ is located at $x = 0$; charge $q_2 = -0.50\ \mu\text{C}$ is located at $x = 0.40$ m. Point P is located at $x = 1.20$ m. What is the magnitude and direction of the electric field at point P due to the two charges?

Strategy   We can determine the field at P due to q_1 and the field at P due to q_2 separately using Coulomb's law and the definition of the electric field. In each case, the electric field points in the direction of the electric force on a *positive*

Figure 16.20
Two point charges on the *x*-axis.

test charge at point P. The sum of these two fields is the electric field at P. We sketch a vector diagram to help add the fields correctly. Since there are two different distances

Continued on next page

Example 16.6 Continued

in the problem, subscripts help to distinguish them. Let the distance between charge 1 and point P be $r_1 = 1.20$ m and the distance between charge 2 and point P be $r_2 = 0.80$ m.

Solution   Charge 1 is positive. We imagine a tiny positive test charge, q_0, located at point P. Since charge 1 repels the positive test charge, the force $\vec{F}_1$ on the test charge due to q_1 is in the positive x-direction (Fig. 16.21). The direction of the electric field due to charge 1 is also in the $+x$-direction since $\vec{E}_1 = \vec{F}_1/q_0$ and $q_0 > 0$. Charge q_2 is negative so it attracts the imaginary test charge along the line joining the two charges; the force $\vec{F}_2$ on the test charge due to q_2 is in the negative x-direction. Therefore $\vec{E}_2 = \vec{F}_2/q_0$ is in the $-x$-direction.

We first find the magnitude of the field $\vec{E}_1$ at P due to q_1 and then repeat the same process to find the magnitude of field $\vec{E}_2$ at P due to q_2. From the given information,

$$E_1 = \frac{k|q_1|}{r_1^2}$$

$$= 8.99 \times 10^9 \, \frac{\text{N} \cdot \text{m}^2}{\text{C}^2} \times \frac{0.60 \times 10^{-6} \, \text{C}}{(1.20 \, \text{m})^2}$$

$$= 3.75 \times 10^3 \, \text{N/C}$$

Now for the magnitude of field $\vec{E}_2$ at P due to charge 2.

$$E_2 = \frac{k|q_2|}{r_2^2}$$

$$= 8.99 \times 10^9 \, \frac{\text{N} \cdot \text{m}^2}{\text{C}^2} \times \frac{0.50 \times 10^{-6} \, \text{C}}{(0.80 \, \text{m})^2}$$

$$= 7.02 \times 10^3 \, \text{N/C}$$

Figure 16.22 shows the vector addition $\vec{E}_1 + \vec{E}_2 = \vec{E}$, which points in the $-x$-direction since $E_2 > E_1$. The magnitude of E at point P is

$$E = 7.02 \times 10^3 \, \text{N/C} - 3.75 \times 10^3 \, \text{N/C} = 3.3 \times 10^3 \, \text{N/C}$$

The electric field at P is 3.3×10^3 N/C in the $-x$-direction.

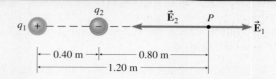

Figure 16.21

Directions of electric field vectors at point P due to charges q_1 and q_2.

Figure 16.22

Vector addition of $\vec{E}_1$ and $\vec{E}_2$.

Discussion   This same method is used to find the electric field at a point due to *any* number of point charges. The direction of the electric field due to each charge alone is the direction of the electric force on an imaginary positive test charge at that point. The magnitude of each electric field is found from Eq. (16-5). Then the electric field vectors are added. If the charges and the point do not all lie on the same line, then the fields can be added by resolving them into x- and y-components and summing the components.

Even when electric fields are not due to a small number of point charges, the principle of superposition still applies: the electric field at any point is the vector sum of the fields at that point caused by each charge or set of charges separately.

Practice Problem 16.6   Electric Field at Point P due to Two Charges

Find the magnitude and direction of the electric field at point P due to charges 1 and 2 located on the x-axis. The charges are $q_1 = +0.040$ μC and $q_2 = +0.010$ μC. Charge q_1 is at the origin, charge q_2 is at $x = 0.30$ m, and point P is at $x = 1.50$ m.

Electric Field Lines

It is often difficult to make a visual representation of an electric field using vector arrows; the vectors drawn at different points may overlap and become impossible to distinguish. Another visual representation of the electric field is a sketch of the **electric field lines**, a set of continuous lines that represent both the magnitude and the direction of the electric field vector as follows:

Interpretation of Electric Field Lines

- The direction of the electric field vector at any point is *tangent to the field line* passing through that point and in the direction indicated by arrows on the field line (Fig. 16.23a).

- The electric field is strong where field lines are close together and weak where they are far apart (Fig. 16.23b). (More specifically, if you imagine a small surface perpendicular to the field lines, the magnitude of the field is proportional to the number of lines that cross the surface divided by the area.)

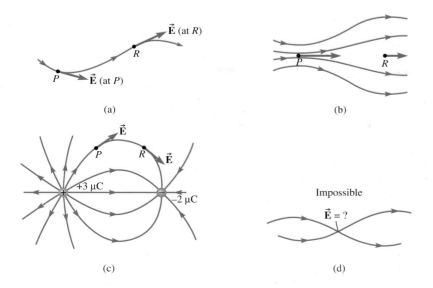

Figure 16.23 Field line rules illustrated. (a) The electric field direction at points P and R. (b) The magnitude of the electric field at point P is larger than the magnitude at R. (c) If 12 lines are drawn starting on a point charge $+3\ \mu C$, then 8 lines must be drawn ending on a $-2\ \mu C$ point charge. (d) If field lines were to cross, the direction of $\vec{E}$ at the intersection would be undetermined.

To help sketch the field lines, these three additional rules are useful:

Rules for Sketching Field Lines

- Field lines start only on positive charges and end only on negative charges.
- The number of lines starting on a positive charge (or ending on a negative charge) is proportional to the magnitude of the charge (Fig. 16.23c). (The total number of lines you draw is arbitrary; the more lines you draw, the better the representation of the field.)
- Field lines never cross. The electric field at any point has a unique direction; if field lines crossed, the field would have two directions at the same point (Fig. 16.23d).

Field Lines for a Point Charge

Figure 16.24 shows sketches of the field lines due to single point charges. The field lines show that the direction of the field is radial (away from a positive charge or toward a negative charge). The lines are close together near the point charge, where the field is strong, and are more spread out farther from the point charge, showing that the field strength diminishes with distance. No other nearby charges are shown in these sketches, so the lines go out to infinity as if the point charge were the only thing in the universe. If the field of view is enlarged, so that other charges are shown, the lines starting on the positive point charge would end on some faraway negative charges, and those that end on the negative charge would start on some faraway positive charges.

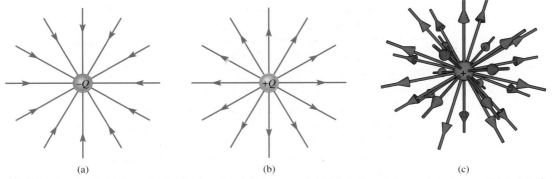

Figure 16.24 Electric field lines due to isolated point charges. (a) Field of negative point charge; (b) field of positive point charge. These sketches show only field lines that lie in a two-dimensional plane. (c) A three-dimensional illustration of electric field lines due to a positive charge.

Electric Field due to a Dipole

Dipole: two equal and opposite point charges

A pair of point charges with equal and opposite charges that are near one another is called a **dipole** (literally *two poles*). To find the electric field due to the dipole at various points by using Coulomb's law would be extremely tedious, but sketching some field lines immediately gives an approximate idea of the electric field (Fig. 16.25).

Because the charges in the dipole have equal charge magnitudes, the same number of lines that start on the positive charge end on the negative charge. Close to either of the charges, the field lines are evenly spaced in all directions, just as if the other charge were not present. As we approach one of the charges, the field due to that charge gets so large ($F \propto 1/r^2$, $r \rightarrow 0$) that the field due to the other charge is negligible in comparison and we are left with the spherically symmetric field due to a single point charge.

The field at other points has contributions from both charges. Figure 16.25 shows, for one point P, how the field vectors ($\vec{E}_-$ and $\vec{E}_+$) due to the two separate charges add, following vector addition rules, to give the total field $\vec{E}$ at point P. Note that the total field $\vec{E}$ is tangent to the field line through point P.

The principles of superposition and symmetry are two powerful tools for determining electric fields. The use of symmetry is illustrated in Conceptual Example 16.7.

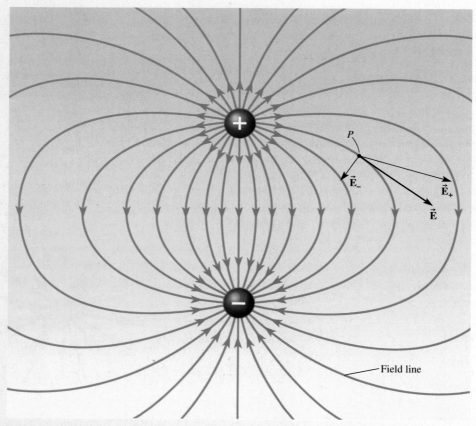

Figure 16.25 Electric field lines for a dipole. The electric field vector $\vec{E}$ at a point P is tangent to the field line through that point and is the sum of the fields ($\vec{E}_-$ and $\vec{E}_+$) due to each of the two point charges.

Conceptual Example 16.7

Field Lines for a Thin Spherical Shell

A thin metallic spherical shell of radius R carries a total charge Q, which is positive. The charge is spread out evenly over the shell's outside surface. Sketch the electric field lines in two different views of the situation: (a) The spherical shell is tiny and you are looking at it from distant points; (b) you are looking at the field inside the shell's cavity. In (a), also sketch $\vec{\mathbf{E}}$ field vectors at two different points outside the shell.

Strategy   Since the charge on the shell is positive, field lines begin on the shell. A sphere is a highly symmetric shape: standing at the center, it looks the same in any chosen direction. This symmetry helps in sketching the field lines.

Solution   (a) A tiny spherical shell located far away cannot be distinguished from a point charge. The sphere looks like a point when seen from a great distance and the field lines look just like those emanating from a positive point charge (Fig. 16.26). The field lines show that the electric field is directed radially away from the center of the shell and that its magnitude decreases with increasing distance, as illustrated by the two $\vec{\mathbf{E}}$ vectors in Fig. 16.26.

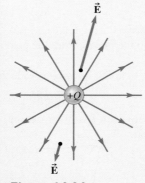

Figure 16.26
Field lines outside the shell are directed radially outward.

(b) Field lines begin on the positive charges on the shell surface. Some go outward, representing the electric field outside the shell, while others may *perhaps* go inward, representing the field inside the shell. Any field lines inside must start evenly spaced on the shell and point directly toward the center of the shell (Fig. 16.27); the lines cannot deviate from the radial direction due to the symmetry of the sphere. But what would happen to the field lines when they reach the center? The lines can only end at the center if a negative point charge is found there—but there is no point charge. If the lines do not end, they would cross at the center. That cannot be

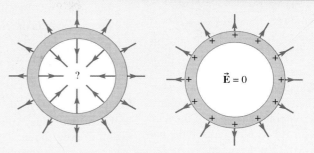

Figure 16.27
If there are field lines inside the shell, they must start on the shell and point radially inward. Then what?

Figure 16.28
There can be no field lines—and therefore no electric field—inside the shell.

right since the field must have a *unique* direction at every point—field lines never cross. The inescapable conclusion: *there are no field lines inside the shell* (Fig. 16.28), so $\vec{\mathbf{E}} = 0$ everywhere inside the shell.

Discussion   We conclude that the electric field *inside* a spherical shell of charge is zero. This conclusion, which we reached using field lines and symmetry considerations, can also be proved using Coulomb's law, the principle of superposition, and some calculus—a much more difficult method!

The field line picture also shows that *the electric field pattern outside a spherical shell is the same as if the charge were all condensed into a point charge at the center of the sphere.*

Conceptual Practice Problem 16.7   Field Lines After a Negative Point Charge Is Inserted

Suppose the spherical shell of evenly distributed positive charge Q has a point charge $-Q$ placed at its center. (a) Sketch the field lines. [*Hint:* Since the charges are equal in magnitude, the number of lines starting on the shell is equal to the number of lines ending on the point charge.] (b) Defend your sketch using the principle of superposition (total field = field due to shell + field due to point charge).

Electrolocation

Long before scientists learned how to detect and measure electric fields, certain animals and fish evolved organs to produce and detect electric fields. *Gymnarchus niloticus* (see the Chapter Opener) has electrical organs running along the length of its body; these organs set up an electric field around the fish (Fig. 16.29). When a nearby object distorts the field lines, *Gymnarchus* detects the change through sensory receptors, mostly near the head, and responds accordingly. This extra sense enables the fish to detect prey or predators in muddy streams where eyes are less useful.

Making the Connection:
electrolocation in fish

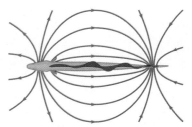

Figure 16.29 The electric field generated by *Gymnarchus*. The field is approximately that of a dipole. The head of the fish is positively charged and the tail is negatively charged.

Figure 16.30 Uniform electric field between two parallel metal plates.

Since *Gymnarchus* relies primarily on electrolocation, where slight changes in the electric field are interpreted as the presence of nearby objects, it is important that it be able to create the same electric field over and over. For this reason, *Gymnarchus* swims by undulating its long dorsal fin while holding its body rigid. Keeping the backbone straight keeps the negative and positive charge centers aligned and at a fixed distance apart. A swishing tail would cause variation in the electric field and that would make electrolocation much less accurate.

16.5   MOTION OF A POINT CHARGE IN A UNIFORM ELECTRIC FIELD

The simplest example of how a charged object responds to an electric field is when the electric field (due to other charges) is **uniform**—that is, has the same magnitude and direction at every point. The field due to a single point charge is *not* uniform; it is radially directed and its magnitude follows the inverse square law. To create a uniform field requires a large number of charges. The most common way to create a (nearly) uniform electric field is to put equal and opposite charges on two parallel metal plates (Fig. 16.30). If the charges are $\pm Q$ and the plates have area A, the magnitude of the field between the plates is

$$E = \frac{Q}{\epsilon_0 A} \qquad (16\text{-}6)$$

(This expression can be derived using Gauss's law—see Section 16.7.) The direction of the field is perpendicular to the plates, from the positively charged plate toward the negatively charged plate.

Assuming the uniform field $\vec{E}$ is known, a point charge q experiences an electric force

$$\vec{F} = q\vec{E} \qquad (16\text{-}4b)$$

If this is the only force acting on the point charge, then the net force is constant and therefore so is the acceleration:

$$\vec{a} = \frac{\vec{F}}{m} = \frac{q\vec{E}}{m}$$

With a constant acceleration, the motion can take one of two forms. If the initial velocity of the point charge is zero or is parallel or antiparallel to the field, then the motion is along a straight line. If the point charge has an initial velocity component perpendicular to the field, then the trajectory is parabolic (just like a projectile in a uniform gravitational field if other forces are negligible). All the tools developed in Chapter 4 to analyze motion with constant acceleration can be used here. The direction of the acceleration is either parallel to $\vec{E}$ (for a positive charge) or antiparallel to $\vec{E}$ (for a negative charge).

Example 16.8

Electron Beam

A cathode ray tube (CRT) is used to accelerate electrons in some televisions, computer monitors, oscilloscopes, and x-ray tubes. Electrons from a heated filament pass through a hole in the cathode; they are then accelerated by an electric field between the cathode and the anode (Fig. 16.31). Suppose an electron passes through the hole in the cathode at a velocity of 1.0×10^5 m/s toward the anode. The electric field is uniform between the anode and cathode and has a magnitude of 1.0×10^4 N/C. (a) What is the acceleration of the electron? (b) If the anode and cathode are separated by 2.0 cm, what is the final velocity of the electron?

Strategy   Because the field is uniform, the acceleration of the electron is constant. Then we can apply Newton's

second law and use any of the methods we previously developed for motion with constant acceleration.

Given: initial speed $v_i = 1.0 \times 10^5$ m/s;
 separation between plates $d = 0.020$ m;
 electric field magnitude $E = 1.0 \times 10^4$ N/C

Look up: electron mass $m_e = 9.109 \times 10^{-31}$ kg;
 electron charge $q = -e = -1.602 \times 10^{-19}$ C

Find: (a) acceleration; (b) final velocity

Solution   (a) First, check that gravity is negligible. The weight of the electron is

$$F_g = mg = 9.109 \times 10^{-31} \text{ kg} \times 9.8 \text{ m/s}^2 = 8.9 \times 10^{-30} \text{ N}$$

Continued on next page

Example 16.8 Continued

The magnitude of the electric force is

$$F_E = eE = 1.602 \times 10^{-19}\,\text{C} \times 1.0 \times 10^4\,\text{N/C} = 1.6 \times 10^{-15}\,\text{N}$$

which is about 14 orders of magnitude larger. Gravity is completely negligible. While between the plates, the electron's acceleration is therefore

$$a = \frac{F}{m_e} = \frac{eE}{m_e} = \frac{1.602 \times 10^{-19}\,\text{C} \times 1.0 \times 10^4\,\text{N/C}}{9.109 \times 10^{-31}\,\text{kg}}$$

$$= 1.76 \times 10^{15}\,\text{m/s}^2$$

To two significant figures, $a = 1.8 \times 10^{15}\,\text{m/s}^2$. Since the charge on the electron is negative, the direction of the acceleration is opposite to the electric field, or to the right in the figure.

(b) The initial velocity of the electron is also to the right. We have a one-dimensional constant acceleration problem since the initial velocity and the acceleration are in the same direction. From Eq. (4-5), the final velocity is

$$v_f = \sqrt{v_i^2 + 2ad}$$

$$= \sqrt{(1.0 \times 10^5)^2 + 2 \times 1.76 \times 10^{15} \times 0.020}\,\text{m/s}$$

$$= 8.4 \times 10^6\,\text{m/s to the right}$$

Discussion   The acceleration of the electrons seems large. This large value might cause some concern, but there is no law of physics against such large accelerations. Note that the final *speed* is less than the speed of light (3×10^8 m/s), the universe's ultimate speed limit.

You may suspect that this problem can also be solved using energy methods. We could indeed find the work done by the electric force and use the work done to find the change in kinetic energy. The energy approach for electric fields is developed in chapter 17.

Practice Problem 16.8   Slowing Some Protons

If a beam of *protons* were projected horizontally to the right through the hole in the cathode (Fig. 16.31) with an initial speed of $v_i = 3.0 \times 10^5$ m/s, with what speed would the protons reach the anode (if they do reach it)?

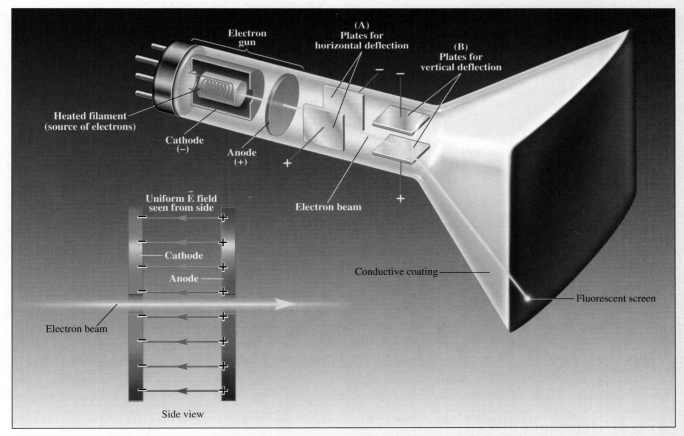

Figure 16.31 In a cathode ray tube (CRT), electrons are accelerated to high speeds by an electric field between the cathode and anode. This CRT, used in an oscilloscope, has two pairs of parallel plates that are used to deflect the electron beam horizontally and vertically.

The electric field is used to speed up the electron beam in a CRT. In an oscilloscope—a device used to measure time-dependent quantities in circuits—it is also used to deflect the beam. An electric field is *not* used to deflect the electron beam in the CRT used in a TV or computer monitor; that function is performed by a magnetic field.

Example 16.9

Deflection of an Electron Projected into a Uniform $\vec{\mathbf{E}}$ Field

An electron is projected horizontally into the uniform electric field directed vertically downward between two parallel plates (Fig. 16.32). The plates are 2.00 cm apart and are of length 4.00 cm. The initial speed of the electron is $v_i = 8.00 \times 10^6$ m/s. As it enters the region between the plates, the electron is midway between the two plates; as it leaves, the electron just misses the upper plate. What is the magnitude of the electric field?

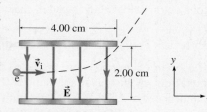

Figure 16.32

An electron deflected by an electric field.

Strategy

Using the x- and y-axes in the figure, the electric field is in the $-y$-direction and the initial velocity of the electron is in the $+x$-direction. The electric force on the electron is *upward* (in the $+y$-direction) since it has a negative charge. Thus, the acceleration of the electron is upward. Since the acceleration is in the $+y$-direction, the x-component of the velocity is constant. If the electron just misses the upper plate, its displacement is $+1.00$ cm in the y-direction and $+4.00$ cm in the x-direction. From v_x and Δx, we can find the time the electron spends between the plates. From Δy and the time, we can find a_y. From the acceleration we find the electric field using Newton's second law, $\sum \vec{\mathbf{F}} = m\vec{\mathbf{a}}$.

We ignore the gravitational force on the electron because we assume it to be negligible. We can test this assumption later.

Given: $\Delta x = 4.00$ cm; $\Delta y = 1.00$ cm; $v_x = 8.00 \times 10^6$ m/s
Find: electric field strength, E

Solution

We start by finding the time the electron spends between the plates from Δx and v_x.

$$\Delta t = \frac{\Delta x}{v_x} = \frac{4.00 \times 10^{-2}\ \text{m}}{8.00 \times 10^6\ \text{m/s}} = 5.00 \times 10^{-9}\ \text{s}$$

From the time spent between the plates and Δy, we find the component of the acceleration in the y-direction.

$$\Delta y = \tfrac{1}{2} a_y (\Delta t)^2$$

$$a_y = \frac{2\,\Delta y}{(\Delta t)^2} = \frac{2 \times 1.00 \times 10^{-2}\ \text{m}}{(5.00 \times 10^{-9}\ \text{s})^2} = 8.00 \times 10^{14}\ \text{m/s}^2$$

This acceleration is produced by the electric force acting on the electron since we assume that no other forces act. From Newton's second law,

$$F_y = qE_y = m_e a_y$$

Solving for E_y, we have

$$E_y = \frac{m_e a_y}{q} = \frac{9.109 \times 10^{-31}\ \text{kg} \times 8.00 \times 10^{14}\ \text{m/s}^2}{-1.602 \times 10^{-19}\ \text{C}}$$

$$= -4.55 \times 10^3\ \text{N/C}$$

Since the field has no x-component, its magnitude is 4.55×10^3 N/C.

Discussion   We have ignored the gravitational force on the electron because we suspect that it is negligible in comparison with the electric force. This should be checked to be sure it is a valid assumption.

$$\vec{\mathbf{F}} = m_e \vec{\mathbf{g}} = 9.109 \times 10^{-31}\ \text{kg} \times 9.80\ \text{N/kg}\ \text{downward}$$

$$= 8.93 \times 10^{-30}\ \text{N downward}$$

$$\vec{\mathbf{F}}_E = q\vec{\mathbf{E}} = -1.602 \times 10^{-19}\ \text{C} \times 4.55 \times 10^3\ \text{N/C downward}$$

$$= 7.29 \times 10^{-16}\ \text{N upward}$$

The electric force is stronger than the gravitational force by a factor of approximately 10^{14}, so the assumption is valid.

Practice Problem 16.9   Deflection of a Proton Projected into a Uniform $\vec{\mathbf{E}}$ Field

If the electron is replaced by a proton projected with the same initial velocity, will the proton exit the region between the plates or will it hit one of the plates? If it does not strike one of the plates, by how much is it deflected by the time it leaves the region of electric field?

16.6   CONDUCTORS IN ELECTROSTATIC EQUILIBRIUM

In Section 16.1, we described how a piece of paper can be polarized by nearby charges. The polarization is the paper's response to an applied electric field. By *applied* we mean a field due to charges *outside the paper*. The separation of charge in the paper produces an electric field of its own. The net electric field at any point—whether inside or outside the paper—is the sum of the applied field and the field due to the separated charges in the paper.

How much charge separation occurs depends on both the strength of the applied field and properties of the atoms and molecules that make up the paper. Some materials are more easily polarized than others. The *most* easily polarized materials are conductors because they contain highly mobile charges that can move freely through the entire volume of the material.

It is useful to examine the distribution of charge in a conductor, whether the conductor has a net charge or lies in an externally applied field, or both. We restrict our attention to a conductor in which the mobile charges are at rest in equilibrium, a situation called **electrostatic equilibrium**. If charge is put on a conductor, mobile charges move about until a stable distribution is attained. The same thing happens when an external field is applied or changed—charges move in response to the external field, but they soon reach an equilibrium distribution.

If the electric field within a conducting material is nonzero, it exerts a force on each of the mobile charges (usually electrons) and makes them move preferentially in a certain direction. With mobile charge in motion, the conductor cannot be in electrostatic equilibrium. Therefore, we can draw this conclusion:

> The electric field is zero at any point within a conducting material in electrostatic equilibrium.

⬤ In **electrostatic equilibrium**, there is no net motion of charge.

Electronic circuits and cables are often shielded from stray electric fields produced by other devices by placing them inside metal enclosures (see Conceptual Question 6). Free charges in the metal enclosure rearrange themselves as the external electric field changes. As long as the charges in the enclosure can keep up with changes in the external field, the external field is canceled inside the enclosure.

The electric field is zero *within* the conducting material, but is not necessarily zero *outside*. If there are field lines outside but none inside, field lines must either start or end at charges on the surface of the conductor. Field lines start or end on charges, so

Making the Connection: electrostatic shielding

> When a conductor is in electrostatic equilibrium, only its surface(s) can have net charge.

At any point within the conductor, there are equal amounts of positive and negative charge. Imbalance between positive and negative charge can occur only on the surface(s) of the conductor.

It is also true that, in electrostatic equilibrium,

> The electric field at the surface of the conductor is perpendicular to the surface.

How do we know that? If the field had a component parallel to the surface, any free charges at the surface would feel a force parallel to the surface and would move in response. Thus, if there is a parallel component at the surface, the conductor cannot be in electrostatic equilibrium.

If a conductor has an irregular shape, the excess charge on its surface(s) is concentrated more where the surface has its smallest radius of curvature (Fig. 16.33a). Think of the charges as being constrained to move along the surfaces of the conductor. On flat surfaces, repulsive forces between neighboring charges push parallel to the surface, making the charges spread apart evenly. On a curved surface, only the components of the repulsive forces parallel to the surface, $F_\parallel$, are effective at making the charges spread apart (Fig. 16.33b). If charges were spread evenly over an irregular surface, the parallel components of the repulsive forces would be smaller for charges on the more sharply curved regions and charge would tend to move toward these regions. Therefore,

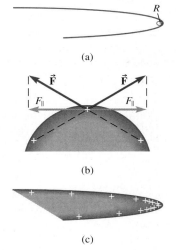

Figure 16.33 (a) The radius of curvature R at the rounded tip of a conductor. (b) Repulsive forces on a charge constrained to move along a curved surface due to two of its neighbors. The parallel components of the forces ($F_\parallel$) determine the spacing between the charges. (c) In electrostatic equilibrium, charge is concentrated where the radius of curvature of the surface is small.

The excess charge on a conductor in electrostatic equilibrium is more concentrated at regions of smallest radius of curvature (Fig. 16.33c).

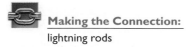

Making the Connection:
lightning rods

Figure 16.34 A lightning rod protects a Victorian house in Mt. Horeb, Wisconsin.

Sharp points on a conducting surface have a small radius of curvature, so charge tends to collect at sharp points.

The electric field lines just outside the conducting surface are more densely packed where the radius of curvature is smallest because each line starts or ends on a surface charge. Since the density of field lines reflects the magnitude of the electric field, the electric field outside the conductor is largest near the sharpest points of the conducting surface.

Lightning rods (invented by Franklin) are often found on the roofs of tall buildings and old farmhouses (Fig. 16.34). The rod comes to a sharp point at the top. When a passing thunderstorm attracts charge to the top of the rod, the strong electric field at the point ionizes nearby air molecules. Neutral air molecules do not transfer net charge when they move, but ionized molecules do, so ionization allows charge to leak gently off the building through the air instead of building up to a dangerously large value. If the rod did not come to a sharp point, the electric field might not be large enough to ionize the air.

The conclusions we have reached about conductors in electrostatic equilibrium can be restated in terms of field line rules:

For a conductor in electrostatic equilibrium,
- There are no field lines within the conducting material;
- Field lines that start or stop on the surface of a conductor are perpendicular to the surface where they intersect it; and
- The density of field lines at the surface of the conductor is greatest at regions of smallest radius of curvature.

Conceptual Example 16.10
Spherical Conductor in a Uniform Applied Field

Two oppositely charged parallel plates produce a uniform electric field between them (Fig. 16.35). An uncharged metal sphere is placed between the plates. Assume that the sphere is small enough that it does not affect the charge distribution on the plates. Sketch the electric field lines between the plates once electrostatic equilibrium is reached.

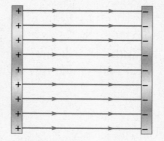

Figure 16.35
Uniform field between two plates.

Strategy We expect electrons in the metal sphere to be attracted to the positive plate, leaving the surface near the positive plate with a negative surface charge. The other side will have a positive surface charge. The electric field is changed by these surface charges, so that it is no longer uniform.

Solution and Discussion There are no field lines inside the metal sphere. The field lines cannot "go around"

the sphere, since then there would be a field component parallel to the sphere's surface. Furthermore, since we already know that there is charge on the sphere's surface, some field lines must start on the positive side and others end on the negative side. The field lines must intersect the sphere perpendicular to the surface. Figure 16.36 shows a field line diagram for the sphere.

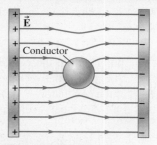

Figure 16.36
Field lines when a metal sphere is placed between the plates.

Conceptual Practice Problem 16.10
Oppositely Charged Spheres

Two metal spheres of the same radius R are given charges of equal magnitude and opposite sign. No other charges are nearby. Sketch the electric field lines when the center-to-center distance between the spheres is approximately $3R$.

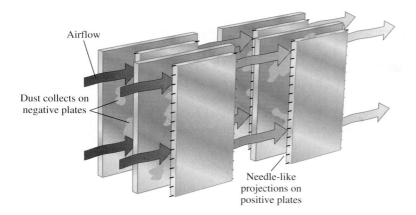

Airflow

Dust collects on
negative plates

Needle-like
projections on
positive plates

Figure 16.37 An electrostatic precipitator.

Making the Connection:

electrostatic precipitator

Electrostatic Precipitator

One direct application of electric fields is the *electrostatic precipitator*—a device that reduces the air pollution emitted from industrial smokestacks (Fig. 16.37). Many industrial processes, such as the burning of fossil fuels in electrical generating plants, release flue gases containing particulates into the air. To reduce the quantity of particulates released, the gases are sent through a precipitator chamber before leaving the smokestack. Many air purifiers sold for use in the home are electrostatic precipitators.

Inside the precipitator chamber is a set of oppositely charged metal plates. The positively charged plates are fitted with needle-like wire projections that serve as discharge points. The electric field is strong enough at these points to ionize air molecules. The particulates are positively charged by contact with the ions. The electric field between the plates then attracts the particulates to the negatively charged collection plates. After enough particulate matter has built up on these plates, it falls to the bottom of the precipitator chamber from where it is easily removed.

16.7 GAUSS'S LAW FOR ELECTRIC FIELDS

Gauss's law is a powerful statement of properties of the electric field. It relates the electric field on a closed surface—*any* closed surface—to the net charge inside the surface. A **closed surface** encloses a volume of space, so that there is an inside and an outside. The surface of a sphere, for instance, is a closed surface, whereas the interior of a circle is not. Gauss's law says: I can tell you how much charge you have inside that "box" without looking inside; I'll just look at the field lines that enter or exit the box.

If a box has no charge inside of it, then the same number of field lines that go into the box must come back out; there is nowhere for field lines to end or to begin. Even if there is charge inside, but the *net* charge is zero, the same number of field lines that start on the positive charge must end on the negative charge, so again the same number of field lines that go in must come out. If there is net positive charge inside, then there will be field lines starting on the positive charge that leave the box; then more field lines come out than go in. If there is net negative charge inside, some field lines that go in end on the negative charge; more field lines go in than come out.

Field lines are a useful device for visualization, but they are not quantifiable in any standard way. In order for Gauss's law to be useful, we formulate it mathematically so that numbers of field lines are not involved. To reformulate the law, there are two conditions to satisfy. First, a mathematical quantity must be found that is proportional to the number of field lines leaving a closed surface. Second, a proportionality must be turned into an equation by solving for the constant of proportionality.

Recall from Section 16.4 that the magnitude of the electric field is proportional to the number of field lines *per unit cross-sectional area*:

$$E \propto \frac{\text{number of lines}}{\text{area}}$$

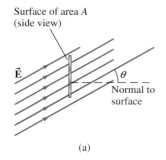

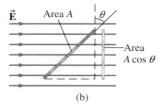

Figure 16.38 (a) Electric field lines crossing through a rectangular surface (side view). The angle between the field lines and the line *perpendicular* to the surface is θ. (b) The number of field lines that cross the surface of area A is the same as the number that cross the perpendicular surface of area $A \cos \theta$.

If a surface of area A is everywhere perpendicular to an electric field of uniform magnitude E, then the number of field lines that cross the surface is proportional to EA, since

$$\text{number of lines} = \frac{\text{number of lines}}{\text{area}} \times \text{area} \propto EA$$

This is only true if the surface is perpendicular to the electric field everywhere. As an analogy, think of rain falling straight down into a bucket. Less rainwater enters the bucket when it is tilted to one side than if the bucket rests with its opening perpendicular to the direction of rainfall. In general, the number of field lines crossing a surface is proportional to the *perpendicular component* of the field times the area:

$$\text{number of lines} \propto E_\perp A = EA \cos \theta$$

where θ is the angle that the field lines make with the normal (perpendicular) to the surface (Fig. 16.38a). Equivalently, Fig. 16.38b shows that the number of lines crossing the surface is the same as the number crossing a surface of area $A \cos \theta$, which is the area perpendicular to the field.

The mathematical quantity that is proportional to the number of field lines crossing a surface is called the **flux of the electric field** (symbol Φ_E; Φ is the Greek capital phi).

Definition of Flux

$$\Phi_E = E_\perp A = EA_\perp = EA \cos \theta \tag{16-7}$$

For a closed surface, flux is defined to be positive if more field lines leave the surface than enter, or negative if more lines enter than leave. Flux is then positive if the net enclosed charge is positive and it is negative if the net enclosed charge is negative.

Since the net number of field lines is proportional to the net charge inside a closed surface, Gauss's law takes the form

$$\Phi_E = \text{constant} \times q$$

where q stands for the *net charge enclosed by the surface*. In Problem 56, you can show that the constant of proportionality is $4\pi k = 1/\epsilon_0$. Therefore,

Gauss's Law

$$\Phi_E = 4\pi k q = q/\epsilon_0 \tag{16-8}$$

Example 16.11

Flux Through a Sphere

What is the flux through a sphere of radius $r = 5.0$ cm that has a point charge $q = -2.0$ μC at its center?

Strategy   In this case, there are two ways to find the flux. The electric field is known from Coulomb's law and it can be used to find the flux; or we can use Gauss's law.

Solution   The electric field at a separation r from a point charge is

$$E = \frac{kq}{r^2}$$

For a negative point charge, the field is radially inward. The field has the same strength everywhere on the sphere,

since the separation from the point charge is constant. Also, the field is always perpendicular to the surface of the sphere ($\theta = 0$ everywhere). Therefore,

$$\Phi_E = EA = \frac{kq}{r^2} \times 4\pi r^2 = 4\pi k q$$

This is exactly what Gauss's law tells us. The flux is independent of the radius of the sphere, since all the field lines cross the sphere regardless of its radius. A negative value of q gives a negative flux, which is correct since the field lines go inward. Then

Continued on next page

Example 16.11 Continued

$$\Phi_E = 4\pi k q$$

$$= 4\pi \times 9.0 \times 10^9 \, \frac{\text{N·m}^2}{\text{C}^2} \times (-2.0 \times 10^{-6} \, \text{C})$$

$$= -2.3 \times 10^5 \, \frac{\text{N·m}^2}{\text{C}}$$

Discussion   In this case, we can find the flux directly because the field at every point on the sphere is constant in magnitude and perpendicular to the sphere. However, Gauss's law tells us that the flux through *any* surface that encloses this charge, no matter what shape or size, must be the same.

Practice Problem 16.11   Flux Through a Side of a Cube

What is the flux through *one side* of a cube that has a point charge −2.0 μC at its center? [*Hint:* Of the total number of field lines, what fraction passes through one side of the cube?]

Using Gauss's Law to Find the Electric Field

As presented so far, Gauss's law is a way to determine how much charge is inside a closed surface given the electric field on the surface. Sometimes it can be turned around and used to *find the electric field* due to a distribution of charges. Why not just use Coulomb's law? In many cases there are such a large number of charges that the charge can be viewed as being continuously spread along a line, or over a surface, or throughout a volume. Microscopically, charge is still limited to multiples of the electronic charge, but when there are large numbers of charges, it is simpler to view the charge as a continuous distribution.

For a continuous distribution, the **charge density** is usually the most convenient way to describe how much charge is present. There are three kinds of charge densities:

• If the charge is spread throughout a volume, the relevant charge density is the charge per unit *volume* (symbol ρ).
• If the charge is spread over a two-dimensional surface, then the charge density is the charge per unit *area* (symbol σ).
• If the charge is spread over a one-dimensional line or curve, the appropriate charge density is the charge per unit *length* (symbol λ).

Gauss's law can be used to calculate the electric field in cases where there is enough *symmetry* to tell us something about the field lines. Example 16.12 illustrates this technique.

Example 16.12

Electric Field at a Distance from a Long Thin Wire

Charge is spread *uniformly* along a long thin wire. The charge per unit length on the wire is λ and is constant. Find the electric field at a distance r from the wire, far from either end of the wire.

Strategy   The electric field at any point is the sum of the electric field contributions from the charge all along the wire. Coulomb's law tells us that the strongest contributions come from the charge on nearby parts of the wire, with contributions falling off as $1/r^2$ for faraway points.

When concerned only with points near the wire, and far from either end, an approximately correct answer is obtained by assuming the wire is *infinitely long*.

How is it a simplification to *add* more charges? When using Gauss's law, a symmetric situation is far simpler than a situation that lacks symmetry. An infinitely long wire with a uniform linear charge density has *axial symmetry*. Sketching the field lines first helps show what symmetry tells us about the electric field.

Continued on next page

Example 16.12 Continued

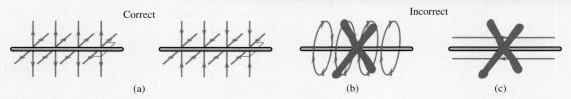

Correct   Incorrect

(a)   (b)   (c)

Figure 16.39

(a) Electric field lines emanating from a long wire, radially outward and radially inward; (b) hypothetical lines circling a wire; (c) hypothetical lines parallel to the wire.

Solution We start by sketching field lines for an infinitely long wire. The field lines either start or stop on the wire (depending on whether the charge is positive or negative). Then what do the field lines do? The only possibility is that they move radially outward (or inward) from the wire. Figure 16.39a shows sketches of the field lines for positive and negative charges, respectively. The wire looks the same from all sides, so a field line could not start to curl around as in Fig. 16.39b: how would it determine which way to go? Also, the field lines cannot go along the wire as in Fig. 16.39c: again, how could the lines decide whether to go right or left? The wire looks exactly the same in both directions.

Once we recognize that the field lines are radial, the next step is to choose a surface. Gauss's law is easiest to handle if the electric field is constant in magnitude and either perpendicular or parallel to the surface. A cylinder with a radius r with the wire as its axis has the field perpendicular to the surface everywhere, since the lines are radial (Fig. 16.40). The magnitude of the field must also be constant on the surface of the cylinder because every point on the cylinder is located an equal distance from the wire. Since a *closed* surface is necessary, the two circular ends of the cylinder are included. The flux through the ends is zero since no field lines pass through; equivalently, the *perpendicular component* of the field is zero.

Since the field is constant in magnitude and perpendicular to the surface, the flux is

$$\Phi_E = E_r A$$

where E_r is the radial component of the field. E_r is positive if the field is radially outward and negative if the field is radially inward. A is the area of a cylinder of radius r and . . . what length? Since the cylinder is imaginary, we can consider an arbitrary length denoted by L. The area of the cylinder is (Appendix A.6)

$$A = 2\pi r L$$

How much charge is enclosed by this cylinder? The charge per unit length is λ and a length L of the wire is inside the cylinder, so the enclosed charge is

$$q = \lambda L$$

which can be either positive or negative. Gauss's law and the definition of flux yield

$$4\pi k q = \Phi_E = E_r A$$

Substituting the expressions for A and q into Gauss's law yields

$$E_r \times (2\pi r L) = 4\pi k \lambda L$$

Solving for E_r,

$$E_r = \frac{2k\lambda}{r}$$

The field direction is radially outward for $\lambda > 0$ and radially inward for $\lambda < 0$.

Discussion The final expression for the electric field does not depend on the arbitrary length L of the cylinder. If L appeared in the answer, we would know to look for a mistake.

We should check the units of the answer: λ is the charge per unit length, so it has SI units

$$[\lambda] = \frac{\text{C}}{\text{m}}$$

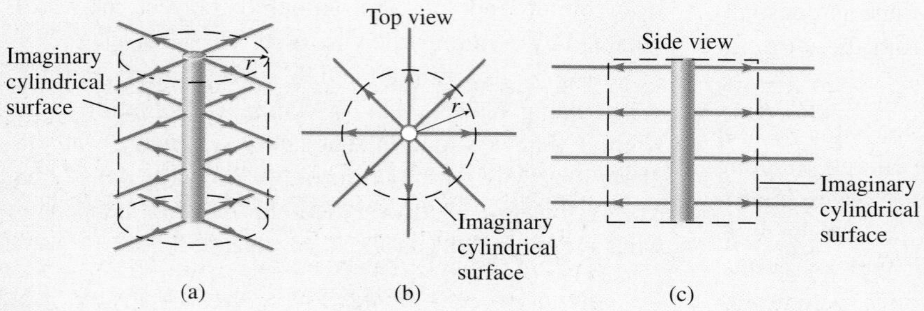

Imaginary cylindrical surface

Top view

r

Imaginary cylindrical surface

Side view

Imaginary cylindrical surface

(a)   (b)   (c)

Figure 16.40

(a) Electric field lines from a wire located along the axis of a cylinder are perpendicular to the surrounding imaginary cylindrical surface. (b) Top and (c) side views of the cylinder and the field lines; the field lines are perpendicular to the cylindrical surface area but parallel to the planes of the top and bottom circular areas.

Continued on next page

Example 16.12 Continued

The constant k has SI units

$$[k] = \frac{N \cdot m^2}{C^2}$$

The factor of 2π is dimensionless and r is a distance. Then

$$\left[\frac{2k\lambda}{r}\right] = \frac{C}{m} \times \frac{N \cdot m^2}{C^2} \times \frac{1}{m} = \frac{N}{C}$$

which is the SI unit of electric field.

The electric field falls off as the inverse of the separation ($E \propto 1/r$). Wait a minute—does this violate Coulomb's law, which says $E \propto 1/r^2$? No, because that is the field at a separation r from a *point charge*. Here the charge is spread out in a line. The different geometry changes the field lines (they come radially outward from a line rather than from a point) and this changes how the field depends on distance.

Conceptual Practice Problem 16.12   Which Area to Use?

In Example 16.12, we wrote the area of a cylinder as $A = 2\pi rL$, which is only the area of the curved surface of the cylinder. The total area of a cylinder includes the area of the circles on each end (top and base): $A_{total} = 2\pi rL + 2\pi r^2$. Why did we not include the area of the ends of the cylinder when calculating flux?

MASTER THE CONCEPTS

- Coulomb's law gives the electric force exerted on one point charge due to another. The magnitude of the force is

$$F = \frac{k|q_1||q_2|}{r^2} \qquad (16\text{-}2)$$

  where the Coulomb constant is

$$k = 8.99 \times 10^9 \frac{N \cdot m^2}{C^2} \qquad (16\text{-}3a)$$

- The direction of the force on one point charge due to another is either directly toward the other charge (if the charges have opposite signs) or directly away (if the charges have the same sign).
- The electric field (symbol $\vec{E}$) is the electric force per unit *charge*. It is a vector quantity.
- If a point charge q is located where the electric field due to all other charges is $\vec{E}$, then the electric force on the point charge is

$$\vec{F}_E = q\vec{E} \qquad (16\text{-}4b)$$

- The SI units of the electric field are N/C.
- Electric field lines are useful for representing an electric field.

- The direction of the electric field at any point is tangent to the field line passing through that point and in the direction indicated by the arrows on the field line.
- The electric field is strong where field lines are close together and weak where they are far apart.
- Field lines never cross.
- Field lines start on positive charges and end on negative charges.
- The number of field lines starting on a positive charge (or ending on a negative charge) is proportional to the magnitude of the charge.
- The principle of superposition says that the electric field due to a collection of charges at any point is the vector sum of the electric fields caused by each charge separately.
- Electric flux:

$$\Phi_E = E_\perp A = EA_\perp = EA \cos \theta \qquad (16\text{-}7)$$

- Gauss's law:

$$\Phi_E = 4\pi kq = q/\epsilon_0 \qquad (16\text{-}8)$$

Conceptual Questions

1. (a) List three similarities between gravity and the electric force. (b) List two differences.

2. Due to the similarity between Newton's law of gravity and Coulomb's law, a friend proposes these hypotheses: perhaps there is no gravitational interaction at all. Instead, what we call gravity might be *electric* forces acting between objects that are almost, but not quite, electrically neutral. Think up as many counterarguments as you can.

3. What makes clothes cling together—or to your body—after they've been through the dryer? Why do they not cling as much if they are taken out of the dryer while slightly damp? In which case would you expect your clothes to cling more, all other things being equal: when the clothes in the dryer are all made of the same material, or when they are made of several different materials?

4. Explain why any net charge on a solid metal conductor is found on the outside surface of the conductor instead of being distributed uniformly throughout the solid.

5. Explain why electric field lines begin on positive charges and end on negative charges. [*Hint:* What is the direction of the electric field near positive and negative charges?]

6. Electronic devices are usually enclosed in metal boxes. One function of the box is to shield the inside components from external electric fields. (a) How does this shielding work? (b) Why is the degree of shielding better for constant or slowly varying fields than for rapidly varying fields? (c) Explain the reasons why it is not possible to shield something from gravitational fields in a similar way.

7. A metal sphere is initially uncharged. After being touched by a charged rod, the metal sphere is positively charged. (a) Is the mass of the sphere larger, smaller, or the same as before it was charged? Explain. (b) What sign of charge is on the rod?

8. Your laboratory partner hands you a glass rod and asks if it has negative charge on it. There is an electroscope in the laboratory. How can you tell if the rod is charged? Can you determine the sign of the charge? If the rod is charged to begin with, will its charge be the same after you have made your determination? Explain.

9. A lightweight plastic rod is rubbed with a piece of fur. A second plastic rod, hanging from a string, is attracted to the first rod and swings toward it. When the second rod touches the first, it is suddenly repelled and swings away. Explain what has happened.

10. The following *hypothetical* reaction shows a neutron (n) decaying into a proton (p^+) and an electron (e^-):

$$n \rightarrow p^+ + e^-$$

At first there is no charge, but then charge seems to be "created." Does this reaction violate the law of charge conservation? Explain. (In Section 29.3, it is shown that the neutron does not decay into just a proton and an electron; the decay products include a third, electrically neutral particle.)

11. A fellow student says that there is *never* an electric field inside a conductor. Do you agree? Explain.

12. Explain why electric field lines never cross.

13. A truck carrying explosive gases either has chains or straps that drag along the ground, or else it has special tires that conduct electricity (ordinary tires are good insulators). Explain why the chains, straps, or conducting tires are necessary.

14. An electroscope consists of a conducting sphere, conducting pole, and two metal foils (Fig. 16.6). The electroscope is initially uncharged. (a) A positively charged rod is allowed to touch the conducting sphere and then is removed. What happens to the foils and what is their charge? (b) Next, another positively

charged rod is brought near to the conducting sphere without touching it. What happens? (c) The positively charged rod is removed and a negatively charged rod is brought near the sphere. What happens?

15. A rod is negatively charged by rubbing it with fur. It is brought near another rod of unknown composition and charge. There is a repulsive force between the two. (a) Is the first rod an insulator or a conductor? Explain. (b) What can you tell about the charge of the second rod?

16. A negatively charged rod is brought near a grounded conductor. After the ground connection is broken, the rod is removed. Is the charge on the conductor positive, negative, or zero? Explain.

17. In some textbooks, the electric field is called the *flux density*. Explain the meaning of this term. Does flux density mean the flux per unit volume? If not, then what does it mean?

18. The word *flux* comes from the Latin "to flow." What does the quantity $\Phi_E = E_\perp A$ have to do with flow? The figure shows some streamlines for the flow of water in a pipe. The streamlines are actually field lines for the *velocity field*. What is the physical significance of the quantity $v_\perp A$? Sometimes physicists call positive charges *sources* of the electric field and negative charges *sinks*. Why?

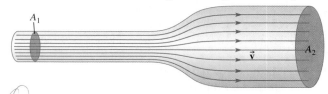

19. The flux through a closed surface is zero. Is the electric field necessarily zero? Is the net charge inside the surface necessarily zero? Explain your answers.

20. Consider a closed surface that surrounds Q_1 and Q_2 but not Q_3 or Q_4. (a) Which charges contribute to the electric field at point *P*? (b) Would the value obtained for the flux through the surface, calculated using only the electric field due to Q_1 and Q_2, be greater than, less than, or equal to that obtained using the total field?

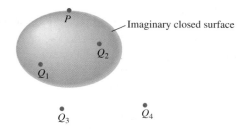

Multiple-Choice Questions

1. An α particle (charge $+2e$ and mass approximately $4m_p$) is on a collision course with a proton (charge $+e$ and mass m_p). Assume that no forces act other than the

electrical repulsion. Which one of these statements about the accelerations of the two particles is true?

(a) $\vec{a}_\alpha = \vec{a}_p$ (b) $\vec{a}_\alpha = 2\vec{a}_p$ (c) $\vec{a}_\alpha = 4\vec{a}_p$
(d) $2\vec{a}_\alpha = \vec{a}_p$ (e) $4\vec{a}_\alpha = \vec{a}_p$ (f) $\vec{a}_\alpha = -\vec{a}_p$
(g) $\vec{a}_\alpha = -2\vec{a}_p$ (h) $\vec{a}_\alpha = -4\vec{a}_p$ (i) $-2\vec{a}_\alpha = \vec{a}_p$
(j) $-4\vec{a}_\alpha = \vec{a}_p$

2. The electric charge on a conductor is

   (a) uniformly distributed throughout the volume.
   (b) confined to the surface and is uniformly distributed.
   (c) mostly on the outer surface, but is not uniformly distributed.
   (d) entirely on the surface and is distributed according to the shape of the object.
   (e) dispersed throughout the volume of the object and distributed according to the object's shape.

3. The electric field at a point in space is a measure of

   (a) the total charge on an object at that point.
   (b) the electric force on any charged object at that point.
   (c) the charge-to-mass ratio of an object at that point.
   (d) the electric force per unit mass on a point charge at that point.
   (e) the electric force per unit charge on a point charge at that point.

4. Two charged particles attract each other with a force of magnitude F acting on each. If the charge of one is doubled and the distance separating the particles is also doubled, the force acting on each of the two particles has magnitude

   (a) $F/2$ (b) $F/4$ (c) F (d) $2F$ (e) $4F$
   (f) None of the above.

5. A charged insulator and an uncharged metal

   (a) exert no electric force on each other.
   (b) repel each other electrically.
   (c) attract each other electrically.
   (d) attract or repel, depending on whether the charge is positive or negative.

6. A tiny charged pellet of mass m is suspended at rest by the electric field between two horizontal, charged metallic plates. 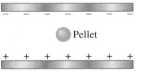 The lower plate has a positive charge and the upper plate has a negative charge. Which statement in the answers here is *not* true?

   (a) The electric field between the plates points vertically upward.
   (b) The pellet is negatively charged.
   (c) The magnitude of the electric force on the pellet is equal to mg.
   (d) If the magnitude of charge on the plates is increased, the pellet begins to move upward.

7. Which of these statements comparing electrical and gravitational forces is correct?

   1. The direction of the electric force exerted by one point particle on another is always the same as the direction of the gravitational force exerted by that particle on the other.
   2. The electric and gravitational forces exerted by two particles on one another are inversely proportional to the separation of the particles.
   3. The electric force exerted by one planet on another is typically stronger than the gravitational force exerted by that same planet on the other.

   (a) 1 only   (b) 2 only   (c) 3 only
   (d) none of them

8. In the figure, which best represents the field lines due to two spheres with equal and opposite charges?

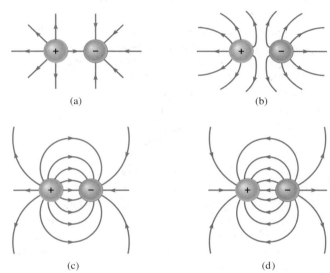

(a)   (b)

(c)   (d)

9. In the figure, put points 1–4 in order of increasing field strength.

   (a) 2, 3, 4, 1   (b) 2, 1, 3, 4   (c) 1, 4, 3, 2
   (d) 4, 3, 1, 2   (e) 2, 4, 1, 3

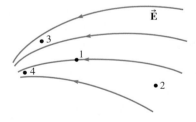

10. Two point charges q and $2q$ lie on the x-axis. Which region(s) on the x-axis include a point where the electric field due to the two point charges is zero?

   (a) to the right of $2q$ (b) between $2q$ and point P
   (c) between point P and q (d) to the left of q
   (e) both (a) and (c)   (f) both (b) and (d)

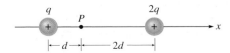

Problems

©   Combination conceptual/quantitative problem

☒   Biological or medical application

No ✦   Easy to moderate difficulty level

✦   More challenging

✦✦   Most challenging

Blue #   Detailed solution in the Student Solutions Manual

1 2   Problems paired by concept

16.1 Electric Charge; 16.2 Electrical Conductors and Insulators

1. Find the total positive charge of all the protons in 1.0 mol of water.

2. Suppose a 1.0-g nugget of pure gold has zero net charge. What would be its net charge after it has 1.0% of its electrons removed?

© 3. A balloon, initially neutral, is rubbed with fur until it acquires a net charge of −0.60 nC. (a) Assuming that only electrons are transferred, were electrons removed from the balloon or added to it? (b) How many electrons were transferred?

© 4. A metallic sphere has a charge of +4.0 nC. A negatively charged rod has a charge of −6.0 nC. When the rod touches the sphere, 8.2×10^9 electrons are transferred. What are the charges of the sphere and the rod now?

© 5. A positively charged rod is brought near two uncharged conducting spheres of the same size that are initially touching each other (diagram a). The spheres are moved apart and then the charged rod is removed (diagram b). (a) What is the sign of the net charge on sphere a in diagram b? (b) In comparison with the charge on sphere a, how much and what sign of charge is on sphere b?

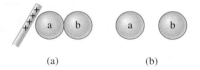

(a)   (b)

6. A metal sphere A has charge Q. Two other spheres, B and C, are identical to A except they have zero net charge. A touches B, then the two spheres are separated. B touches C, then those spheres are separated. Finally, C touches A and those two spheres are separated. How much charge is on each sphere?

7. Repeat Problem 6 with a slight change. The difference this time is that sphere C is grounded when it is touching B, but C is not grounded at any other time. What is the final charge on each sphere?

8. Five conducting spheres are charged as shown. All have the same magnitude net charge except E, whose net charge is zero. Which pairs

are attracted to each other and which are repelled by each other when they are brought near each other, but well away from the other spheres?

16.3 Coulomb's Law

9. If the electrical force of repulsion between two 1-C charges is 10 N, how far apart are they?

10. Two small metal spheres are 25.0 cm apart. The spheres have equal amounts of negative charge and repel each other with a force of 0.036 N. What is the charge on each sphere?

✦ 11. A total charge of 7.50×10^{-6} C is distributed on two different small metal spheres. When the spheres are 6.00 cm apart, they each feel a repulsive force of 20.0 N. How much charge is on each sphere?

12. How many electrons must be removed from each of two 5.0-kg copper spheres to make the electric force of repulsion between them equal in magnitude to the gravitational attraction between them?

13. What is the ratio of the electric force to the gravitational force between a proton and an electron separated by 5.3×10^{-11} m (the radius of a hydrogen atom)?

14. Three point charges are fixed in place in a right triangle. What is the electric force on the −0.60-μC charge due to the other two charges?

15. Three point charges are fixed in place in a right triangle. What is the electric force on the +1.0-μC charge due to the other two charges?

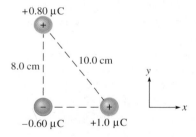

Problems 14 and 15

✦ 16. A tiny sphere with a charge of 7.0 μC is attached to a spring. Two other tiny charged spheres, each with a charge of −4.0 μC, are placed in the positions shown in the figure and the spring stretches 5.0 cm from its previous equilibrium position toward the two spheres. Calculate the spring constant.

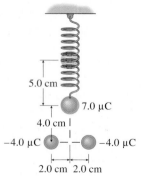

17. A +2.0-nC point charge is 3.0 cm away from a −3.0-nC point charge. (a) What are the magnitude and direction of the electric force acting on the +2.0-nC charge? (b) What is the magnitude

and direction of the electric force acting on the −3.0-nC charge?

18. Two Styrofoam balls with the same mass $m = 9.0 \times 10^{-8}$ kg and the same positive charge Q are suspended from the same point by insulating threads of length $L = 0.98$ m. The separation of the balls is $d = 0.020$ m. What is the charge Q?

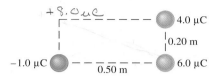

19. Two metal spheres separated by a distance much greater than either sphere's radius have equal mass m and equal electric charge q. What is the ratio of charge to mass q/m in C/kg if the electrical and gravitational forces balance?

20. In the figure, a third point charge $−q$ is placed at point P. What is the electric force on $−q$ due to the other two point charges?

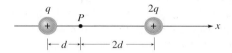

21. A K$^+$ ion and a Cl$^−$ ion are directly across from each other on opposite sides of a membrane 9.0 nm thick. What is the electric force on the K$^+$ ion due to the Cl$^−$ ion? Ignore the presence of other charges.

22. Two point charges are separated by a distance r and repel each other with a force F. If their separation is reduced to 0.25 times the original value, what is the magnitude of the force of repulsion between them?

✦ 23. Using the three point charges of Example 16.3, find the magnitude of the force on q_2 due to the other two charges, q_1 and q_3. [*Hint:* After finding the force on q_2 due to q_1, separate that force into x- and y-components.]

✦ 24. An equilateral triangle has a point charge $+q$ at each of the three vertices (A, B, C). Another point charge Q is placed at D, the midpoint of the side BC. Solve for Q if the total electric force on the charge at A due to the charges at B, C, and D is zero.

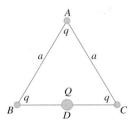

16.4 The Electric Field

25. Three point charges are placed on the x-axis. A charge of 3.00 μC is at the origin. A charge of −5.00 μC is at 20.0 cm, and a charge of 8.00 μC is at 35.0 cm. What is the force on the charge at the origin?

26. Positive point charges are placed at three corners of a rectangle, as shown in the figure. (a) What is the elec-

tric field at the fourth corner? (b) A small object with a charge of +8.0 μC is placed at the fourth corner. What force acts on the object?

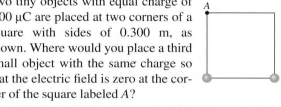

27. Two tiny objects with equal charge of 7.00 μC are placed at two corners of a square with sides of 0.300 m, as shown. Where would you place a third small object with the same charge so that the electric field is zero at the corner of the square labeled A?

28. A small sphere with a charge of −0.60 μC is placed in a uniform electric field of magnitude 1.2×10^6 N/C pointing to the west. What is the magnitude and direction of the force on the sphere due to the electric field?

29. The electric field across a cellular membrane is 1.0×10^7 N/C directed into the cell. (a) If a pore opens, which way do sodium ions (Na$^+$) flow—into the cell or out of the cell? (b) What is the magnitude of the electric force on the sodium ion? The charge on the sodium ion is $+e$.

30. Sketch the electric field lines near two isolated and equal (a) positive point charges and (b) negative point charges. Include arrowheads to show the field directions.

31. Sketch the electric field lines in the plane of the page due to the charges shown in the diagram.

Q $−2Q$ Q

32. What are the magnitude and direction of the acceleration of an electron at a point where the electric field has magnitude 6100 N/C and is directed due north?

33. What are the magnitude and direction of the acceleration of a proton at a point where the electric field has magnitude 33 kN/C and is directed straight up?

34. What are the magnitude and direction of the electric field midway between two point charges, −15 μC and +12 μC, that are 8.0 cm apart?

35. In the figure, what is the electric field at point P?

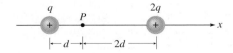

36. Two point charges, $q_1 = +20.0$ nC and $q_2 = +10.0$ nC, are located on the x-axis at $x = 0$ and $x = 1.00$ m, respectively. Where on the x-axis is the electric field equal to zero?

✦ 37. Two electric charges, $q_1 = +20.0$ nC and $q_2 = +10.0$ nC, are located on the x-axis at $x = 0$ m and $x = 1.00$ m, respectively. What is the magnitude of the electric field at the point $x = 0.50$ m, $y = 0.50$ m?

38. Two equal charges (Q = +1.00 nC) are situated at the diagonal corners A and B of a square of side 1.0 m. What is the magnitude of the electric field at point D?

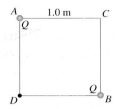

39. Suppose a charge q is placed at point $x = 0$, $y = 0$. A second charge q is placed at point $x = 8.0$ m, $y = 0$. What charge must be placed at the point $x = 4.0$ m, $y = 0$ in order that the field at the point $x = 4.0$ m, $y = 3.0$ m be zero?

40. An electron traveling horizontally from west to east enters a region where a uniform electric field is directed upward. What is the direction of the electric force exerted on the electron once it has entered the field?

41. A negative point charge $-Q$ is situated near a large metal plate that has a total charge of $+Q$. Sketch the electric field lines.

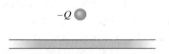

16.5 Motion of a Point Charge in a Uniform Electric Field

42. An electron is placed in a uniform electric field of strength 232 N/C. If the electron is at rest at the origin of a coordinate system at $t = 0$ and the electric field is in the positive x-direction, what are the x- and y-coordinates of the electron at $t = 2.30$ ns?

43. An electron is projected horizontally into the space between two oppositely charged metal plates. The electric field between the plates is 500.0 N/C, directed up. (a) While in the field, what is the force on the electron? (b) If the vertical deflection of the electron as it leaves the plates is 3.00 mm, how much has its kinetic energy increased due to the electric field?

44. A horizontal beam of electrons initially moving at 4.0×10^7 m/s is deflected vertically by the vertical electric field between oppositely charged parallel plates. The magnitude of the field is 2.00×10^4 N/C. (a) What is the direction of the field between the plates? (b) What is the charge per unit area on the plates? (c) What is the vertical deflection d of the electrons as they leave the plates?

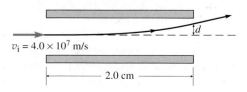

45. A particle with mass 2.30 g and charge +10.0 μC enters through a small hole in a metal plate with a speed of 8.50 m/s at an angle of 55.0°. The uniform $\vec{E}$ field in the region above the plate has magnitude 6.50×10^3 N/C and is directed downward. The region above the metal plate is essentially a vacuum, so there is no air resistance. (a) Can you neglect the force of gravity when solving for the horizontal distance traveled by the particle? Why or why not? (b) How far will the particle travel, Δx, before it hits the metal plate?

46. Consider the same situation as in Problem 45, but with a proton entering through the small hole at the same angle with a speed of $v = 8.50 \times 10^5$ m/s. (a) Can you neglect the force of gravity when solving this problem for the horizontal distance traveled by the proton? Why or why not? (b) How far will the proton travel, Δx, before it hits the metal plate?

47. Some forms of cancer can be treated using proton therapy in which proton beams are accelerated to high energies, then directed to collide into a tumor, killing the malignant cells. Suppose a proton accelerator is 4.0 m long and must accelerate protons from rest to a speed of 1.0×10^7 m/s. Ignore any relativistic effects (Chapter 26) and determine the magnitude of the average electric field that could accelerate these protons.

48. After the electrons in Example 16.8 pass through the anode, they are moving at a speed of 8.4×10^6 m/s. They next pass between a pair of parallel plates [(A) in Fig. 16.31]. The plates each have an area of 2.50 cm by 2.50 cm and they are separated by a distance of 0.50 cm. The uniform electric field between them is 1.0×10^3 N/C and the plates are charged as shown. (a) In what direction are the electrons deflected? (b) By how much are the electrons deflected after passing through these plates?

49. After the electrons pass through the parallel plates in Problem 48, they pass between another set of parallel plates [(B) in Fig. 16.31]. These plates also have an area of 2.50 cm by 2.50 cm and are separated by a distance of 0.50 cm. (a) In what direction must the field be oriented so that the electrons are deflected vertically upward? (b) If we neglect the gravitational force, how strong must the field be between these plates in order for the electrons to be deflected by 2.0 mm? (c) How much less will the electrons be deflected if we *do* include the gravitational force?

16.6 Conductors in Electrostatic Equilibrium

50. A hollow conducting sphere of radius R carries a negative charge $-q$. (a) Write expressions for the electric field $\vec{E}$ inside ($r < R$) and outside ($r > R$) the sphere.

Also indicate the direction of the field. (b) Sketch a graph of the field strength as a function of r. [*Hint:* See Conceptual Example 16.7.]

✦ 51. A conducting sphere is placed within a conducting spherical shell. The conductors are in electrostatic equilibrium. The inner sphere has a radius of 1.50 cm, the inner radius of the

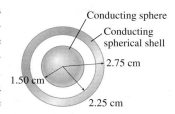

spherical shell is 2.25 cm, and the outer radius of the shell is 2.75 cm. If the inner sphere has a charge of 230 nC, and the spherical shell has zero net charge, (a) what is the magnitude of the electric field at a point 1.75 cm from the center? (b) What is the electric field at a point 2.50 cm from the center? (c) What is the electric field at a point 3.00 cm from the center? [*Hint:* What must be true about the electric field inside a conductor in electrostatic equilibrium?]

 52. A conducting sphere that carries a total charge of −6 μC is placed at the center of a conducting spherical shell that carries a total charge of +1 μC. The conductors are in electrostatic equilibrium. Determine the charge on the *outer surface* of the shell. [*Hint:* Sketch a field line diagram.]

 53. A conducting sphere that carries a total charge of +6 μC is placed at the center of a conducting spherical shell that also carries a total charge of +6 μC. The conductors are in electrostatic equilibrium. (a) Determine the charge on the inner surface of the shell. (b) Determine the total charge on the outer surface of the shell.

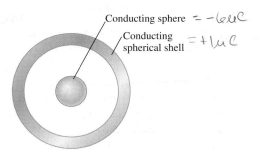

Problems 52 and 53

✦ 54. A conductor in electrostatic equilibrium contains a cavity in which there are two point charges: $q_1 = +5$ μC and $q_2 = -12$ μC. The conductor itself carries a net charge −4 μC. How much charge is on (a) the inner surface of the conductor? (b) the outer surface of the conductor?

✦ 55. In fair weather, over flat ground, there is a downward electric field of about 150 N/C. (a) Assume that the Earth is a conducting sphere with charge on its surface. If the electric field just outside is 150 N/C pointing radially inward, calculate the total charge on the Earth and the charge per unit area. (b) At an altitude of 250 m

above the Earth's surface, the field is only 120 N/C. Calculate the charge density (charge per unit volume) of the air (assumed constant). [*Hint:* See Conceptual Example 16.7.]

16.7 Gauss's Law for Electric Fields

56. In this problem, you can show from Coulomb's law that the constant of proportionality in Gauss's law must be $1/\epsilon_0$. Imagine a sphere with its center at a point charge q. (a) Write an expression for the electric flux in terms of the field strength E and the radius r of the sphere. [*Hint:* The field strength E is the same everywhere on the sphere and the field lines cross the sphere perpendicular to its surface.] (b) Use Gauss's law in the form $\Phi_E = cq$ (where c is the constant of proportionality) and the electric field strength given by Coulomb's law to show that $c = 1/\epsilon_0$.

57. An object with a charge of 0.890 μC is placed at the center of a cube. What is the electric flux through one surface of the cube?

58. (a) Find the electric flux through each side of a cube of edge length a in a uniform electric field of magnitude E. The field direction is perpendicular to two of the faces. (b) What is the total flux through the cube?

59. In a uniform electric field of magnitude E, the field lines cross through a rectangle of area A at an angle of 60.0° with respect to the plane of the rectangle. What is the flux through the rectangle?

✦ 60. An electron is suspended at a distance of 1.20 cm above a uniform line of charge. What is the linear charge density of the line of charge? Ignore end effects.

✦ 61. A thin, flat sheet of charge has a uniform surface charge density σ ($\sigma/2$ on each side). (a) Sketch the field lines due to the sheet. (b) Sketch the field lines for an infinitely large sheet with the same charge density. (c) For the infinite sheet, how does the field strength depend on the distance from the sheet? [*Hint:* Refer to your field line sketch.] (d) For points close to the finite sheet and far from its edges, can the sheet be approximated by an infinitely large sheet? [*Hint:* Again, refer to the field line sketches.] (e) Use Gauss's law to show that the magnitude of the electric field near a sheet of uniform charge density σ is $E = \sigma/(2\epsilon_0)$.

✦ 62. A flat *conducting* sheet of area A has a charge q on *each surface*. (a) What is the electric field inside the sheet? (b) Use Gauss's law to show that the electric field just outside the sheet is $E = q/(\epsilon_0 A) = \sigma/\epsilon_0$. (c) Does this contradict the result of Problem 61? Compare the field line diagrams for the two situations.

✦ 63. A *parallel-plate capacitor* consists of two flat metal plates of area A separated by a small distance d. The plates are given equal and opposite net charges ±q. (a) Sketch the field lines and use your sketch to explain why almost all of the charge is on the inner surfaces of the plates. (b) Use Gauss's law to show that the electric field between the plates and away from the edges is $E = q/(\epsilon_0 A) = \sigma/\epsilon_0$. (c) Does this agree with or contradict the result of Problem 62? Explain. (d) Use the principle of superposition and the result of Problem 61 to arrive at this same answer. [*Hint:* The inner surfaces of the two plates are thin, flat sheets of charge.]

64. (a) Use Gauss's law to prove that the electric field *outside* any spherically symmetric charge distribution is the same as if all of the charge were concentrated into a point charge. (b) Now use Gauss's law to prove that the electric field *inside* a spherically symmetric charge distribution is zero if none of the charge is at a distance from the center less than that of the point where we determine the field.

65. Using the results of Problem 64, we can find the electric field at any radius for any spherically symmetric charge distribution. A solid sphere of charge of radius R has a total charge of q uniformly spread throughout the sphere. (a) Find the magnitude of the electric field for $r \geq R$. (b) Find the magnitude of the electric field for $r \leq R$. (c) Sketch a graph of $E(r)$ for $0 \leq r \leq 3R$.

66. A coaxial cable consists of a wire of radius a surrounded by a thin metal cylindrical shell of radius b. The wire has a uniform linear charge density $\lambda > 0$ and the outer shell has a uniform linear charge density $-\lambda$. (a) Sketch the field lines for this cable. (b) Find expressions for the magnitude of the electric field in the regions $r \leq a$, $a < r < b$, and $b \leq r$.

67. Power lines have a limit on the maximum size of the electric field they produce. In most states, a maximum of 5 kN/C at about 20 m from the wires is allowed. This is quite large compared to the Earth's fair-weather electric field of about 100 N/C. Assume that the charge on the wire is static (not true, but a simplification here) and use the formula for the electric field for a wire derived in Example 16.12 to determine how much charge per unit length is on the wire.

68. Two concentric, infinitely long cylinders have radii r_1 and r_2 ($r_2 > r_1$), and corresponding surface charge densities σ_1 and σ_2. (a) Use Gauss's law to determine the electric field strength as a function of r between the two cylinders. (b) Sketch a graph of the electric field strength between the two cylinders as a function of r. Assume $\sigma_2 = 2\sigma_1 > 0$.

Comprehensive Problems

69. A charge of 63.0 nC is located at a distance of 3.40 cm from a charge of −47.0 nC. What are the *x*- and *y*-

components of the electric field at a point P that is directly above the 63.0-nC charge at a distance of 1.40 cm? Point P and the two charges are on the vertices of a right triangle.

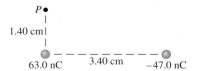

70. Consider two protons (charge $+e$), separated by a distance of 2.0×10^{-15} m (as in a typical atomic nucleus). The electric force between these protons is equal in magnitude to the gravitational force on an object of what mass near the Earth's surface?

71. In lab tests it was found that rats can detect electric fields of about 5.0 kN/C or more. If a point charge of 1.0 μC is sitting in a maze, how close must the rat come to the charge in order to detect it?

72. A raindrop inside a thundercloud has charge $-8e$. What is the electric force on the raindrop if the electric field at its location (due to other charges in the cloud) has magnitude 2.0×10^6 N/C and is directed upward?

73. A thin wire with positive charge evenly spread along its length is shaped into a semicircle. What is the direction of the electric field at the center of curvature of the semicircle? Explain.

74. A very small charged block with a mass of 2.35 g is placed on an insulated, frictionless plane inclined at an angle of 17.0° with respect to the horizontal. The block does not slide down the plane because of a 465-N/C uniform electric field that points parallel to the surface downward along the plane. What is the sign and magnitude of the charge on the block?

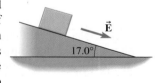

75. In a cathode ray tube, electrons initially at rest are accelerated by a uniform electric field of magnitude 4.0×10^5 N/C during the first 5.0 cm of the tube's length; then they move at essentially constant velocity another 45 cm before hitting the screen. (a) Find the speed of the electrons when they hit the screen. (b) How long does it take them to travel the length of the tube?

76. An electron beam in an oscilloscope is deflected by the electric field produced by oppositely charged metal plates. If the electric field between the plates is 2.00×10^5 N/C directed downward, what is the force on each electron when it passes between the plates?

77. A point charge $q_1 = +5.0$ μC is fixed in place at $x = 0$ and a point charge $q_2 = -3.0$ μC is fixed at $x = -20.0$ cm. Where can we place a point charge $q_3 = -8.0$ μC so that the net electric force on q_1 due to q_2 and q_3 is zero?

78. Point charges are arranged on the vertices of a square with sides of 2.50 cm. Starting at the upper left corner

and going clockwise, we have charge A with a charge of 0.200 μC, B with a charge of –0.150 μC, C with a charge of 0.300 μC, and D with a mass of 2.00 g, but with an unknown charge. Charges A, B, and C are fixed in place, and D is free to move. Particle D's instantaneous acceleration at point D is 248 m/s^2 in a direction 30.8° below the negative x-axis. What is the charge on D?

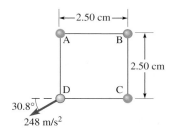

79. The Bohr model of the hydrogen atom proposes that the electron orbits around the proton in a circle of radius 5.3×10^{-11} m. The electric force is responsible for the radial acceleration of the electron. What is the speed of the electron in this model?

◆ 80. What is the electric force on the chloride ion in the lower right-hand corner in the diagram? Since the ions are in water, the "effec-

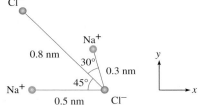

tive charge" on the chloride ions (Cl$^-$) is -2×10^{-21} C and that of the sodium ions (Na$^+$) is $+2 \times 10^{-21}$ C. The effective charge is a way to account for the partial shielding due to nearby water molecules. Assume that all four ions are coplanar.

Ⓒ 81. (a) What would the net charges on the Sun and Earth have to be if the electric force instead of the gravitational force were responsible for keeping the Earth in its orbit? There are many possible answers, so restrict yourself to the case where the magnitude of the charges is proportional to the masses. (b) If the magnitude of the charges of the proton and electron were not exactly equal, astronomical bodies would have net charges that are approximately proportional to their masses. Could this possibly be an explanation for the Earth's orbit?

◆ 82. A dipole consists of two equal and opposite point charges ($\pm q$) separated by a distance d. (a) Write an expression for the electric field at a point $(0, y)$ on the dipole axis. Specify the direction of the field in all four regions: $y > \frac{1}{2}d$, $0 < y < \frac{1}{2}d$, $-\frac{1}{2}d < y < 0$, and $y < -\frac{1}{2}d$. (b) At distant points

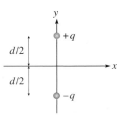

Problems 82 and 83

($|y| \gg d$), write a simpler, approximate expression for the field. To what power of y is the field proportional? Does this conflict with Coulomb's law? [*Hint:* Use the binomial approximation $(1 \pm x)^n \approx 1 \pm nx$ for $x \ll 1$.]

◆ 83. A dipole consists of two equal and opposite point charges ($\pm q$) separated by a distance d. (a) Write an expression for the magnitude of the electric field at a point $(x, 0)$ a large distance ($x \gg d$) from the midpoint of the charges on a line perpendicular to the dipole axis. [*Hint:* Use small angle approximations.] (b) Give the direction of the field for $x > 0$ and for $x < 0$.

84. In a thunderstorm, charge is separated through a complicated mechanism that is ultimately powered by the Sun. A simplified model of the charge in a thundercloud represents the positive charge accumulated at the top and the negative charge at the bottom as a pair

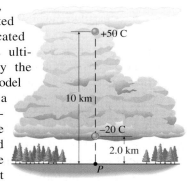

of point charges. (a) What is the magnitude and direction of the electric field produced by the two point charges at point P, which is just above the surface of the Earth? (b) Thinking of the Earth as a conductor, what sign of charge would accumulate on the surface near point P? (This accumulated charge increases the magnitude of the electric field near point P.)

85. Two point charges are located on the x-axis: a charge of +6.0 nC at $x = 0$ and an unknown charge q at $x = 0.50$ m. No other charges are nearby. If the electric field is zero at the point $x = 1.0$ m, what is q?

86. Three equal charges are placed on three corners of a square. If the force that Q_a exerts on Q_b has magnitude F_{ba} and the force that Q_a exerts on Q_c has magnitude F_{ca}, what is the ratio of F_{ca} to F_{ba}?

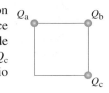

Ⓒ 87. Two otherwise identical conducting spheres carry charges of +5.0 μC and –1.0 μC. They are initially a large distance L apart. The spheres are brought together, touched together, and then returned to their original separation L. What is the ratio of the magnitude of the force on either sphere after they are touched to that before they were touched?

Ⓒ 88. In the diagram, regions A and C extend far to the left and right, respectively. The electric field due to the two point charges is zero at some point in which region or regions? Explain.

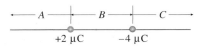

© 89. Two metal spheres of radius 5.0 cm carry net charges of +1.0 μC and +0.2 μC. (a) What (approximately) is the magnitude of the electrical repulsion on either sphere when their centers are 1.00 m apart? (b) Why cannot Coulomb's law be used to find the force of repulsion when their centers are 12 cm apart? (c) Would the actual force be larger or smaller than the result of using Coulomb's law with $r = 12$ cm? Explain.

✦ 90. A dipole consists of two opposite charges (q and $-q$) separated by a fixed distance d. The dipole is placed in an electric field in the $+x$-direction of magnitude E. The dipole axis makes an angle θ with the electric field as shown in the diagram. (a) Calculate the net electric force acting on the dipole. (b) Calculate the net torque acting on the dipole due to the electric forces as a function of θ. Let counterclockwise torque be positive. (c) Evaluate the net torque for $\theta = 0°$, $\theta = 36.9°$, and $\theta = 90.0°$. Let $q = \pm 3.0$ μC, $d = 7.0$ cm, and $E = 2.0 \times 10^4$ N/C.

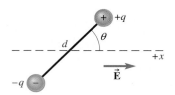

Answers to Practice Problems

16.1 7.5×10^{10} electrons

16.2 As the positively charged rod is moved away, the free electrons of the electroscope spread out more evenly. Since there is less net positive charge on the leaves, they do not hang as far apart.

16.3 6.8×10^{-3} N, 31° CW from the $-y$-direction

16.4 6.2×10^{-4} N

16.5 $\theta = 49.1°$

16.6 220 N/C to the right

16.7

(a) Inside the shell, field lines run from the positive charge spread about the surface to the negative charge located at the center of the shell.

(b) Outside the shell, we can imagine the charge $+Q$ all concentrated at the center of the sphere where it cancels the $-Q$ of the point charge. Therefore, $E = 0$ outside. Inside, the shell produces no electric field (as we found in the Example), so the field is just that due to the point charge $-Q$.

16.8 2.3×10^5 m/s to the right

16.9 The proton is deflected downward, but it has a much smaller acceleration because it has a much larger mass than the electron ($m_p = 1.673 \times 10^{-27}$ kg). The proton's acceleration vertically downward is 4.36×10^{11} m/s^2. The y-displacement, after spending 5.00×10^{-9} s between the plates, is 5.44×10^{-6} m, or 5.44×10^{-4} cm. The proton is barely deflected at all before leaving the region between the plates.

16.10

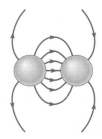

16.11 -3.8×10^4 N·m^2/C

16.12 On the ends, $\vec{E}$ is *parallel* to the surface, so the component of $\vec{E}$ perpendicular to the ends is zero and the flux through the ends is zero. No field lines *pass through* the ends of the cylinder.

Chapter 7

Electric Potential

A tool widely used in medicine to diagnose the condition of the heart is the electrocardiogram (EKG). The EKG data is displayed on a graph that shows a pattern repeated with each beat of the heart. What physical quantity is measured in an EKG? (See p. 609 for the answer.)

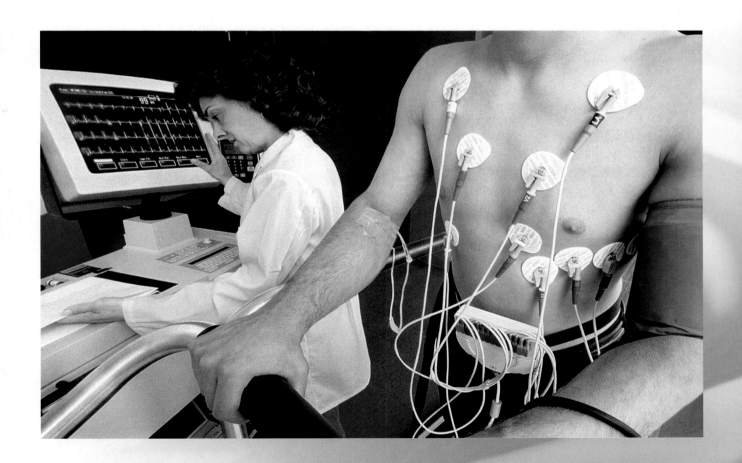

17.1   ELECTRIC POTENTIAL ENERGY

● **Potential energy** is energy stored in a field.

In Chapter 6, we learned about gravitational potential energy—energy stored in a gravitational field. **Electric potential energy** is the energy stored in an *electric* field (Fig. 17.1). For both gravitational and electric potential energy, the *change* in potential energy when objects move around is equal in magnitude but opposite in sign to the work done by the field:

$$\Delta U = -W_{\text{field}} \tag{6-8}$$

The minus sign indicates that, when the field does positive work W_{field} on an object, the *object's* energy is increased by an amount W_{field}. That amount of energy is *taken from* stored potential energy. The field dips into its "potential energy bank account" and gives the energy to the object, so the potential energy decreases when the force does positive work.

Some of the many similarities between gravitational and electric potential energy include:

- In both cases, the potential energy depends on only the *positions* of various objects, not on the *path* they took to get to those positions.
- Only *changes* in potential energy are physically significant, so we are free to assign the potential energy to be zero at any *one* convenient point. The potential energy in a given situation depends on the choice of the point where $U = 0$, but *changes* in potential energy are *not* affected by this choice.
- For two point particles, we usually choose $U = 0$ when the particles are infinitely far apart.
- Both the gravitational and electrical forces exerted by one point particle on another are inversely proportional to the square of the distance between them ($F \propto 1/r^2$). As a result, the gravitational and electric potential energies have the *same distance dependence* ($U \propto 1/r$, with $U = 0$ at $r = \infty$).
- The gravitational force and the gravitational potential energy for a pair of point particles are proportional to the product of the masses of the particles:

$$F = \frac{Gm_1m_2}{r^2} \tag{2-6}$$

$$U_{\text{g}} = -\frac{Gm_1m_2}{r} \quad (U_{\text{g}} = 0 \text{ at } r = \infty) \tag{6-14}$$

Figure 17.1 (a) An object moving through a gravitational field; the gravitational potential energy changes. (b) A charged particle moving through an *electric* field; the *electric* potential energy changes.

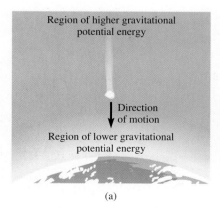

(a)

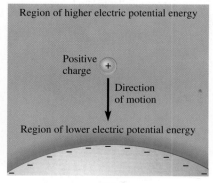

(b)

The electric force and the electric potential energy for a pair of point particles are proportional to the product of the *charges* of the particles:

$$F = \frac{k|q_1||q_2|}{r^2} \qquad (16\text{-}2)$$

$$U_E = \frac{kq_1q_2}{r} \quad (U_E = 0 \text{ at } r = \infty) \qquad (17\text{-}1)$$

● Electric potential energy for a pair of point charges a distance r apart

The negative sign in Eq. (6-14) indicates that gravity is always an attractive force: if two particles move closer together (r decreases), gravity does positive work and ΔU is negative—some gravitational potential energy is converted to other forms of energy. If the two particles move farther apart, the gravitational potential energy increases.

Why is there no negative sign in Eq. (17-1)? If the two charges have opposite signs, the force is an attractive one. The potential energy should be negative, as it is for the attractive force of gravity. With opposite signs, the product q_1q_2 is negative and the potential energy has the correct sign (Fig. 17.2). If the two charges instead have the same sign—both positive or both negative—the product q_1q_2 is positive. The electric force between two like charges is *repulsive*; the potential energy *increases* as they move closer together. Thus, Eq. (17-1) automatically gives the correct sign in every case.

Coulomb's law is written in terms of the *magnitudes* of the charges ($|q_1||q_2|$) since it gives the *magnitude* of a vector quantity—the force. In the potential energy expression [Eq. (17-1)], we do *not* write the absolute value bars. The signs of the two charges determine the sign of the potential energy, a scalar quantity that can be positive, negative, or zero.

If potential energy is negative, it *increases* when its absolute value gets smaller (just as -6 is *greater* than -8).

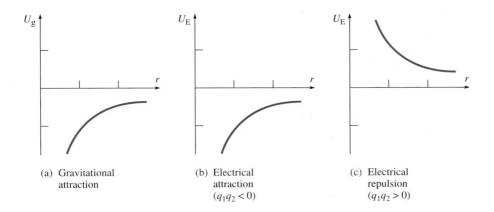

(a) Gravitational attraction

(b) Electrical attraction ($q_1q_2 < 0$)

(c) Electrical repulsion ($q_1q_2 > 0$)

Figure 17.2 Potential energies for pairs of point particles as a function of separation distance r. In each case, we choose $U = 0$ at $r = \infty$. For an attractive force, (a) and (b), the potential energy is negative. If two particles start far apart where $U = 0$, they "fall" spontaneously toward each other as the potential energy *decreases*. For a repulsive force (c), the potential energy is positive. If two particles start far apart, they have to be pushed together by an external agent that does work to increase the potential energy.

Example 17.1

Electric Potential Energy in a Thundercloud

In a thunderstorm, charge is separated through a complicated mechanism that is ultimately powered by the Sun. A simplified model of the charge in a thundercloud represents the positive charge accumulated at the top and the negative charge at the bottom as a pair of point charges (Fig. 17.3). (a) What is the electric potential energy of the pair of point charges, assuming that $U = 0$ when the two charges are infinitely far apart?

(b) Explain the sign of the potential energy in light of the fact that *positive* work must be done by external forces in the thundercloud to *separate* the charges.

Strategy   (a) The electric potential energy for a pair of point charges is given by Eq. (17-1), where $U = 0$ at infinite separation is assumed. The algebraic signs of the charges

Continued on next page

Example 17.1 Continued

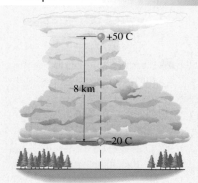

Figure 17.3

Charge separation in a thundercloud.

are included when finding the potential energy. (b) The work done by an external force to separate the charges is equal to the *change* in the electric potential energy as the charges are *moved apart* by forces acting within the thundercloud.

Solution and Discussion (a) The general expression for electric potential energy for two point charges is

$$U_E = \frac{kq_1q_2}{r}$$

We substitute the known values into the equation for electric potential energy.

$$U_E = 8.99 \times 10^9 \ \frac{N \cdot m^2}{C^2} \times \frac{(+50 \ C) \times (-20 \ C)}{8000 \ m}$$

$$= -1 \times 10^9 \ J$$

(b) Recall that we chose $U = 0$ at infinite separation. Negative potential energy therefore means that, *if the two point charges started infinitely far apart*, their electric potential energy would decrease as they are brought together—in the absence of other forces they would "fall" spontaneously toward one another. However, in the thundercloud, the unlike charges *start close together* and are moved *farther apart* by an external force; the external agent must do *positive* work to increase the potential energy and move the charges *apart*. Initially, when the charges are close together, the potential energy is *less than* -1×10^9 J; the *change* in potential energy as the charges are moved apart is *positive*.

Practice Problem 17.1   Two Point Charges with Like Signs

Two point charges, $Q = +6.0 \ \mu C$ and $q = +5.0 \ \mu C$, are separated by 15.0 m. (a) What is the electric potential energy? (b) Charge q is free to move—no other forces act on it—while Q is fixed in place. Both are initially at rest. Does q move toward or away from charge Q? (c) How does the motion of q affect the electric potential energy? Explain how energy is conserved.

Potential Energy due to Several Point Charges

To find the potential energy due to more than two point charges, we add the potential energies of each *pair* of charges. For three point charges, there are three pairs, so the potential energy is

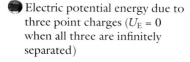

Electric potential energy due to three point charges ($U_E = 0$ when all three are infinitely separated)

$$U_E = k\left(\frac{q_1q_2}{r_{12}} + \frac{q_1q_3}{r_{13}} + \frac{q_2q_3}{r_{23}}\right) \tag{17-2}$$

where, for instance, r_{12} is the distance between q_1 and q_2. The potential energy in Eq. (17-2) is the negative of the work done by the electric field as the three charges are put into their positions, *starting from infinite separation*. If there are more than three charges, the potential energy is a sum just like Eq. (17-2), which includes *one* term for each *pair* of charges. Be sure not to count the potential energy of the same pair twice. If the potential energy expression has a term $(q_1q_2)/r_{12}$, it must not also have a term $(q_2q_1)/r_{21}$.

Example 17.2

Electric Potential Energy due to Three Point Charges

Find the electric potential energy for the array of charges shown in Fig. 17.4. Charge $q_1 = +4.0 \ \mu C$ is located at (0.0, 0.0) m; charge $q_2 = +2.0 \ \mu C$ is located at (3.0, 4.0) m; and charge $q_3 = -3.0 \ \mu C$ is located at (3.0, 0.0) m.

Strategy With three charges, there are three pairs to include in the potential energy sum [Eq. (17-2)]. The charges are given; we need only find the distance between each pair. Subscripts are useful to identify the three dis-

tances; r_{12}, for example, means the distance between q_1 and q_2.

Solution From Fig. 17.4, $r_{13} = 3.0$ m and $r_{23} = 4.0$ m. The Pythagorean theorem enables us to find r_{12}:

$$r_{12} = \sqrt{3.0^2 + 4.0^2} \ m = \sqrt{25} \ m = 5.0 \ m$$

Continued on next page

Example 17.2 Continued

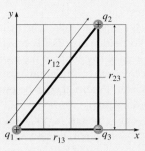

Figure 17.4
Three point charges.

The potential energy has one term for each pair:

$$U_E = k\left(\frac{q_1 q_2}{r_{12}} + \frac{q_1 q_3}{r_{13}} + \frac{q_2 q_3}{r_{23}}\right)$$

Substituting numerical values,

$$U_E = 8.99 \times 10^9 \, \frac{\text{N·m}^2}{\text{C}^2} \times \left[\frac{(+4.0)(+2.0)}{5.0} + \frac{(+4.0)(-3.0)}{3.0} + \frac{(+2.0)(-3.0)}{4.0}\right] \times 10^{-12} \, \frac{\text{C}^2}{\text{m}}$$

$$= -0.035 \, \text{J}$$

Discussion To interpret the answer, assume that the three charges start far apart from each other. As the charges are brought together and put into place, the electric fields do a total work of +0.035 J. Once the charges are in place, an external agent would have to supply 0.035 J of energy to separate them again.

Conceptual Practice Problem 17.2
Four Charges

When finding the potential energy due to four point charges, how many *pairs* of charges are there?

17.2 ELECTRIC POTENTIAL

Imagine that a collection of point charges is somehow fixed in place while another charge q can move. Moving q may involve changes in electric potential energy since the distances between it and the fixed charges may change. Just as the electric field is defined as the electric force per unit charge, the **electric potential** V is defined as the electric potential energy *per unit charge* (Fig. 17.5).

Potential: electric potential energy per unit charge

$$V = \frac{U_E}{q} \tag{17-3}$$

In Eq. (17-3), U_E is the electric potential energy *as a function of the position of the moveable charge (q).* Then the electric potential V is also a function of the position of charge q.

The SI unit of electric potential is the joule per coulomb, which is named the volt (symbol V) after the Italian scientist Alessandro Volta (1745–1827). Volta invented the voltaic pile, an early form of battery. *Electric potential* is often shortened to *potential.* It is also informally called "voltage," especially in connection with electric circuits, just as weight is sometimes called "tonnage." Be careful to distinguish *electric potential* from *electric potential energy.* It is all too easy to confuse the two, but they are not interchangeable.

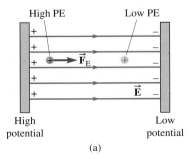

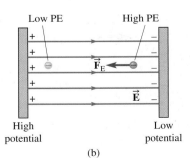

Figure 17.5 The electric *force* on a charge is always in the direction of lower electric potential energy. The electric *field* is always in the direction of lower *potential.*

● Definition of the volt

$$1 \text{ V} = 1 \text{ J/C} \qquad (17\text{-}4)$$

Since potential energy and charge are scalars, potential is also a scalar. The principle of superposition is easier to apply to potentials than to fields since fields must be added as vectors. Given the potential at various points, it is easy to calculate the potential energy change when a charge moves from one point to another. Potentials do not have direction in space; they are added just as any other scalar. Potentials can be either positive or negative and so must be added with their algebraic signs.

Since only changes in potential energy are significant, only changes in potential are significant. We are free to choose the potential arbitrarily at any one point. Equation (17-3) assumes that the potential is zero infinitely far away from the collection of fixed charges.

If the potential at a point due to a collection of fixed charges is V, then when a charge q is placed at that point, the electric potential energy is

$$U_E = qV \qquad (17\text{-}5)$$

Potential Difference

When a point charge q moves from point A to point B, it moves through a *potential difference*

$$\Delta V = V_f - V_i = V_B - V_A \qquad (17\text{-}6)$$

The potential difference is the change in electric potential energy per unit charge:

$$\Delta U_E = q\,\Delta V \qquad (17\text{-}7)$$

The electric force on a charge is always directed toward regions of lower electric potential energy, just as the gravitational force on an object is directed toward regions of lower gravitational potential energy (that is, downward). For a positive charge, lower potential energy means lower potential (Fig. 17.5a), but for a negative charge, lower potential energy means *higher* potential (Fig. 17.5b). This shouldn't be surprising, since the force on a negative charge is opposite to the direction of $\vec{\mathbf{E}}$, while the force on a positive charge is in the direction of $\vec{\mathbf{E}}$. Since the electric field points toward lower potential energy for positive charges,

$$\vec{\mathbf{E}} \text{ points in the direction of decreasing } V.$$

Example 17.3

A Battery-Powered Lantern

 A battery-powered lantern is switched on for 5.0 min. During this time, electrons with total charge -8.0×10^2 C flow through the lamp; 9600 J of electric potential energy is converted to light and heat. Through what potential difference do the electrons move?

Strategy   Equation (17-7) relates the change in electric potential energy to the potential difference. We could apply Eq. (17-7) to a single electron, but since all of the electrons move through the same potential difference, we can let q be the total charge of the electrons and ΔU_E be the total change in electric potential energy.

Solution   The total charge moving through the lamp is $q = -800$ C. The change in electric potential energy is *negative* since it is converted into other forms of energy. Therefore,

$$\Delta V = \frac{\Delta U_E}{q} = \frac{-9600 \text{ J}}{-8.0 \times 10^2 \text{ C}} = +12 \text{ V}$$

Discussion   The sign of the potential difference is positive: negative charges decrease the electric potential energy when they move through a potential increase.

Continued on next page

Example 17.3 Continued

Conceptual Practice Problem 17.3   An Electron Beam

A beam of electrons is deflected as it moves between oppositely charged parallel plates (Fig. 17.6). Which plate is at the higher potential?

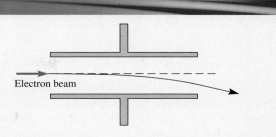

Figure 17.6

An electron beam deflected by a pair of oppositely charged plates.

Potential due to a Point Charge

If q is in the vicinity of one other point charge Q, the potential energy is

$$U = \frac{kQq}{r} \tag{17-1}$$

when Q and q are separated by a distance r. Therefore, the electric potential at a distance r from a point charge Q is

$$V = \frac{kQ}{r} \quad (V = 0 \text{ at } r = \infty) \tag{17-8}$$

● Potential due to a point charge

The potential at a point P due to N point charges is the sum of the potentials due to each charge:

$$V = \sum V_i = \sum \frac{kQ_i}{r_i} \quad \text{for } i = 1, 2, 3, \dots, N \tag{17-9}$$

where r_i is the distance from the ith point charge Q_i to point P.

Example 17.4

Potential due to Three Point Charges

Charge $Q_1 = +4.0 \ \mu C$ is located at $(0.0, 3.0)$ cm; charge $Q_2 = +2.0 \ \mu C$ is located at $(1.0, 0.0)$ cm; and charge $Q_3 = -3.0 \ \mu C$ is located at $(2.0, 2.0)$ cm (Fig. 17.7). (a) Find the electric potential at point A ($x = 0.0$, $y = 1.0$ cm) due to the three charges. (b) A point charge $q = -5.0$ nC moves from a great distance to point A. What is the change in electric potential energy?

Strategy   The potential at A is the sum of the potentials due to each point charge. The first step is to find the distance from each charge to point A. We call these distances r_1, r_2, and r_3 to avoid using the wrong one by mistake. Then we add the potentials due to each of the three charges at A.

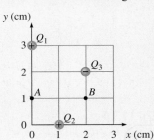

Figure 17.7

An array of three point charges.

Solution   (a) From the grid, $r_1 = 2.0$ cm. The distance from Q_2 to point A is the diagonal of a square that is 1.0 cm on a side. Thus, $r_2 = \sqrt{2.0}$ cm $= 1.414$ cm. The third charge is located at a distance equal to the hypotenuse of a right triangle with sides of 2.0 cm and 1.0 cm. From the Pythagorean theorem,

$$r_3 = \sqrt{1.0^2 + 2.0^2} \text{ cm} = \sqrt{5.0} \text{ cm} = 2.236 \text{ cm}$$

The potential at A is the sum of the potentials due to each point charge:

$$V = k \sum \frac{Q_i}{r_i}$$

Substituting numerical values:

$$V_A = 8.99 \times 10^9 \ \frac{\text{N} \cdot \text{m}^2}{\text{C}^2} \times$$

$$\left(\frac{+4.0 \times 10^{-6} \text{ C}}{0.020 \text{ m}} + \frac{+2.0 \times 10^{-6} \text{ C}}{0.01414 \text{ m}} + \frac{-3.0 \times 10^{-6} \text{ C}}{0.02236 \text{ m}} \right)$$

$$= +1.863 \times 10^6 \text{ V}$$

Continued on next page

Example 17.4 Continued

To two significant figures, the potential at point A is $+1.9 \times 10^6$ V.

(b) The change in potential energy is
$$\Delta U_E = q \, \Delta V$$
Here ΔV is the potential difference through which charge q moves. If we assume that q starts from an infinite distance, then $V_i = 0$. Therefore,
$$\Delta U_E = q(V_A - 0) = (-5.0 \times 10^{-9} \, \text{C}) \times (+1.863 \times 10^6 \, \text{J/C} - 0)$$
$$= -9.3 \times 10^{-3} \, \text{J}$$

Discussion The positive sign of the potential indicates that a positive charge at point A would have positive potential energy. To bring in a positive charge from far away, the potential energy must be increased and therefore positive work must be done by the agent bringing in the charge. A negative charge at that point, on the other hand, has negative potential energy. When q moves from a potential of zero to a positive potential, the potential increase causes a potential energy decrease ($q < 0$).

In Practice Problem 17.4, you are asked to find the work done by the field as q moves from A to B. The force is not constant in magnitude or direction, so we cannot just multiply force component times distance. In principle, the problem could be solved this way using calculus; but using the potential difference gives the same result without vector components or calculus.

Practice Problem 17.4   Potential at Point B

Find the potential due to the same array of charges at point B ($x = 2.0$ cm, $y = 1.0$ cm) and the work done by the electric field if $q = -5.0$ nC moves from A to B.

Conceptual Example 17.5

Field and Potential at the Center of a Square

Four equal positive point charges q are fixed at the corners of a square of side s (Fig. 17.8). (a) Is the electric field zero at the center of the square? (b) Is the potential zero at the center of the square?

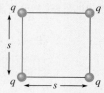

Figure 17.8
Four equal point charges at the corners of a square.

Strategy and Solution (a) The electric field at the center is the *vector* sum of the fields due to each of the point charges. Figure 17.9 shows the field vectors at the center of the square due to each charge. Each of these vectors has the same magnitude since the center is equidistant from each corner and the four charges are the same. From symmetry, the vector sum of the electric fields is zero.

(b) Since potential is a scalar rather than a vector, the potential at the center of the square is the *scalar* sum of the potentials due to each charge. These potentials are all equal since the distances and charges are the same. Each is positive since $q > 0$. The total potential at the center of the square is
$$V = 4 \frac{kq}{r}$$

where $r = s/\sqrt{2}$ is the distance from a corner of the square to the center.

Discussion In this example, the electric field is zero at a point where the potential is not zero. In other cases, there may be points where the potential is zero while the electric field at the same points is not zero. Never assume that the potential at a point is zero because the electric field is zero or *vice versa*. If the electric field is zero at a point, it means that a point charge placed at that point would feel no net electric force. If the potential is zero at a point, it means zero total work would be done by the electric field as a point charge moves from infinity to that point.

Practice Problem 17.5   Field and Potential for a Different Set of Charges

Find the electric field and the potential at the center of a square of side 2.0 cm with a charge of $+9.0 \, \mu$C at one corner and with charges of $-3.0 \, \mu$C at the other three corners (Fig. 17.10).

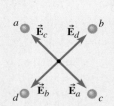

Figure 17.9
Electric field vectors due to each of the point charges at the center of the square.

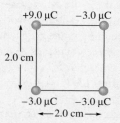

Figure 17.10
Charges for Practice Problem 17.5.

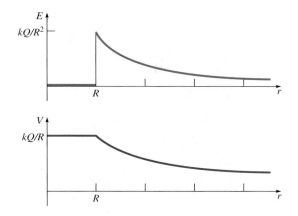

Figure 17.11 The electric field and the potential due to a hollow conducting sphere of radius R and charge Q as a function of r, the distance from the center.

Potential due to Spherical Conductors

In Section 16.4, we saw that the field outside a charged conducting sphere is the same as if all of the charge were concentrated into a point charge located at the center of the sphere. As a result, the electric potential due to a conducting sphere is similar to the potential due to a point charge.

Figure 17.11 shows graphs of the electric field strength and the potential as functions of the distance r from the center of a hollow conducting sphere of radius R and charge Q. The electric field inside the conducting sphere (from $r = 0$ to $r = R$) is zero. The magnitude of the electric field is greatest at the surface of the conductor and then drops off as $1/r^2$. Outside the sphere, the electric field is the same as for a charge Q located at $r = 0$.

The potential is chosen to be zero for $r = \infty$. The electric field outside the sphere ($r \geq R$) is the same as the field at a distance r from a *point charge Q*. Therefore, for any point at a distance $r \geq R$ from the center of the sphere, the potential is the same as the potential at a distance r from a point charge Q:

$$V = \frac{kQ}{r} \quad (r \geq R) \tag{17-8}$$

For a positive charge Q, the potential is positive; and it is negative for a negative charge. At the surface of the sphere, the potential is

$$V = \frac{kQ}{R}$$

Since the field inside the conductor is zero, the potential *anywhere inside* the sphere is the same as the potential at the surface of the sphere. Thus, for $r < R$, the potential is *not* the same as for a point charge. The magnitude of the potential due to a point charge continues to increase as $r \to 0$.

Van de Graaff Generator

An apparatus designed to charge a conductor to a high potential difference is the van de Graaff generator (Fig. 17.12). A large conducting sphere is supported on an insulating cylinder. In the cylinder, a motor-driven conveyor belt collects negative charge either by rubbing or from some other source of charge at the base of the cylinder. The charge is carried by the conveyor belt to the top of the cylinder, where it is collected by small metal rods and transferred to the conducting sphere. As more and more charge is deposited onto the conducting sphere, the charges repel each other and move as far away from each other as possible, ending up on the outer surface of the conducting sphere.

Inside the conducting sphere, the electric field is zero, so no repulsion from charges already on the sphere is felt by the charge on the conveyor belt. Thus, a large quantity of

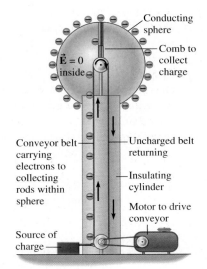

Figure 17.12 The van de Graaff generator.

Making the Connection:

van de Graaff generator

Figure 17.13 A hair-raising experience. A person touching the dome of a van de Graaff while electrically isolated from ground reaches the same potential as the dome. Although the effects are quite noticeable, there is no danger to the person since the whole body is at the same potential. A large potential *difference* between two parts of the person's body would be dangerous or lethal.

charge can build up on the conducting sphere so that an extremely high potential difference can be established. Potential differences of millions of volts can be attained with a large sphere (Fig. 17.13). Commercial van de Graaff generators supply the large potential differences required to produce intense beams of high energy x-rays. The x-rays are used in medicine for cancer therapy; industrial uses include radiography (to detect tiny defects in machine parts) and the polymerization of plastics. Old science fiction movies often show sparks jumping from generators of this sort.

Example 17.6

Minimum Radius Required for a van de Graaff

You wish to charge a van de Graaff to a potential of 240 kV. On a day with average humidity, an electric field of 8.0×10^5 N/C or greater ionizes air molecules, allowing charge to leak off the van de Graaff. Find the minimum radius of the conducting sphere under these conditions.

Strategy We set the potential of a conducting sphere equal to $V_{max} = 240$ kV and require the electric field strength just outside the sphere to be less than $E_{max} = 8.0 \times 10^5$ N/C. Since both $\vec{E}$ and V depend on the charge on the sphere and its radius, we should be able to eliminate the charge and solve for the radius.

Solution The potential of a conducting sphere with charge Q and radius R is

$$V = \frac{kQ}{R}$$

The electric field strength just outside the sphere is

$$E = \frac{kQ}{R^2}$$

Comparing the two expressions, we see that $E = V/R$ just outside the sphere. Now let $V = V_{max}$ and require $E < E_{max}$:

$$E = \frac{V_{max}}{R} < E_{max}$$

Solving for R,

$$R > \frac{V_{max}}{E_{max}} = \frac{2.4 \times 10^5 \text{ V}}{8.0 \times 10^5 \text{ N/C}}$$

$$R > 0.30 \text{ m}$$

The minimum radius is 30 cm.

Discussion To achieve a large potential difference, a large conducting sphere is required. A small sphere—or a conductor with a sharp point, which is like part of a sphere with a small radius of curvature—cannot be charged to a high potential. Even a relatively small potential on a conductor with a sharp point, such as a lightning rod, enables charge to leak off into the air since the strong electric field ionizes the nearby air.

The equation $E = V/R$ derived in this example is *not* a general relationship between field and potential. The general relationship is discussed in Section 17.3.

Practice Problem 17.6   A Small Conducting Sphere

What is the largest potential that can be achieved on a conducting sphere of radius 0.5 cm? Assume $E_{max} = 8.0 \times 10^5$ N/C.

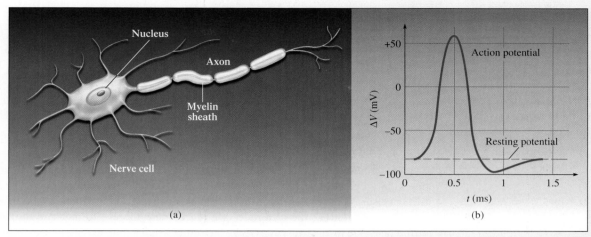

Figure 17.14 (a) The structure of a neuron. (b) The action potential. The graph shows the potential difference between the inside and outside of the cell membrane at a point along the axon as a function of time.

Potential Differences in Biological Systems

In general, the inside and outside of a biological cell are *not* at the same potential. The potential difference across a cell membrane is due to different concentrations of ions in the fluids inside and outside the cell. These potential differences are particularly note-worthy in nerve and muscle cells.

A nerve cell or *neuron* consists of a cell body and a long extension, called an *axon* (Fig. 17.14a). Human axons are 10–20 μm in diameter. When the axon is in its resting state, negative ions on the inner surface of the membrane and positive ions on the outer surface cause the fluid inside to be at a potential of about –85 mV relative to the fluid outside.

A nerve impulse is a change in the potential difference across the membrane that gets propagated along the axon. The cell membrane at the end stimulated suddenly becomes permeable to positive sodium ions for about 0.2 ms. Sodium ions flow into the cell, changing the polarity of the charge on the inner surface of the membrane. The potential difference across the cell membrane changes from about –85 mV to +60 mV. The reversal of polarity of the potential difference across the membrane is called the *action potential* (Fig. 17.14b). The action potential propagates down the axon at a speed of about 30 m/s.

Restoration of the resting potential involves both the diffusion of potassium and the pumping of sodium ions out of the cell—called *active transport*. As much as 20% of the resting energy requirements of the body are used for the active transport of sodium ions.

Similar polarity changes occur across the membranes of muscle cells. When a nerve impulse reaches a muscle fiber, it causes a change in potential, which propagates along the muscle fiber and signals the muscle to contract.

Muscle cells, including those in the heart, have a layer of negative ions on the inside of the membrane and positive ions on the outside. Just before each heartbeat, positive ions are pumped into the cells, neutralizing the potential difference. Just as for the action potential in neurons, the *depolarization* of muscle cells begins at one end of the cell and proceeds toward the other end. Depolarization of various cells occurs at different times. When the heart relaxes, the cells are polarized again.

An electrocardiogram (EKG) measures the potential difference between points on the chest as a function of time (Fig. 17.15). The depolarization and polarization of the cells in the heart causes potential differences that can be measured using electrodes connected to the skin. The potential difference measured by the electrodes is amplified and recorded on a chart recorder or a computer (Fig. 17.16).

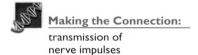

Making the Connection:

transmission of
nerve impulses

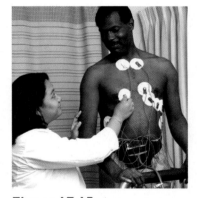

Figure 17.15 A stress test. The EKG is a graph of the potential difference measured between two electrodes as a function of time. These potential differences reveal whether the heart functions normally during exercise.

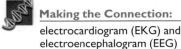

Making the Connection:

electrocardiogram (EKG) and
electroencephalogram (EEG)

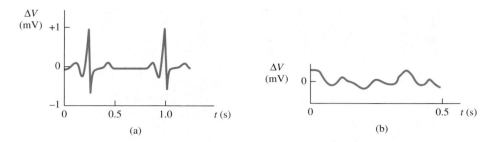

Figure 17.16 (a) A normal EKG indicates that the heart is healthy. (b) An abnormal or irregular EKG indicates a problem. This EKG indicates ventricular fibrillation.

Potential differences other than those due to the heart are used for diagnostic purposes. In an electroencephalogram (EEG), the electrodes are placed on the head. The EEG measures potential differences caused by electrical activity in the brain. In an electroretinogram (ERG), the electrodes are placed near the eye to measure the potential differences due to electrical activity in the retina when stimulated by a flash of light.

17.3   THE RELATIONSHIP BETWEEN ELECTRIC FIELD AND POTENTIAL

In this section, we explore the relationship between electric field and electric potential in detail, starting with visual representations of each.

Equipotential Surfaces

A field line sketch is a useful visual representation of the electric field. Is there a similar way to represent the electric potential? There cannot be "potential lines" since potential doesn't have direction. Instead, we can create something analogous to a contour map. An **equipotential surface** has the same potential at every point on the surface. The idea is similar to the lines of constant elevation on a topographic map, which show where the elevation is the same (Fig. 17.17). Since the potential difference between any two points on such an equipotential surface is zero, no work is done by the field when a charge moves from one point on the surface to another.

Equipotential surfaces and field lines are closely related. Suppose you want to move a charge in a direction so that the potential stays constant. In order for the field to do no work on the charge, the displacement must be perpendicular to the electric force (and therefore perpendicular to the field). As long as you always move the charge in a direction perpendicular to the field, the work done by the field is zero and the potential stays the same.

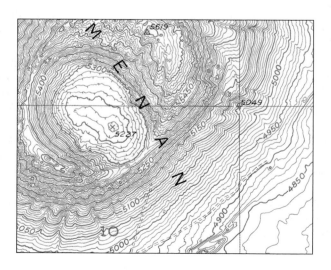

Figure 17.17 A topographic map showing lines of constant elevation in feet.

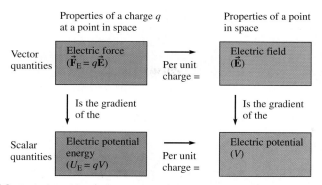

Figure 17.18 Relationships between force, field, potential energy, and potential.

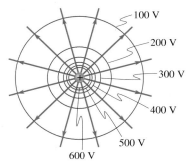

An equipotential surface is perpendicular to the electric field lines at all points.

Conversely, if you want to move a charge in a direction that *maximizes* the change in potential, you would move parallel or antiparallel to the electric field. Only the component of displacement perpendicular to an equipotential surface changes the potential. Think of a contour map: the steepest slope—the quickest change of elevation—is perpendicular to the lines of constant elevation. The electric field is sometimes called the **potential gradient**, where the word *gradient* suggests *grade* or *slope* (see Fig. 17.18). On a contour map, a hill is steepest where the lines of constant elevation are close together; a diagram of equipotential surfaces is similar.

If equipotential surfaces are drawn such that the potential difference between adjacent surfaces is constant, then the surfaces are closer together where the field is stronger.

The electric field always points in the direction of maximum potential decrease.

The simplest equipotential surfaces are those for a single point charge. The potential due to a point charge depends only on the distance from the charge, so the equipotential surfaces are spheres with the charge at the center (Fig. 17.19). There are an infinite number of equipotential surfaces, so we customarily draw a few surfaces equally spaced in potential—just like a contour map that shows places of equal elevation in 5-m increments.

Figure 17.19 Equipotential surfaces near a positive point charge. The circles represent the intersection of the spherical surfaces with the plane of the page. The potential decreases as we move away from a positive charge. The electric field lines are perpendicular to the spherical surfaces and point toward lower potentials. The spacing between equipotential surfaces increases with increasing distance since the electric field gets weaker.

Conceptual Example 17.7

Equipotential Surfaces for Two Point Charges

Sketch some equipotential surfaces for two point charges $+Q$ and $-Q$.

Strategy and Solution   One way to draw a set of equipotential surfaces is to first draw the field lines. Then we construct the equipotential surfaces by sketching lines that are perpendicular to the field lines at all points. Close to either point charge, the field is primarily due to the nearby charge, so the surfaces are nearly spherical.

Figure 17.20 shows a sketch of the field lines and equipotential surfaces for the two charges.

Discussion   This two-dimensional sketch shows only the intersection of the equipotential surfaces with the plane of the page. Except for the plane midway between the two charges, the equipotentials are closed surfaces that enclose one of the charges. Equipotential surfaces very close to either charge are approximately spherical.

Continued on next page

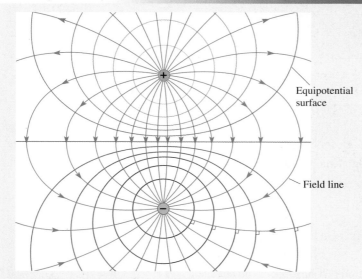

Figure 17.20

A sketch of the equipotential surfaces (purple) and electric field lines (green) for two point charges of the same magnitude but opposite in sign.

Equipotential surface

Field line

Conceptual Practice Problem 17.7
Equipotential Surfaces for Two Positive Charges

Sketch some equipotential surfaces for two equal positive point charges.

Potential in a Uniform Electric Field

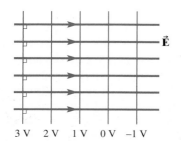

3 V   2 V   1 V   0 V   –1 V

Figure 17.21 Field lines and equipotential surfaces (at 1-V intervals) in a uniform field. The equipotential surfaces are equally spaced *planes* perpendicular to the field lines.

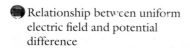
Relationship between uniform electric field and potential difference

In a uniform electric field, the field lines are equally spaced parallel lines. Since equipotential surfaces are perpendicular to field lines, the equipotential surfaces are a set of parallel planes (Fig. 17.21). The potential decreases from one plane to the next in the direction of $\vec{E}$. Since the spacing of equipotential planes depends on the magnitude of $\vec{E}$, in a uniform field planes at equal potential increments are equal distances apart.

To find a quantitative relationship between the field strength and the spacing of the equipotential planes, imagine moving a point charge $+q$ a distance d in the direction of an electric field of magnitude E. The work done by the electric field is

$$W_E = F_E d = qEd$$

The change in electric potential energy is

$$\Delta U_E = -W_E = -qEd$$

From the definition of potential, the potential change is

$$\Delta V = \frac{\Delta U_E}{q} = -Ed \qquad (17\text{-}10)$$

The negative sign in Eq. (17-10) is correct because potential *decreases* in the direction of the electric field.

Equation (17-10) implies that the SI unit of electric field (N/C) can also be written *volts per meter* (V/m):

$$1 \text{ N/C} = 1 \text{ V/m} \qquad (17\text{-}11)$$

In Fig. 17.21, the equipotential planes differ in potential by 1 V. If the electric field magnitude is 25 N/C = 25 V/m, then the distance between the planes is

$$\frac{1 \text{ V}}{25 \text{ V/m}} = 0.04 \text{ m}$$

Where the field is strong, the equipotential surfaces are close together: with a large number of volts per meter, it doesn't take many meters to change the potential a given number of volts.

Potential Inside a Conductor

In Section 16.6, we learned that $E = 0$ at every point inside a conductor in electrostatic equilibrium (when no charges are moving). If the potential gradient (the field) is zero at every point, then the potential does not change as we move from one point to another. If there were potential differences within the conductor, then charges would move in response. Positive charge would be accelerated by the field toward regions of lower potential and negative charge would be accelerated toward higher potential. If there are no moving charges, then the field is zero everywhere and no potential differences exist within the conductor. Therefore:

> In electrostatic equilibrium, every point within a conducting material must be at the same potential.

17.4   CONSERVATION OF ENERGY FOR MOVING CHARGES

When a charge moves from one position to another in an electric field, the change in electric potential energy must be accompanied by a change in other forms of energy so that the total energy is constant. Energy conservation simplifies problem solving just as it does with gravitational or elastic potential energy.

If no other forces act on a point charge, then as it moves in an electric field, the sum of the kinetic and electric potential energy is constant:

$$K_i + U_i = K_f + U_f = \text{constant}$$

Changes in gravitational potential energy are negligible compared with changes in electric potential energy when the gravitational force is much weaker than the electric force.

Example 17.8

Electron Gun

In an electron gun, electrons are accelerated from the cathode toward the anode, which is at a potential higher than the cathode (see Fig. 16.31). If the potential difference between the cathode and anode is 12 kV, at what speed do the electrons move as they reach the anode? Assume that the initial kinetic energy of the electrons as they leave the cathode is negligible.

Strategy   Using energy conservation, we set the sum of the initial kinetic and potential energies equal to the sum of the final kinetic and potential energies. The initial kinetic energy is taken to be zero. Once we find the final kinetic energy, we can solve for the speed.

Known: $K_i = 0$; $\Delta V = +12$ kV

Find: v

Solution   The change in electric potential energy is
$$\Delta U = U_f - U_i = q\,\Delta V$$
From conservation of energy,
$$K_i + U_i = K_f + U_f$$

Solving for the final kinetic energy,
$$K_f = K_i + (U_i - U_f) = K_i - \Delta U$$
$$= 0 - q\,\Delta V$$
To find the speed, we set $K_f = \frac{1}{2}mv^2$.
$$\tfrac{1}{2}mv^2 = -q\,\Delta V$$
Solving for the speed,
$$v = \sqrt{\frac{-2q\,\Delta V}{m}}$$
For an electron,
$$q = -e = -1.602 \times 10^{-19}\ \text{C}$$
$$m = 9.109 \times 10^{-31}\ \text{kg}$$
Substituting numerical values,
$$v = \sqrt{\frac{-2 \times (-1.602 \times 10^{-19}\ \text{C}) \times (12{,}000\ \text{V})}{9.109 \times 10^{-31}\ \text{kg}}}$$
$$= 6.5 \times 10^7\ \text{m/s}$$

Continued on next page

Example 17.8 Continued

Discussion The answer is more than 20% of the speed of light (3×10^8 m/s). A more accurate calculation of the speed, accounting for Einstein's theory of relativity, is 6.4×10^7 m/s.

Using conservation of energy to solve this problem makes it clear that the final speed depends only on the potential difference between the cathode and anode, not on the distance between them. To solve the problem using Newton's second law, even if the electric field is uniform, we have to assume some distance d between the cathode and anode. Using d, we can find the magnitude of the electric field

$$E = \frac{\Delta V}{d}$$

The acceleration of the electron is

$$a = \frac{F_E}{m} = \frac{eE}{m} = \frac{e\,\Delta V}{md}$$

Now we can find the final speed. Since the acceleration is constant,

$$v = \sqrt{v_i^2 + 2ad} = \sqrt{0 + 2 \times \frac{e\Delta V}{md} \times d}$$

The distance d cancels and gives the same result as the energy calculation.

Practice Problem 17.8   **Proton Accelerated**

A proton is accelerated from rest through a potential difference. Its final speed is 2.00×10^6 m/s. What is the potential difference? The mass of the proton is 1.673×10^{-27} kg.

17.5   CAPACITORS

Can a useful device be built to store electric potential energy? Yes. Many such devices, called *capacitors*, are found in every piece of electronic equipment (Fig. 17.22).

A **capacitor** is a device that stores electric potential energy by storing separated positive and negative charges. It consists of two conductors separated by either vacuum or an insulating material. Charge is separated, with positive charge put on one of the conductors and an equal amount of negative charge on the other conductor. Work must be done to separate positive charge from negative charge, since there is an attractive force between the two. The work done to separate the charge ends up as electric potential energy. An electric field arises between the two conductors, with field lines beginning on the conductor with positive charge and ending on the conductor with negative charge (Fig. 17.23). The stored potential energy is associated with this electric field. We can recover the stored energy—that is, convert it into some other form of energy—by letting the charges come together again.

The simplest form of capacitor is a **parallel plate capacitor**, consisting of two parallel metal plates, each of the same area A, separated by a distance d. A charge $+Q$ is put on one plate and a charge $-Q$ on the other. For now, assume there is air between the plates. One way to charge the plates is to connect the positive terminal of a battery to one and the negative terminal to the other. The battery removes electrons from one

Figure 17.22 The arrows indicate a few of the many capacitors on a circuit board from the inside of an amplifier.

plate, leaving it positively charged, and puts them on the other plate, leaving it with an equal magnitude of negative charge. In order to do this, the battery has to do work—some of the battery's chemical energy is converted into electric potential energy.

In general, the field between two such plates does not have to be uniform (Fig. 17.23). However, if the plates are close together, then a good approximation is to say that the charge is evenly spread on the inner surfaces of the plates and none is found on the outer surfaces. The plates in a real capacitor are almost always close enough that this approximation is valid.

With charge evenly spread on the inner surfaces, a uniform electric field exists between the two plates. We can neglect the nonuniformity of the field near the edges as long as the plates are close together. The electric field lines start on positive charges and end on negative charges. If charge of magnitude Q is evenly spread over each plate with surface of area A, then the *surface charge density* (the charge per unit area) is denoted by σ, the Greek letter sigma:

$$\sigma = Q/A \qquad (17\text{-}12)$$

In Problem 48, you can show that the magnitude of the electric field just outside a conductor is

Electric field just outside a conductor:

$$E = 4\pi k\sigma = \sigma/\epsilon_0 \qquad (17\text{-}13)$$

Recall that the constant $\epsilon_0 = 1/(4\pi k) = 8.85 \times 10^{-12}\ \text{C}^2/(\text{N}\cdot\text{m}^2)$ is called the *permittivity of free space* [Eq. (16-3b)]. Since the field between the plates of the capacitor is uniform, Eq. (17-13) gives the magnitude of the field *everywhere* between the plates.

What is the potential difference between the plates? Since the field is uniform, the *magnitude* of the potential difference is

$$\Delta V = Ed \qquad (17\text{-}10)$$

The field is proportional to the charge and the potential difference is proportional to the field; therefore, *the charge is proportional to the potential difference.* That turns out to be true for any capacitor, not just a parallel plate capacitor. The constant of proportionality between charge and potential difference depends only on geometric factors (sizes and shapes of the plates) and the material between the plates. Conventionally, this proportionality is written

Definition of capacitance:

$$Q = C\,\Delta V \qquad (17\text{-}14)$$

where Q is the magnitude of the charge on each plate and ΔV is the magnitude of the potential *difference* between the plates. The constant of proportionality C is called the **capacitance**. Think of capacitance as the capacity to hold charge for a given potential difference. The SI units of capacitance are coulombs per volt, which is called the *farad* (symbol F). Capacitances are commonly measured in μF (microfarads), nF (nanofarads), or pF (picofarads) because the farad is a rather large unit; a pair of plates with area 1 m² spaced 1 mm apart has a capacitance of only about $10^{-8}\ \text{F} = 10\ \text{nF}$.

We can now find the capacitance of a parallel plate capacitor. The electric field is

$$E = \frac{\sigma}{\epsilon_0} = \frac{Q}{\epsilon_0 A}$$

where A is the inner surface area of each plate. If the plates are a distance d apart, then the *magnitude* of the potential difference is

$$\Delta V = Ed = \frac{Qd}{\epsilon_0 A}$$

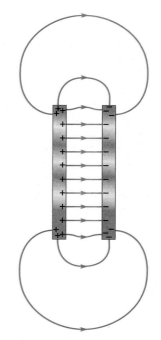

Figure 17.23 Side view of two parallel metal plates with charges of equal magnitude and opposite sign. There is a potential difference between the two plates; the positive plate is at the higher potential.

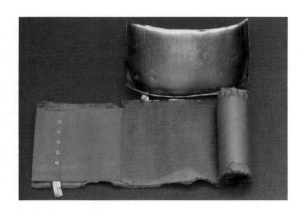

Figure 17.24 A disassembled capacitor, showing the foil conducting plates and the thin sheet of insulating material.

By rearranging, this can be rewritten in the form $Q = \text{constant} \times \Delta V$:

$$Q = \frac{\epsilon_0 A}{d}\Delta V$$

Comparing with the definition of capacitance, the capacitance of a parallel plate capacitor is

Capacitance of parallel plate capacitor:

$$C = \frac{\epsilon_0 A}{d} = \frac{A}{4\pi k d} \qquad (17\text{-}15)$$

To produce a large capacitance, we make the plate area large and the plate spacing small. To get large areas while still keeping the physical size of the capacitor reasonable, the plates are often made of thin conducting foil that is rolled, with the insulating material sandwiched in between, into a cylinder (Fig. 17.24). The effect of using an insulator other than air or vacuum is discussed in Section 17.6.

Example 17.9

Computer Keyboard

In one kind of computer keyboard, each key is attached to one plate of a parallel plate capacitor; the other plate is fixed in position (Fig. 17.25). The capacitor is maintained at a constant potential difference of 5.0 V by an external circuit. When the key is pressed down, the top plate moves closer to the bottom plate, changing the capacitance and causing charge to flow through the circuit. If each plate is a square of side 6.0 mm and the plate separation changes from 4.0 mm to 1.2 mm when a key is pressed, how much charge flows through the circuit? Does the charge on the capacitor increase or decrease? Assume that there is air between the plates instead of a flexible insulator.

Strategy Since we are given the area and separation of the plates, we can find the capacitance from Eq. (17-15). The charge is then found from the product of the capacitance and the potential difference across the plates: $Q = C\,\Delta V$.

Solution The capacitance of a parallel plate capacitor is given by Eq. (17-15):

$$C = \frac{A}{4\pi k d}$$

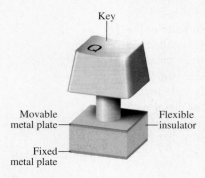

Key

Movable metal plate —

Flexible insulator

Fixed — metal plate

Figure 17.25

Basically, this kind of computer key is merely a capacitor with a variable plate spacing. A circuit detects the change in the plate spacing as charge flows from one plate through an external circuit to the other plate.

Continued on next page

Example 17.9 Continued

The area is $A = (6.0 \text{ mm})^2$. Since the potential difference ΔV is kept constant, the change in the magnitude of the charge on the plates is

$$Q_f - Q_i = C_f \Delta V - C_i \Delta V$$

$$= \left(\frac{A}{4\pi k d_f} - \frac{A}{4\pi k d_i}\right)\Delta V = \frac{A\Delta V}{4\pi k}\left(\frac{1}{d_f} - \frac{1}{d_i}\right)$$

Substituting numerical values,

$$Q_f - Q_i = \frac{(0.0060 \text{ m})^2 \times 5.0 \text{ V}}{4\pi \times 8.99 \times 10^9 \text{ N·m}^2/\text{C}^2} \times \left(\frac{1}{0.0012 \text{ m}} - \frac{1}{0.0040 \text{ m}}\right)$$

$$= +9.3 \times 10^{-13} \text{ C} = +0.93 \text{ pC}$$

Since ΔQ is positive, the magnitude of charge on the plates increases.

Discussion   If the plates move closer together, the capacitance increases. A greater capacitance means that more charge can be stored for a given potential difference. Therefore, the magnitude of the charge increases.

Practice Problem 17.9   Capacitance and the Charge Stored

A parallel plate capacitor has plates of area 1.0 m^2 and a separation of 1.0 mm. The potential difference between the plates is 2.0 kV. Find the capacitance and the magnitude of the charge on each plate. Which of these quantities depends on the potential difference?

Other devices are based on a capacitor with one moveable plate. In a *condenser microphone* (Fig. 17.26), one plate moves in and out in response to a sound wave. (*Condenser* is a synonym for capacitor.) The capacitor is maintained at a constant potential difference; as the plate spacing changes, charge flows onto and off the plates. The moving charge—an electric current—is amplified to generate an electrical signal. The design of many *tweeters* (speakers for high-frequency sounds) is just the reverse; in response to an electrical signal, one plate moves in and out, generating a sound wave.

Capacitors have many other uses. Each RAM (random-access memory) chip in a computer contains millions of microscopic capacitors. Each of the capacitors stores one bit (binary digit). To store a 1, the capacitor is charged; to store a 0, it is discharged. The insulation of the capacitors from their surroundings is not perfect, so charge would leak off if it were not periodically refreshed—which is why the contents of RAM are lost when the computer's power is turned off.

Besides storing charge and electrical energy, capacitors are also useful for the uniform electric field between the plates. This field can be used to accelerate or deflect charges in a controlled way. The oscilloscope—a device used to display time-dependent

Making the Connection:
condenser microphone

Making the Connection:
random-access memory (RAM) chips

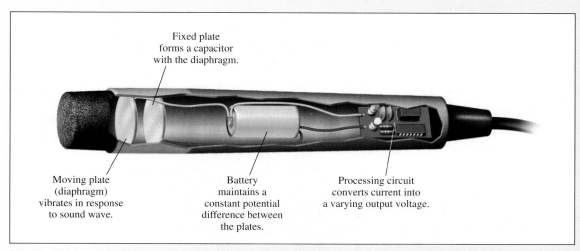

Figure 17.26 This microphone uses a capacitor with one moving plate to create an electrical signal.

potential differences in electric circuits—is a cathode ray tube that sends electrons between the plates of two capacitors (see Fig. 16.31). One of the capacitors deflects the electrons vertically; the other deflects them horizontally.

Discharging a Capacitor

If we connect one plate of a charged capacitor to the other with a conducting wire, charge moves along the wire until there is no longer a difference in potential between the plates.

Making the Connection:

camera flash

PHYSICS AT HOME

The next time you are taking flash pictures with a camera, try to take two pictures one right after the other. Unless you have a professional-quality camera, the flash does not work the second time. There is a minimum time interval of a few seconds between successive flashes. Many cameras have an indicator light to show when the flash is ready.

Did you ever wonder how the small battery in a camera produces such a bright flash? Compare the brightness of a flashlight with the same type of battery. By itself, a small battery cannot pump charge fast enough to produce the bright flash needed. During the time when the flash is inoperative, the battery charges a capacitor. Once the capacitor is fully charged, the flash is ready. When the picture is taken, the capacitor is discharged through the bulb, producing a bright flash of light.

17.6   DIELECTRICS

There is a problem inherent in trying to store a large charge in a capacitor. To store a large charge without making the potential difference excessively large, we need a large capacitance. Capacitance is inversely proportional to the spacing d between the plates. One problem with making the spacing small is that the air between the plates of the capacitor breaks down at an electric field of about 3000 V/mm with dry air (less for humid air). The breakdown allows a spark to jump across the gap so the stored charge is lost.

One way to overcome this difficulty is to put a better insulator than air between the plates. Some insulating materials, which are also called **dielectrics**, can withstand electric fields larger than those that cause air to break down and act as a conductor rather than as an insulator. Another advantage of placing a dielectric between the plates is that the capacitance itself is increased.

For a parallel plate capacitor in which a dielectric fills the entire space between the plates, the capacitance is

Capacitance of parallel plate capacitor with dielectric:

$$C = \kappa \frac{\epsilon_0 A}{d} = \kappa \frac{A}{4\pi k d} \qquad (17\text{-}16)$$

The effect of the dielectric is to increase the capacitance by a factor κ (Greek letter kappa), which is called the **dielectric constant**. The dielectric constant is a dimensionless number: the ratio of the capacitance with the dielectric to the capacitance without the dielectric. The value of κ varies from one dielectric material to another. Equation (17-16) is more general than Eq. (17-15), which applies only when $\kappa = 1$. When there is vacuum between the plates, $\kappa = 1$ by definition. Air has a dielectric constant that is only slightly larger than 1; for most practical purposes we can take $\kappa = 1$ for air also. The flexible insulator in a computer key (Example 17.9) increases the capacitance by a factor of κ. Thus, the amount of charge that flows when the key is pressed is larger than the value we calculated.

Table 17.1

Dielectric Constants and Dielectric Strengths for Materials at 20°C (in order of increasing dielectric constant)

Material	Dielectric Constant κ	Dielectric Strength (kV/mm)
Vacuum	1 (exact)	—
Air (dry, 1 atm)	1.00054	3
Paraffined paper	2.0–3.5	40–60
Teflon	2.1	60
Rubber (vulcanized)	3.0–4.0	16–50
Paper (bond)	3.0	8
Mica	4.5–8.0	150–220
Bakelite	4.4–5.8	12
Glass	5–10	8–13
Diamond	5.7	100
Porcelain	5.1–7.5	10
Rubber (neoprene)	6.7	12
Titanium dioxide ceramic	70–90	4
Water	80	—
Strontium titanate	310	8
Nylon 11	410	27
Barium titanate	6000	—

The dielectric constant depends on the insulating material used. Table 17.1 gives dielectric constants and the breakdown limit, or **dielectric strength**, for several materials. The dielectric strength is the electric field strength at which dielectric breakdown occurs and the material becomes a conductor. Since $\Delta V = Ed$ for a uniform field, the dielectric strength determines the maximum potential difference that can be applied across a capacitor per meter of plate spacing.

Do not confuse dielectric constant and dielectric strength; they are not related. The dielectric constant determines how much charge can be stored for a given potential difference, while dielectric strength determines how large a potential difference can be applied to a capacitor before dielectric breakdown occurs.

Polarization in a Dielectric

What is happening microscopically to a dielectric between the plates of a capacitor? Recall that polarization is a separation of the charge in an atom or molecule. The atom or molecule remains neutral, but the center of positive charge no longer coincides with the center of negative charge.

Figure 17.27 is a simplified diagram to indicate polarization of an atom. The unpolarized atom with a central positive charge is encircled by a cloud of electrons, so that the center of the negative charge coincides with the center of the positive charge. When a positively charged rod is brought near the atom, it repels the positive charge in the atoms and attracts the negative. This separation of the charges means the centers of positive and negative charge no longer coincide; they are distorted by the influence of the charged rod.

In Fig. 17.28a, a slab of dielectric material has been placed between the plates of a capacitor. The charges on the capacitor plates induce a polarization of the dielectric. The polarization occurs throughout the material, so the positive charge is slightly displaced relative to the negative charge.

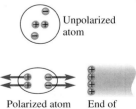

Figure 17.27 A positively charged rod induces polarization in a nearby atom.

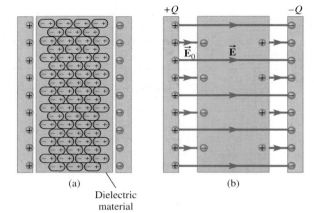

Figure 17.28 (a) Polarization of molecules in a dielectric material. (b) A dielectric with $\kappa = 2$ between the plates of a parallel plate capacitor. The electric field inside the dielectric ($\vec{\mathbf{E}}$) is smaller than the field outside ($\vec{\mathbf{E}}_0$).

Throughout the bulk of the dielectric, there are still equal amounts of positive and negative charge. The net effect of the polarization of the dielectric is a layer of positive charge on one face and negative charge on the other (Fig. 17.28b). Each conducting plate faces a layer of opposing charge.

The layer of opposing charge induced on the surface of the dielectric helps attract more charge to the conducting plate, for the same potential difference, than would be there without the dielectric. Since capacitance is charge per unit potential difference, the capacitance must have increased. The dielectric constant of a material is a measure of the ease with which the insulating material can be polarized. A larger dielectric constant indicates a more easily polarized material. Thus, neoprene rubber ($\kappa = 6.7$) is more easily polarized than Teflon ($\kappa = 2.1$).

The induced charge on the faces of the dielectric reduces the strength of the electric field in the dielectric compared to the field outside. Some of the electric field lines end on the surface of the insulating dielectric material; fewer lines penetrate the dielectric and thus the field is weaker. With a weaker field, there is a smaller potential difference between the plates (recall that for a uniform field, $\Delta V = Ed$). A smaller potential difference makes it easier to put more charge on the capacitor. We have succeeded in having the capacitor store more charge with a smaller potential difference. Since there is a limiting potential difference before breakdown occurs, this is an important factor for reaching maximum charge storage capability.

Suppose a dielectric is immersed in an external electric field E_0. The *definition* of the **dielectric constant** is the ratio of the electric field in vacuum E_0 to the electric field E inside the dielectric material:

Definition of dielectric constant:

$$\kappa = \frac{E_0}{E} \qquad \text{(17-17)}$$

Polarization *weakens* the field, so $\kappa > 1$. The electric field inside the dielectric (E) is

$$E = E_0/\kappa$$

In a capacitor, the dielectric is immersed in an applied field E_0 due to the charges on the plates. By reducing the field between the plates to E_0/κ, the dielectric reduces the potential difference between the plates by the same factor $1/\kappa$. Since $Q = C \Delta V$, multiplying ΔV by $1/\kappa$ for a given charge Q means the capacitance is multiplied by a factor of κ due to the dielectric [see Eq. (17-16)].

Example 17.10

Parallel Plate Capacitor with Dielectric

A parallel plate capacitor has plates of area 1.00 m^2 and spacing of 0.500 mm. The insulator has dielectric constant 4.9 and dielectric strength 18 kV/mm. (a) What is the capacitance? (b) What is the maximum charge that can be stored on this capacitor?

Strategy   Finding the capacitance is a straightforward application of Eq. (17-16). The dielectric strength and the plate spacing determine the maximum potential difference; using the capacitance we can find the maximum charge.

Solution   (a) The capacitance is

$$C = \kappa \frac{A}{4\pi k d}$$

$$= 4.9 \times \frac{1.00 \text{ m}^2}{4\pi \times 8.99 \times 10^9 \text{ N·m}^2/\text{C}^2 \times 5.00 \times 10^{-4} \text{ m}}$$

$$= 8.67 \times 10^{-8} \text{ F} = 86.7 \text{ nF}$$

(b) The maximum potential difference is

$$\Delta V = 18 \text{ kV/mm} \times 0.500 \text{ mm} = 9.0 \text{ kV}$$

Using the definition of capacitance, the maximum charge is

$$Q = C \Delta V = 8.67 \times 10^{-8} \text{ F} \times 9.0 \times 10^3 \text{ V} = 7.8 \times 10^{-4} \text{ C}$$

Discussion   Check: Each plate has a surface charge density of magnitude $\sigma = Q/A$ [Eq. (17-12)]. If the capacitor plates had this same charge density with no dielectric between them, the electric field between the plates would be [Eq. (17-13)]:

$$E_0 = 4\pi k \sigma = \frac{4\pi k Q}{A} = 8.8 \times 10^7 \text{ V/m}$$

From Eq. (17-17), the dielectric reduces the field strength by a factor of 4.9:

$$E = \frac{E_0}{\kappa} = \frac{8.8 \times 10^7 \text{ V/m}}{4.9} = 1.8 \times 10^7 \text{ V/m} = 18 \text{ kV/mm}$$

Thus, with the charge found in (b), the electric field has its maximum possible value.

Practice Problem 17.10   Changing the Dielectric

If the dielectric were replaced with one having twice the dielectric constant and half the dielectric strength, what would happen to the capacitance and the maximum charge?

Example 17.11

Neuron Capacitance

A neuron can be modeled as a parallel plate capacitor, where the membrane serves as the dielectric and the oppositely charged ions are the charges on the "plates" (Fig. 17.29). Find the capacitance of a neuron and the number of ions (assumed to be singly charged) required to establish a potential difference of 85 mV. Assume that the membrane has a dielectric constant of $\kappa = 3.0$, a thickness of 10.0 nm, and an area of $1.0 \times 10^{-10} \text{ m}^2$.

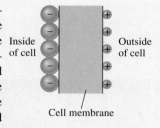

Inside of cell   Outside of cell

Cell membrane

Figure 17.29

Cell membrane as a dielectric.

Strategy   Since we know κ, A, and d, we can find the capacitance. Then, from the potential difference and the capacitance, we can find the magnitude of charge Q on each side of the membrane. A singly charged ion has a charge of magnitude e, so Q/e is the number of ions on each side.

Solution   From Eq. (17-16),

$$C = \kappa \frac{A}{4\pi k d}$$

Substituting numerical values,

$$C = 3.0 \times \frac{1.0 \times 10^{-10} \text{ m}^2}{4\pi \times 8.99 \times 10^9 \text{ N·m}^2/\text{C}^2 \times 10.0 \times 10^{-9} \text{ m}}$$

$$= 2.66 \times 10^{-13} \text{ F} = 0.27 \text{ pF}$$

From the definition of capacitance,

$$Q = C \Delta V = 2.66 \times 10^{-13} \text{ F} \times 0.085 \text{ V}$$

$$= 2.26 \times 10^{-14} \text{ C} = 0.023 \text{ pC}$$

Each ion has a charge of magnitude $e = +1.602 \times 10^{-19} \text{ C}$. The number of ions on each side is therefore,

$$\text{number of ions} = \frac{2.26 \times 10^{-14} \text{ C}}{1.602 \times 10^{-19} \text{ C/ion}} = 1.4 \times 10^5 \text{ ions}$$

Continued on next page

Example 17.11 Continued

Discussion   To see if the answer is reasonable, we can estimate the average distance between the ions. If 10^5 ions are evenly spread over a surface of area 10^{-10} m^2, then the area per ion is 10^{-15} m^2. Assuming each ion to occupy a square of area 10^{-15} m^2, the distance from one ion to its nearest neighbor is the side of the square $s = \sqrt{10^{-15} \text{ m}^2} = 30$ nm. The size of a typical atom or ion is 0.2 nm. Since the distance between ions is much larger than the size of an ion, the answer is plausible; if the dis-

tance between ions came out to be less than the size of an ion, the answer would not be plausible.

Practice Problem 17.11   Action Potential

How many ions must cross the membrane to change the potential difference from -0.085 V (with negative charge inside and positive outside) to $+0.060$ V (with negative charge outside and positive charge inside)?

Making the Connection:

thunderclouds and lightning

Lightning

Lightning (Fig. 17.30) involves the dielectric breakdown of air. Charge separation occurs within a thundercloud; the top of the cloud becomes positive and the lower part becomes negative (Fig. 17.31a). How this charge separation occurs is not completely understood, but one leading hypothesis is that collisions between ice particles or between an ice particle and a droplet of water tend to transfer electrons from the smaller particle to the larger. Updrafts in the thundercloud lift the smaller, positively charged particles to the top of the cloud, while the larger, negatively charged particles settle nearer the bottom of the cloud.

The negative charge at the bottom of the thundercloud induces positive charge on the Earth just underneath the cloud. When the electric field between the cloud and Earth reaches the breakdown limit for moist air (about 3.3×10^5 V/m), negative charge jumps from the cloud, moving in branching steps of about 50 m each. This stepwise progression of negative charges from the cloud is called a *stepped leader* (Fig. 17.31b).

Since the average electric field strength is $\Delta V/d$, the largest field occurs where d is the smallest—between tall objects and the stepped leader. *Positive streamers*—stepwise progressions of positive charge from the surface—reach up into the air from the tallest objects. If a positive streamer connects with one of the stepped leaders, a lightning channel is completed; electrons rush to the ground, lighting up the bottom of the channel. The rest of the channel then glows as more electrons rush down. The other stepped leaders also glow, but less brightly than the main channel because they contain fewer electrons. The flash of light starts at the ground and moves upward so it is called a *return stroke* (Fig. 17.31c). A total of about -20 to -25 C of charge is transferred from the thundercloud to the surface.

Figure 17.30 Lightning illuminates the sky near the West Virginia state capitol building.

Figure 17.31 (a) Charge separation in a thundercloud. A thunderstorm acts as a giant heat engine; work is done by the engine to separate positive charge from negative charge. (b) A stepped leader extends from the bottom of the cloud toward the surface. (c) When a positive streamer from the surface connects to a stepped leader, a complete path—a column of ionized air—is formed for charge to move between the cloud and the surface.

How can you protect yourself during a thunderstorm? Stay indoors or in an automobile if possible. If you are caught out in the open, keep low to prevent yourself from being the source of positive streamers. Do not stand under a tall tree; if lightning strikes the tree, charge traveling down the tree and then along the surface puts you in grave danger. Do not lie flat on the ground, or you risk the possibility of a large potential difference developing between your feet and head when a lightning strike travels through the ground. Go to a nearby ditch or low spot if there is one. Crouch with your head low and your feet as close together as possible to minimize the potential difference between your feet.

17.7   ENERGY STORED IN A CAPACITOR

A capacitor not only stores charge; it also stores energy. Figure 17.32 shows what happens when a battery is connected to an initially uncharged capacitor. Electrons are pumped off the upper plate and onto the lower until the potential difference between the capacitor plates is equal to the potential difference ΔV maintained by the battery.

The energy stored in the capacitor can be found by summing the work done by the battery to separate the charge. As the amount of charge on the plates increases, the potential difference ΔV through which charge must be moved also increases. Suppose we look at this process at some instant of time when one plate has charge $+q_i$, the other has charge $-q_i$, and the potential difference between the plates is ΔV_i.

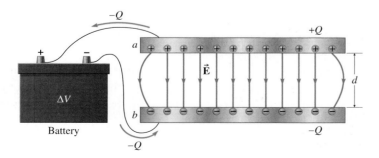

Figure 17.32 A parallel plate capacitor charged by a battery. Electrons with total charge $-Q$ are moved from the upper plate to the lower, leaving the plates with charges of equal magnitude and opposite sign.

To avoid writing a collection of minus signs, we imagine transferring positive charge instead of the negative charge; the result is the same whether we move negative or positive charges. From the definition of capacitance,

$$\Delta V_i = \frac{q_i}{C}$$

Now the battery transfers a little more charge Δq_i from one plate to the other, increasing the electric potential energy. If Δq_i is small, the potential difference is approximately constant during the transfer. The increase in energy is

$$\Delta U_i = \Delta q_i \times \Delta V_i$$

The total energy U stored in the capacitor is the sum of all the electric potential energy increases, ΔU_i:

$$U = \sum \Delta U_i = \sum \Delta q_i \times \Delta V_i$$

We can find this sum using a graph of the potential difference ΔV_i as a function of the charge q_i (Fig. 17.33). The graph is a straight line since $\Delta V_i = q_i/C$. The energy increase $\Delta U_i = \Delta q_i \times \Delta V_i$ when a small amount of charge is transferred is represented on the graph by the area of a rectangle of height ΔV_i and width Δq_i.

Summing the energy increases means summing the areas of a series of rectangles of increasing height. Thus, the total energy stored in the capacitor is represented by the triangular area under the graph. If the final values of the charge and potential difference are Q and ΔV, then

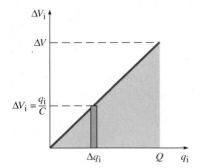

Figure 17.33 The total energy transferred is the area under the curve $\Delta V_i = q_i/C$.

> **Energy stored in a capacitor:**
> $$U = \text{area of triangle} = \tfrac{1}{2}(\text{base} \times \text{height})$$
> $$U = \tfrac{1}{2} Q \Delta V \qquad \text{(17-18a)}$$

The factor of $\frac{1}{2}$ reflects the fact that the potential difference through which the charge was moved increases from zero to ΔV; the *average* potential difference through which the charge was moved is $\Delta V/2$. To move charge Q through an average potential difference of $\Delta V/2$ requires $Q \Delta V/2$ of work.

Equation (17-18a) can be written in other useful forms, using the definition of capacitance to eliminate either Q or ΔV.

$$U = \frac{1}{2}Q\Delta V = \frac{1}{2}(C\Delta V) \times \Delta V = \frac{1}{2}C(\Delta V)^2 \qquad \text{(17-18b)}$$

$$U = \frac{1}{2}Q\Delta V = \frac{1}{2}Q \times \frac{Q}{C} = \frac{Q^2}{2C} \qquad \text{(17-18c)}$$

Example 17.12

A Defibrillator

Fibrillation is a chaotic pattern of heart activity that is ineffective at pumping blood and is therefore life threatening. A device known as a *defibrillator* is used to shock the heart back to a normal beat pattern. The defibrillator discharges a capacitor through paddles on the skin, so that some of the charge flows through the heart (Fig. 17.34). (a) If an 11.0-μF capacitor is charged to 6.00 kV and then discharged through paddles into a patient's body, how much energy is stored in the capacitor? (b) How much charge flows through the patient's body if the capacitor discharges completely?

Strategy There are three equivalent expressions for energy stored in a capacitor. Since the capacitance and the potential difference are given, Eq. (17-18b) is the most direct. Since the capacitor is completely discharged, all of the charge initially on the capacitor flows through the patient's body.

Solution (a) The energy stored in the capacitor is

$$U = \tfrac{1}{2}C(\Delta V)^2 = \tfrac{1}{2} \times 11.0 \times 10^{-6}\,\text{F} \times (6.00 \times 10^3\,\text{V})^2 = 198\,\text{J}$$

Continued on next page

Example 17.12 Continued

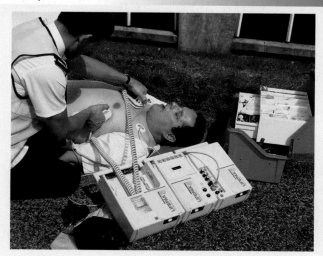

Figure 17.34

A paramedic uses a defibrillator to resuscitate a patient.

(b) The charge initially on the capacitor is

$$Q = C\,\Delta V = 11.0 \times 10^{-6}\,\text{F} \times 6.00 \times 10^{3}\,\text{V} = 0.0660\,\text{C}$$

Discussion   To test our result, we make a quick check:

$$U = \frac{Q^2}{2C} = \frac{(0.0660\,\text{C})^2}{2 \times 11.0 \times 10^{-6}\,\text{F}} = 198\,\text{J}$$

Practice Problem 17.12   Charge and Stored Energy for a Parallel Plate Capacitor

A parallel plate capacitor of area 0.24 m² has a plate separation, in air, of 8.00 mm. The potential difference between the plates is 0.800 kV. Find (a) the charge on the plates and (b) the stored energy.

Energy Stored in an Electric Field

Potential energy is energy of interaction or field energy. The energy stored in a capacitor is stored in the electric field between the plates. We can use the energy stored in a capacitor to calculate how much energy *per unit volume* is stored in an electric field E. Why energy per unit volume? Two capacitors can have the same electric field but store different amounts of energy. The larger capacitor stores more energy, proportional to the volume of space between the plates.

In a parallel plate capacitor, the energy stored is

$$U = \frac{1}{2}C(\Delta V)^2 = \frac{1}{2}\kappa \frac{A}{4\pi kd}(\Delta V)^2$$

Assuming the field is uniform between the plates, the potential difference is

$$\Delta V = Ed$$

Substituting Ed for ΔV,

$$U = \frac{1}{2}\kappa \frac{A}{4\pi kd}(Ed)^2 = \frac{1}{2}\kappa \frac{Ad}{4\pi k}E^2$$

We recognize Ad as the volume of space between the plates of the capacitor. This is the volume in which the energy is stored—$E = 0$ outside an ideal parallel plate capacitor. Then the **energy density** u—the electric potential energy per unit volume—is

$$u = \frac{U}{Ad} = \frac{1}{2}\kappa \frac{1}{4\pi k}E^2 = \frac{1}{2}\kappa \epsilon_0 E^2 \qquad (17\text{-}19)$$

The energy density is proportional to the square of the field strength. This is true in general, not just for a capacitor; there is energy associated with any electric field.

MASTER THE CONCEPTS

- Electric potential energy can be stored in an electric field. The electric potential energy of two point charges separated by a distance r is

$$U_E = \frac{k q_1 q_2}{r} \quad (U_E = 0 \text{ at } r = \infty) \quad (17\text{-}1)$$

- The signs of q_1 and q_2 determine whether the electric potential energy is positive or negative. For more than two charges, the electric potential energy is the scalar sum of the individual potential energies for each *pair* of charges.

- The electric potential V at a point is the electric potential energy per unit charge:

$$V = \frac{U_E}{q} \quad (17\text{-}3)$$

In Eq. (17-3), U_E is the electric potential energy due to the interaction of a moveable charge q with a collection of fixed charges and V is the electric potential due to that collection of fixed charges. Both U_E and V are functions of the position of the moveable charge q.

- Electric potential, like electric potential energy, is a scalar quantity. The SI unit for potential is the volt (1 V = 1 J/C).

- If a point charge q moves through a potential difference ΔV, then the change in electric potential energy is

$$\Delta U_E = q \, \Delta V \quad (17\text{-}7)$$

- The electric potential at a distance r from a point charge Q is

$$V = \frac{kQ}{r} \quad (V = 0 \text{ at } r = \infty) \quad (17\text{-}8)$$

The potential at a point P due to N point charges is the sum of the potentials due to each charge.

- An equipotential surface has the same potential at every point on the surface. An equipotential surface is perpendicular to the electric field at all points. No change in electric potential energy occurs when a charge moves from one position to another on an equipotential surface. If equipotential surfaces are drawn such that the potential difference between adjacent surfaces is constant, then the surfaces are closer together where the field is stronger.

- The electric field always points in the direction of maximum potential decrease.

- The potential difference that occurs when you move a distance d in the direction of a uniform electric field of magnitude E is

$$\Delta V = -Ed \quad (17\text{-}10)$$

- The electric field has units of

$$\text{N/C} = \text{V/m} \quad (17\text{-}11)$$

- In electrostatic equilibrium, every point in a conductor must be at the same potential.

- A capacitor consists of two conductors (the *plates*) that are given opposite charges. A capacitor stores charge and electric potential energy. Capacitance is the ratio of the magnitude of charge on each plate (Q) to the electric potential difference between the plates (ΔV). Capacitance is measured in farads (F).

$$Q = C \Delta V \quad (17\text{-}14)$$
$$1 \text{ F} = 1 \text{ C/V}$$

- The capacitance of a parallel plate capacitor is

$$C = \kappa \frac{A}{4 \pi k d} = \kappa \frac{\epsilon_0 A}{d} \quad (17\text{-}16)$$

where A is the area of each plate, d is their separation, and ϵ_0 is the permittivity of free space [$\epsilon_0 = 1/(4\pi k)$ = 8.854×10^{-12} C^2/(N·m^2)]. If vacuum separates the plates, $\kappa = 1$; otherwise, $\kappa > 1$ is the dielectric constant of the dielectric (the insulating material). If a dielectric is immersed in an external electric field, the dielectric constant is the ratio of the external electric field E_0 to the electric field E in the dielectric.

$$\kappa = \frac{E_0}{E} \quad (17\text{-}17)$$

- The dielectric constant is a measure of the ease with which the insulating material can be polarized.

- The dielectric strength is the electric field strength at which dielectric breakdown occurs and the material becomes a conductor.

- The energy stored in a capacitor is

$$U = \frac{1}{2} Q \, \Delta V = \frac{1}{2} C (\Delta V)^2 = \frac{Q^2}{2C} \quad (17\text{-}18)$$

- The energy density u—the electric potential energy per unit volume—associated with an electric field is

$$u = \frac{1}{2} \kappa \frac{1}{4 \pi k} E^2 = \frac{1}{2} \kappa \epsilon_0 E^2 \quad (17\text{-}19)$$

Conceptual Questions

1. A negatively charged particle with charge $-q$ is far away from a positive charge $+Q$ that is fixed in place. As $-q$ moves closer to $+Q$, (a) does the electric field do positive or negative work? (b) Does $-q$ move through a potential increase or a potential decrease? (c) Does the electric potential energy increase or decrease? (d) Repeat questions (a)–(c) if the fixed charge is instead negative $(-Q)$.

2. Dry air breaks down for a voltage of about 3000 V/mm. Is it possible to build a parallel plate capacitor with a plate spacing of 1 mm that can be charged to a potential difference greater than 3000 V? If so, explain how.

3. A bird is perched on a high-voltage power line whose potential varies between -100 kV and $+100$ kV. Why is the bird not electrocuted?

4. A positive charge is initially at rest in an electric field and is free to move. Does the charge start to move toward a position of higher or lower potential? What happens to a negative charge in the same situation?

5. Points A and B are at the same potential. What is the total work that must be done by an external agent to move a charge from A to B? Does your answer mean that no external force need be applied? Explain.

6. A point charge moves to a region of higher potential and yet the electric potential energy *decreases*. How is this possible?

7. Why are all parts of a conductor at the same potential in electrostatic equilibrium?

8. If $E = 0$ at a single point, then a point charge placed at that point will feel no electric force. What does it mean if the *potential* is zero at a point? Are there any assumptions behind your answer?

9. If $E = 0$ everywhere throughout a region of space, what do we know is true about the potential at points in that region?

10. If the potential increases as you move from point P in the $+x$-direction, but the potential does not change as you move from P in the y- or z-directions, what is the direction of the electric field at P?

11. If the potential is the same at every point throughout a region of space, is the electric field the same at every point in that region? What can you say about the magnitude of $\vec{E}$ in the region? Explain.

12. If a uniform electric field exists in a region of space, is the potential the same at all points in the region? Explain.

13. When we talk about the potential difference between the plates of a capacitor, shouldn't we really specify two *points*, one on each plate, and talk about the potential difference between those points? Or doesn't it matter which points we choose? Explain.

14. A swimming pool is filled with water (total mass M) to a height h. Explain why the gravitational potential energy of the water (taking $U = 0$ at ground level) is $\frac{1}{2}Mgh$. Where does the factor of $\frac{1}{2}$ come from? How much work must be done to fill the pool, if there is a ready supply of water at ground level? What does this have to do with capacitors? [*Hint:* Make an analogy between the capacitor and the pool. What is analogous to the water? What quantity is analogous to M? What quantity is analogous to gh?]

15. The charge on a capacitor doubles. What happens to its capacitance?

16. During a thunderstorm, some cows gather under a large tree. One cow stands facing directly toward the tree. Another cow stands at about the same distance from the tree, but it faces sideways (tangent to a circle centered on the tree). Which cow do you think is more likely to be killed if lightning strikes the tree? [*Hint:* Think about the potential difference between the cows' front and hind legs in the two positions.]

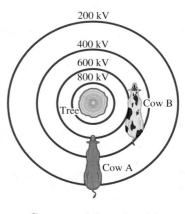

Conceptual Question 16 and Problem 51

17. If we know the potential at a single point, what (if anything) can we say about the magnitude of the electric field at that same point?

18. In Fig. 17.13, why is the person touching the dome of the van de Graaff generator not electrocuted even though there may be a potential difference of hundreds of thousands of volts between her and the ground?

19. The electric field just above Earth's surface on a clear day in an open field is about 150 V/m downward. Which is at a higher potential: the Earth or the upper atmosphere?

20. A parallel plate capacitor has the space between the plates filled with a slab of dielectric with $\kappa = 3$. While the capacitor is connected to a battery, the dielectric slab is removed. Describe *quantitatively* what happens to the capacitance, the potential difference, the charge on the plates, the electric field, and the energy stored in the capacitor as the slab is removed. [*Hint:* First figure out which quantities remain constant.]

21. Repeat Question 20 if the capacitor is charged and then disconnected from the battery before removing the dielectric slab.

22. A charged parallel plate capacitor has the space between the plates filled with air. The capacitor has been disconnected from the battery that charged it. Describe *quantitatively* what happens to the capacitance, the potential difference, the charge on the plates,

the electric field, and the energy stored in the capacitor as the plates are moved closer together. [*Hint:* First figure out which quantities remain constant.]

C 23. A positive charge +2 μC and a negative charge –5 μC lie on a line. In which region or regions (*A, B, C*) is there a point on the line a finite distance away where the potential is zero? Explain your reasoning. Are there any points where both the electric field and the potential are zero?

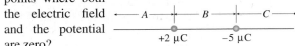

24. Explain why the woman's hair in Fig. 17.13 stands on end. Why are the hairs directed approximately radially away from her scalp? [*Hint:* Think of her head as a conducting sphere.]

Multiple-Choice Questions

In all problems, we assign the potential due to a point charge to be zero at an infinite distance from the charge.

1. Two charges are located at opposite corners (*A* and *C*) of a square. We do not know the magnitude or sign of these charges. What can be said about the potential at corner *B* relative to the potential at corner *D*?

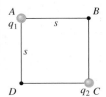

   (a) It is the same as that at *D*.
   (b) It is different from that at *D*.
   (c) It is the same as that at *D* only if the charges at *A* and *C* are equal.
   (d) It is the same as that at *D* only if the charges at *A* and *C* are equal in magnitude and opposite in sign.

2. Among these choices, which is/are correct units for electric field?

   (a) N/kg only   (b) N/C only
   (c) N only   (d) N·m/C only
   (e) V/m only   (f) both N/C and V/m

3. In the diagram, the potential is zero at which of the points *A*–*E*?

   (a) *B*, *D*, and *E*
   (b) *B* only
   (c) *A*, *B*, and *C*
   (d) all five points
   (e) all except *B*

   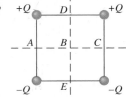

4. Which of these units can be used to measure electric potential?

   (a) N/C   (b) J   (c) V·m   (d) V/m   (e) $\dfrac{N \cdot m}{C}$

5. A parallel plate capacitor is attached to a battery that supplies a constant potential difference. While the battery is still attached, the parallel plates are separated a little more. Which statement describes what happens?

(a) The electric field increases and the charge on the plates decreases.
(b) The electric field remains constant and the charge on the plates increases.
(c) The electric field remains constant and the charge on the plates decreases.
(d) Both the electric field and the charge on the plates decrease.

6. A capacitor has been charged with $+Q$ on one plate and $-Q$ on the other plate. Which of these statements is true?

   (a) The potential difference between the plates is QC.
   (b) The energy stored is $\frac{1}{2}Q\Delta V$.
   (c) The energy stored is $\frac{1}{2}Q^2C$.
   (d) The potential difference across the plates is $Q^2/(2C)$.
   (e) None of the statements above is true.

7. Two solid metal spheres of different radii are far apart. The spheres are connected by a fine metal wire. Some charge is placed on one of the spheres. After electrostatic equilibrium is reached, the wire is removed. Which of these quantities will be the *same* for the two spheres?

   (a) the charge on each sphere
   (b) the electric field inside each sphere, at the same distance from the center of the spheres
   (c) the electric field just outside the surface of each sphere
   (d) the electric potential at the surface of each sphere
   (e) both (b) and (c)   (f) both (b) and (d)
   (g) both (a) and (c)

8. A large negative charge $-Q$ is located in the vicinity of points *A* and *B*. Suppose a positive charge $+q$ is moved at constant speed from *A* to *B* by an external agent. Along which of the paths shown in the figure will the work done by the field be the greatest?

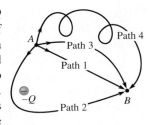

   (a) path 1   (b) path 2   (c) path 3   (d) path 4
   (e) Work is the same along all four paths.

9. A tiny charged pellet of mass *m* is suspended at rest between two horizontal, charged metallic plates. The lower plate has a positive charge and the upper plate has a negative charge. Which statement in the answers here is *not* true?

   (a) The electric field between the plates points vertically upward.
   (b) The pellet is negatively charged.
   (c) The magnitude of the electric force on the pellet is equal to *mg*.
   (d) The plates are at different potentials.

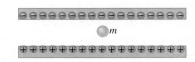

10. Two positive 2.0-µC point charges are placed as shown in part (a) of the figure. The distance from each charge to the point P is 0.040 m. Then the charges are rearranged as shown in part (b) of the figure. Which statement is now true concerning $\vec{E}$ and V at point P?

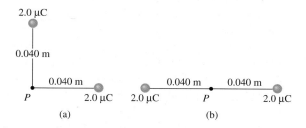

(a)

(b)

(a) The electric field and the electric potential are both zero.

(b) $\vec{E} = 0$, but V is the same as before the charges were moved.

(c) $V = 0$, but $\vec{E}$ is the same as before the charges were moved.

(d) $\vec{E}$ is the same as before the charges were moved, but V is less than before.

(e) Both $\vec{E}$ and V have changed and neither is zero.

11. In the diagram, which two points are closest to being at the same potential?

(a) A and D (b) B and C
(c) B and D (d) A and C

12. In the diagram, which point is at the lowest potential?

(a) A (b) B
(c) C (d) D

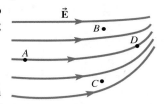

Multiple-Choice
Questions 11 and 12

Problems

 Combination conceptual/quantitative problem

 Biological or medical application

No ✦   Easy to moderate difficulty level

✦   More challenging

✦✦   Most challenging

Blue # Detailed solution in the Student Solutions Manual

1 2   Problems paired by concept

17.1 Electric Potential Energy

1. Two point charges, +5.0 µC and –2.0 µC, are separated by 5.0 m. What is the electric potential energy?

$Q = +5.0\ \mu C$ $q = -2.0\ \mu C$
$\leftarrow r = 5.0\ m \rightarrow$

2. A hydrogen atom has a single proton at its center and a single electron at a distance of approximately 0.0529 nm from the proton. (a) What is the electric potential energy

in joules? (b) What is the significance of the sign of the answer?

3. How much work is done by an applied force that moves two charges of 6.5 µC that are initially very far apart to a distance of 4.5 cm apart?

4. The nucleus of a helium atom contains two protons that are approximately 1 fm apart. How much work must be done by an external agent to bring the two protons from an infinite separation to a separation of 1.0 fm?

5. How much work does it take for an external force to set up the arrangement of charged objects in the diagram on the corners of a right triangle when the three objects are initially very far away from each other?

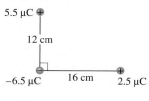

6. Two point charges (+10.0 nC and –10.0 nC) are located 8.00 cm apart. What is the *total* electric potential energy of the three charges when a third point charge of –4.2 nC is placed at points a, b, and c in turn? (Let $U = 0$ when *all three* charges are separated by an infinite distance.)

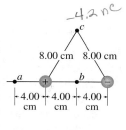

7. Find the electric potential energy for the following array of charges: charge $q_1 = +4.0\ \mu C$ is located at $(x, y) = (0.0, 0.0)$ m; charge $q_2 = +3.0\ \mu C$ is located at $(4.0, 3.0)$ m; and charge $q_3 = -1.0\ \mu C$ is located at $(0.0, 3.0)$ m.

8. (a) In the diagram, how much work is done *by the electric field* as a charge of +2.00 nC moves from infinity to each of the three points a, b, and c? (b) How much work is done *by the field* as the charge (+2.00 nC) moves from a to b and from b to c in turn?

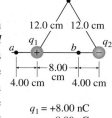

17.2 Electric Potential

9. Find the electric field and the potential at the center of a square of side 2.0 cm with charges of +9.0 µC at each corner.

10. Find the electric field and the potential at the center of a square of side 2.0 cm with a charge of +9.0 µC at one corner of the square and with charges of –3.0 µC at the remaining three corners.

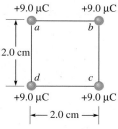

11. A charge $Q = -50.0$ nC is located 0.30 m from point A and 0.50 m from point B. (a) What is the potential at A? (b) What is the potential at B? (c) If a point charge q is moved from A to B while Q is fixed in place, through what potential difference does it move? Does its potential increase or decrease? (d) If $q = -1.0$ nC, what is the change in electric potential energy as it moves from A to B? Does the potential energy increase or decrease? (e) How much work is done by the electric field due to charge Q as q moves from A to B?

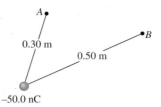

12. A charge of $+2.0$ mC is located at $x = 0$, $y = 0$ and a charge of -4.0 mC is located at $x = 0$, $y = 3.0$ m. What is the electric potential due to these charges at a point with coordinates $x = 4.0$ m, $y = 0$?

13. The electric potential at a distance of 20.0 cm from a point charge is $+1.0$ kV (assuming $V = 0$ at infinity). (a) Is the point charge positive or negative? (b) At what distance is the potential $+2.0$ kV?

14. A spherical conductor with a radius of 75.0 cm has an electric field of magnitude 8.40×10^5 V/m just outside its surface. What is the electric potential just outside the surface, assuming the potential is zero far away from the conductor?

15. An array of four charges is arranged along the x-axis at intervals of 1.0 m. (a) If two of the charges are $+1.0$ μC and two are -1.0 μC, draw a configuration of these charges that minimizes the potential at $x = 0$. (b) If three of the charges are the same, $q = +1.0$ μC, and the charge at the far right is -1.0 μC, what is the potential at the origin?

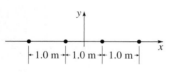

16. At a point P, a distance R_0 from a positive charge Q_0, the electric field has a magnitude $E_0 = 100$ N/C and the electric potential is $V_0 = 10$ V. The charge is now increased by a factor of three, becoming $3Q_0$. (a) At what distance, R_E, from the charge $3Q_0$ will the electric field have the same value, $E = E_0$; and (b) at what distance, R_V, from the charge $3Q_0$ will the electric potential have the same value, $V = V_0$?

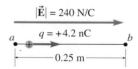

17. Charges of $+2.0$ nC and -1.0 nC are located at opposite corners, A and C, respectively, of a square which is 1.0 m on a side. What is the electric potential at a third corner, B, of the square (where there is no charge)?

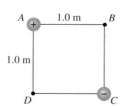

18. (a) Find the electric potential at points a and b for charges of $+4.2$ nC and -6.4 nC located as shown in the figure. (b) What is the potential difference ΔV for a trip from a to b? (c) How much work must be done by an external agent to move a point charge of $+1.50$ nC from a to b?

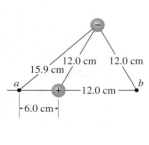

19. (a) Find the potential at points a and b in the diagram for charges $Q_1 = +2.50$ nC and $Q_2 = -2.50$ nC. (b) How much work must be done by an external agent to bring a point charge q from infinity to point b?

✦ 20. (a) Find the potentials at points a, b, and c for the arrangement of charges in the figure. (b) How much work must be done by an external agent to move a charge $(+2.00$ nC$)$ from a to b and from b to c in turn? (If you have done Problem 8, compare your answers.)

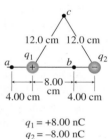

$q_1 = +8.00$ nC
$q_2 = -8.00$ nC

17.3 The Relationship Between Electric Field and Potential

21. By rewriting each unit in terms of kg, m, s, and C, show that 1 N/C = 1 V/m.

22. A uniform electric field has magnitude 240 N/C and is directed to the right. A particle with charge $+4.2$ nC moves along the straight line from a to b. (a) What is the electric force that acts on the particle? (b) What is the work done on the particle by the electric field? (c) What is the potential difference $V_a - V_b$ between points a and b?

$|\vec{E}| = 240$ N/C

$q = +4.2$ nC

0.25 m

23. In a region where there is an electric field, the electric forces do $+8.0 \times 10^{-19}$ J of work on an electron as it moves from point X to point Y. (a) Which point, X or Y, is at a higher potential? (b) What is the potential difference, $V_Y - V_X$, between point Y and point X?

24. Suppose a uniform electric field of magnitude 100.0 N/C exists in a region of space. How far apart are a pair of equipotential surfaces whose potentials differ by 1.0 V?

25. Draw some electric field lines and a few equipotential surfaces outside a negatively charged hollow conducting sphere. What shape are the equipotential surfaces?

26. Draw some electric field lines and a few equipotential surfaces outside a positively charged conducting cylinder. What shape are the equipotential surfaces?

27. It is believed that a large electric fish known as *Torpedo occidentalis* uses electricity to shock its victims. A typical fish can deliver a potential difference of 0.20 kV for a duration of 1.5 ms. This pulse delivers charge at a rate of 18 C/s. (a) What is the rate at which work is done by the electric organs during a pulse? (b) What is the total amount of work done during one pulse?

28. A positive point charge is located at the center of a hollow spherical metal shell with zero net charge. (a) Draw some electric field lines and sketch some equipotential surfaces for this arrangement. (b) Sketch graphs of the electric field magnitude and the potential as functions of r.

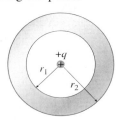

29. A positively charged oil drop is injected into a region of uniform electric field between two oppositely charged, horizontally oriented plates. If the electric force on the drop is found to be 9.6×10^{-16} N and the electric field magnitude is 3000 V/m, what is the magnitude of the charge on the drop in terms of the elementary charge e?

30. A positively charged oil drop of mass 1.0×10^{-15} kg is placed in the region of a uniform electric field between two oppositely charged, horizontal plates. The drop is found to remain stationary under the influence of the Earth's gravitational field and the uniform electric field of 6.1×10^4 N/C. What is the magnitude of the charge on the drop?

17.4 Conservation of Energy for Moving Charges

31. Point P is at a potential of 500.0 kV and point S is at a potential of 200.0 kV. The space between these points is evacuated. When a charge of $+2e$ moves from P to S, by how much does its kinetic energy change?

32. An electron is accelerated from rest through a potential difference ΔV. If the electron reaches a speed of 7.26×10^6 m/s, what is the potential difference? Be sure to include the correct sign. (Does the electron move through an increase or a decrease in potential?)

33. As an electron moves through a region of space, its speed decreases from 8.50×10^6 m/s to 2.50×10^6 m/s. The electric force is the only force acting on the electron. (a) Did the electron move to a higher potential or a lower potential? (b) Across what potential difference did the electron travel?

34. The figure shows a graph of electric potential versus position along the x-axis. An electron is originally at point A, moving in the positive x-direction. How much kinetic energy does it need to have at point A in order to be able to reach point E (with no forces acting on the electron other than those due to the indicated potential)? Points B, C, and D have to be passed on the way.

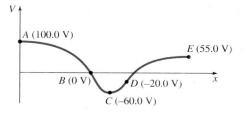

Problems 34 and 35

35. Repeat Problem 34 for a proton rather than an electron.

36. A helium nucleus (charge $+2e$) moves through a potential difference $\Delta V = -0.50$ kV. Its initial kinetic energy is 1.20×10^{-16} J. What is its final kinetic energy?

37. A beam of electrons of mass m_e is deflected vertically by the uniform electric field between two oppositely charged, parallel metal plates. The plates are a distance d apart and the potential difference between the plates is ΔV. (a) What is the direction of the electric field between the plates? (b) If the y-component of the electrons' velocity as they leave the region between the plates is v_y, derive an expression for the time it takes each electron to travel through the region between the plates in terms of ΔV, v_y, m_e, d, and e. (c) Does the electric potential energy of an electron increase, decrease, or stay constant while it moves between the plates? Explain.

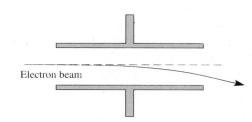

38. An electron (charge $-e$) is projected horizontally into the space between two oppositely charged parallel plates. The electric field between the plates is 500.0 N/C upward. If the vertical deflection of the electron as it leaves the plates has magnitude 3.0 mm, how much has its kinetic energy increased due to the electric field? [*Hint:* First find the potential difference through which the electron moves.]

17.5 Capacitors

39. If a capacitor has a capacitance of 10.2 μF and we wish to lower the potential difference across the plates by 60.0 V, how much charge will we have to remove?

40. A parallel plate capacitor has a capacitance of 2.0 μF and plate separation of 1.0 mm. (a) How much potential difference can be placed across the capacitor before dielectric breakdown of air occurs ($E_{max} = 3 \times 10^6$ V/m)? (b) What is the magnitude of the greatest charge the capacitor can store before breakdown?

41. A parallel plate capacitor is charged by connecting it to a 12-V battery. The battery is then disconnected from the capacitor, leaving the plates with a 12-V potential difference. The parallel plates are then pulled so that the air spacing between the plates is enlarged slightly. What is the effect (a) on the electric field between the plates? (b) on the potential difference between the plates?

42. A parallel plate capacitor has a capacitance of 1.20 nF. There is a charge of magnitude 0.800 μC on each plate. (a) What is the potential difference between the plates? (b) If the plate separation is doubled, while the charge is kept constant, what will happen to the potential difference?

43. A variable capacitor is made of two parallel semicircular plates with air between them. One plate is fixed in place and the other

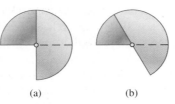

(a)   (b)

can be rotated. The electric field is zero everywhere except in the region where the plates overlap. When the plates are directly across from each other, the capacitance is 0.694 pF. (a) What is the capacitance when the movable plate is rotated so that only one-half its area is across from the stationary plate? (b) What is the capacitance when the movable plate is rotated so that two-thirds of its area is across from the stationary plate?

44. A shark is able to detect the presence of electric fields as small as 1.0 μV/m. To get an idea of the magnitude of this field, suppose you have a parallel plate capacitor connected to a 1.5-V battery. How far apart must the parallel plates be to have an electric field of 1.0 μV/m between the plates?

45. Two metal spheres have charges of equal magnitude, 3.2×10^{-14} C, but opposite sign. If the potential difference between the two spheres is 4.0 mV, what is the capacitance? [Hint: The "plates" are not parallel, but the definition of capacitance holds.]

46. Suppose you were to wrap the Moon in aluminum foil and place a charge Q on it. What is the capacitance of the Moon in this case? [Hint: It is not necessary to have two oppositely charged conductors to have a capacitor. Use the definition of potential for a spherical conductor and the definition of capacitance to get your answer.]

47. A tiny hole is made in the center of the negatively and positively charged plates of a capacitor, allowing a

beam of electrons to pass through and emerge from the far side. If 40.0 V are applied across the capacitor plates and the electrons enter through the hole in the negatively charged plate with a speed of 2.50×10^6 m/s, what is the speed of the electrons as they emerge from the hole in the positive plate?

48. A spherical conductor of radius R carries a total charge Q. (a) Show that the magnitude of the electric field just outside the sphere is $E = \sigma/\epsilon_0$, where σ is the charge per unit area on the conductor's surface. (b) Construct an argument to show why the electric field at a point P just outside *any* conductor in electrostatic equilibrium has magnitude $E = \sigma/\epsilon_0$, where σ is the local surface charge density. [Hint: Consider a tiny area of an arbitrary conductor and compare it to an area of the same size on a spherical conductor with the same charge density. Think about the number of field lines starting or ending on the two areas.]

17.6 Dielectrics

49. A 6.2-cm by 2.2-cm parallel plate capacitor has the plates separated by a distance of 2.0 mm. (a) When 4.0×10^{-11} C of charge is placed on this capacitor, what is the electric field between the plates? (b) If a dielectric with dielectric constant of 5.5 is placed between the plates while the charge on the capacitor stays the same, what is the electric field in the dielectric?

50. Before a lightning strike can occur, the breakdown limit for *damp* air must be reached. If this occurs for an electric field of 3.33×10^5 V/m, what is the maximum possible height above the Earth for the bottom of a thundercloud, which is at a potential 1.00×10^8 V below Earth's surface potential, if there is to be a lightning strike?

51. Two cows, with approximately 1.8 m between their front and hind legs, are standing under a tree during a thunderstorm. See the diagram with Conceptual Question 16. (a) If the equipotential surfaces about the tree just after a lightning strike are as shown, what is the average electric field between Cow A's front and hind legs? (b) Which cow is more likely to be killed? Explain.

52. A parallel plate capacitor has a charge of 0.020 μC on each plate with a potential difference of 240 V. The parallel plates are separated by 0.40 mm of bakelite. What is the capacitance of this capacitor?

53. Two metal spheres are separated by a distance of 1.0 cm and a power supply maintains a constant potential difference of 900 V between them. The spheres are brought closer to each other until a spark flies between them. If the dielectric strength of dry air is 3.0×10^6 V/m, what is the distance between the spheres at this time?

54. To make a parallel plate capacitor, you have available two flat plates of aluminum (area 120 cm^2), a sheet of paper (thickness = 0.10 mm, κ = 3.5), a sheet of glass (thickness = 2.0 mm, κ = 7.0), and a slab of paraffin (thickness = 10.0 mm, κ = 2.0). (a) What is the largest capacitance possible using one of these dielectrics? (b) What is the smallest?

55. A capacitor can be made from two sheets of aluminum foil separated by a sheet of waxed paper. If the sheets of aluminum are 0.30 m by 0.40 m and the waxed paper, of slightly larger dimensions, is of thickness 0.030 mm and dielectric constant κ = 2.5, what is the capacitance of this capacitor?

56. In capacitive electrostimulation, electrodes are placed on opposite sides of a limb. A potential difference is applied to the electrodes, which is believed to be beneficial in treating bone defects and breaks. If the capacitance is measured to be 0.59 pF, the electrodes are 4.0 cm^2 in area, and the limb is 3.0 cm in diameter, what is the (average) dielectric constant of the tissue in the limb?

17.7 Energy Stored in a Capacitor

57. A certain capacitor stores 450 J of energy when it holds 8.0×10^{-2} C of charge. What is (a) the capacitance of this capacitor and (b) the potential difference across the plates?

58. What is the maximum electric energy density possible in dry air without dielectric breakdown occurring?

59. A parallel plate capacitor has a charge of 5.5×10^{-7} C on one plate and -5.5×10^{-7} C on the other. The distance between the plates is increased by 50% while the charge on each plate stays the same. What happens to the energy stored in the capacitor?

60. A large parallel plate capacitor has plate separation of 1.00 cm and plate area of 314 cm^2. The capacitor is connected across a voltage of 20.0 V and has air between the plates. How much work is done on the capacitor as the plate separation is increased to 2.00 cm?

61. Figure 17.31b shows a thundercloud before a lightning strike has occurred. The bottom of the thundercloud and the Earth's surface might be modeled as a charged parallel plate capacitor. The base of the cloud, which is roughly parallel to the Earth's surface, serves as the negative plate and the region of Earth's surface under the cloud serves as the positive plate. The separation between the cloud base and the Earth's surface is small compared to the length of the cloud. (a) Find the capacitance for a thundercloud of base dimensions 4.5 km by 2.5 km located 550 m above the Earth's surface. (b) Find the energy stored in this capacitor if the charge magnitude is 18 C.

62. A parallel plate capacitor of capacitance 6.0 μF has the space between the plates filled with a slab of glass with

κ = 3.0. The capacitor is charged by attaching it to a 1.5-V battery. After the capacitor is disconnected from the battery, the dielectric slab is removed. Find (a) the capacitance, (b) the potential difference, (c) the charge on the plates, and (d) the energy stored in the capacitor after the glass is removed.

(1)   (2)   (3)

63. A parallel plate capacitor is composed of two square plates, 10.0 cm on a side, separated by an air gap of 0.75 mm. (a) What is the charge on this capacitor when there is a potential difference of 150 V between the plates? (b) What energy is stored in this capacitor?

64. The capacitor of Problem 63 is initially charged to a 150-V potential difference. The plates are then physically separated by another 0.750 mm in such a way that none of the charge can leak off the plates. Find (a) the new capacitance and (b) the new energy stored in the capacitor. Explain the result using conservation of energy.

65. Capacitors are used in many applications where you need to supply a short burst of energy. A 100.0-μF capacitor in an electronic flash lamp supplies an average power of 10.0 kW to the lamp for 2.0 ms. (a) To what potential difference must the capacitor initially be charged? (b) What is its initial charge?

66. A parallel plate capacitor has a charge of 0.020 μC on each plate with a potential difference of 240 V. The parallel plates are separated by 0.40 mm of air. What energy is stored in this capacitor?

67. A parallel plate capacitor has a capacitance of 1.20 nF. There is a charge of 0.80 μC on each plate. How much work must be done by an external agent to double the plate separation while keeping the charge constant?

68. A defibrillator is used to restart a person's heart after it stops beating. Energy is delivered to the heart by discharging a capacitor through the body tissues near the heart. If the capacitance of the defibrillator is 9 μF and the energy delivered is to be 300 J, to what potential difference must the capacitor be charged?

69. A defibrillator consists of a 15-μF capacitor that is charged to 9.0 kV. (a) If the capacitor is discharged in 2.0 ms, how much charge passes through the body tissues? (b) What is the average power delivered to the tissues?

70. The bottom of a thundercloud is at a potential of -1.00×10^8 V with respect to Earth's surface. If a charge of -25.0 C is transferred to the Earth during a lightning strike, find the electric potential energy released. (Assume that the system acts like a capacitor—as charge flows, the potential difference decreases to zero.)

✦ 71. (a) If the bottom of a thundercloud has a potential of -1.00×10^9 V with respect to the Earth and a charge of -20.0 C is discharged from the cloud to the Earth during a lightning strike, how much electric potential energy is released? (Assume that the system acts like a capacitor—as charge flows, the potential difference decreases to zero.) (b) If a tree is struck by the lightning bolt and 10.0% of the energy released vaporizes sap in the tree, about how much sap is vaporized? (Assume the sap to have the same latent heat as water.) (c) If 10.0% of the energy released from the lightning strike could be stored and used by a homeowner who uses 400.0 kW·hr of electricity per month, for how long could the lightning bolt supply electricity to the home?

Comprehensive Problems

72. Charges of -12.0 nC and -22.0 nC are separated by 0.700 m. What is the potential midway between the two charges?

73. Two point charges ($+10.0$ nC and -10.0 nC) are located 8.00 cm apart. (a) What is the potential energy of a point charge of -4.2 nC when it is placed at points a, b, and c in turn? Let $U = 0$ when the -4.2 nC charge is far away (but the other two are still in place). (b) How much work would an external force have to do to move the point charge from b to a?

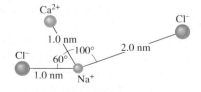

74. If an electron moves from one point at a potential of -100.0 V to another point at a potential of $+100.0$ V, how much work is done by the electric field?

75. A van de Graaff generator has a metal sphere of radius 15 cm. To what potential can it be charged before the electric field at its surface exceeds 3.0×10^6 N/C (which is sufficient to break down dry air and initiate a spark)?

76. Find the potential at the sodium ion, Na^+, which is surrounded by two chloride ions, Cl^-, and a calcium ion, Ca^{2+}, in water as shown in the diagram. The effective charge of the positive sodium ion in water is 2.0×10^{-21} C, of the negative chlorine ion is -2.0×10^{-21} C, and of the positive calcium ion is 4.0×10^{-21} C.

77. An infinitely long conducting cylinder sits near an infinite conducting sheet (side view in the diagram). The cylinder and sheet have equal and opposite charges; the cylinder is positive. (a) Sketch some electric field lines. (b) Sketch some equipotential surfaces.

78. Two parallel plates are 4.0 cm apart. The bottom plate is charged positively and the top plate is charged negatively, producing a uniform electric field of 5.0×10^4 N/C in the region between the plates. What is the time required for an electron, which starts at rest at the upper plate, to reach the lower plate? (Assume a vacuum exists between the plates.)

79. In 1911, Ernest Rutherford discovered the nucleus of the atom by observing the scattering of helium nuclei from gold nuclei. If a helium nucleus with a mass of 6.68×10^{-27} kg, a charge of $+2e$, and an initial velocity of 1.50×10^7 m/s is projected head-on toward a gold nucleus with a charge of $+79e$, how close will the helium atom come to the gold nucleus before it stops and turns around? Assume the gold nucleus is held in place by other gold atoms and does not move.

✦ 80. Draw some electric field lines and a few equipotential surfaces outside a positively charged metal cube. [*Hint:* What shape are the equipotential surfaces close to the cube? What shape are they far away?]

81. The potential difference across a cell membrane is -90 mV. If the membrane's thickness is 10 nm, what is the magnitude of the electric field in the membrane? Assume the field is uniform.

82. A beam of electrons traveling with a speed of 3.0×10^7 m/s enters a uniform, downward electric field of magnitude 2.0×10^4 N/C between the deflection plates of an oscilloscope. The initial velocity of the electrons is perpendicular to the field. The plates are 6.0 cm long. (a) What is the direction and magnitude of the change in velocity of the electrons while they are between the plates? (b) How far are the electrons deflected in the $\pm y$-direction while between the plates?

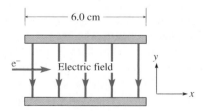

83. A negatively charged particle of mass 5.00×10^{-19} kg is moving with a speed of 35.0 m/s when it enters the region between two parallel capacitor plates. The velocity of the charge is parallel to the plate surfaces and in the positive x-direction. The plates are square with a side of 1.00 cm and the voltage across the plates is 3.00 V. If the particle is initially 1.00 mm from both

plates, and it just barely clears the positive plate after traveling 1.00 cm through the region between the plates, how many excess electrons are on the particle? You may neglect gravitational and edge effects.

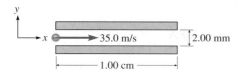

84. (a) Show that it was valid to neglect the gravitational force in Problem 83. (b) What are the components of velocity of the particle when it emerges from the plates?

85. Refer to Problem 83. One capacitor plate has an excess of electrons and the other has a matching deficit of electrons. What is the number of excess electrons?

86. A parallel plate capacitor has a charge of 0.020 μC on each plate with a potential difference of 240 V. The parallel plates are separated by 0.40 mm of air. (a) What is the capacitance for this capacitor? (b) What is the area of a single plate? (c) At what voltage will the air between the plates become ionized? Assume a dielectric strength of 3.0 kV/mm for air.

87. A 200.0-μF capacitor is placed across a 12.0-V battery. When a switch is thrown, the battery is removed from the capacitor and the capacitor is connected across a heater that is immersed in 1.00 cm^3 of water. Assuming that all the energy from the capacitor is delivered to the water, what is the temperature change of the water?

88. The potential difference across a cell membrane from outside to inside is initially at −90 mV (when in its resting phase). When a stimulus is applied, Na$^+$ ions are allowed to move into the cell such that the potential changes to +20 mV for a short amount of time. (a) If the membrane capacitance per unit area is 1 μF/cm^2, how much charge moves through a membrane of area 0.05 cm^2? (b) The charge on Na$^+$ is +e. How many ions move through the membrane?

89. An axon has the outer part of its membrane positively charged and the inner part negatively charged. The membrane has a thickness of 4.4 nm and a dielectric constant $\kappa = 5$. If we model the axon as a parallel plate capacitor whose area is 5 μm^2, what is its capacitance?

90. It has only been fairly recently that 1.0-F capacitors have been readily available. A typical 1.0-F capacitor can withstand up to 5.00 V. To get an idea why it isn't easy to make a 1.0-F capacitor, imagine making a 1.0-F parallel plate capacitor using titanium dioxide ($\kappa = 90.0$, breakdown strength 4.00 kV/mm) as the dielectric. (a) Find the minimum thickness of the titanium dioxide such that the capacitor can withstand 5.00 V. (b) Find the area of the plates so that the capacitance is 1.0 F.

91. A cell membrane has a surface area of 1.0×10^{-7} m^2, a dielectric constant of 5.2, and a thickness of 7.5 nm.

The membrane acts like the dielectric in a parallel plate capacitor; a layer of positive ions on the outer surface and a layer of negative ions on the inner surface act as the capacitor plates. The potential difference between the "plates" is 90.0 mV. (a) How much energy is stored in this capacitor? (b) How many positive ions are there on the outside of the membrane? Assume that all the ions are singly charged (charge +e).

92. A parallel plate capacitor is connected to a battery. The space between the plates is filled with air. The electric field strength between the plates is 20.0 V/m. Then, *with the battery still connected*, a slab of dielectric ($\kappa = 4.0$) is inserted between the plates. The thickness of the dielectric is half the distance between the plates. Find the electric field inside the dielectric.

93. An electron beam is deflected upward through 3.0 mm while traveling in a vacuum between two deflection plates 12.0 mm apart. The potential difference between the deflecting plates is 100.0 kV and the kinetic energy of each electron as it enters the space between the plates is 2.0×10^{-15} J. What is the kinetic energy of each electron when it leaves the space between the plates?

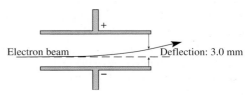

94. A point charge $q = -2.5$ nC is initially at rest adjacent to the negative plate of a capacitor. The charge per unit area on the plates is 4.0 μC/m^2 and the space between the plates is 6.0 mm. (a) What is the potential difference between the plates? (b) What is the kinetic energy of the point charge just before it hits the positive plate, assuming no other forces act on it?

95. An alpha particle (helium nucleus, charge +2e) starts from rest and travels a distance of 1.0 cm under the influence of a uniform electric field of magnitude 10.0 kV/m. What is the final kinetic energy of the alpha particle?

96. A parallel plate capacitor is attached to a battery that supplies a constant voltage. While the battery remains attached to the capacitor, the distance between the parallel plates increases by 25%. What happens to the energy stored in the capacitor?

97. A parallel plate capacitor is attached to a battery that supplies a constant voltage. While the battery is still attached, a dielectric of dielectric constant $\kappa = 3.0$ is inserted so that it just fits between the plates. What is the energy stored in the capacitor after the dielectric is inserted in terms of the energy U_0 before the dielectric was inserted?

98. The inside of a cell membrane is at a potential of 90.0 mV lower than the outside. How much work does the electric field do when a sodium ion (Na^+) with a charge of $+e$ moves through the membrane from outside to inside?

99. (a) Calculate the capacitance per unit length of an axon of radius 5.0 µm (see Fig. 17.14). The membrane acts as an insulator between the conducting fluids inside and outside the neuron. The membrane is 6.0 nm thick and has a dielectric constant of 7.0. (*Note:* The membrane is thin compared to the radius of the axon, so the axon can be treated as a parallel plate capacitor.) (b) In its resting state (no signal being transmitted), the potential of the fluid inside is about 85 mV lower than the outside. Therefore, there must be small net charges $\pm Q$ on either side of the membrane. Which side has positive charge? What is the magnitude of the charge density on the surfaces of the membrane?

100. A 4.00-µF air gap capacitor is connected to a 100.0-V battery until the capacitor is fully charged. The battery is removed and then a dielectric of dielectric constant 6.0 is inserted between the plates without allowing any charge to leak off the plates. (a) Find the energy stored in the capacitor before and after the dielectric is inserted. [*Hint:* First find the new capacitance and potential difference.] (b) Does an external agent have to do positive work to insert the dielectric or to remove the dielectric? Explain.

Answers to Practice Problems

17.1 (a) +0.018 J; (b) away from Q; (c) U decreases as the separation increases. The potential energy decrease accompanies an increase in kinetic energy as q moves faster and faster.

17.2 six pairs (with subscripts 12, 13, 14, 23, 24, 34)

17.3 the lower plate

17.4 $V_B = -1.5 \times 10^5$ V; work (done by $\vec{E}$) $= -\Delta U_E = -0.010$ J

17.5 $\vec{E} = 5.4 \times 10^8$ N/C away from the +9.0-µC charge; $V = 0$

17.6 4 kV

17.7

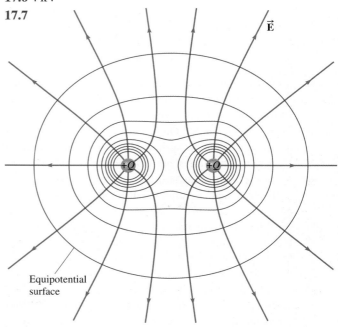

17.8 –20.9 kV (Note that a positive charge gains kinetic energy when it moves through a potential decrease; a negative charge gains kinetic energy when it moves through a potential increase.)

17.9 8.9 nF; 18 µC; charge (capacitance is independent of potential difference)

17.10 C doubles; maximum charge is unchanged

17.11 2.4×10^5 ions

17.12 (a) 0.21 µC; (b) 85 µJ

Electric Current and Circuits

Graham's car won't start; the battery is dead after he left the headlights on overnight. In a kitchen drawer are several 1.5-V flashlight batteries. Graham decides to connect eight of them together, being careful to connect the positive terminal of one to the negative terminal of the next, just the way two 1.5-V batteries are connected inside a flashlight to provide 3.0 V. Eight 1.5-V batteries should provide 12 V, the same as a car battery, he reasons. Will this scheme work? (See p. 649 for the answer.)

Concepts & Skills to Review

- conductors and insulators (Section 16.2)
- electric potential (Section 17.2)
- capacitors (Section 17.5)
- solving simultaneous equations (Appendix A.2)
- power (Section 6.8)

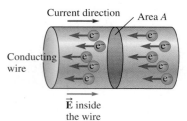

Figure 18.1 Close-up picture of a wire that carries an electric current. The current is the rate of flow of charge through an area perpendicular to the direction of flow.

18.1   ELECTRIC CURRENT

A net flow of charge is called an **electric current**. When a conductor is in electrostatic equilibrium, there are no currents; the electric field within the conducting material is zero and the entire conductor is at the same potential. If we can keep a conductor from reaching electrostatic equilibrium by maintaining a potential difference between two points of a conductor, then the electric field within the conducting material is not zero and a sustained current exists in the conductor.

The *current* (symbol I) is defined as the net amount of charge passing per unit time through an area perpendicular to the flow direction (Fig. 18.1). The magnitude of the current tells us the rate of the net flow of charge. If Δq is the net charge that passes through the shaded surface in Fig. 18.1 during a time interval Δt, then the current in the wire is defined as

Definition of current:

$$I = \frac{\Delta q}{\Delta t} \tag{18-1}$$

Currents are not necessarily steady. In order for Eq. (18-1) to define the instantaneous current, we must use a sufficiently small time interval Δt.

The SI unit of current, equal to one coulomb per second, is the ampere (A), named for the French scientist André-Marie Ampère (1775–1836). The ampere is one of the SI base units; the coulomb is a derived unit defined as one ampere-second:

$$1 \text{ C} = 1 \text{ A·s}$$

Small currents are more conveniently measured in milliamperes (mA = 10^{-3} A) or in microamperes (μA = 10^{-6} A). The word amperes is often shortened to *amps*; for smaller currents, we speak of *milliamps* or *microamps*.

According to convention, the direction of an electric current is defined as the direction in which *positive* charge is transported. Benjamin Franklin established this convention (and decided which kind of charge would be called positive) long before scientists understood that the mobile charges (or *charge carriers*) in metals are electrons. If electrons move to the left in a metal wire, the direction of the current is to the *right*; negative charge moving to the left has the same effect on the net distribution of charge as positive charge moving to the right.

In most situations, the motion of positive charge in one direction causes the same macroscopic effects as the motion of negative charge in the opposite direction. In circuit analysis, we always draw currents in the conventional direction regardless of the sign of the charge carriers.

- Direction of current = direction of flow of positive charge

Example 18.1

Current in a Clock

Two wires of cross-sectional area 1.6 mm² connect the terminals of a battery to the circuitry in a clock. During a time interval of 0.040 s, 5.0×10^{14} electrons move to the right through a cross section of one of the wires. (Actually, electrons pass through the cross section in both

Continued on next page

Example 18.1 Continued

directions; the number that cross to the right is 5.0×10^{14} more than the number that cross to the left.) What is the magnitude and direction of the current in the wire?

Strategy   Current is the rate of flow of charge. We are given the number N of electrons; multiplying by the elementary charge e gives the magnitude of moving charge Δq.

Solution   The magnitude of the charge of 5.0×10^{14} electrons is

$$\Delta q = Ne = 5.0 \times 10^{14} \times 1.60 \times 10^{-19}\, C = 8.0 \times 10^{-5}\, C$$

The magnitude of the current is therefore,

$$I = \frac{\Delta q}{\Delta t} = \frac{8.0 \times 10^{-5}\, C}{0.040\, s} = 0.0020\, A = 2.0\, mA$$

Negatively charged electrons moving to the right means that the direction of conventional current—the direction in which positive charge is effectively being transported—is to the *left*.

Discussion   To find the magnitude of the current, we use the *magnitude* of the charge on the electron. We *do* treat current as a signed quantity when analyzing circuits. We arbitrarily choose a direction for current when the actual direction is not known. If the calculations result in a negative current, the negative sign reveals that the actual direction of the current is opposite the chosen direction. The negative sign merely means the current flows in the direction opposite to the one we assumed.

In this problem, the cross-sectional area of the wire was extraneous information. To find the current, we need only the quantity of charge and the time for the charge to pass.

Practice Problem 18.1   Current in a Calculator

(a) If 0.320 mA of current flow through a calculator, how many electrons pass through per second? (b) How long does it take for 1.0 C of charge to pass through the calculator?

Electric Current in Liquids and Gases

Electric currents can exist in liquids and gases as well as in solid conductors. In an ionic solution, both positive and negative charges contribute to the current by moving in opposite directions (Fig. 18.2). The electric field is to the right, away from the positive electrode and toward the negative electrode. In response, positive ions move in the direction of the electric field (to the right) and negative ions move in the opposite direction (to the left). Since positive and negative charges are moving in opposite directions, they both contribute to current in the *same* direction. Thus, we can find the magnitudes of the currents separately due to the motion of the negative charges and the positive charges and *add* them to find the total current. The direction of the current in Fig. 18.2 is to the right.

If positive and negative charges were moving in the *same* direction, they would represent currents in *opposite* directions and the individual currents would be *subtracted* to find the net current. Just remember this example: In a water pipe, there is an enormous amount of moving charge (the protons and electrons in the neutral water molecules), but equal quantities of positive and negative charges are moving in the same direction. As a result, the net electric current in the pipe is zero; there is no net transport of charge.

Currents also exist in gases. Figure 18.3 shows a neon sign. A large potential difference is applied to the metal electrodes inside a glass container of neon gas. There are always some positive ions present in a gas due to bombardment by cosmic rays and natural

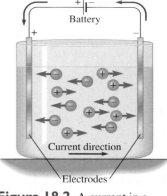

Figure 18.2 A current in a solution of potassium chloride consists of positive ions (K^+) and negative ions (Cl^-) moving in opposite directions. The direction of the current is the direction in which the positive ions move.

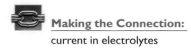

Making the Connection:

current in electrolytes

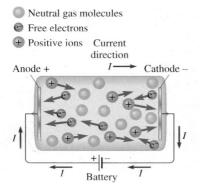

Figure 18.3 Simplified diagram of a neon sign. The neon gas inside the glass tube is ionized by a large potential difference between the electrodes.

radioactivity. The positive ions are accelerated by the electric field toward the cathode; if they have sufficient energy, they can knock electrons loose when they collide with the cathode. These electrons are accelerated toward the anode; they ionize more gas molecules as they pass through the container. Collisions between electrons and ions produce the characteristic red light of a neon sign. Fluorescent lights are similar, but the collisions produce ultraviolet radiation; a coating on the inside of the glass absorbs the ultraviolet and emits visible light.

18.2   EMF AND CIRCUITS

To maintain a current in a conducting wire, we need to maintain a potential difference between the ends of the wire. One way to do that is to connect the ends of the wire to the terminals of a battery (one end to each of the two terminals). An *ideal* battery maintains a constant potential difference between its terminals, regardless of how fast it must pump charge to do so. An ideal battery is analogous to an ideal water pump that maintains a constant pressure difference between intake and output regardless of the volume flow rate.

The potential difference maintained by an ideal battery is called the battery's **emf** (symbol $\mathscr{E}$). Emf originally stood for *electromotive force*, but emf is *not* a measure of the force applied to a charge or to a collection of charges; emf cannot be expressed in newtons. Rather, emf is measured in units of potential (volts) and is a measure of the work done by the battery per unit charge. To avoid this confusion, we just write "emf" (pronounced *ee-em-eff*). If the amount of charge pumped by an ideal battery of emf $\mathscr{E}$ is q, then the work done by the battery is

Work done by an ideal battery:

$$W = \mathscr{E}q \qquad (18\text{-}2)$$

Any device that pumps charge is called a *source of emf* (or just an *emf*). Generators, solar cells, and fuel cells are other sources of emf. Fuel cells, used in the space shuttle and perhaps someday in cars and homes, are similar to batteries, but their reactants are supplied externally. Many living organisms also contain sources of emf (Fig. 18.4). The signals transmitted by the human nervous system are electrical in nature, so our bodies contain sources of emf. The same circuit symbol is used for *any* source of constant emf (—+|—). All emfs are energy conversion devices; they convert some other form of energy into electrical energy. The energy sources used by emfs include chemical energy (batteries, fuel cells, biological sources of emf), sunlight (solar cells), and mechanical energy (generators).

In Fig. 18.5, imagine that the flow of water represents electric current (the flow of charge) in a circuit. The people act as a pump, taking water from the place where its potential energy is lowest and doing the work necessary to carry it uphill to the place

The circuit symbol for a battery is —+|— . Of the two vertical lines, the long line represents the terminal at higher potential and the short line represents the terminal at lower potential. Since many batteries consist of more than one chemical cell, an alternate form is —|||— .

Figure 18.4 The South American electric eel (*Electrophorous electricus*) has hundreds of thousands of cells (called *electroplaques*) that supply emf. The current supplied by the electroplaques is used to stun its enemies and to kill its prey.

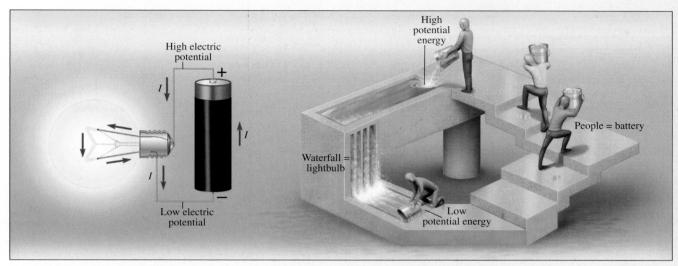

Figure 18.5 Using the flow of water as an analogy to what happens in an electric circuit.

where its potential energy is highest. The water then runs downhill, encountering resistance to its flow (the sluice gate) along the way. A battery (or other source of emf) plays a role something like that of the people who carry buckets of water. Thinking of current as the movement of positive charge, a battery takes positive charge from the place where its *electric potential* is lowest (the negative terminal of the battery) and does the work necessary to move it to the place where the electric potential is highest (the positive terminal). Then the charge flows through some device that offers resistance to the flow of current—perhaps a lightbulb or a CD player—before returning to the negative terminal of the battery.

A 9-V battery (such as the kind used in a smoke detector) maintains its positive terminal 9 V higher than its negative terminal—as long as conditions permit the battery to be treated as ideal. Since a volt is a joule per coulomb, the battery does 9 J of work for every coulomb of charge that it pumps. The battery does work by converting some of its stored chemical energy into electrical energy. When a battery is dead, its supply of chemical energy has been depleted and it can no longer pump charge. Some batteries can be recharged by forcing charge to flow through them in the opposite direction, reversing the direction of the electrochemical reaction and converting electrical energy into chemical energy.

Batteries come with various emfs (12 V, 9 V, 1.5 V, etc.) as well as in various sizes (Fig. 18.6). The size of a battery does *not* determine its emf. Common battery sizes AAA, AA, A, C, and D all provide the same emf (1.5 V). However, the larger batteries have a larger quantity of the chemicals and thus store more chemical energy. A larger battery can supply more energy by pumping more charge than a smaller one, even though the two do the same amount of work *per unit charge*. The amount of charge that a battery can pump is often measured in A·h (ampere-hours). Another difference is that larger batteries can generally pump charge *faster*—in other words, they can supply larger currents.

Circuits

For currents to continue to flow, a complete circuit is required. That is, there must be a continuous conducting path from one terminal of the emf to one or more devices and then back to the other terminal. In Fig. 18.7a,b there is one complete circuit for the current to travel from the positive terminal of the battery, through a wire, through the lightbulb filament, through another wire, into the battery at the negative terminal, and through the battery to return to the positive terminal. Since this circuit has only a single

Figure 18.6 Batteries come in many sizes and shapes. In the back is a lead-acid automobile battery. In front, from left to right are three types of rechargeable nickel-cadmium batteries, seven batteries commonly used in flashlights, cameras, and watches, and a zinc graphite dry cell.

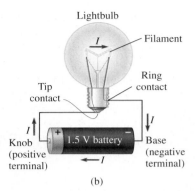

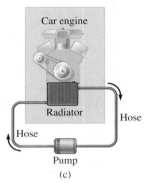

(a)   (b)   (c)

Figure 18.7 (a) Connecting a battery to a lightbulb. The bulb only lights up when current flows through its filament. (b) To maintain current flow, a complete circuit must exist. Note the use of the arrows to indicate the direction of current flow in the wires, lightbulb, and battery. (c) An analogous circuit dealing with the flow of water rather than of charge.

loop for current to flow, the current must be the same everywhere. Think of the battery as a water pump, the wires as hoses, and the lightbulb as the engine block and radiator of an automobile (Fig. 18.7c). Water must flow from the pump, through a hose, through the engine and radiator, through another hose, and back to the pump. The volume flow rate in this single-loop "water circuit" is the same everywhere. Current does not get "used up" in the lightbulb any more than water gets used up in the radiator.

In this chapter, we consider only circuits in which the current in any branch always moves in the same direction—a **direct current** (dc) circuit. In Chapter 21, we study **alternating current** (ac) circuits, in which the currents periodically reverse direction.

18.3   MICROSCOPIC VIEW OF CURRENT IN A METAL: THE FREE-ELECTRON MODEL

Figure 18.1 showed a simplified picture of the conduction electrons in a metal, all moving with the same constant velocity due to an electric field. Why do the electrons not move with a constant *acceleration* due to a constant electric force? To answer this question and to understand the relationship between electric field and current in a metal, we need a more accurate picture of the motion of the electrons.

In the absence of an applied electric field, the conduction electrons in a metal are in constant random motion at high speed—about 10^6 m/s in copper. The electrons suffer frequent collisions with each other and with ions (the atomic nuclei with their bound electrons). In copper, a given conduction electron collides 4×10^{13} times per second, traveling on average about 40 nm between collisions. A collision can change the direction of the electron's motion, so each electron moves in a random path similar to that of a gas molecule (Fig. 18.8a). The average *velocity* of the conduction electrons in a metal is zero in the absence of an electric field, so there is no net transport of charge.

If a uniform electric field exists within the metal, the electric force on the conduction electrons gives them a uniform acceleration between collisions (when the net force due to nearby ions and other conduction electrons is small). The electrons still move about in random directions like gas molecules, but the electric force makes them move on average a little faster in the direction of the force than in the opposite direction— much like air molecules in a gentle breeze. As a result, the electrons slowly drift in the direction of the electric force (Fig. 18.8b). The electrons now have a nonzero average velocity called the **drift velocity** $\vec{v}_D$ (which corresponds to the wind velocity for air molecules). The magnitude of the drift velocity (the *drift speed*) is much smaller than the instantaneous speeds of the electrons—typically less than 1 mm/s—but since it is nonzero, there is a net transport of charge.

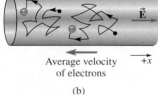

Figure 18.8 (a) Random paths followed by two conduction electrons in a metal wire in the absence of an electric field. (b) An electric field in the +x-direction gives the electrons a constant acceleration in the –x-direction between collisions. *On average,* the electrons drift in the –x-direction. The current in the wire is in the +x-direction.

It might seem that a uniform acceleration should make the electrons move faster and faster. If there were no collisions, they would. An electron has a uniform acceleration *between collisions*, but every collision sends it off in some new direction with a different speed. Each collision between an electron and an ion is an opportunity for the electron to transfer some of its kinetic energy to the ion. The net result is that the drift velocity is constant and energy is transferred from the electrons to the ions at a constant rate. As an analogy, think of an object falling at its terminal velocity. If there were no air resistance, gravity would give the object a constant acceleration. The average force on the object due to collisions with molecules in the air is equal and opposite to the gravitational force, so it falls with a constant velocity and zero acceleration.

Relationship Between Current and Drift Velocity

To find out how current depends on drift velocity, we use a simplified model in which all the electrons move at a constant velocity $\vec{v}_D$ (Fig. 18.9). The number of conduction electrons per unit volume (n) is a characteristic of a particular metal. Suppose we calculate the current by finding how much charge moves through the shaded area in a time Δt. During that time, every electron moves a distance $v_D \Delta t$ to the left. Thus, every conduction electron in a volume $Av_D \Delta t$ moves through the shaded area. The number of electrons in this volume is $N = nAv_D \Delta t$; the magnitude of the charge is

$$\Delta Q = Ne = neAv_D \Delta t$$

Therefore, the magnitude of the current in the wire is

$$I = \frac{\Delta Q}{\Delta t} = neAv_D \qquad (18\text{-}3)$$

Remember that, since electrons carry negative charge, the direction of current flow is opposite the direction of motion of the electrons. The electric force on the electrons is opposite the electric field, so the current is in the direction of the electric field in the wire.

Equation (18-3) can be generalized to systems where the current carriers are not necessarily electrons, simply by replacing e with the charge of the carriers. In materials called semiconductors, there may be both positive and negative carriers. The negative carriers are electrons; the positive carriers are "missing" electrons (called *holes*) that act as particles with charge $+e$. The electrons and holes drift in opposite directions; both contribute to the current. Since the concentrations of electrons and holes may be different and they may have different drift speeds, the current is

$$I = n_+ eAv_+ + n_- eAv_- \qquad (18\text{-}4)$$

In Eq. (18-4), v_+ and v_- are drift *speeds*—both are positive.

When we turn on a light by flipping a wall switch, current flows through the lightbulb almost instantaneously. We do *not* have to wait for electrons to move from the switch to the lightbulb—which is a good thing, since it would be a long wait (see Example 18.2). Conduction electrons are present all along the wires that form the circuit. When the switch is closed; the *electric field* extends into the entire circuit almost instantaneously. The electrons start to drift as soon as the electric field is nonzero.

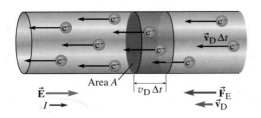

Area A

$\vec{E} \rightarrow$ $v_D \Delta t$ $\vec{F}_E$
$I \rightarrow$ $\vec{v}_D$

Figure 18.9 Simplified picture of the conduction electrons moving at a uniform velocity $\vec{v}_D$. In a time Δt, each electron moves a distance $v_D \Delta t$. The black vector arrows show the displacement of each electron during Δt. All of the conduction electrons within a distance $v_D \Delta t$ pass through the shaded cross-sectional area in a time Δt.

Example 18.2

Drift Speed in Household Wiring

A #12 gauge copper wire, commonly used in household wiring, has a diameter of 2.053 mm. There are 8.00×10^{28} conduction electrons per cubic meter in copper. (a) If the wire carries a constant dc current of 5.00 A, what is the drift speed of the electrons? (b) Explain why a thinner copper wire carrying a current of 5.00 A has a *larger* drift speed.

Strategy   From the diameter, we can find the cross-sectional area A of the wire. The number of conduction electrons per cubic meter is n in Eq. (18-3). Then Eq. (18-3) enables us to solve for the drift speed. In (b), we consider how to get the same number of electrons per second flowing through a smaller cross-sectional area.

Solution   (a) The cross-sectional area of the wire is

$$A = \pi r^2 = \tfrac{1}{4}\pi d^2$$

The drift speed is given by

$$v_D = \frac{I}{neA} =$$

$$\frac{5.00 \text{ A}}{8.00 \times 10^{28} \text{ m}^{-3} \times 1.602 \times 10^{-19} \text{ C} \times \tfrac{1}{4}\pi \times (2.053 \times 10^{-3} \text{ m})^2}$$

$$= 1.18 \times 10^{-4} \text{ m·s}^{-1} = 0.118 \text{ mm/s}$$

(b) A thinner wire has fewer conduction electrons in a given length—the number per unit *volume* is the same but now the cross-sectional area is smaller. To produce the same current using fewer electrons, the electrons must

move faster. This reasoning is confirmed by Eq. (18-3). The wire is still copper, so n is the same; the magnitude of the charge on the electron is also the same. If I is the same but A is smaller, v_D must be larger.

Discussion   The drift speed may seem surprisingly small: at an average speed of 0.118 mm/s, it takes an electron over 2 h to move one meter along the wire! How can 5 C/s—a respectable amount of current—be carried by electrons with such small average velocities? Because there are so many of them. As a check: the number of conduction electrons per unit length of wire is

$$nA = 8.00 \times 10^{28} \text{ m}^{-3} \times \tfrac{1}{4}\pi \times (2.053 \times 10^{-3} \text{ m})^2$$

$$= 2.65 \times 10^{23} \text{ electrons/m}$$

Then the number of conduction electrons in a 0.118 mm length of wire is

$$2.65 \times 10^{23} \text{ electrons/m} \times 0.118 \times 10^{-3} \text{ m} = 3.13 \times 10^{19} \text{ electrons}$$

The magnitude of the total charge of these electrons is

$$3.13 \times 10^{19} \text{ electrons} \times 1.602 \times 10^{-19} \text{ C/electron} = 5.01 \text{ C}$$

Practice Problem 18.2   Current and Drift Speed in a Silver Wire

A silver wire has a diameter of 2.588 mm and contains 5.80×10^{28} conduction electrons per cubic meter. A battery of 1.50 V pushes 880 C through the wire in 45 min. Find (a) the current and (b) the drift speed in the wire.

18.4   RESISTANCE AND RESISTIVITY

Resistance

Suppose we maintain a potential difference across the ends of a conductor. How does the current I that flows through the conductor depend on the potential difference ΔV across the conductor? For many conductors, the I is proportional to ΔV. Georg Ohm (1789–1854) first observed this relationship, which is now called **Ohm's law**:

Ohm's Law

$$I \propto \Delta V \qquad\qquad (18\text{-}5)$$

Ohm's law is not a universal law of physics like the conservation laws. It does not apply at all to some materials, whereas even materials that obey Ohm's law for a wide range of potential differences fail to do so when ΔV becomes too large. Hooke's law ($F \propto \Delta x$ or stress $\propto$ strain) is similar; it applies to many materials under many circumstances but is not a fundamental law of physics. Any *homogeneous* material follows Ohm's law for *some* range of potential differences; metals that are good conductors follow Ohm's law over a *wide* range of potential differences.

Ohm was inspired to look at the relationship between current and potential difference by Fourier's observation that the rate of heat flow through a conductor of heat is proportional to the temperature difference across it. Another analogous situation is the flow of oil (or any viscous fluid) through a pipe. Poiseuille's law says that the rate of flow of the fluid is proportional to the pressure difference between the ends of the pipe.

The electrical **resistance** R is defined to be the ratio of the potential difference (or *voltage*) ΔV across a conductor to the current I through the material:

Definition of resistance:

$$R = \frac{\Delta V}{I} \qquad (18\text{-}6)$$

In SI units, electrical resistance is measured in ohms (symbol Ω, the Greek capital omega), defined as

$$1\ \Omega = 1\ \text{V/A} \qquad (18\text{-}7)$$

For a given potential difference, a large current flows through a conductor with a small resistance, while a small current flows through a conductor with a large resistance.

An *ohmic* conductor—one that follows Ohm's law—has a resistance that is constant, regardless of the potential difference applied. Equation (18-6) is *not* a statement of Ohm's law, since it does not require that the resistance be constant; it is the *definition of resistance* for nonohmic conductors as well as for ohmic conductors. For an ohmic conductor, a graph of current versus potential difference is a straight line through the origin with slope $1/R$ (Fig. 18.10a). For some nonohmic systems, the graph of I versus ΔV is dramatically nonlinear (Fig. 18.10b,c).

Resistivity

Resistance depends on size and shape. Returning to the analogy with fluid flow: a longer pipe offers more resistance to fluid flow than does a short pipe and a wider pipe offers less resistance than a narrow one. By analogy, we expect a long wire to have higher resistance than a short one (everything else being the same) and a thicker wire to have a lower resistance than a thin one. The electrical resistance of a conductor of length L and cross-sectional area A can be written:

$$R = \rho \frac{L}{A} \qquad (18\text{-}8)$$

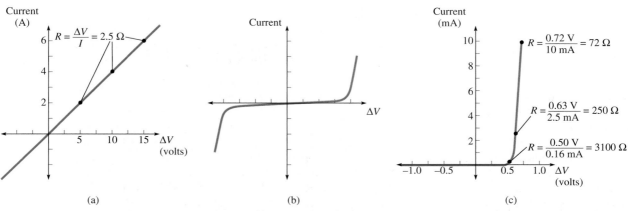

Figure 18.10 (a) Current as a function of potential difference for a tungsten wire. The resistance is the same for any value of ΔV on the graph, so the wire is an ohmic conductor. Similar graphs for (b) the gas in a fluorescent light and (c) a diode are far from linear; these systems are nonohmic.

Table 18.1

Resistivities and Temperature Coefficients at 20°C

	ρ ($\Omega \cdot$m)	α (°C^{-1})		ρ ($\Omega \cdot$m)	α (°C^{-1})
Conductors			**Semiconductors (pure)**		
Silver	1.59×10^{-8}	3.8×10^{-3}	Carbon	3.5×10^{-5}	-0.5×10^{-3}
Copper	1.67×10^{-8}	4.05×10^{-3}	Germanium	0.6	-50×10^{-3}
Gold	2.35×10^{-8}	3.4×10^{-3}	Silicon	2300	-70×10^{-3}
Aluminum	2.65×10^{-8}	3.9×10^{-3}			
Tungsten	5.40×10^{-8}	4.50×10^{-3}			
Iron	9.71×10^{-8}	5.0×10^{-3}	**Insulators**		
Lead	21×10^{-8}	3.9×10^{-3}	Glass	10^{10}–10^{14}	
Platinum	10.6×10^{-8}	3.64×10^{-3}	Lucite	$> 10^{13}$	
Manganin	44×10^{-8}	0.002×10^{-3}	Quartz (fused)	$> 10^{16}$	
Constantan	49×10^{-8}	0.002×10^{-3}	Rubber (hard)	10^{13}–10^{16}	
Mercury	96×10^{-8}	0.89×10^{-3}	Teflon	$> 10^{13}$	
Nichrome	108×10^{-8}	0.4×10^{-3}	Wood	10^{8}–10^{11}	

Equation (18-8) assumes a uniform distribution of current across the cross section of the conductor.

The constant of proportionality ρ (Greek letter rho), which is an intrinsic characteristic of a particular material at a particular temperature, is called the **resistivity** of the material. The SI unit for resistivity is $\Omega \cdot$m. Table 18.1 lists resistivities for various substances at 20°C. The resistivities of good conductors are small. The resistivities of pure semiconductors are significantly larger. By doping semiconductors (introducing controlled amounts of impurities), their resistivities can be changed dramatically, which is one reason that semiconductors are used to make computer chips and other electronic devices (Fig. 18.11). Insulators have very large resistivities (about a factor of 10^{20} larger than for conductors). The inverse of resistivity is called *conductivity* [SI units $(\Omega \cdot$m$)^{-1}$].

Why is resistance proportional to length? Suppose we have two otherwise identical wires with different lengths. If the wires carry the same current, they must have the same drift speed; to have the same drift speed, the electric field must be the same. Since for a uniform field $\Delta V = EL$, the potential differences across the wires are proportional to their lengths. Therefore, $R = \Delta V/I$ is proportional to length.

Why is resistance inversely proportional to area? Suppose we have two otherwise identical wires with different areas. Applying the same potential difference produces the same drift speed, but the thicker wire has more conduction electrons per unit length. Since $I = neAv_D$ [Eq. (18-3)], the current is proportional to the area and $R = \Delta V/I$ is inversely proportional to area.

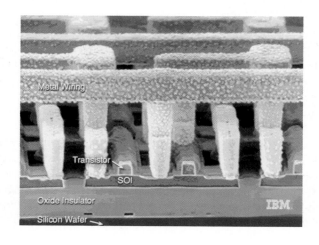

Figure 18.11 A scanning electron microscope view of a microprocessor chip. Much of the chip is made of silicon. By introducing impurities into the silicon in a controlled way, some regions act as insulating material, others as conducting wires, and others as the transistors—circuit elements that act as switches. SOI stands for silicon on insulator, a technology that reduces the heat generated within a chip.

Example 18.3

Resistance of an Extension Cord

(a) A 30.0-m-long extension cord is made from two #19 gauge copper wires. (One wire carries current *to* an appliance, while the other wire carries current *from* it.) What is the resistance of each wire at 20.0°C? The diameter of #19 gauge wire is 0.912 mm. (b) If the copper wire is to be replaced by an aluminum wire of the same length, what is the minimum diameter so that the new wire has a resistance no greater than the old?

Strategy   After calculating the cross-sectional area of the copper wire from its diameter, we find the resistance of the copper wire from Eq. (18-8). The resistivities of copper and aluminum are found in Table 18.1.

Solution   (a) From Table 18.1, the resistivity of copper is

$$\rho = 1.67 \times 10^{-8}\ \Omega\cdot\text{m}$$

The wire's cross-sectional area is

$$A = \tfrac{1}{4}\pi d^2 = \tfrac{1}{4}\pi (9.12 \times 10^{-4}\ \text{m})^2 = 6.533 \times 10^{-7}\ \text{m}^2$$

Resistance is resistivity times length over area:

$$R = \rho \frac{L}{A}$$

$$= \frac{1.67 \times 10^{-8}\ \Omega\cdot\text{m} \times 30.0\ \text{m}}{6.533 \times 10^{-7}\ \text{m}^2}$$

$$= 0.767\ \Omega$$

(b) We want the resistance of the aluminum wire to be less than or equal to the resistance of the copper wire ($R_a \leq R_c$):

$$\frac{\rho_a L}{\tfrac{1}{4}\pi d_a^2} \leq \frac{\rho_c L}{\tfrac{1}{4}\pi d_c^2}$$

which simplifies to $\rho_a d_c^2 \leq \rho_c d_a^2$. Solving for d_a yields

$$d_a \geq d_c \sqrt{\frac{\rho_a}{\rho_c}} = 0.912\ \text{mm} \times \sqrt{\frac{2.65 \times 10^{-8}\ \Omega\cdot\text{m}}{1.67 \times 10^{-8}\ \Omega\cdot\text{m}}} = 1.15\ \text{mm}$$

Discussion   Check: the resistance of an aluminum wire of diameter 1.149 mm is

$$R = \frac{\rho L}{A} = \frac{2.65 \times 10^{-8}\ \Omega\cdot\text{m} \times 30.0\ \text{m}}{\tfrac{1}{4}\pi (1.149 \times 10^{-3}\ \text{m})^2} = 0.767\ \Omega$$

Aluminum has a higher resistivity, so the wire must be thicker to have the same resistance.

Extension cords are rated according to the maximum safe current they can carry. For an appliance that draws a larger current, a thicker extension cord must be used; otherwise, the potential difference across the wires would be too large ($\Delta V = IR$).

Practice Problem 18.3   Resistance of a Lightbulb Filament

Find the resistance at 20°C of a tungsten lightbulb filament of length 4.0 cm and diameter 0.020 mm.

Resistivity Depends on Temperature

Resistivity does not depend on the size or shape of the material, but it does depend on temperature. Two factors primarily determine the resistivity of a metal: the number of conduction electrons per unit volume and the rate of collisions between an electron and an ion. The second of these factors is sensitive to changes in temperature. At a higher temperature, the internal energy is greater; the ions vibrate with larger amplitudes. As a result, the electrons collide more frequently with the ions. With less time to accelerate between collisions, they acquire a smaller drift speed; thus, the current is smaller for a given electric field. Therefore, as the temperature of a metal is raised, its resistivity increases. The metal filament in a glowing incandescent lightbulb reaches a temperature of about 3000 K; its resistance is significantly higher than at room temperature.

For many materials, the relation between resistivity and temperature is linear over a fairly wide range of temperatures (about 500°C):

$$\rho = \rho_0 (1 + \alpha\, \Delta T) \qquad (18\text{-}9)$$

Here ρ_0 is the resistivity at temperature T_0 and ρ is the resistivity at temperature $T = T_0 + \Delta T$. The quantity α is called the **temperature coefficient of resistivity** and has SI units °C^{-1} or K^{-1}. Temperature coefficients for some materials are listed in Table 18.1.

The relationship between resistivity and temperature is the basis of the *resistance thermometer*. The resistance of a conductor is measured at a reference temperature and at the temperature to be measured; the change in the resistance is then used to calculate

Temperature dependence of resistivity

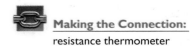

Making the Connection:
resistance thermometer

the unknown temperature. For measurements over limited temperature ranges, the linear relationship of Eq. (18-9) can be used in the calculation; over larger temperature ranges, the resistance thermometer must be calibrated to account for the nonlinear variation of resistivity with temperature. Materials with high melting points (such as tungsten) can be used to measure high temperatures.

Note that for semiconductors, $\alpha < 0$. A negative temperature coefficient means that the resistivity *decreases* with increasing temperature. It is still true, as for metals that are good conductors, that the collision rate increases with temperature. However, in semiconductors the number of carriers (conduction electrons and/or holes) per unit volume increases dramatically with increasing temperature; with more carriers, the resistivity is smaller.

Some materials become *superconductors* ($\rho = 0$) at low temperatures. Once a current is started in a superconducting loop, it continues to flow indefinitely *without* a source of emf. Experiments with superconducting currents have lasted more than two years without any measurable change in the current. Mercury was the first superconductor discovered (by Dutch scientist Kammerlingh Onnes in 1911). As the temperature of mercury is decreased, its resistivity gradually decreases—as for any metal—but at mercury's critical temperature ($T_C = 4.15$ K) its resistivity suddenly becomes zero. Many other superconductors have since been discovered. In the past two decades, scientists have created ceramic materials with much higher critical temperatures than those previously known. Above their critical temperatures, the ceramics are insulators.

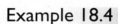

Example 18.4

Change in Resistance with Temperature

The nichrome heating element of a toaster has a resistance of 12.0 Ω when it is red-hot (1200°C). What is the resistance of the element at room temperature (20°C)? Ignore changes in the length or diameter of the element due to temperature.

Strategy Since we assume the length and cross-sectional area to be the same, the resistances at the two temperatures are proportional to the resistivities at those temperatures:

$$\frac{R}{R_0} = \frac{\rho L/A}{\rho_0 L/A} = \frac{\rho}{\rho_0}$$

Thus, we do not need the length or cross-sectional area of the heating element.

Given: $T_0 = 20°C$; $R = 12.0$ Ω at $T = 1200°C$.
To find: R_0

Solution   From Eq. (18-9),

$$\frac{R}{R_0} = \frac{\rho L/A}{\rho_0 L/A} = \frac{\rho}{\rho_0} = 1 + \alpha \Delta T$$

The change in temperature is

$$\Delta T = T - T_0 = 1200°C - 20°C = 1180°C$$

For nichrome, Table 18.1 gives

$$\alpha = 0.4 \times 10^{-3} \ °C^{-1}$$

Solving for R_0 yields

$$R_0 = \frac{R}{1 + \alpha \Delta T} = \frac{12.0 \ \Omega}{1 + 0.4 \times 10^{-3} \ °C^{-1} \times 1180°C} = 8 \ \Omega$$

Discussion   Why do we write only one significant figure? Since the temperature change is so large (1180°C), the result must be considered an estimate. The relationship between resistivity and temperature may not be linear over such a large temperature range.

Practice Problem 18.4   Using a Resistance Thermometer

A platinum resistance thermometer has a resistance of 225 Ω at 20.0°C. When the thermometer is placed in a furnace, its resistance rises to 448 Ω. What is the temperature of the furnace? Assume the temperature coefficient of resistivity is constant over the temperature range in this problem.

Resistors

A **resistor** is a circuit element designed to have a known resistance. Resistors are found in virtually all electronic devices (Fig. 18.12). In circuit analysis, it is customary to write the relationship between voltage and current for a resistor as $V = IR$. Remember that V actually stands for the potential *difference* between the ends of the resistor even though the symbol Δ is omitted. Sometimes V is called the *voltage drop*. Current in a resistor flows in the direction of the electric field, which points from higher to lower potential. Therefore, if you move across a resistor in the direction of current flow, the voltage *drops* by an amount *IR*. Remember a useful analogy: water flows downhill (toward lower potential energy); electric current *in a resistor* flows toward lower potential.

Internal Resistance of a Battery

Figure 18.13a shows a circuit we've seen before. Figure 18.13b is a *circuit diagram* of the circuit. The lightbulb is represented by the symbol for a resistor (*R*). The battery is represented by two symbols surrounded by a dashed line. The battery symbol represents an *ideal* emf and the resistor (*r*) represents the *internal resistance* of the battery. If the internal resistance of a source of emf is negligible, then we just draw the symbol for an ideal emf.

When the current through a source of emf is zero, the **terminal voltage**—the potential difference between its terminals—is equal to the emf. When the source supplies current to a *load* (a lightbulb, a toaster, or any other device that uses electrical energy), its terminal voltage is less than the emf; there is a voltage drop due to the internal resistance of the source. If the current is *I* and the internal resistance is *r*, then the voltage drop across the internal resistance is *Ir* and the terminal voltage is

$$V = \mathcal{E} - Ir \qquad (18\text{-}10)$$

When the current is small enough, the voltage drop *Ir* due to the internal resistance is negligible compared to $\mathcal{E}$; then we can treat the emf as ideal ($V \approx \mathcal{E}$). A flashlight that is left on for a long time gradually dims because, as the chemicals in a battery are depleted, the internal resistance increases. As the internal resistance increases, the terminal voltage $V = \mathcal{E} - Ir$ decreases; thus, the voltage across the lightbulb decreases and the light gets dimmer.

Figure 18.12 The little cylinders on this computer circuit board are resistors. The colored bands specify the resistance of the resistor.

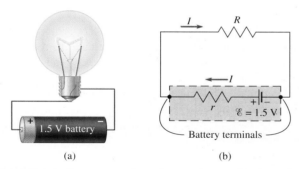

(a)   (b)

Figure 18.13 (a) A lightbulb connected to a battery by conducting wires. (b) A circuit diagram for the same circuit. The emf and the internal resistance of the battery are enclosed by a dashed line as a reminder that in reality the two are not separate; we can't make a connection to the "wire" between the two!

In a circuit diagram, the symbol —VVV— represents a resistor or any other device in a circuit that dissipates electrical energy.
A straight line ——— represents a conducting wire with negligible resistance. (If a wire's resistance is appreciable, then we draw it as a resistor.)

Conceptual Example 18.5

Starting a Car Using Flashlight Batteries

Discuss the merits of Graham's scheme to start his car using eight D-cell flashlight batteries, each of which provides an emf of 1.50 V and has an internal resistance of 0.10 Ω. (A current of several hundred amps is required to turn the starter motor in a car, while the current through the bulb in a flashlight is typically less than 1 A.)

Strategy We consider not only the values of the emfs, but also whether the batteries can supply the required *current*.

Solution and Discussion Connecting eight 1.5-V batteries as in a flashlight—with the positive terminal of one connected to the negative terminal of the next—does provide an emf of 12 V. Each battery does 1.5 J of work per coulomb of charge; if the charge must pass through all eight batteries in turn, the total work done is 12 J per coulomb of charge.

Continued on next page

Conceptual Example 18.5 Continued

When the batteries are used to power a device that draws a *small* current (because the resistance of the load R is large compared to the internal resistance r of each battery), the terminal voltage of each battery is nearly 1.5 V and the terminal voltage of the combination is nearly 12 V. For instance, in a flashlight that draws 0.50 A of current, the terminal voltage of a D-cell is

$$V = \mathscr{E} - Ir = 1.50 \text{ V} - 0.50 \text{ A} \times 0.10 \text{ }\Omega = 1.45 \text{ V}$$

However, the current required to start the car is large. As the current increases, the terminal voltage decreases. We can estimate the *maximum* current that a battery can supply by setting its terminal voltage to zero (the smallest possible value):

$$V = \mathscr{E} - I_{max}r = 0$$

$$I_{max} = \mathscr{E}/r = (1.5 \text{ V})/(0.10 \text{ }\Omega) = 15 \text{ A}$$

(This estimate is optimistic since the battery's chemical energy would be rapidly depleted and the internal resistance would increase dramatically.) The flashlight batteries cannot supply a current large enough to start the car.

Practice Problem 18.5   Terminal Voltage of a Battery in a Clock

The current supplied by an alkaline D-cell (1.500 V emf, 0.100 Ω internal resistance) in a clock is 50.0 mA. What is the terminal voltage of the battery?

PHYSICS AT HOME

Turn on the headlights of a car and then start the car. Notice that the headlights dim considerably. If the car battery were an *ideal* emf of 12 V, it would continue to supply 12 V to the headlights regardless of how much current is drawn from it. Due to the internal resistance of the battery, the terminal voltage of the battery is significantly less than 12 V when it supplies a few hundred amps of current to the starter.

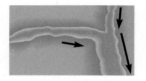

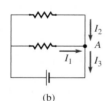

(a)

(b)

Figure 18.14 (a) The rate at which water flows into the junction from the two streams is equal to the rate at which water flows out of the junction into the larger stream. Equivalently, we can say that the net rate of flow of water into the junction is zero. (b) An analogous junction in an electric circuit.

18.5   KIRCHHOFF'S RULES

Two rules, developed by Gustav Kirchhoff (1824–1887), are essential in circuit analysis. **Kirchhoff's junction rule** states that the sum of the currents that flow into a junction—any electrical connection—must equal the sum of the currents that flow out of the same junction. The junction rule is a consequence of the law of conservation of charge. Since charge does not continually build up at a junction, the *net* rate of flow of charge into the junction must be zero.

> **Kirchhoff's Junction Rule**
>
> $$\sum I_{in} - \sum I_{out} = 0 \qquad (18\text{-}11)$$

Figure 18.14a shows two streams joining to form a larger stream. Figure 18.14b shows an analogous junction (point A) in an electric circuit. Applying the junction rule to point A results in the equation $I_1 + I_2 - I_3 = 0$.

Kirchhoff's loop rule is an expression of energy conservation applied to changes in potential in a circuit. Recall that the electric potential must have a unique value at any point; the potential at a point cannot depend on the path one takes to arrive at that point. Therefore, if a closed path is followed in a circuit, beginning and ending at the same point, the algebraic sum of the potential changes must be zero (Fig. 18.15). Think of taking a hike in the mountains, starting and returning at the same spot. No matter what path you take, the algebraic sum of all your elevation changes must equal zero.

> **Kirchhoff's Loop Rule**
>
> $$\sum \Delta V = 0 \qquad (18\text{-}12)$$

for any path in a circuit that starts and ends at the same point. (Potential rises are positive; potential drops are negative.)

Be careful to get the signs right when applying the loop rule. If you follow a path through a resistor going in the same direction as the current, the potential drops ($\Delta V = -IR$). If your path takes you through a resistor in a direction opposite to the current ("upstream"), the potential rises ($\Delta V = +IR$). For an emf, the potential drops if you move from the positive terminal to the negative ($\Delta V = -\mathscr{E}$); it rises if you move from the negative to the positive ($\Delta V = +\mathscr{E}$).

18.6   SERIES AND PARALLEL CIRCUITS

Resistors in Series

When one or more electrical devices are wired so that the *same current* flows through each one, the devices are said to be wired in **series** (Figs. 18.16 and 18.17). The circuit of Fig. 18.17a shows two resistors in series. The straight lines represent wires, which we assume to have negligible resistance. Negligible resistance means negligible voltage drop ($V = IR$), so *points connected by wires of negligible resistance are at the same potential.* The junction rule, applied to any of the points A–D, tells us that the same current flows through the emf and the two resistors.

Let's apply the loop rule to a clockwise loop $DABCD$. From D to A we move from the negative terminal to the positive terminal of the emf, so $\Delta V = +1.5$ V. Since we move around the loop *with* the current, the potential *drops* as we move across each resistor. Therefore,

$$1.5 \text{ V} - IR_1 - IR_2 = 0$$

The same current I flows through the two resistors in series. Factoring out the common current I,

$$I(R_1 + R_2) = 1.5 \text{ V}$$

The current I would be the same if a single equivalent resistor $R_{eq} = R_1 + R_2$ replaced the two resistors in series:

$$IR_{eq} = I(R_1 + R_2) = 1.5 \text{ V}$$

Figure 18.17b shows how the circuit diagram can be redrawn to indicate the simplified, equivalent circuit.

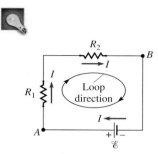

Figure 18.15 Applying the loop rule. If we start at point A and walk around the loop in the direction shown (clockwise), the loop rule gives $\sum \Delta V = -IR_1 - IR_2 + \mathscr{E} = 0$. (Starting at B and walking counterclockwise gives $\sum \Delta V = +IR_2 + IR_1 - \mathscr{E} = 0$, an equivalent equation.)

Series: same current through each device

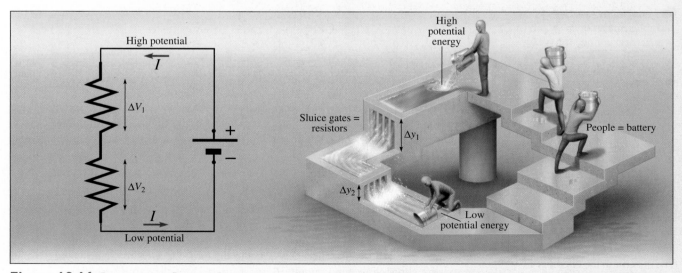

Figure 18.16 Just as water flows at the same mass flow rate through each of the two sluice gates, the same current flows through two resistors in series. Just as $\Delta y_1 + \Delta y_2 = \Delta y$, the potential difference ΔV across a series pair is the sum of the two potential differences.

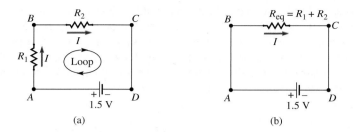

Figure 18.17 (a) A circuit with two resistors in series. (b) Replacing the two resistors with an equivalent resistor.

We can generalize this result to any number of resistors in series:

For any number N of resistors connected in series,

$$R_{eq} = \sum R_i = R_1 + R_2 + \cdots + R_N \qquad (18\text{-}13)$$

Note that the equivalent resistance for two or more resistors in series is *larger* than *any* of the resistances.

Making the Connection:

battery connection in a flashlight

Emfs in Series

In many devices, batteries are connected in series with the positive terminal of one connected to the negative terminal of the next. This provides a larger emf than a single battery can (Fig. 18.18). The emfs of batteries connected in this way are added just as series resistances are added. However, there is a disadvantage in connecting batteries in series: the internal resistance is larger because the internal resistances are in series as well.

Sources can be connected in series with the emfs in opposition. A common use for such a circuit is in a battery charger. In Fig. 18.19, as we move from point C to B to A, the potential decreases by $\mathscr{E}_2$ and then increases by $\mathscr{E}_1$, so the net emf is $\mathscr{E}_1 - \mathscr{E}_2$.

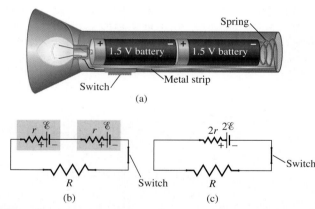

Figure 18.18 (a) Two 1.5-V batteries connected in series in a flashlight to supply 3.0 V. (b) Circuit diagram, including the internal resistances of the batteries. (c) Simplified circuit diagram, where the two batteries are combined into a single source of emf $2\mathscr{E}$ with internal resistance $2r$.

The symbol ⎯⎯/•⎯⎯ represents an open switch (no electrical connection). The symbol ⎯⎯•—•⎯⎯ represents a closed switch.

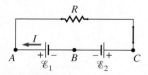

Figure 18.19 Circuit for charging a rechargeable battery (shown as emf $\mathscr{E}_2$). The source supplying the energy to charge the battery must have a larger emf ($\mathscr{E}_1 > \mathscr{E}_2$). The net emf in the circuit is $\mathscr{E}_1 - \mathscr{E}_2$; the current is $I = (\mathscr{E}_1 - \mathscr{E}_2)/R$ (where R includes the internal resistances of the sources).

Capacitors in Series

Figure 18.20a shows three capacitors connected in series. We want to find the equivalent capacitance C_{eq} that would store the same amount of charge as each of the three capacitors (Fig. 18.20b). When the switch is closed, the emf pumps charge until the potential difference between points A and D is equal to the emf. Since there are no voltage drops across the connecting wires, points B and b must be at the same potential. Likewise, points C and c are at the same potential. Applying Kirchhoff's loop rule yields

$$\mathscr{E} - V_{AB} - V_{BC} - V_{CD} = 0 \qquad (18\text{-}14)$$

The magnitude of the charge on the three capacitors is the same. Why? Suppose that the battery puts charge $+Q$ on plate A. Then, since capacitor plates store opposite charges of equal magnitude, plate B has charge $-Q$. Plates B and b and their connecting wire are not connected to anything else, so their net charge must remain zero. Charge just shifts between plates B and b; therefore, plate b has charge $+Q$. Continuing the same line of reasoning leads to the conclusion that *capacitors in series have the same charge.* Since $Q = C\Delta V$,

$$V_{AB} = \frac{Q}{C_1}, \quad V_{BC} = \frac{Q}{C_2}, \quad \text{and} \quad V_{CD} = \frac{Q}{C_3}$$

The equivalent capacitance is defined by $\mathscr{E} = Q/C_{eq}$. Substituting into Eq. (18-14) yields

$$\frac{Q}{C_{eq}} - \frac{Q}{C_1} - \frac{Q}{C_2} - \frac{Q}{C_3} = 0$$

The equivalent capacitance is given by

$$\frac{1}{C_{eq}} = \frac{1}{C_1} + \frac{1}{C_2} + \frac{1}{C_3}$$

This reasoning can be extended to the general case for any number of capacitors connected in series.

For N capacitors connected in series,

$$\frac{1}{C_{eq}} = \sum \frac{1}{C_i} = \frac{1}{C_1} + \frac{1}{C_2} + \cdots + \frac{1}{C_N} \tag{18-15}$$

Note that the equivalent capacitor stores the same magnitude of charge as *each* of the capacitors it replaces.

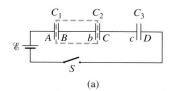

Figure 18.20 (a) Three capacitors connected in series. (b) Equivalent circuit.

Resistors in Parallel

When one or more electrical devices are wired so that the *potential difference across them is the same*, the devices are said to be wired in **parallel** (Fig. 18.21). In Fig. 18.22, an emf is connected to three resistors in parallel with one another. The left side of each resistor is at the same potential since they are all connected by wires of negligible resistance.

Parallel: same potential difference across each device

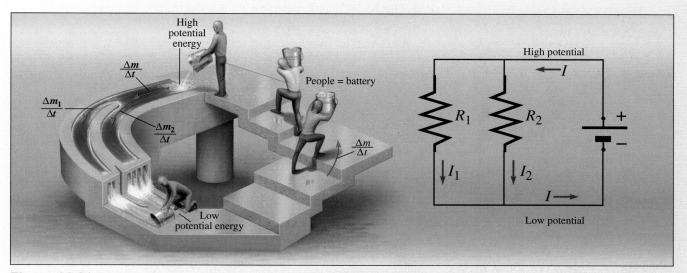

Figure 18.21 Some water flows through one branch and some through the other. The mass flow rate before the water channels divide and after they come back together is equal to the sum of the flow rates in the two branches. The elevation change Δy for the two branches is equal since they start and end at the same elevations. For two resistors in parallel, the currents *add;* the potential differences are *equal.*

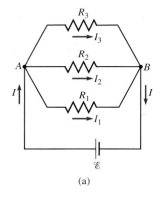

(a)

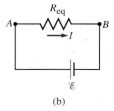

(b)

Figure 18.22 (a) Three resistors connected in parallel. (b) The equivalent circuit.

Likewise, the right side of each resistor is at the same potential. Thus, there is a common potential difference across the three resistors. Applying the junction rule to point A yields

$$+I - I_1 - I_2 - I_3 = 0 \quad \text{or} \quad I = I_1 + I_2 + I_3 \tag{18-16}$$

How much of the current I from the emf flows through each resistor? The current divides such that the potential difference $V_A - V_B$ must be the same along each of the three paths—and it must equal the emf $\mathscr{E}$. From the definition of resistance,

$$\mathscr{E} = I_1 R_1 = I_2 R_2 = I_3 R_3$$

Therefore, the currents are

$$I_1 = \frac{\mathscr{E}}{R_1}, \quad I_2 = \frac{\mathscr{E}}{R_2}, \quad I_3 = \frac{\mathscr{E}}{R_3}$$

Substituting the currents into Eq. (18-16) yields

$$I = \frac{\mathscr{E}}{R_1} + \frac{\mathscr{E}}{R_2} + \frac{\mathscr{E}}{R_3}$$

Dividing by $\mathscr{E}$ yields

$$\frac{I}{\mathscr{E}} = \frac{1}{R_1} + \frac{1}{R_2} + \frac{1}{R_3}$$

The three parallel resistors can be replaced by a single equivalent resistor R_{eq}. In order for the same current to flow, R_{eq} must be chosen so that $\mathscr{E} = I R_{\text{eq}}$. Then $I/\mathscr{E} = 1/R_{\text{eq}}$ and

$$\frac{1}{R_{\text{eq}}} = \frac{1}{R_1} + \frac{1}{R_2} + \frac{1}{R_3}$$

Although we examined three resistors in parallel, the result applies to any number of resistors in parallel:

> For N resistors connected in parallel,
> $$\frac{1}{R_{\text{eq}}} = \sum \frac{1}{R_i} = \frac{1}{R_1} + \frac{1}{R_2} + \cdots + \frac{1}{R_N} \tag{18-17}$$

Note that the equivalent resistance for two or more resistors in parallel is *smaller* than *any* of the resistances ($1/R_{\text{eq}} > 1/R_i$, so $R_{\text{eq}} < R_i$). Note also that the equivalent resistance for resistors in *parallel* is found in the same way as the equivalent capacitance for capacitors in *series*. The reason is that resistance is defined as $R = \Delta V / I$ and capacitance as $C = Q / \Delta V$. One has ΔV in the numerator, the other in the denominator.

Example 18.6

Current for Two Parallel Resistors

(a) Find the equivalent resistance for the two resistors in Fig. 18.23 if $R_1 = 20.0\ \Omega$ and $R_2 = 40.0\ \Omega$. (b) What is the ratio of the current through R_1 to the current through R_2?

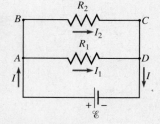

Figure 18.23

Circuit with parallel resistors for Example 18.6.

Strategy Points A and B are at the same potential; points C and D are at the same potential. Therefore, the voltage drops across the two resistors are equal; the two resistors are in parallel. The ratio of the currents can be found by equating the potential differences in the two branches in terms of the current and resistance.

Solution (a) The equivalent resistance for two parallel resistors is

$$\frac{1}{R_{\text{eq}}} = \frac{1}{R_1} + \frac{1}{R_2} = \frac{1}{20.0\ \Omega} + \frac{1}{40.0\ \Omega} = 0.0750\ \Omega^{-1}$$

$$R_{\text{eq}} = \frac{1}{0.0750\ \Omega^{-1}} = 13.3\ \Omega$$

(b) The potential differences across the resistors are equal

$$I_1 R_1 = I_2 R_2$$

Therefore,

$$\frac{I_1}{I_2} = \frac{R_2}{R_1} = \frac{40.0\ \Omega}{20.0\ \Omega} = 2.00$$

Continued on next page

Example 18.6 Continued

Discussion   Note that the current in each branch of the circuit is inversely proportional to the resistance of that branch. Since R_2 is twice R_1, it has half as much current flowing through it. At the junction of two or more parallel branches, the current does not all flow through the "path of least resistance," but *more* current flows through the branch of least resistance than through the branches with larger resistances.

Practice Problem 18.6   Three Resistors in Parallel

Find the equivalent resistance from point A to point B for the three resistors in Fig. 18.24.

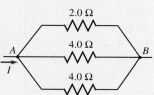

Figure 18.24

Three parallel resistors.

Example 18.7

Equivalent Resistance for Network in Series and Parallel

(a) Find the equivalent resistance for the network of resistors in Fig. 18.25.
(b) Find the current through the resistor R_2 if $\mathscr{E} = 0.60$ V.

Strategy   We simplify the network of resistors in a series of steps. At first, the only series or parallel combination is the two resistors in parallel between points B and C. No other pair of resistors has either the same current (for series) or the same voltage drop (for parallel). We replace those two with an equivalent resistor, redraw the circuit, and look for new series or parallel combinations, continuing until the entire network reduces to a single resistor.

Solution   (a) For the two 2.0-Ω resistors in parallel between points B and C,

$$R_{eq} = \left(\frac{1}{R_3} + \frac{1}{R_4}\right)^{-1} = \left(\frac{1}{2.0\ \Omega} + \frac{1}{2.0\ \Omega}\right)^{-1} = 1.0\ \Omega$$

We redraw the circuit, replacing the two parallel resistors with an equivalent 1.0-Ω resistor.

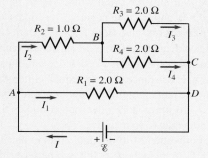

Figure 18.25

Network of resistors for Example 18.7.

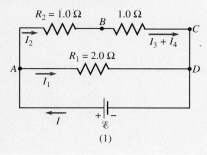

(1)

The two 1.0-Ω resistors are in series since the same current must flow through them. They can be replaced with a single resistor,

$$R_{eq} = 1.0\ \Omega + 1.0\ \Omega = 2.0\ \Omega$$

The network of resistors now becomes

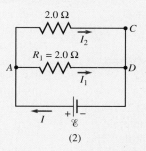

(2)

As before, the equivalent resistance for two 2.0-Ω resistors in parallel is 1.0 Ω. The network of resistors reduces to a single equivalent 1.0-Ω resistor.

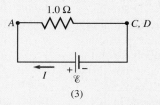

(3)

(b) The current through R_2 is I_2 (Fig. 18.25). From circuit diagram (2), when I_2 flows through an equivalent resistance of 2.0 Ω, the voltage drop is 0.60 V. Therefore,

$$I_2 = \frac{0.60\ \text{V}}{2.0\ \Omega} = 0.30\ \text{A}$$

Discussion   To reduce complicated arrangements of resistors to an equivalent resistance, look for resistors in

Continued on next page

Example 18.7 Continued

parallel (resistors connected so that they must have the same potential difference) and resistors in series (connected so that they must have the same current). Replace all parallel and series combinations of resistors with equivalents. Then look for new parallel and series combinations in the simplified circuit. Repeat until there is only one resistor remaining.

Practice Problem 18.7   Three Resistors Connected

Find the equivalent resistance that can be placed between points A and B to replace the three equal resistors shown

in Fig. 18.26. First try to decide whether these resistors are in series or parallel. Label the black dots with A or B by tracing the straight lines from A or B to their connections at one side or another of the resistors. Redraw the diagram if that helps you decide.

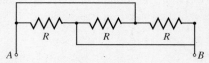

Figure 18.26

Three connected resistors.

Emfs in Parallel

Two or more sources of *equal* emf are often connected in parallel with all the positive terminals connected together and all the negative terminals connected together (Fig. 18.27a). The equivalent emf for any number of equal sources in parallel is the same as the emf of each source. The advantage of connecting sources in this way is not to achieve a larger emf, but rather to lower the internal resistance and thus supply more current. In Fig. 18.27a, the two internal resistances (r) are equal. Since they are in parallel—note that points A and B are at the same potential—the equivalent internal resistance for the parallel combination is $\frac{1}{2}r$. To jump-start a car, one connects the two batteries in parallel, positive to positive and negative to negative.

We need not concern ourselves with unequal emfs in parallel or with arrangements like that shown in Fig. 18.27b. In such cases the two batteries drain each other and supply little or no current to the rest of the circuit.

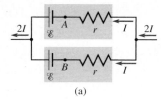

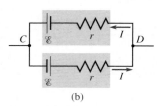

Figure 18.27 (a) Two identical batteries (with internal resistances r) in parallel. The combination provides an emf $\mathscr{E}$ and can supply twice as much current as one battery since the equivalent internal resistance is $\frac{1}{2}r$. (b) Two identical batteries connected backwards. Points C and D are at the same potential, so the batteries supply no emf to the rest of the circuit; they just drain each other. If two car batteries are connected in this way, the large current that would flow would be dangerous.

Figure 18.28 (a) Three capacitors in parallel. (b) When the switch is closed, each capacitor is charged until the potential difference between its plates is equal to $\mathscr{E}$. If the capacitances are unequal, the charges on the capacitors are unequal.

Capacitors in Parallel

Capacitors in series have the same charge but may have different potential differences. Capacitors in parallel share a common potential difference but may have different charges. Suppose three capacitors are in parallel (Fig. 18.28). After the switch is closed, the source of emf pumps charge onto the plates of the capacitors until the potential difference across each capacitor is equal to the emf $\mathscr{E}$. Suppose that the total magnitude of charge pumped by the battery is Q. If the magnitude of charge on the three capacitors is q_1, q_2, and q_3, respectively, conservation of charge requires that

$$Q = q_1 + q_2 + q_3$$

The relation between the potential difference across a capacitor and the charge on either plate of the capacitor is $q = C\,\Delta V$. For each capacitor, $\Delta V = \mathscr{E}$. Therefore,

$$Q = q_1 + q_2 + q_3 = C_1\mathscr{E} + C_2\mathscr{E} + C_3\mathscr{E} = (C_1 + C_2 + C_3)\mathscr{E}$$

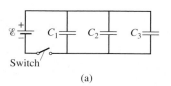

(a)

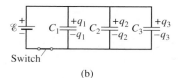

(b)

We can replace the three capacitors with a single equivalent capacitor. In order for it to store charge of magnitude Q for a potential difference $\mathcal{E}$, $Q = C_{eq}\mathcal{E}$. Therefore, $C_{eq} = C_1 + C_2 + C_3$. Once again, this result can be extended to the general case for any number of capacitors connected in parallel.

For N capacitors connected in parallel,

$$C_{eq} = \sum C_i = C_1 + C_2 + \cdots + C_N \qquad \text{(18-18)}$$

18.7 CIRCUIT ANALYSIS USING KIRCHHOFF'S RULES

Sometimes a circuit cannot be simplified by replacing parallel and series combinations alone. In such cases, we apply Kirchhoff's rules directly and solve the resulting equations simultaneously.

Problem-Solving Strategy: Using Kirchhoff's Rules to Analyze a Circuit

1. Replace any series or parallel combinations with their equivalents.
2. Assign variables to the currents in each branch of the circuit ($I_1, I_2, \ldots$) and choose directions for each current. Draw the circuit with the current directions indicated by arrows. It does not matter whether or not you choose the correct direction.
3. Apply Kirchhoff's junction rule to *all but one* of the junctions in the circuit. (Applying it to every junction produces one redundant equation.) Remember that current into a junction is positive; current out of a junction is negative.
4. Apply Kirchhoff's loop rule to enough loops so that, together with the junction equations, you have the same number of equations as unknown quantities. For each loop, choose a starting point and a direction to go around the loop. Be careful with signs. For a resistor, if your path through a resistor goes *with* the current ("downstream"), there is a potential drop; if your path goes *against* the current ("upstream"), the potential rises. For an emf, the potential drops or rises depending on whether you move from the positive terminal to the negative or *vice versa*; the direction of the current is irrelevant. A helpful method is to write "+" and "−" signs on the ends of each resistor and emf to indicate which end is at the higher potential and which is at the lower potential.
5. Solve the loop and junction equations simultaneously. If a current comes out negative, the direction of the current is opposite to the direction you chose.
6. Check your result using one or more loops or junctions. A good choice is a loop that you did not use in the solution.

Example 18.8

A Two-Loop Circuit

Find the currents through each branch of the circuit of Fig. 18.29.

Strategy First we look for series and parallel combinations. R_1 and $\mathcal{E}_1$ are in series, but since one is a resistor and one an emf we cannot replace them with a single equivalent circuit element. No pair of resistors is either in series or in parallel. R_1 and R_2 might look like they're in parallel, but the emf $\mathcal{E}_1$ keeps points A and F at different potentials, so they are not. The two emfs might look like they're in series, but the junction at point F means that

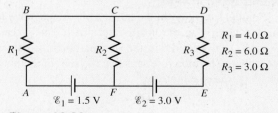

Figure 18.29

Circuit to be analyzed using Kirchhoff's rules.

$R_1 = 4.0\ \Omega$
$R_2 = 6.0\ \Omega$
$R_3 = 3.0\ \Omega$

Continued on next page

Example 18.8 Continued

the current through the two is not the same. Since there are no series or parallel combinations to simplify, we proceed to apply Kirchhoff's rules directly.

Solution   First we assign the currents variable names and directions on the circuit diagram:

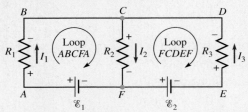

Points C and F are junctions between the three branches of the circuit. We choose current I_1 for branch $FABC$, current I_3 for branch $FEDC$, and current I_2 for branch CF.

Now we can apply the junction rule. There are two junctions; we can choose either one. For point C, I_1 and I_3 flow into the junction and I_2 flows out of the junction. The resulting equation is

$$I_1 + I_3 - I_2 = 0 \qquad (1)$$

Before applying the loop rule, we write "+" and "−" signs on each resistor and emf to show which side is at the higher potential and which at the lower, given the directions assumed for the currents. In a resistor, current flows from higher to lower potential. The emf symbol uses the longer line for the positive terminal and the shorter line for the negative terminal.

Now we choose a closed loop and add up the potential rises and drops as we travel around the loop. Suppose we start at point A and travel around loop $ABCFA$. The starting point and direction to go around the loop are arbitrary choices, but once made, we stick with it regardless of the directions of the currents. From A to B, we move in the same direction as the current I_1. The current through a resistor travels from higher to lower potential, so going from A to B is a potential drop: $\Delta V_{A \to B} = -I_1 R_1$.

From B to C, since the wire is assumed to have negligible resistance, there is no potential rise or drop. From C to F, we move with current I_2, so there is another potential drop: $\Delta V_{C \to F} = -I_2 R_2$.

Finally, from F to A, we move from the negative terminal of an emf to the positive terminal. The potential *rises*: $\Delta V_{F \to A} = +\mathcal{E}_1$. A was the starting point, so the loop is complete. The loop rule says that the sum of the potential changes is equal to zero:

$$-I_1 R_1 - I_2 R_2 + \mathcal{E}_1 = 0 \qquad (2)$$

We must choose another loop since we have not yet gone through resistor R_3 or emf $\mathcal{E}_2$. There are two choices possible: the right-hand loop (such as $FCDEF$) or the outer loop ($ABCDEFA$). Let's choose $FCDEF$.

From F to C, we move *against* the current I_2 ("upstream"). The potential rises: $\Delta V_{F \to C} = +I_2 R_2$. From C to D, the potential does not change. From D to E, we again move upstream, so $\Delta V_{D \to E} = +I_3 R_3$. From E to F, we move through a source of emf from the negative to the positive terminal. The potential increases: $\Delta V_{E \to F} = +\mathcal{E}_2$. Then the loop rule gives

$$+I_2 R_2 + I_3 R_3 + \mathcal{E}_2 = 0 \qquad (3)$$

Now we have three equations and three unknowns (the three currents). To solve them simultaneously, we first substitute known numerical values:

$I_1 + I_3 - I_2 = 0 \qquad (1)$
$-(4.0\ \Omega)I_1 - (6.0\ \Omega)I_2 + 1.5\ \text{V} = 0 \qquad (2)$
$(6.0\ \Omega)I_2 + (3.0\ \Omega)I_3 + 3.0\ \text{V} = 0 \qquad (3)$

To solve simultaneous equations, we can solve one equation for one variable and substitute into the other equations, thus eliminating one variable. Solving Eq. (1) for I_1 yields $I_1 = -I_3 + I_2$. Substituting in Eq. (2):

$$-(4.0\ \Omega)(-I_3 + I_2) - (6.0\ \Omega)I_2 + 1.5\ \text{V} = 0$$

Simplifying,

$$4.0 I_3 - 10.0 I_2 = -1.5\ \text{V}/\Omega = -1.5\ \text{A} \qquad (2a)$$

Eqs. (2a) and (3) now have only two unknowns. We can eliminate I_3 if we multiply Eq. (2a) by 3 and Eq. (3) by 4 so that I_3 has the same coefficient.

$$12.0 I_3 - 30.0 I_2 = -4.5\ \text{A} \quad 3 \times \text{Eq. (2a)}$$
$$12.0 I_3 + 24.0 I_2 = -12.0\ \text{A} \quad 4 \times \text{Eq. (3)}$$

Subtracting one from the other,

$$54.0 I_2 = -7.5\ \text{A}$$

Now we can solve for I_2:

$$I_2 = -\frac{7.5}{54.0}\ \text{A} = -0.139\ \text{A}$$

Substituting the value of I_2 into Eq. (2a) enables us to solve for I_3:

$$4 I_3 + 10 \times 0.139\ \text{A} = -1.5\ \text{A}$$

$$I_3 = \frac{-1.5 - 1.39}{4}\ \text{A} = -0.723\ \text{A}$$

Equation (1) now gives I_1:

$$I_1 = -I_3 + I_2 = +0.723\ \text{A} - 0.139\ \text{A} = +0.584\ \text{A}$$

Rounding to two significant figures, the currents are $I_1 = +0.58\ \text{A}$, $I_3 = -0.72\ \text{A}$, and $I_2 = -0.14\ \text{A}$. Since I_3 and I_2 came out negative, the actual directions of the currents in those branches are opposite to the ones we arbitrarily chose.

Continued on next page

Example 18.8 Continued

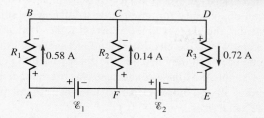

Discussion   Note that it did not matter that we chose some of the current directions wrong. It also doesn't matter which loops we choose (as long as we cover every branch of the circuit), which starting point we use for a loop, or which direction we go around a loop.

The hardest thing about applying Kirchhoff's rules is getting the signs correct. It is also easy to make an algebraic mistake when solving simultaneous equations. Therefore, it is a good idea to check the answer. A good way to check is to write down a loop equation for a loop that was not used in the solution (see Practice Problem 18.8).

Practice Problem 18.8   Verifying the Solution with the Loop Rule

Apply Kirchhoff's loop rule to loop *CBAFEDC* to verify the solution of Example 18.8.

18.8   POWER AND ENERGY IN CIRCUITS

From the definition of electric potential, if a charge q moves through a potential difference ΔV, the change in electric potential energy is

$$\Delta U_E = q\,\Delta V \qquad (17\text{-}7)$$

From energy conservation, a change in electric potential energy means that conversion between two forms of energy takes place. For example, a battery converts stored chemical energy into electric potential energy. A resistor converts electric potential energy into internal energy. The *rate* at which the energy conversion takes place is the *power P*. Since current is the rate of flow of charge, $I = q/\Delta t$ and

Power

$$P = \frac{\Delta U_E}{\Delta t} = \frac{q}{\Delta t}\,\Delta V = I\,\Delta V \qquad (18\text{-}19)$$

Thus, the power for *any circuit element* is the product of current and potential difference. We can verify that current times voltage comes out in the correct units for power by substituting coulombs per second for amperes and joules per coulomb for volts:

$$A \times V = \frac{C}{s} \times \frac{J}{C} = \frac{J}{s} = W$$

According to the definition of emf, if the amount of charge pumped by an ideal source of constant emf $\mathscr{E}$ is q, then the work done by the battery is

$$W = \mathscr{E}q \qquad (18\text{-}2)$$

The power supplied by the emf is the rate at which it does work:

$$P = \frac{\Delta W}{\Delta t} = \mathscr{E}\frac{q}{\Delta t} = \mathscr{E}I \qquad (18\text{-}20)$$

Since $\Delta V = \mathscr{E}$ for an ideal emf, Eqs. (18-20) and (18-19) are equivalent.

Power Dissipated by a Resistor

If an emf causes current to flow through a resistor, what happens to the energy supplied by the emf? Why must the emf continue supplying energy to maintain the current?

Current flows in a metal wire when an emf gives rise to a potential difference between one end and the other. The electric field makes the conduction electrons drift in the direction of lower electric potential energy (higher potential). If there were no

The term *power dissipated* means *the rate at which energy is dissipated.* "Power" is not dissipated in a resistor; *energy* is.

collisions between electrons and atoms in the metal, the average kinetic energy of the electrons would continually increase. However, the electrons frequently collide with atoms; each such collision is an opportunity for an electron to give away some of its kinetic energy. For a steady current, the average kinetic energy of the conduction electrons does not increase; the rate at which the electrons gain kinetic energy (due to the electric field) is equal to the rate at which they lose kinetic energy (due to collisions). The net effect is that the energy supplied by the emf increases the vibrational energy of the atoms. The vibrational energy of the atoms is part of the internal energy of the metal, so the temperature of the metal rises.

From the definition of resistance, the potential drop across a resistor is

$$V = IR$$

Dissipation: the conversion of energy from an organized form to a disorganized form

Then the rate at which energy is dissipated in a resistor can be written

$$P = I \times IR = I^2 R \qquad (18\text{-}21a)$$

or

$$P = \frac{V}{R} \times V = \frac{V^2}{R} \qquad (18\text{-}21b)$$

Is the power dissipated in a resistor directly proportional to the resistance [Eq. (18-21a)] or inversely proportional to the resistance [Eq. (18-21b)]? It depends on the situation. For two resistors with the *same current* (such as two resistors in series), the power is directly proportional to resistance—the voltage drops are not the same. For two resistors with the same voltage drop (such as two resistors in parallel), the power is inversely proportional to resistance; this time the currents are not the same.

Dissipation in a resistor is not necessarily undesirable. In any kind of electric heater—in portable or baseboard heaters, electric stoves and ovens, toasters, hair dryers, and electric clothes dryers—and in incandescent lights, the dissipation of energy and the resulting temperature increase of a resistor are put to good use.

Power Supplied by an Emf with Internal Resistance

If the source has internal resistance, then the net power supplied is *less* than $\mathscr{E}I$. Some of the energy supplied by the emf is dissipated by the internal resistance. The net power supplied to the rest of the circuit is

$$P = \mathscr{E}I - I^2 r \qquad (18\text{-}22)$$

where r is the internal resistance of the source. Equation (18-22) agrees with Eq. (18-19); remember that the potential difference is *not* equal to the emf when there is internal resistance (see Problem 72).

Example 18.9

Two Flashlights

A flashlight is powered by two batteries in series. Each has an emf of 1.50 V and an internal resistance of 0.10 Ω. The batteries are connected to the lightbulb by wires of total resistance 0.40 Ω. At normal operating temperature, the resistance of the filament is 9.70 Ω. (a) Calculate the power dissipated by the bulb—that is, the rate at which energy in the form of heat and light flows away from it. (b) Calculate the power dissipated by the wires and the net power supplied by the batteries. (c) A second flashlight uses *four* such batteries in series and the same resistance

wires. A bulb of resistance 42.1 Ω (at operating temperature) dissipates approximately the same power as the bulb in the first flashlight. Verify that the power dissipated is nearly the same and calculate the power dissipated by the wires and the net power supplied by the batteries.

Strategy   All the circuit elements are in series. We can simplify the circuit by replacing all the resistors (including the internal resistances of the batteries) with one series

Continued on next page

Example 18.9 Continued

equivalent and the two emfs with one equivalent emf. Doing so enables us to find the current. Then we can use Eq. (18-21a) to find the power in the wires and in the filament. Equation (18-21b) could be used, but would require an extra step: finding the voltage drops across the resistors. Equation (18-22) gives the net power supplied by the batteries.

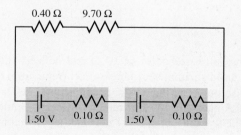

Figure 18.30
Circuit for the first flashlight.

Solution   (a) Figure 18.30 is a sketch of the circuit for the first flashlight. To find the power dissipated in the lightbulb, we need either the current through it or the voltage drop across it. We can find the current in this single-loop circuit by replacing the two ideal emfs with a series equivalent emf of $\mathscr{E}_{eq} = 3.00$ V and all the resistors by a series equivalent resistance of

$$R_{eq} = 9.70\ \Omega + 0.40\ \Omega + 2 \times 0.10\ \Omega = 10.30\ \Omega$$

Then the current is

$$I = \frac{\mathscr{E}_{eq}}{R_{eq}} = \frac{3.00\ \text{V}}{10.30\ \Omega} = 0.2913\ \text{A}$$

The power dissipated by the filament is

$$P_f = I^2 R = (0.2913\ \text{A})^2 \times 9.70\ \Omega = 0.823\ \text{W}$$

(b) The power dissipated by the wires is

$$P_w = I^2 R = (0.2913\ \text{A})^2 \times 0.40\ \Omega = 0.034\ \text{W}$$

The net power supplied by the batteries is

$$P_b = \mathscr{E}_{eq}I - I^2 r_{eq}$$

where $r_{eq} = 0.20\ \Omega$ is the series equivalent for the two internal resistances. Then

$$P_b = 3.00\ \text{V} \times 0.2913\ \text{A} - (0.2913\ \text{A})^2 \times 0.20\ \Omega = 0.857\ \text{W}$$

(c) In the second circuit, $\mathscr{E}_{eq} = 6.00$ V and

$$R_{eq} = 42.1\ \Omega + 0.40\ \Omega + 4 \times 0.10\ \Omega = 42.90\ \Omega$$

The current is

$$I = \frac{\mathscr{E}_{eq}}{R_{eq}} = \frac{6.00\ \text{V}}{42.90\ \Omega} = 0.13986\ \text{A}$$

The power dissipated by the filament is

$$P_f = I^2 R = (0.13986\ \text{A})^2 \times 42.1\ \Omega = 0.824\ \text{W}$$

which is only 0.1% more than the filament in the first flashlight. The power dissipated by the wires is

$$P_w = I^2 R = (0.13986\ \text{A})^2 \times 0.40\ \Omega = 0.0078\ \text{W}$$

The series equivalent for the four internal resistances is $r_{eq} = 0.40\ \Omega$, so the net power supplied by the batteries is

$$P_b = \mathscr{E}_{eq}I - I^2 r_{eq}$$

$$= 6.00\ \text{V} \times 0.13986\ \text{A} - 0.0078\ \text{W} = 0.831\ \text{W}$$

Discussion   Note that in each case, the net power supplied by the batteries is equal to the total power dissipated in the wires and the filament. Since there is nowhere else for the energy to go, the wires and filament must dissipate energy—convert electrical energy to light and heat—at the same rate that the battery supplies electrical energy.

The power supplied to the two filaments is about the same in the two cases. However, the power dissipated by the wires in the second flashlight is a bit less than one-fourth as much as in the first. By using a larger emf, the current required to supply a given amount of power is smaller. The current is smaller because the load resistance (the resistance of the filament) is larger. A smaller current means the power dissipated in the wires is smaller. Utility companies distribute power over long distances using high-voltage wires for exactly this reason: the smaller the current, the smaller the power dissipated in the wires.

Practice Problem 18.9   A Simplified Flashlight Circuit

A flashlight takes two 1.5-V batteries connected in series. If the current that flows to the bulb in the flashlight is 0.35 A, find the power delivered to the lightbulb and the amount of energy dissipated after the light has been in the "on position" for three minutes. Treat the batteries as ideal and ignore the resistance of the wires. [*Hint:* It is not necessary to calculate the resistance of the filament since in this case the voltage drop across it is equal to the emf.]

18.9   MEASURING CURRENTS AND VOLTAGES

Current and potential difference in a circuit can be measured with instruments called **ammeters** and **voltmeters**, respectively. A multimeter functions as an ammeter or a voltmeter, depending on the setting of a switch. Meters can be either digital or analog; the latter uses a rotating pointer to indicate the value of current or voltage on a calibrated scale. At the heart of an analog voltmeter or analog ammeter is a **galvanometer**, a sensitive detector of current whose operation is based on magnetic forces.

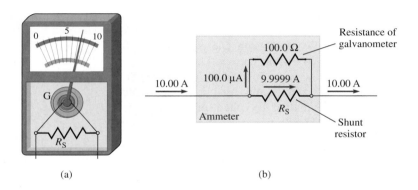

Figure 18.31 (a) An ammeter constructed from a galvanometer. (b) The circuit diagram for the ammeter. The galvanometer is represented as a 100.0-Ω resistor.

Suppose a particular galvanometer has a resistance of 100.0 Ω and deflects full scale for a current of 100 μA. We want to build an ammeter to measure currents from 0 to 10 A—when a current of 10 A passes through the meter, the needle should deflect full scale. Therefore, when a current of 10 A goes through the ammeter, 100 μA should go through the galvanometer; the other 9.9999 A must bypass the galvanometer. We put a resistor in parallel with the galvanometer so that the 10 A current branches, sending 100 μA to deflect the needle and 9.9999 A through the *shunt resistor* (Fig. 18.31a).

Example 18.10

Constructing an Ammeter from a Galvanometer

If the internal resistance of a galvanometer (Fig. 18.31a) is 100.0 Ω and it deflects full scale for a current of 100.0 μA, what resistance should the shunt resistor have to make an ammeter for measuring currents up to 10.00 A?

Strategy When 10.00 A flows into the ammeter, 100.0 μA should go through the galvanometer and the remaining 9.9999 A should go through the shunt resistor (Fig. 18.31b). Since the two are in parallel, the potential difference across the galvanometer is equal to the potential difference across the shunt resistor.

Solution The voltage drop across the galvanometer when it deflects full scale is

$$V = IR = 100.0 \text{ μA} \times 100.0 \text{ Ω}$$

The voltage drop across the shunt resistor must be the same, so

$$V = 100.0 \text{ μA} \times 100.0 \text{ Ω} = 9.9999 \text{ A} \times R_S$$

$$R_S = \frac{100.0 \text{ μA} \times 100.0 \text{ Ω}}{9.9999 \text{ A}} = 0.001000 \text{ Ω} = 1.000 \text{ mΩ}$$

Discussion The resistance of the ammeter is

$$\left(\frac{1}{0.001000 \text{ Ω}} + \frac{1}{100.0 \text{ Ω}} \right)^{-1} = 1.000 \text{ mΩ}$$

A good ammeter should have a small resistance. When an ammeter is used to measure the current in a branch of a circuit, it must be inserted *in series* in that branch—the ammeter can only measure whatever current passes through it. Adding a small resistance in series has only a slight effect on the circuit.

Practice Problem 18.10   Changing the Ammeter Scale

If the ammeter measures currents from 0 to 1.00 A, what shunt resistance should be used? What is the resistance of the ammeter? Use the same galvanometer as in Example 18.10.

🔴 An ammeter must have a small resistance.

In order to give accurate measurements, an ammeter must have a small resistance so its presence in the circuit does not change the current significantly from its value in the absence of the ammeter. An ideal ammeter has zero resistance.

It is also possible to construct a voltmeter by connecting a resistor (R_S) *in series* with the galvanometer (R_S, Fig. 18.32). The series resistor R_S is chosen so that the current through the galvanometer makes it deflect full scale when the desired full-scale voltage appears across the voltmeter. A voltmeter measures the potential difference between its terminals; to measure the potential difference across a resistor, for example, the voltmeter

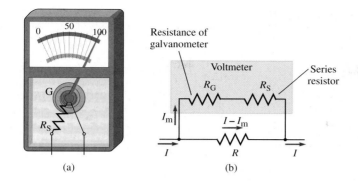

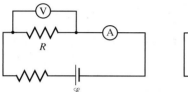

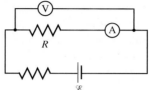

(a)   (b)

Figure 18.32 (a) A voltmeter constructed from a galvanometer. (b) Circuit diagram of the voltmeter measuring the voltage across the resistor *R*.

Figure 18.33 Two ways to arrange meters to measure a resistance *R*. If the meters were ideal (an ammeter with zero resistance and a voltmeter with infinite resistance), the two arrangements would give exactly the same measurement. Note the symbols used for the meters.

A voltmeter must have a large resistance.

is connected in parallel with the resistor, with one terminal connected to each side of the resistor. So as not to affect the circuit too much, a good voltmeter must have a large resistance; then when measurements are taken, the current through the voltmeter (I_m) is small compared to *I* and the potential difference across the parallel combination is nearly the same as when the voltmeter is disconnected. An ideal voltmeter has infinite resistance.

To measure a resistance in a circuit, we can use a voltmeter to measure the potential difference across the resistor and an ammeter to measure the current through the resistor (Fig. 18.33). By definition, the ratio of the voltage to the current is the resistance.

18.10   *RC* CIRCUITS

Circuits containing both resistors and capacitors have many important applications. *RC circuits* are commonly used to control timing. When windshield wipers are set to operate intermittently, the charging of a capacitor to a certain voltage is the trigger that turns them on. The time delay between wipes is determined by the resistance and capacitance in the circuit; adjusting a variable resistor changes the length of the time delay. Similarly, an *RC* circuit controls the time delay in strobe lights and in some pacemakers. We can also use the *RC* circuit as a simplified model of the transmission of nerve impulses.

Charging *RC* Circuit

In Fig. 18.34, switch *S* is initially open and the capacitor is uncharged. When the switch is closed, current begins to flow and charge starts to build up on the plates of the capacitor. At any instant, Kirchhoff's loop law requires that

$$\mathscr{E} - V_R - V_C = 0$$

where V_R and V_C are the voltage drops across the resistor and capacitor, respectively. As charge accumulates on the capacitor plates, it becomes increasingly difficult to push more charge onto them.

Just after the switch is closed, the potential difference across the resistor is equal to the emf since the capacitor is uncharged. Initially, a relatively large current $I_0 = \mathscr{E}/R$ flows. As the voltage drop across the capacitor increases, the voltage drop across the resistor

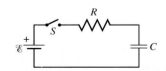

Figure 18.34 An *RC* circuit.

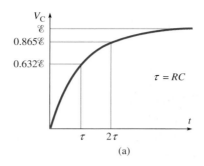
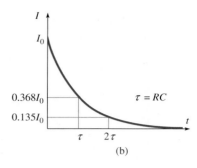

Figure 18.35 (a) The potential difference across the capacitor as a function of time as the capacitor is charged. (b) The current through the resistor as a function of time.

decreases, and thus the current decreases. Long after the switch is closed, the potential difference across the capacitor is nearly equal to the emf and the current is small.

Using calculus, it can be shown that the voltage across the capacitor involves an exponential function (see Fig. 18.35):

● Charging capacitor

$$V_C(t) = \mathscr{E}(1 - e^{-t/\tau}) \qquad (18\text{-}23)$$

where $e \approx 2.718$ is the base of the natural logarithm and the quantity $\tau = RC$ is called the **time constant** for the RC circuit.

● Time constant

$$\tau = RC \qquad (18\text{-}24)$$

The product RC has time units:

$$[R] = \frac{\text{volts}}{\text{amps}} \quad \text{and} \quad [C] = \frac{\text{coulombs}}{\text{volts}} \quad \text{so} \quad [RC] = \frac{\text{C}}{\text{A}} = \text{s}$$

The time constant is a measure of how fast the capacitor charges. At $t = \tau$, the voltage across the capacitor is

$$V_C(t = \tau) = \mathscr{E}(1 - e^{-1}) \approx 0.632\mathscr{E}$$

Since $Q = CV_C$, when one time constant has elapsed, the capacitor has 63.2% of its final charge.

From Eq. (18-23), we can use the loop rule to find the current.

$$\mathscr{E} - IR - \mathscr{E}(1 - e^{-t/\tau}) = 0$$

Solving for I,

● Charging *or* discharging

$$I(t) = \frac{\mathscr{E}}{R}e^{-t/\tau} \qquad (18\text{-}25)$$

At $t = \tau$, the current is

$$I(t = \tau) = \frac{\mathscr{E}}{R}e^{-1} \approx 0.368\,\frac{\mathscr{E}}{R}$$

When one time constant has elapsed, the current is reduced to 36.8% of its initial value. The voltage drop across the resistor as a function of time can be found from $V_R = IR$.

Example 18.11

An *RC* Circuit with Two Capacitors in Series

Two 0.500-μF capacitors in series are connected to a 50.0-V battery through a 4.00-MΩ resistor at $t = 0$ (Fig. 18.36). The capacitors are initially uncharged. (a) Find the charge on the capacitors at $t = 1.00$ s and $t = 3.00$ s. (b) Find the current in the circuit at the same two times.

Strategy First we find the equivalent capacitance of two 0.500-μF capacitors in series. Then we can find the time constant using the equivalent capacitance.

Continued on next page

Example 18.11 Continued

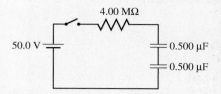

Figure 18.36

The circuit for Example 18.11.

Equation (18-23) gives the voltage across the equivalent capacitor at any time t; once we know the voltage, we can find the charge from $Q = CV_C$. The charge on each of the two capacitors is equal to the charge on the equivalent capacitor. The current decreases exponentially according to Eq. (18-25).

Solution   (a) For two equal capacitors C in series,

$$\frac{1}{C_{eq}} = \frac{1}{C} + \frac{1}{C} = \frac{2}{C}$$

Then $C_{eq} = \frac{1}{2}C = 0.250 \ \mu F$. The time constant is

$$\tau = RC_{eq} = 4.00 \times 10^6 \ \Omega \times 0.250 \times 10^{-6} \ F = 1.00 \ s$$

The final charge on the capacitor is

$Q_f = C_{eq}\mathcal{E} = 0.250 \times 10^{-6} \ F \times 50.0 \ V = 12.5 \times 10^{-6} \ C = 12.5$ μC

At any time t, the charge on each capacitor is

$$Q(t) = C_{eq}V_C(t) = C_{eq}\mathcal{E}(1 - e^{-t/\tau}) = Q_f(1 - e^{-t/\tau})$$

At $t = 1.00$ s, $t/\tau = 1.00$; the charge on each capacitor is

$$Q = Q_f(1 - e^{-1.00}) = 12.5 \ \mu C \times (1 - e^{-1.00}) = 7.90 \ \mu C$$

At $t = 3.00$ s, $t/\tau = 3.00$; the charge on each capacitor is

$$Q = Q_f(1 - e^{-3.00}) = 12.5 \ \mu C \times (1 - e^{-3.00}) = 11.9 \ \mu C$$

(b) The initial current is

$$I_0 = \frac{\mathcal{E}}{R} = \frac{50.0 \ V}{4.00 \times 10^6 \ \Omega} = 12.5 \ \mu A$$

At a time t,

$$I = I_0 e^{-t/\tau}$$

At $t = 1.00$ s,

$$I = I_0 e^{-1.00} = 12.5 \ \mu A \times e^{-1.00} = 4.60 \ \mu A$$

At $t = 3.00$ s,

$$I = I_0 e^{-3.00} = 12.5 \ \mu A \times e^{-3.00} = 0.622 \ \mu A$$

Discussion   The solution can be checked using the loop rule. At $t = \tau$, we found that $Q = 7.90 \ \mu C$ and $I = 4.60 \ \mu A$. Then at $t = \tau$,

$$V_C = \frac{Q}{C_{eq}} = \frac{7.90 \ \mu C}{0.250 \ \mu F} = 31.6 \ V$$

and

$$V_R = IR = 4.60 \ \mu A \times 4.00 \ M\Omega = 18.4 \ V$$

Since 31.6 V + 18.4 V = 50.0 V = $\mathcal{E}$, the loop rule is satisfied.

Notice the pattern: the current is multiplied by $1/e$ during a time interval equal to the time constant. Thus, for a current of 4.60 μA at $t = \tau$, we expect a current of 4.60 μA $\times 1/e = 1.69 \ \mu A$ at $t = 2\tau$ and a current of 1.69 μA $\times 1/e = 0.622 \ \mu A$ at $t = 3\tau$.

Practice Problem 18.11   Another *RC* Circuit

At $t = 0$ a capacitor of 0.050 μF is connected through a 5.0-MΩ resistor to a 12-V battery. Initially the capacitor is uncharged. Find the initial current, the charge on the capacitor at $t = 0.25$ s, the current at $t = 1.00$ s, and the final charge on the capacitor.

Discharging *RC* Circuit

In Fig. 18.37, the capacitor is first charged to a voltage $\mathcal{E}$ by closing switch S_1 with switch S_2 open. Once the capacitor is fully charged, S_1 is opened and then S_2 is closed at $t = 0$. Now the capacitor acts like a battery in the sense that it supplies energy in the circuit, though not at a constant potential difference. As the potential difference between the plates causes current to flow, the capacitor discharges.

The loop rule requires that the voltages across the capacitor and resistor be equal in magnitude. As the capacitor discharges, the voltage across it decreases. A decreasing voltage across the *resistor* means that the current must be decreasing. The current as a

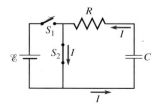

Figure 18.37 A capacitor is discharged through a resistor R.

Discharging capacitor

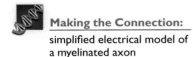

Making the Connection:

camera flash attachments

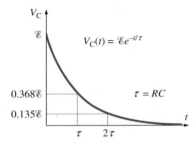

Making the Connection:

simplified electrical model of a myelinated axon

Figure 18.38 Decreasing voltage across a capacitor as it discharges through a resistor.

function of time is the same as for the charging circuit [Eq. (18-25)] with time constant $\tau = RC$. The voltage across the capacitor begins at its maximum value $\mathscr{E}$ and decreases exponentially (Fig. 18.38):

$$V_C(t) = \mathscr{E}e^{-t/\tau} \tag{18-26}$$

The bulb in a camera flash needs a burst of current much larger than a small battery can supply (due to the battery's internal resistance). Therefore, the battery charges a capacitor (Fig. 18.39). When the capacitor is fully charged, the flash is ready; when the picture is taken, the capacitor is discharged quickly through the bulb. The resistance of the bulb is small so that the capacitor discharges quickly. After taking a picture, there is a delay of a second or two while the capacitor recharges. The time constant is longer for the charging circuit due to the internal resistance of the battery.

RC Circuits in Neurons

An RC time constant also determines the speed at which nerve impulses travel. Figure 18.40a is a simplified model of a myelinated axon. Inside the axon is a fluid called the *axoplasm*, which is a conductor due to the presence of ions. Outside is the *interstitial fluid*, a conducting fluid with a much lower resistivity. Between the *nodes of Ranvier*, the cell membrane is covered with a *myelin sheath*—an insulator that reduces the capacitance of the section of axon (by increasing the distance between the conducting fluids) and reduces the leakage current that flows through the membrane.

A section of axon between nodes is modeled as an RC circuit in Fig. 18.40b. The interstitial fluid has little resistance, so it is modeled as a conducting wire. Current I travels inside the axon through the axoplasm (resistor R). The capacitor consists of the two conducting fluids as the plates, with the membrane and myelin sheath acting as insulator. For a section of axon 1 mm long with radius 5 μm, the resistance and capacitance are approximately $R = 13$ MΩ and $C = 1.6$ pF. The time constant is therefore,

$$\tau = RC = 13 \text{ MΩ} \times 1.6 \text{ pF} \approx 20 \text{ μs}$$

An estimate of how fast the electrical impulse travels is

$$v \approx \frac{\text{length of section}}{\tau} = \frac{1 \text{ mm}}{20 \text{ μs}} = 50 \text{ m/s}$$

This simple estimate is remarkably accurate; nerve impulses in a human myelinated axon of radius 5 μm travel at speeds ranging from 60 to 90 m/s.

Both R and C depend on the radius r of the axon. In humans, r ranges from under 2 μm to over 10 μm. The capacitance is proportional to r due to the larger plate area, but the resistance is inversely proportional to r^2 due to the larger cross-sectional area of the "wire." Thus, $RC \propto 1/r$ and $v \propto r$. The largest radius axons—those with the largest signal speeds—are those that must carry signals over relatively long distances.

Figure 18.39 A flash attachment for a camera. The large gray cylinder is the capacitor.

Figure 18.40 (a) A simplified picture of two sections of myelinated axon. (b) A simplified RC circuit model of a section of axon between nodes of Ranvier.

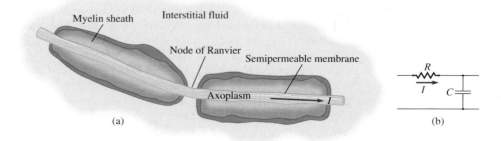

18.11 ELECTRICAL SAFETY

Effects of Current on the Human Body

Electric currents passing through the body interfere with the operation of the muscles and the nervous system. Large currents also cause burns due to the energy dissipated in the tissues. A current of around 1 mA or less causes an unpleasant sensation but usually no other effect. The maximum current that can pass through the body without causing harm is about 5 mA. A current of 10 to 20 mA results in muscle contractions or paralysis; paralysis may prevent the person from letting go of the source of the current.

Currents of 100 to 300 mA may cause ventricular fibrillation (uncontrolled, arrhythmic contractions of the heart) if they pass through or near the heart. In this condition, the person will die unless treated with a defibrillator to shock the heart back into a normal rhythm. Through the defibrillator paddles, a brief spurt of current of several amps is sent into the body near the heart (see Fig. 17.34). The shocked heart suffers a sudden muscular contraction, after which it may return to a normal state with regular contractions.

Most of the electrical resistance of the body is due to the skin. The fluids inside the body are good conductors due to the presence of ions. The total resistance of the body between distant points *when the skin is dry* ranges from around 10 kΩ to 1 MΩ. The resistance is much lower when the skin is wet—around 1 kΩ or even less.

A *short circuit* (a low resistance path) may occur between the circuitry inside an appliance to metal on the outside of the appliance. A person touching the appliance would then have one hand at 120 V with respect to ground. (To simplify the discussion, we treat the emf as if it were dc rather than ac.) If his feet are in a wet tub, which makes good electrical contact to the grounded water pipes, he might have a resistance as low as 500 Ω. Then a current of magnitude 120 V/500 Ω = 0.24 A = 240 mA flows through the body past the heart. Ventricular fibrillation is likely to occur. If the person were not standing in the tub, but had one hand on the hair dryer and another hand on a metal faucet, which is also grounded through the household plumbing, he is still in trouble. The electrical resistance of a person from one damp hand to the other might be around 1600 Ω, resulting in a current of 75 mA, which could still be lethal.

An electrified fence (Fig. 18.41) keeps farm animals in a pasture or wild animals out of a garden. One terminal of an emf is connected to the wire; the wire is insulated from the fence posts by ceramic insulators. The other terminal of the emf is connected to ground by a metal rod driven into the ground. When an animal or person touches the metal wire, the circuit is completed from the wire through the body and back to the ground (Fig. 18.41). The current flowing through the body is limited so that it produces an unpleasant sensation without being dangerous.

Grounding of Appliances

A two-pronged plug does not protect against a short circuit. The case of the appliance is supposed to be insulated from the wiring inside. If, by accident, a wire breaks loose or its insulation becomes frayed, a short circuit might occur, providing a low-resistance path directly to the metal case of the appliance. If a person touches the case, which is now at a high potential, the current travels through the person and back to the ground (Fig. 18.42a).

With a three-pronged plug, the case of the appliance is connected directly to ground through the third prong (Fig. 18.42b). Then, if a short circuit occurs, the person touching the case does not complete the circuit to the ground. Instead the current travels from the case directly to the ground through low-resistance wiring via the third prong in the wall outlet. For safety reasons, the metal cases of many electrical appliances are grounded.

Hospitals must take care that patients, connected to various monitors and IVs, are protected from a possible short circuit. For this reason the patient's bed, as well as anything else that the patient might touch, is insulated from the ground. Then if the patient touches something at a high potential, there is no ground connection to complete the circuit through the patient's body.

Making the Connection:
defibrillator

Remember that the symbol ⏚ represents a connection to ground.

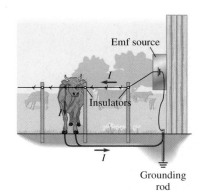

Figure 18.41 An electric fence. The circuit is completed when a person touches the wire.

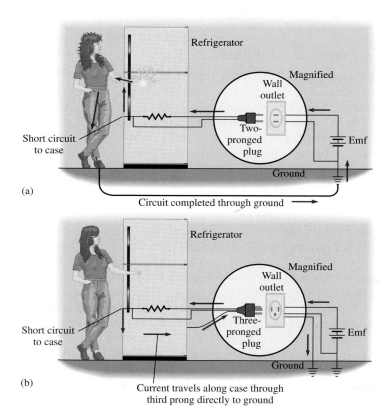

Figure 18.42 (a) If a refrigerator were connected with a two-pronged plug to a wall outlet, a short circuit to the case of the refrigerator allows the circuit to be completed through the body of a person touching the refrigerator. (b) If a short circuit occurs with a three-pronged plug, the person is safe.

Making the Connection:

household wiring

Fuses and Circuit Breakers

A simple fuse is made from an alloy of lead and tin that melts at a low temperature. The fuse is put in series with the circuit and is designed to melt—due to I^2R heating—if the current to the circuit exceeds a given value. The melted fuse is an open switch, interrupting the circuit and stopping the current. Many appliances are protected by fuses. Replacing a fuse with one of a higher current rating is dangerous because too much current may go through the appliance, damaging it or causing a fire.

Most household wiring is protected from overheating by circuit breakers instead of fuses. When too much current flows, perhaps because too many appliances are connected to the same circuit, a bimetallic strip or an electromagnet "trips" the circuit breaker, making it an open switch. After the problem causing the overload is corrected, the circuit breaker can be reset by flipping it back into the closed position.

Household wiring is arranged so that several appliances can be connected in parallel to a single circuit with one side of the circuit (the *neutral* side) grounded and the other side (the *hot* side) at a potential of 120 V with respect to ground (in our simplified dc model). Within one house or apartment, there are many such circuits; each one is protected by a circuit breaker (or fuse) placed in the hot side of the circuit. If a short circuit occurs, the large current that results trips the circuit breaker. If the breaker were placed on the grounded side, a blown circuit breaker would leave the hot side hot, possibly allowing a hazardous condition to continue. For the same reason, wall switches for overhead lights and for wall outlets are placed on the hot side.

MASTER THE CONCEPTS

- Electric current is the rate of net flow of charge:

$$I = \frac{\Delta q}{\Delta t} \qquad (18\text{-}1)$$

The SI unit of current is the ampere (1 A = 1 C/s), one of the base units of the SI. By convention, the direction of current is the direction of flow of positive charge. If the carriers are negative, the direction of the current is opposite the direction of motion of the carriers.

- A complete circuit is required for a continuous flow of charge.

- The current in a metal is proportional to the drift speed (v_D) of the conduction electrons, the number of electrons per unit volume (n), and the cross-sectional area of the metal (A):

$$I = \frac{\Delta Q}{\Delta t} = neAv_D \qquad (18\text{-}3)$$

- Electrical resistance is the ratio of the potential difference across a conducting material to the current through the material. It is measured in ohms: 1 Ω = 1 V/A.

Ohm's Law
$\Delta V = IR$

$$R = \frac{\Delta V}{I} \qquad (18\text{-}6)$$

For an ohmic conductor, R is independent of ΔV and I; then ΔV is proportional to I.

- The electrical resistance of a wire is directly proportional to its length and inversely proportional to its cross-sectional area:

$$R = \rho \frac{L}{A} \qquad (18\text{-}8)$$

- The resistivity ρ is an intrinsic characteristic of a particular material at a particular temperature and is measured in Ω·m. For many materials, resistivity varies linearly with temperature:

$$\rho = \rho_0 (1 + \alpha \Delta T) \qquad (18\text{-}9)$$

- A device that pumps charge is called a source of emf. The emf $\mathcal{E}$ is work done per unit charge [$W = \mathcal{E}q$, Eq. (18-2)]. The terminal voltage may differ from the emf due to the internal resistance r of the source:

$$V = \mathcal{E} - Ir \qquad (18\text{-}10)$$

- Kirchhoff's junction rule: $\sum I_{in} - \sum I_{out} = 0$ at any junction [Eq. (18-11)]. Kirchhoff's loop rule: $\sum \Delta V = 0$ for any path in a circuit that starts and ends at the same point [Eq. (18-12)]. Potential rises are positive; potential drops are negative.

- Circuit elements wired in series have the same current through them. Circuit elements wired in parallel have the same potential difference across them.

- The power—the rate of conversion between electrical energy and another form of energy—for any circuit element is

$$P = I \Delta V \qquad (18\text{-}19)$$

The SI unit for power is the watt (W). Electrical energy is dissipated (transformed into internal energy) in a resistor.

- The quantity $\tau = RC$ is called the time constant for an RC circuit. The currents and voltages are

$$V_C(t) = \mathcal{E}(1 - e^{-t/\tau}) \quad \text{(charging)} \quad (18\text{-}23)$$

$$V_C(t) = \mathcal{E}e^{-t/\tau} \quad \text{(discharging)} \quad (18\text{-}26)$$

$$I(t) = \frac{\mathcal{E}}{R} e^{-t/\tau} \quad \text{(both)} \quad (18\text{-}25)$$

Conceptual Questions

1. Draw a circuit diagram for automobile headlights, connecting two separate bulbs and a switch to a single battery so that: (1) one switch turns both bulbs on and off and (2) one bulb still lights up even if the other bulb burns out.

2. Ammeters often contain fuses that protect them from large currents, while voltmeters seldom do. Explain.

3. Why do lightbulbs usually burn out just after they are switched on and not when they have been on for a while?

4. Jeff needs a 100-Ω resistor for a circuit, but he only has a box of 300-Ω resistors. What can he do?

5. A friend says that electric current "follows the path of least resistance." Is that true? Explain.

6. Compare the resistance of an ideal ammeter with that of an ideal voltmeter. Which has the larger resistance? Why?

7. Why does the resistivity of a metallic conductor increase with increasing temperature?

8. Suppose a battery is connected to a network of resistors and capacitors. What happens to the energy supplied by the battery?

9. Why are electric stoves and clothes dryers supplied with 240 V, but lights, radios, and clocks are supplied with 120 V?

10. Why are ammeters connected in series with a circuit element in which the current is to be measured and voltmeters connected in parallel across the element for which the potential difference is to be measured?

11. Is it more dangerous to touch a "live" electric wire when your hands are dry or wet, everything else being equal? Explain.

12. Is the electric field inside a conductor always zero? If not, when is it not zero? Explain.

13. Some batteries can be "recharged." Does that mean that the battery has a supply of charge that is depleted as the battery is used? If "recharging" does not literally mean to put charge back into the battery, what *does* it mean?

14. A battery is connected to a clock by copper wires as shown. What is the direction of current through the clock (*B* to *C* or *C* to *B*)? What is the direction of current through the battery (*D* to *A* or *A* to *D*)? Which terminal of the battery is at the higher potential (*A* or *D*)? Which side of the clock is at the higher potential (*B* or *C*)? Does current *always* flow from higher to lower potential? Explain.

15. Think of a wire of length *L* as two wires of length *L*/2 in series. Construct an argument for why the resistance of a wire must be proportional to its length.

16. Think of a wire of cross-sectional area *A* as two wires of area *A*/2 in parallel. Construct an argument for why the resistance of a wire must be inversely proportional to its cross-sectional area.

17. An electrician working on "live" circuits wears insulated shoes and keeps one hand behind his or her back. Why?

18. A 15-A circuit breaker trips repeatedly. Explain why it would be dangerous to replace it with a 20-A circuit breaker.

19. A bird perched on a power line is not harmed, but if you are pruning a tree and your metal pole saw comes in contact with the same wire, you risk being electrocuted. Explain.

20. When batteries are connected in parallel, they should have the same emf. However, batteries connected in series need not have the same emf. Explain.

21. (a) If the resistance R_1 decreases, what happens to the voltage drop across R_3? The switch *S* is still open, as in the figure. (b) If the resistance R_1 decreases, what happens to the voltage drop across R_2? The switch *S* is still open, as in the figure. (c) In the circuit shown, if the switch *S* is closed, what happens to the current through R_1?

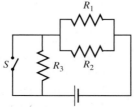

22. Four identical lightbulbs are placed in two different circuits with identical batteries. Bulbs *A* and *B* are connected in series with the battery. Bulbs *C* and *D* are connected in parallel across the battery. (a) Rank the brightness of the bulbs. (b) What happens to the brightness of bulb *B* if bulb *A* is replaced by a wire? (c) What happens to the brightness of bulb *C* if bulb *D* is removed from the circuit?

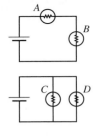

23. Three identical lightbulbs are connected in a circuit as shown in the diagram. (a) What happens to the brightness of the remaining bulbs if bulb *A* is removed from the circuit and replaced by a wire? (b) What happens to the brightness of the remaining bulbs if bulb *B* is removed from the circuit? (c) What happens to the brightness of the remaining bulbs if bulb *B* is replaced by a wire?

Multiple-Choice Questions

1. In an ionic solution, sodium ions (Na^+) are moving to the right and chlorine ions (Cl^-) are moving to the left. In which direction is the current due to the motion of (1) the sodium ions and (2) the chlorine ions?
   (a) Both are to the right.
   (b) Current due to Na^+ is to the left; current due to Cl^- is to the right.
   (c) Current due to Na^+ is to the right; current due to Cl^- is to the left.
   (d) Both are to the left.

2. A capacitor and a resistor are connected through a switch to an emf. At the instant just after the switch is closed,

   (a) the current in the circuit is zero.
   (b) the voltage across the capacitor is $\mathcal{E}$.
   (c) the voltage across the resistor is zero.
   (d) the voltage across the resistor is $\mathcal{E}$.
   (e) Both (a) and (c) are true.

3. Which is a unit of energy?
   (a) $A^2 \cdot \Omega$ (b) $V \cdot A$ (c) $\Omega \cdot m$
   (d) $\dfrac{N \cdot m}{V}$ (e) $\dfrac{A}{C}$ (f) $V \cdot C$

4. How does the resistance of a piece of conducting wire change if both its length and diameter are doubled?
   (a) Remains the same   (b) 2 times as much
   (c) 4 times as much   (d) 1/2 as much
   (e) 1/4 as much

Each of the graphs for questions 5 and 6 shows a relation between the potential drop across (V) and the current through (I) a circuit element.

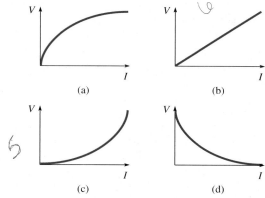

(a)

(b)

(c)

(d)

Multiple-Choice Questions 5 and 6

5. Which depicts a circuit element whose resistance increases with increasing current?

6. Which depicts an ohmic circuit element?

7. The electrical properties of copper and rubber are different because
   (a) the positive charges are free to move in copper and stationary in rubber.
   (b) many electrons are free to move in copper but nearly all are bound to molecules in rubber.
   (c) the positive charges are free to move in rubber but are stationary in copper.
   (d) many electrons are free to move in rubber but nearly all are bound to molecules in copper.

8. Consider these four statements. Choose true or false for each one in turn and then find the answer that matches your choices for all four together.
   (1) An ammeter should draw very little current compared with that in the rest of the circuit.
   (2) An ammeter should have a high resistance compared with the resistances of the other elements in the circuit.
   (3) To measure the current in a circuit element, the ammeter should be connected in series with that element.
   (4) Connecting the ammeter in series with a circuit element causes at least a small reduction of the current in that element.
   (a) (1) true, (2) true, (3) false, (4) false
   (b) (1) true, (2) false, (3) true, (4) true
   (c) (1) false, (2) false, (3) true, (4) false
   (d) (1) false, (2) false, (3) true, (4) true
   (e) (1) false, (2) true, (3) true, (4) true
   (f) (1) false, (2) false, (3) false, (4) true

9. A 12-V battery with internal resistance 0.5 Ω has initially no load connected across its terminals. Then the switches S_1 and S_2 are closed successively. The voltmeter (assumed ideal) has which set of successive readings?

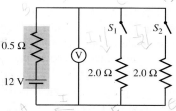

(a) 12 V, 11 V, 10 V   (b) 12 V, 12 V, 12 V
(c) 12 V, 9.6 V, 7.2 V   (d) 12 V, 9.6 V, 8 V
(e) 12 V, 8 V, 4 V   (f) 12 V, zero, zero

10. Which of these is equal to the emf of a battery?
    (a) the chemical energy stored in the battery
    (b) the terminal voltage of the battery when no current flows
    (c) the maximum current that the battery can supply
    (d) the amount of charge the battery can pump
    (e) the chemical energy stored in the battery divided by the net charge of the battery

Problems

© Combination conceptual/quantitative problem

🔬 Biological or medical application

No ✦ Easy to moderate difficulty level

✦ More challenging

✦✦ Most challenging

Blue # Detailed solution in the Student Solutions Manual

| 1 | 2 | Problems paired by concept

18.1 Electric Current

1. A battery charger delivers a current of 3.0 A for 4.0 h to a 12-V storage battery. What is the total charge that passes through the battery in that time?

2. The current in a wire is 0.500 A. (a) How much charge flows past a point in the wire in 10.0 s? (b) How many electrons pass the same point in 10.0 s?

3. (a) What is the direction of the current in the vacuum tube shown in the figure? (b) Electrons hit the anode at a rate of 6.0×10^{12} per second. What is the current in the tube?

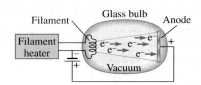

Filament   Glass bulb   Anode

Filament heater   Vacuum

4. In an ion accelerator, 3.0×10^{13} helium-4 nuclei (charge $+2e$) per second strike a target. What is the beam current?

5. The current in the electron beam of a computer monitor is 320 μA. How many electrons per second hit the screen?

6. A potential difference is applied between the electrodes in a gas discharge tube. In 1.0 s, 3.8×10^{16} electrons and 1.2×10^{16} singly charged positive ions move in opposite directions through a surface perpendicular to the length of the tube. What is the current in the tube?

7. Two electrodes are placed in a calcium chloride solution and a potential difference is maintained between them. If 3.8×10^{16} Ca^{2+} ions and 6.2×10^{16} Cl^- ions per second move in opposite directions through an imaginary area between the electrodes, what is the current in the solution?

18.2 Emf and Circuits

8. A Vespa scooter and a Toyota automobile might both use a 12-V battery, but the two batteries are of different sizes and can pump different amounts of charge. Suppose the scooter battery can pump 4.0 kC of charge and the automobile battery can pump 30.0 kC of charge. How much energy can each battery deliver, assuming the batteries are ideal?

9. What is the energy stored in a small battery if it can move 675 C through a potential difference of 1.20 V?

10. The label on a 12.0-V truck battery states that it is rated at 180.0 A·h (ampere-hours). Treat the battery as ideal. (a) How much charge in coulombs can be pumped by the battery? [*Hint:* Convert A·h to A·s.] (b) How much electrical energy can the battery supply? (c) Suppose the radio in the truck is left on when the engine is not running. The radio draws a current of 3.30 A. How long does it take to drain the battery if it starts out fully charged?

11. The starter motor in a car draws 220.0 A of current from the 12.0-V battery for 1.20 s. (a) How much charge is pumped by the battery? (b) How much electrical energy is supplied by the battery?

12. A solar cell provides an emf of 0.45 V. (a) If the cell supplies a constant current of 18.0 mA for 9.0 h, how much electrical energy does it supply? (b) What is the power—the rate at which it supplies electrical energy?

18.3 Microscopic View of Current in a Metal: The Free-Electron Model

13. Two copper wires, one double the diameter of the other, have the same current flowing through them. If the thinner wire has a drift speed v_1, and the thicker wire has a drift speed v_2, how do the drift speeds of the charge carriers compare?

14. A current of 2.50 A is carried by a copper wire of radius 1.00 mm. If the density of the conduction electrons is 8.47×10^{28} m^{-3}, what is the drift speed of the conduction electrons?

15. A current of 10.0 A is carried by a copper wire of diameter 1.00 mm. If the density of the conduction electrons is 8.47×10^{28} m^{-3}, how long does it take for a conduction electron to move 1.00 m along the wire?

16. A silver wire of diameter 1.0 mm carries a current of 150 mA. The density of conduction electrons in silver is 5.8×10^{28} m^{-3}. How long (on average) does it take for a conduction electron to move 1.0 cm along the wire?

17. A strip of doped silicon 260 μm wide contains 8.8×10^{22} conduction electrons per cubic meter and an insignificant number of holes. When the strip carries a current of 130 μA, the drift speed of the electrons is 44 cm/s. What is the thickness of the strip?

18. A gold wire of 0.50 mm diameter has 5.90×10^{28} conduction electrons/m^3. If the drift speed is 6.5 μm/s, what is the current in the wire?

◆ 19. A copper wire of cross-sectional area 1.00 mm^2 has a current of 2.0 A flowing along its length. What is the drift speed of the conduction electrons? Assume 1.3 conduction electrons per copper atom. The mass density of copper is 9.0 g/cm^3 and its atomic mass is 64 g/mol.

◆ 20. An aluminum wire of diameter 2.6 mm carries a current of 12 A. How long on average does it take an electron to move 12 m along the wire? Assume 3.5 conduction electrons per aluminum atom. The mass density of aluminum is 2.7 g/cm^3 and its atomic mass is 27 g/mol.

18.4 Resistance and Resistivity

21. A 12-Ω resistor has a potential difference of 16 V across it. What current flows through the resistor?

22. 83 mA of current flow through the resistor in the diagram. (a) What is the resistance of the resistor? (b) In what direction does the current flow through the resistor?

23. A copper wire and an aluminum wire of the same length have the same resistance. What is the ratio of the diameter of the copper wire to that of the aluminum wire?

24. A bird sits on a high-voltage power line with its feet 2.0 cm apart. The wire is made from aluminum, is 2.0 cm in diameter, and carries a current of 150 A. What is the potential difference between the bird's feet?

 25. A person can be killed if a current as small as 50 mA passes near the heart. An electrician is working on a humid day with hands damp from perspiration. Suppose his resistance from one hand to the other is 1 kΩ and he is touching two wires, one with each hand. (a) What potential difference between the two wires would cause a 50-mA current from one hand to the other? (b) An electrician working on a "live" circuit keeps one hand behind his or her back. Why?

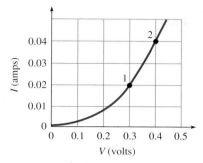

Problems 26 and 108

26. An electrical device has the current-voltage (I-V) graph shown. What is its resistance at (a) point 1 and (b) point 2? [*Hint:* Use the definition of resistance.]

27. If 46 m of nichrome wire is to have a resistance of 10.0 Ω at 20°C, what diameter wire should be used?

28. The resistance of a conductor is 19.8 Ω at 15.0°C and 25.0 Ω at 85.0°C. What is the temperature coefficient of resistance of the material?

29. A common flashlight bulb is rated at 0.300 A and 2.90 V (the values of current and voltage under operating conditions). If the resistance of the bulb's tungsten filament at room temperature (20.0°C) is 1.10 Ω, estimate the temperature of the tungsten filament when the bulb is turned on.

30. Find the maximum current that a fully charged D-cell can supply—if only briefly—such that its terminal voltage is at least 1.0 V. Assume an emf of 1.5 V and an internal resistance of 0.10 Ω.

31. A battery has a terminal voltage of 12.0 V when no current flows. Its internal resistance is 2.0 Ω. If a 1.0-Ω resistor is connected across the battery terminals, what is the terminal voltage and what is the current through the 1.0-Ω resistor?

32. (a) What are the ratios of the resistances of (a) silver and (b) aluminum wire to the resistance of copper wire (R_{Ag}/R_{Cu} and R_{Al}/R_{Cu}) for wires of the same length and the same diameter? (c) Which material is the best conductor, for wires of equal length and diameter?

✦ 33. A wire with cross-sectional area A carries a current I. Show that the electric field strength E in the wire is proportional to the current per unit area (I/A) and identify the constant of proportionality. [*Hint:* Assume a length L of wire. How is the potential difference across the wire related to the electric field in the wire? (Which is uniform?) Use $V = IR$ and the connection between resistance and resistivity.]

Ⓒ 34. A copper wire has a resistance of 24 Ω at 20°C. An aluminum wire has three times the length and twice the radius of the copper wire. The resistivity of copper is 0.6 times that of aluminum. Both Al and Cu have temperature coefficients of resistivity of 0.004°C⁻¹. (a) What is the resistance of the aluminum wire at

20°C? (b) The graph shows a V-I plot for the copper wire. What is the resistance of the wire when operating steadily at a current of 10 A? (c) What must the temperature of the copper wire have been when operating at 10 A? Ignore changes in the wire's dimensions.

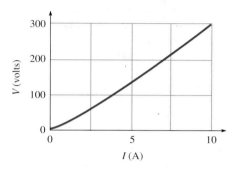

35. Refer to Problem 34. With the copper wire connected to an ideal battery, the current increases greatly when the wire is immersed in liquid nitrogen. Ignoring changes in the wire's dimensions, state whether each of the following quantities increases, decreases, or stays the same as the wire is cooled: the electric field in the wire, the resistivity, and the drift speed. Explain your answers.

18.6 Series and Parallel Circuits

36. Suppose a collection of five batteries is connected as shown. (a) What is the equivalent emf of the collection? Treat them as ideal sources of emf. (b) What is the current through the resistor if its value is 3.2 Ω?

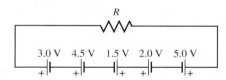

37. Suppose four batteries are connected in series as shown. (a) What is the equivalent emf of the set of four batteries? Treat them as ideal sources of emf. (b) If the current in the circuit is 0.40 A, what is the value of the resistor R?

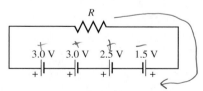

38. (a) Find the equivalent capacitance between points A and B for the three capacitors in parallel. (b) What is the charge on the 6.0-μF capacitor if a 44.0-V emf is connected to the terminals A and B for a long time?

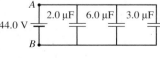

39. (a) Find the equivalent capacitance between points A and B for the five capacitors in parallel. (b) If a 16.0-V

emf is connected to the terminals A and B, what is the charge on a single equivalent capacitor that replaces the parallel combination? (c) What is the charge on the 3.0-μF capacitor?

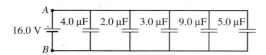

40. (a) What is the resistance between points A and B? (b) A 276-V emf is connected to the terminals A and B. What is the current in the 12-Ω resistor?

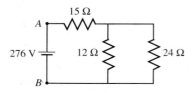

41. (a) What is the equivalent resistance between points A and B if $R = 1.0$ Ω? (b) If a 20-V emf is connected to the terminals A and B, what is the current in the 2.0-Ω resistor?

42. If a 93.5-V emf is connected to the terminals A and B and the current in the 4.0-Ω resistor is 17 A, what is the value of the unknown resistor R?

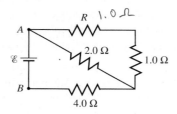

Problems 41 and 42

43. (a) What is the equivalent capacitance between points A and B if $C = 1.0$ μF? (b) What is the charge on the 4.0-μF capacitor when it is fully charged?

44. The capacitance across A and B is 1.63 μF. (a) What is the capacitance of the unknown capacitor C? (b) What is the charge on the 4.0-μF capacitor when it is fully charged?

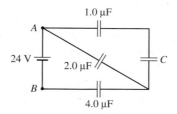

Problems 43 and 44

45. A 24-V emf is connected to the terminals A and B. (a) What is the current in one of the 2.0-Ω resistors?

(b) What is the current in the 6.0-Ω resistor? (c) What is the current in the leftmost 4.0-Ω resistor?

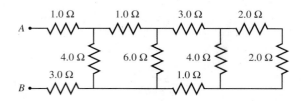

46. (a) Find the equivalent resistance between points A and B for the combination of resistors shown. (b) An 18-V emf is connected to the terminals A and B. What is the current through the 1.0-Ω resistor connected directly to point A? (c) What is the current in the 8.0-Ω resistor?

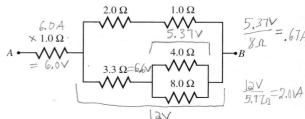

47. (a) What is the resistance between points A and B? Each resistor has the same resistance R. [*Hint:* Redraw the circuit.] (b) What is the resistance between points B and C? (c) If a 32-V emf is connected to the terminals A and B and if each $R = 2.0$ Ω, what is the current in one of the resistors?

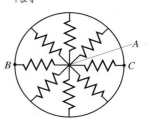

48. (a) Find the equivalent resistance between points A and B for the combination of resistors shown. (b) What is the potential difference across each of the 4.0-Ω resistors? (c) What is the current in the 3.0-Ω resistor?

49. (a) Find the value of a single capacitor to replace the three capacitors in the diagram. (b) What is the potential difference across the 12-μF capacitor at the left side of the diagram? (c) What is the charge on the 12-μF capacitor to the far right side of the circuit?

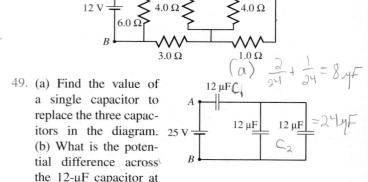

50. A 6.0-pF capacitor is needed to construct a circuit. The only capacitors available are rated as 9.0 pF. How can a combination of 9.0-pF capacitors be assembled so that the equivalent capacitance of the combination is 6.0 pF? (There are many possible solutions. Just find *one* of them—preferably one that uses a small number of 9.0-pF capacitors.)

51. (a) Find the equivalent resistance between terminals A and B to replace all of the resistors in the diagram. (b) What current flows through the emf? (c) What is the current through the 4.00-Ω resistor at the bottom?

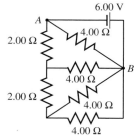

18.7 Circuit Analysis Using Kirchhoff's Rules

52. Find the current in each branch of the circuit. Specify the direction of each.

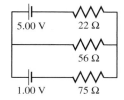

53. Find the current in each branch of the circuit. Specify the direction of each.

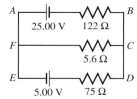

54. Find the unknown emf and the unknown currents in the circuit.

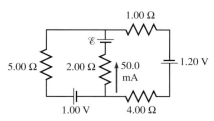

55. Find the unknown emf and the unknown resistor in the circuit.

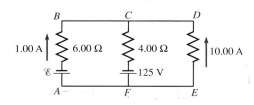

56. The figure shows a simplified circuit diagram for an automobile. The equivalent resistor R represents the total electrical load due to spark plugs, lights, radio, fans, starter, rear window defroster, and the like in parallel. (a) If R = 0.850 Ω, find the current in each branch. What is the terminal voltage of the battery? Is the battery charging or discharging? (b) For what range of values of R is the battery discharging?

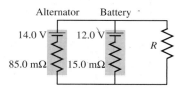

18.8 Power and Energy in Circuits

57. What is the power dissipated by the resistor in the circuit if the emf is 2.00 V?

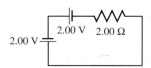

58. Refer to the figure with Problem 57. What is the power dissipated by the resistor in the circuit if R = 5.00 Ω?

59. What is the current in a 60.0-W bulb when connected to a 120-V emf?

60. What is the resistance of a 40.0-W, 120-V lightbulb?

61. If a chandelier has a label stating 120 V, 5.0 A, can its power rating be determined? If so, what is it?

62. A portable CD player does not have a power rating listed, but it has a label stating that it draws a maximum current of 250.0 mA. The player uses three 1.50-V batteries connected in series. What is the maximum power consumed?

63. How much work are the batteries in the circuit doing in every 10.0-s time interval?

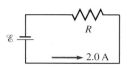

64. Show that $A^2 \times \Omega = W$ (amperes squared times ohms = watts).

65. Consider the circuit in the diagram. (a) Draw the simplest equivalent circuit and label the values of the resistor(s).

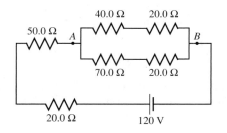

$V_1 = \dfrac{\varepsilon}{1+\frac{c_1}{c_2}} = \dfrac{25V}{1+\frac{12}{24}} = \dfrac{25V}{1.5\mu F} = 17V$

(b) What current flows from the battery? (c) What is the potential difference between points A and B? (d) What current flows through each branch between points A and B? (e) Determine the power dissipated in the 50.0-Ω resistor, the 70.0-Ω resistor, and the 40.0-Ω resistor.

66. Two immersion heaters, A and B, are both connected to a 120-V supply. Heater A can raise the temperature of 1.0 L of water from 20.0°C to 90.0°C in 2.0 min, while heater B can raise the temperature of 5.0 L of water from 20.0°C to 90.0°C in 5.0 min. What is the ratio of the resistance of heater A to the resistance of heater B?

67. (a) What is the equivalent resistance of this circuit if R_1 = 10.0 Ω and R_2 = 15.0 Ω? (b) What current flows through R_1? (c) What is the voltage drop across R_2? (d) What current flows through R_2? (e) How much power is dissipated in R_2?

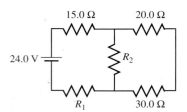

68. At what rate is electrical energy converted to internal energy in the 4.00-Ω and 5.00-Ω resistors in the figure?

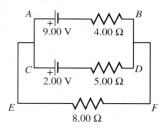

69. In her bathroom, Mindy has an overhead heater that consists of a coiled wire made of nichrome that gets hot when turned on. The wire has a length of 3.0 m when it is uncoiled. The heating element is attached to the normal 120-V wiring and when the wire is glowing red hot it has a temperature of about 420°C and dissipates 2200 W of power. Nichrome has a resistivity of 108×10^{-8} $\Omega \cdot$m at 20°C and a temperature coefficient of resistivity of 0.00040°C^{-1}. (a) What is the resistance of the heater when it is turned on? (b) What current does the wire carry? (c) If the wire has a circular cross section, what is its diameter? Ignore the small changes in the wire's diameter and length due to changes in temperature. (d) When the heater is first turned on, it has not yet heated up, so it is operating at 20°C. What is the current through the wire when it is first turned on?

70. During a "brownout," which occurs when the power companies cannot keep up with high demand, the voltage of the household circuits drops below its normal 120 V. (a) If the voltage drops to 108 V, what would be the power consumed by a "100-W" lightbulb (that is, a lightbulb that consumes 100.0 W when connected to 120 V)? Ignore (for now) changes in the resistance of the lightbulb filament. (b) More realistically, the lightbulb filament will not be as hot as usual during the brownout. Does this make the power drop more or less than that you calculated in part (a)? Explain.

71. A battery has a 6.00-V emf and an internal resistance of 0.600 Ω. (a) What is the voltage across its terminals when the current drawn from the battery is 1.20 A? (b) What is the power supplied by the battery?

✦ 72. A source of emf $\mathcal{E}$ has internal resistance r. (a) What is the terminal voltage when the source supplies a current I? (b) The net power supplied is the terminal voltage times the current. Starting with $P = I\Delta V$, derive Eq. (18-22) for the net power supplied by the source. Interpret each of the two terms. (c) Suppose that a battery of emf $\mathcal{E}$ and internal resistance r is being recharged: another emf sends a current I through the battery in the reverse direction (from positive terminal to negative). At what rate is electrical energy converted to chemical energy in the recharging battery? (d) What is the power supplied by the recharging circuit to the battery?

18.9 Measuring Currents and Voltages

73. An ammeter with a full scale deflection for I = 10.0 A has an internal resistance of 24 Ω. We need to use this ammeter to measure currents up to 12.0 A. The lab instructor advises that we get a resistor and use it to protect the ammeter. (a) What size resistor do we need and how should it be connected to the ammeter, in series or in parallel? (b) How do we interpret the ammeter readings?

74. A galvanometer has a coil resistance of 50.0 Ω. It is to be made into an ammeter with a full-scale deflection equal to 10.0 A. If the galvanometer deflects full scale for a current of 0.250 mA, what size shunt resistor should be used?

75. A galvanometer has a coil resistance of 34.0 Ω. It is to be made into a voltmeter with a full-scale deflection equal to 100.0 V. If the galvanometer deflects full scale for a current of 0.120 mA, what size resistor should be placed in series with the galvanometer?

76. A galvanometer is to be turned into a voltmeter that deflects full scale for a potential difference of 100.0 V. What size resistor should be placed in series with the galvanometer if it has an internal resistance of 75 Ω and deflects full scale for a current of 2.0 mA?

77. Many voltmeters have a switch by which one of several series resistors can be selected. Thus, the same meter can be used with different full-scale voltages. What size series resistors should be used in the voltmeter of Problem 76 to give it full-scale voltages of (a) 50.0 V and (b) 500.0 V?

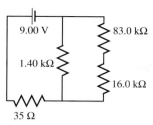

35 Ω

Problems 78, 79, and 115

78. Redraw the circuit (a) to show how an ammeter would be added to the circuit to measure the current through the 1.40-kΩ resistor; (b) to show how a voltmeter would be added to measure the voltage drop across the 83.0-kΩ resistor.

79. (a) Find the current through the 1.40-kΩ resistor. (b) An ammeter with a resistance of 240 Ω is used to measure the current through the 1.40-kΩ resistor. What is the ammeter reading?

✦ **80.** A voltmeter has a switch that enables voltages to be measured with a maximum of 25.0 V or 10.0 V. For a range of voltages to 25.0 V, the switch connects a resistor of magnitude 9850 Ω in series with the galvanometer; for a range of voltages to 10.0 V, the switch connects a resistor of magnitude 3850 Ω in series with the galvanometer. Find the coil resistance of the galvanometer and the galvanometer current that causes a full-scale deflection. [*Hint:* There are two unknowns, so you will need to solve two equations simultaneously.]

18.10 *RC* Circuits

81. In the circuit shown, assume the battery emf is 20.0 V, $R = 1.00$ MΩ, and $C = 2.00$ μF. The switch is closed at $t = 0$. At what time t will the voltage across the capacitor be 15.0 V?

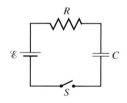

82. In the circuit, $R = 30.0$ kΩ and $C = 0.10$ μF. The capacitor is allowed to charge fully and then the switch is changed from position a to position b. What will the voltage across the resistor be 8.4 ms later?

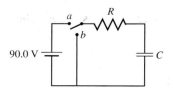

83. A capacitor is charged to an initial voltage $V_0 = 9.0$ V. The capacitor is then discharged by connecting its terminals through a resistor. The current $I(t)$ through this resistor, determined by measuring the voltage $V_R(t) = I(t)R$ with an oscilloscope, is shown in the graph. (a) Find the capacitance C, the resistance R, and the total energy dissipated in the resistor. (b) At what time is the energy in the capacitor half its initial value? (c) Graph the voltage across the capacitor, $V_C(t)$, as a function of time.

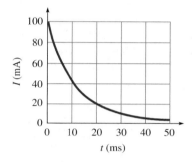

84. A charging *RC* circuit controls the intermittent windshield wipers in a car. The emf is 12.0 V. The wipers are triggered when the voltage across the 125-μF capacitor reaches 10.0 V; then the capacitor is quickly discharged (through a much smaller resistor) and the cycle repeats. What resistance should be used in the charging circuit if the wipers are to operate once every 1.80 s?

85. Capacitors are used in many applications where one needs to supply a short burst of relatively large current. A 100.0-μF capacitor in an electronic flash lamp supplies a burst of current that dissipates 20.0 J of energy (as light and heat) in the lamp. (a) To what potential difference must the capacitor initially be charged? (b) What is its initial charge? (c) Approximately what is the resistance of the lamp if the current reaches 5.0% of its original value in 2.0 ms?

86. A defibrillator passes a brief burst of current through the heart to restore normal beating. In one such defibrillator, a 50.0-μF capacitor is charged to 6.0 kV. Paddles are used to make an electrical connection to the patient's chest. A pulse of current lasting 1.0 ms partially discharges the capacitor through the patient. The electrical resistance of the patient (from paddle to paddle) is 240 Ω. (a) What is the initial energy stored in the capacitor? (b) What is the initial current through the patient? (c) How much energy is dissipated in the patient during the 1.0 ms? (d) If it takes 2.0 s to recharge the capacitor, compare the average power supplied by the power source to the average power delivered to the patient. (e) Referring to your answer to part (d), explain one reason a capacitor is used in a defibrillator.

87. Consider the circuit shown with $R_1 = 25$ Ω, $R_2 = 33$ Ω, $C_1 = 12$ μF, $C_2 = 23$ μF, $C_3 = 46$ μF, and $V = 6.0$ V.

(a) Draw an equivalent circuit with one resistor and one capacitor and label it with the values of the equivalent resistor and capacitor. (b) A long time after switch S is closed, what are the charge on capacitor C_1 and the current in resistor R_1? (c) What is the time constant of the circuit? (d) At what time after switch S is closed is the voltage across the combination of three capacitors 50% of its final value?

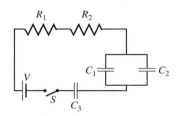

88. A charged capacitor is discharged through a resistor. The current $I(t)$ through this resistor, determined by measuring the voltage $V_R(t) = I(t)R$ with an oscilloscope, is shown in the graph. The total energy dissipated in the resistor is 2.0×10^{-4} J. (a) Find the capacitance C, the resistance R, and the initial charge on the capacitor. [*Hint:* You will need to solve three equations simultaneously for the three unknowns. You can find both the initial current and the time constant from the graph.] (b) At what time is the stored energy in the capacitor 5.0×10^{-5} J?

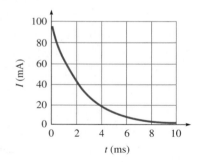

89. In the circuit, the capacitor is initially uncharged. At $t = 0$ switch S is closed. Find the currents I_1 and I_2 and voltages V_1 and V_2 (assuming $V_3 = 0$) at points 1 and 2 at the following times: (a) $t = 0$ (i.e., just after the switch is closed), (b) $t = 1.0$ ms, and (c) $t = 5.0$ ms.

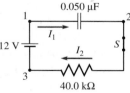

90. In the circuit, the initial energy stored in the capacitor is 25 J. At $t = 0$ the switch is closed. (a) Sketch a graph of the voltage across the resistor (V_R) as a function of t. Label the vertical axis with key numerical value(s) and units. (b) At what time is the energy stored in the capacitor 1.25 J?

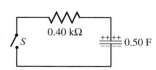

91. A 20-μF capacitor is discharged through a 5-kΩ resistor. The initial charge on the capacitor is 200 μC. (a) Sketch a graph of the current through the resistor as a function of time. Label both axes with numbers and units. (b) What is the initial power dissipated in the resistor? (c) What is the total energy dissipated?

92. (a) In a charging RC circuit, how many time constants have elapsed when the capacitor has 99.0% of its final charge? (b) How many time constants have elapsed when the capacitor has 99.90% of its final charge? (c) How many time constants have elapsed when the current has 1.0% of its initial value?

93. A capacitor is charged by a 9.0-V battery. The charging current $I(t)$ is shown. (a) What, approximately, is the total charge on the capacitor in the end? [*Hint:* During a short time interval Δt, the amount of charge that flows in the circuit is $I\Delta t$.] (b) Using your answer to (a), find the capacitance C of the capacitor. (c) Find the total resistance R in the circuit. (d) At what time is the stored energy in the capacitor half of its maximum value?

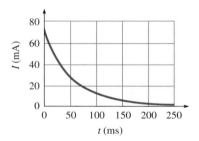

18.11 Electrical Safety

94. In the physics laboratory, Oscar measured the resistance between his hands to be 2.0 kΩ. Being curious by nature, he then took hold of two conducting wires that were connected to the terminals of an emf with a terminal voltage of 100.0 V. (a) What current passes through Oscar? (b) If one of the conducting wires is grounded and the other has an alternate path to ground through a 15-Ω resistor (so that Oscar and the resistor are in parallel), how much current would pass through Oscar if the maximum current that can be drawn from the emf is 1.00 A?

95. A person bumps into a set of batteries with an emf of 100.0 V that can supply a maximum power of 5.0 W. If the man's resistance between the points where he contacts the batteries is 1.0 kΩ, how much current passes through him?

96. The wiring circuit for a typical room is shown schematically. (a) Of the six locations for a circuit breaker indicated by *A, B, C, D, E,* and *F,* which one would best protect the household against a short circuit in any one of the three appliances? Explain. (b) The

room circuit is supplied with 120 V. Suppose the heater draws 1500 W, the lamp draws 300 W, and the microwave draws 1200 W. The circuit breaker is rated at 20.0 A. Can all three devices be operated without tripping the breaker? Explain.

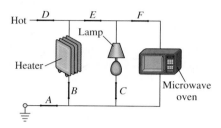

97. Several possibilities are listed for what might or might not happen if the insulation in the current-carrying wires of the figure breaks down and point *b* makes electrical contact with point *c*. Discuss each possibility. (a) The person touching the microwave oven gets a shock; (b) the cord begins to smoke; (c) a fuse blows out; (d) an electrical fire breaks out inside the kitchen wall.

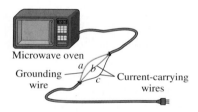

Comprehensive Problems

98. A 1.5-V flashlight battery can maintain a current of 0.30 A for 4.0 h before it is exhausted. How much chemical energy is converted to electrical energy in this process? (Assume zero internal resistance of the battery.)

99. In the diagram, the positive terminal of the 12-V battery is grounded—it is at zero potential. At what potential is point *X*?

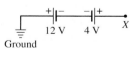

100. In the circuit shown, an emf of 150 V is connected across a resistance network. What is the current through R_2? Each of the resistors has a value of 10 Ω.

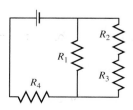

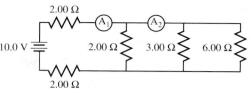

Problems 101 and 102

101. A_1 and A_2 represent ammeters with negligible resistance. What are the values of the currents (a) in A_1 and (b) in A_2?

102. Repeat Problem 101 if each of the ammeters has resistance 0.200 Ω.

103. (a) What is the resistance of the heater element in a 1500-W hair dryer that plugs into a 120-V outlet? (b) What is the current through the hair dryer when it is turned on? (c) At a cost of $0.10 per kW·h, how much does it cost to run the hair dryer for 5.00 min? (d) If you were to take the hair dryer to Europe where the voltage is 240 V, how much power would your hair dryer be using in the brief time before it is ruined? (e) What current would be flowing through the hair dryer during this time?

104. A string of 25 decorative lights has bulbs rated at 9.0 W and the bulbs are connected in parallel. The string is connected to a 120-V power supply. (a) What is the resistance of each of these lights? (b) What is the current through each bulb? (c) What is the total current coming from the power supply? (d) The string of bulbs has a fuse that will blow if the current is greater than 2.0 A. How many of the bulbs can you replace with 10.4-W bulbs without blowing the fuse?

105. About 5.0×10^4 m above Earth's surface, the atmosphere is sufficiently ionized that it behaves as a conductor. The Earth and the ionosphere form a giant spherical capacitor, with the lower atmosphere acting as a leaky dielectric. (a) Find the capacitance C of the Earth-ionosphere system by treating it as a *parallel plate* capacitor. Why is it OK to do that? [*Hint:* Compare the Earth's radius to the distance between the "plates."] (b) The fair-weather electric field is about 150 V/m, downward. How much energy is stored in this capacitor? (c) Due to radioactivity and cosmic rays, some air molecules are ionized even in fair weather. The resistivity of air is roughly 3.0×10^{14} Ω·m. Find the resistance of the lower atmosphere and the total current that flows between the Earth's surface and the ionosphere. [*Hint:* Since we treat the system as a parallel plate capacitor, treat the atmosphere as a dielectric of *uniform thickness* between the plates.] (d) If there were no lightning, the capacitor would discharge. In this model, how much time would elapse before the Earth's charge were reduced to 1% of its normal value? (Thunderstorms are the sources of emf that maintain the charge on this leaky capacitor.)

© 106. A 2.00-µF capacitor is charged using a 5.00-V battery and a 3.00-µF capacitor is charged using a 10.0-V battery. (a) What is the total energy stored in the two capacitors? (b) The batteries are disconnected and the two capacitors are connected together (+ to + and − to −). Find the charge on each capacitor and the total energy in the two capacitors after they are connected. (c) Explain what happened to the "missing" energy. [*Hint:* The wires that connect the two have some resistance.]

107. In a pacemaker used by a heart patient, a capacitor with a capacitance of 25 µF is charged to 1.0 V and then discharged through the heart every 0.80 s. What is the average discharge current?

108. A certain electrical device has the current-voltage (*I-V*) graph shown with Problem 26. What is the power dissipated at points 1 and 2?

109. A 1.5-horsepower motor operates on 120 V. Ignoring I^2R losses, how much current does it draw?

© 110. Three identical lightbulbs are connected with wires to an ideal battery. The two terminals on each socket connect to the two terminals of its lightbulb. Wires do *not* connect with one another where they appear to cross in the picture. Neglect the change of the resistances of the filaments due to temperature changes. (a) Which of the schematic circuit diagrams correctly represent(s) the circuit? (List more than one choice if more than one diagram is correct.) (b) Which bulb(s) is/are the brightest? Which is/are the dimmest? Or are they all the same? Explain. (c) Find the current through each bulb if the filament resistances are each 24.0 Ω and the emf is 6.0 V.

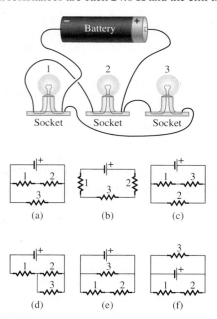

111. Near Earth's surface the air contains both negative and positive ions, due to radioactivity in the soil and cosmic rays from space. As a simplified model, assume there are 600.0 singly charged positive ions per cm³ and 500.0 singly charged negative ions per cm³; ignore the presence of multiply charged ions. The electric field is 100.0 V/m, directed downward. (a) In which direction do the positive ions move? The negative ions? (b) What is the direction of the current due to these ions? (c) The measured resistivity of the air in the region is 4.0×10^{13} Ω·m. Calculate the drift speed of the ions, assuming it to be the same for positive and negative ions. [*Hint:* Consider a vertical tube of air of length *L* and cross-sectional area *A*. How is the potential difference across the tube related to the electric field strength?] (d) If these conditions existed over the entire surface of the Earth, what is the total current due to the movement of ions in the air?

© 112. A portable radio requires an emf of 4.5 V. Oliver has only two nonrechargeable 1.5-V batteries, but he finds a larger 6.0-V battery. (a) How can he arrange the batteries to produce an emf of 4.5 V? Draw a circuit diagram. (b) Is it advisable to use this combination with his radio? Explain.

113. We can model some of the electrical properties of an unmyelinated axon as an electrical cable covered with defective insulation so that current leaks out of the axon to the surrounding fluid. We assume the axon consists of a cylindrical membrane filled with conducting fluid. A current of ions can travel along the axon in this fluid and can also leak out through the membrane. The inner radius of the cylinder is 5.0 µm; the membrane thickness is 8.0 nm. (a) If the resistivity of the axon fluid is 2.0 Ω·m, calculate the resistance of a 1.0-cm length of axon to current flow along its length. (b) If the resistivity of the porous membrane is 2.5×10^7 Ω·m, calculate the resistance of the wall of a 1.0-cm length of axon to current flow across the membrane. (c) Find the length of axon for which the two resistances are equal. This length is a rough measure of the distance a signal can travel without amplification.

114. A piece of gold wire of length *L* has a resistance R_0. Suppose the wire is drawn out so that its length increases by a factor of three. What is the new resistance *R* in terms of the original resistance?

115. A voltmeter with a resistance of 670 kΩ is used to measure the voltage across the 83.0-kΩ resistor in the figure with Problems 78 and 79. What is the voltmeter reading?

116. A gold wire and an aluminum wire have the same dimensions and carry the same current. The electron density (in electrons/cm³) in aluminum is three times larger than the density in gold. How do the drift speeds of the electrons in the two wires, v_{Au} and v_{Al}, compare?

© 117. (a) Given two identical, ideal batteries (emf = $\mathscr{E}$) and two identical lightbulbs (resistance = *R* assumed constant), design a circuit to make both bulbs glow as brightly as possible. (b) What is the power dissipated by each bulb? (c) Design a circuit to make both bulbs glow, but one more brightly than the other. Identify the brighter bulb.

118. Two circuits are constructed using identical, ideal batteries (emf = $\mathscr{E}$) and identical lightbulbs (resistance = *R*). If

each bulb in circuit 1 dissipates 5.0 W of power, how much power does each bulb in circuit 2 dissipate? Ignore changes in the resistance of the bulbs due to temperature changes.

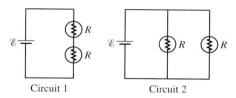

Circuit 1   Circuit 2

119. Given two identical, ideal batteries of emf $\mathscr{E}$ and two identical lightbulbs of resistance R (assumed constant), find the total power dissipated in the circuit in terms of $\mathscr{E}$ and R.

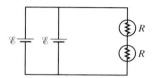

120. Consider a 60.0-W lightbulb and a 100.0-W lightbulb designed for use in a household lamp socket at 120 V. (a) What are the resistances of these two bulbs? (b) If they are wired together in a series circuit, which bulb shines brighter (dissipates more power)? Explain. (c) If they are connected in parallel in a circuit, which bulb shines brighter? Explain.

121. A 500-W electric heater unit is designed to operate with an applied potential difference of 120 V. (a) If the local power company imposes a voltage reduction to lighten its load, dropping the voltage to 110 V, by what percentage does the heat output of the heater drop? (Assume the resistance does not change.) (b) If you took the variation of resistance with temperature into account, would the actual drop in heat output be larger or smaller than calculated in part (a)?

122. Copper and aluminum are being considered for the cables in a high-voltage transmission line where each must carry a current of 50 A. The resistance of each cable is to be 0.15 Ω per kilometer. (a) If this line carries power from Niagara Falls to New York City (approximately 500 km), how much power is lost along the way in the cable? Compute for each choice of cable material (b) the necessary cable diameter and (c) the mass per meter of the cable. The electrical resistivities for copper and aluminum are given in Table 18.1; the mass density of copper is 8920 kg/m³ and that of aluminum is 2702 kg/m³.

123. The circuit is used to study the charging of a capacitor. (a) At $t = 0$, the switch is closed. What initial charging current is measured by the ammeter? (b) After the current has decayed to zero, what are the voltages at points A, B, and C?

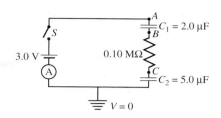

124. A battery with an emf of 1.0 V is connected to a 1.0-kΩ resistor and a diode (a nonohmic device) as shown in part (a) of the figure. The current that flows through the diode for a given voltage drop is shown in part (b) of the figure. (a) What is the current through the diode? (b) What is the current through the battery? (c) What is the total power dissipated in the diode and resistor? (d) Suppose the battery emf were increased so that the power dissipated in the 1.0-kΩ resistor doubled. Would you expect the power dissipated in the diode to double? If not, would it increase by a factor greater than 2 or less than 2? Explain briefly.

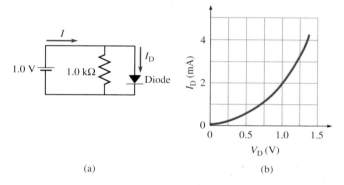

(a)   (b)

125. A parallel plate capacitor is constructed from two square conducting plates of length $L = 0.10$ m on a side. There is air between the plates, which are separated by a distance $d = 89$ μm. The capacitor is connected to a 10.0-V battery. (a) After the capacitor is fully charged, what is the charge on the upper plate? (b) The battery is disconnected from the plates and the capacitor is discharged through a resistor $R = 0.100$ MΩ. Sketch the current through the resistor as a function of time t ($t = 0$ corresponds to the time when R is connected to the capacitor). (c) How much energy is dissipated in R over the whole discharging process?

126. Poiseuille's law [Eq. (9-15)] gives the volume flow rate of a viscous fluid through a pipe. (a) Show that Poiseuille's law can be written in the form $\Delta P = IR$, where $I = \Delta V/\Delta t$ represents the volume flow rate and R is a constant of proportionality called the fluid flow *resistance*. (b) Find R in terms of the viscosity of the

fluid and the length and radius of the pipe. (c) If two or more pipes are connected in series so that the volume flow rate through them is the same, do the resistances of the pipes add as for electrical resistors ($R_{eq} = R_1 + R_2 + \cdots$)? Explain. (d) If two or more pipes are connected in parallel, so the pressure drop across them is the same, do the reciprocals of the resistances add as for electrical resistors ($1/R_{eq} = 1/R_1 + 1/R_2 + \cdots$)? Explain.

127. The *Wheatstone bridge* is a circuit used to measure unknown resistances. The bridge in the figure is balanced—no current flows through the galvanometer. What is the unknown resistance R_x? [*Hint:* What is the potential difference between points A and B?]

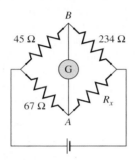

18.1 (a) 2.00×10^{15} electrons; (b) 52 min

18.2 (a) 0.33 A; (b) 6.7 μm/s

18.3 6.9 Ω

18.4 292°C

18.5 1.495 V

18.6 1.0 Ω

18.7 $\frac{1}{3}R$ (the resistors are in parallel)

18.8 $+(0.58 \text{ A})(4.0 \,\Omega) - 1.5 \text{ V} - 3.0 \text{ V} + (0.72 \text{ A})(3.0 \,\Omega) = 0.0$

18.9 1.1 W; 190 J

18.10 10.0 mΩ; 10.0 mΩ

18.11 2.4 μA; 0.38 μC; 44 nA; 0.60 μC

REVIEW AND SYNTHESIS: CHAPTERS 16–18

Review Exercises

1. A hollow metal sphere carries a charge of 6.0 μC. An identical sphere carries a charge of 18.0 μC. The two spheres are brought into contact with each other, then separated. How much charge is on each?

2. A hollow metal sphere carries a charge of 6.0 μC. A second hollow metal sphere with a radius that is double the size of the first carries a charge of 18.0 μC. The two spheres are brought into contact with each other, then separated. How much charge is on each?

3. Three point charges are placed on the corners of an equilateral triangle having sides of 0.150 m. What is the total electrical force on the 2.50-μC charge?

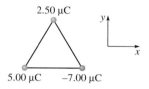

4. Two point charges are located on a coordinate system as follows: $Q_1 = -4.5$ μC at $x = 1.00$ cm and $y = 1.00$ cm and $Q_2 = 6.0$ μC at $x = 3.00$ cm and $y = 1.00$ cm. (a) What is the electric field at point P located at $x = 1.00$ cm and $y = 4.00$ cm? (b) When a 5.0-g tiny particle with a charge of -2.0 μC is placed at point P and released, what is its initial acceleration?

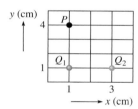

5. Object A has mass 90.0 g and hangs from an insulated thread. When object B, which has a charge of +130 nC, is held nearby, A is attracted to it. In equilibrium, A hangs at an angle $\theta = 7.20°$ with respect to the vertical and is 5.00 cm to the left of B. (a) What is the charge on A? (b) What is the tension in the thread?

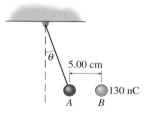

6. A lightbulb filament is made of tungsten. At room temperature of 20.0°C the filament has a resistance of 10.0 Ω. (a) What is the power dissipated in the lightbulb immediately after it is connected to a 120-V emf (when the filament is still at 20.0°C)? (b) After a brief time, the lightbulb filament has changed temperature and it glows brightly. The current is now 0.833 A. What is the resistance of the lightbulb now? (c) What is the power dissipated in the lightbulb when it is glowing brightly as in part (b)? (d) What is the temperature of the filament when it is glowing brightly? (e) Explain why lightbulbs usually burn out when they are first turned on rather than after they have been glowing for a long time.

7. Electrons in a cathode ray tube start from rest and are accelerated through a potential difference of 12.0 kV. They are moving in the +x-direction when they enter the space between the plates of a parallel plate capacitor. There is a potential difference of 320 V between the plates. The plates have length 8.50 cm and are separated by 1.10 cm. The electron beam is deflected in the negative y-direction by the electric field between the plates. What is the change in the y-position of the beam as it leaves the capacitor?

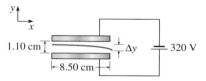

8. A 35.0-nC charge is placed at the origin and a 55.0-nC charge is placed on the +x-axis, 2.20 cm from the origin. (a) What is the electric potential at a point halfway between these two objects? (b) What is the electric potential at a point on the +x-axis 3.40 cm from the origin? (c) How much work does it take for an external agent to move a 45.0-nC charge from the point in (b) to the point in (a)?

9. In the circuit shown, $R_1 = 15.0$ Ω, $R_2 = R_4 = 40.0$ Ω, $R_3 = 20.0$ Ω, and $R_5 = 10.0$ Ω. (a) What is the equivalent resistance of this circuit? (b) What current flows through resistor R_1? (c) What is the total power dissipated by this circuit? (d) What is the potential difference across R_3? (e) What current flows through R_3? (f) What is the power dissipated in R_3?

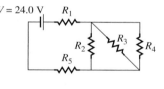

10. An electron with a velocity of 10.0 m/s in the positive y-direction enters a region where there is a uniform electric field of 200 V/m in the positive x-direction. What are the x- and y-components of the electron's displacement 2.40 μs after entering the electric-field region if no other forces act on it?

11. A proton is fired directly at a lithium nucleus. If the proton's velocity is 5.24×10^5 m/s when it is far from the nucleus, how close will the two particles get to each other before the proton stops and turns around?

12. An electron is suspended in a vacuum between two oppositely charged horizontal parallel plates. The separation between the plates is 3.00 mm. (a) What are the signs of the charge on the upper and on the lower plates? (b) What is the voltage across the plates?

13. Consider the circuit in the diagram. (a) After the switch S has been closed for a long time, what is the current through the 12-Ω resistor? (b) What is the voltage across the capacitor?

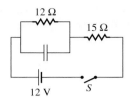

14. Consider the circuit in the diagram. Current $I_1 = 2.50$ A. Find the values of (a) I_2, (b) I_3, and (c) R_3.

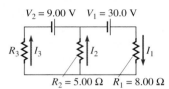

15. A large parallel plate capacitor has plate separation of 1.00 cm and plate area of 314 cm². The capacitor is connected across an emf of 20.0 V and has air between the plates. With the emf still connected, a slab of strontium titanate is inserted so that it completely fills the gap between the plates. Does the charge on the plates increase or decrease? By how much?

Ⓒ 16. A *potentiometer* is a circuit to measure emfs. In the diagram with switch S_1 closed and S_2 open, there is no current through the galvanometer G for $R_1 = 20.0\ \Omega$ with a standard cell $\mathcal{E}_s$ of 2.00 V. With switch S_2 closed and S_1 open, there is no current through the galvanometer G for $R_2 = 80.0\ \Omega$. (a) What is the unknown emf $\mathcal{E}_x$? (b) Explain why the potentiometer accurately measures the emf even for a source with substantial internal resistance.

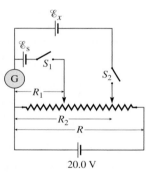

17. In the circuit, $\mathcal{E} = 45.0$ V and $R = 100.0\ \Omega$. If a voltage $V_x = 30.0$ V is needed for a circuit, what should resistance R_x be?

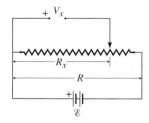

Ⓒ 18. An ideal emf $\mathcal{E}$ is used to charge a capacitor C through a
✦ resistor R. (a) What is the final charge on the capacitor? (b) What is the final energy stored in the capacitor? (c) What is the total electrical energy supplied by the emf? [*Hint:* Use your answer to part (a).] (d) Explain why the final energy stored in the capacitor is less than the total electrical energy supplied by the emf.

19. A parallel plate capacitor has 10.0-cm-diameter circular plates that are separated by 2.00 mm of dry air. (a) What is the maximum charge that can be on this capacitor? (b) A neoprene dielectric is placed between the plates, filling the entire region between the plates. What is the new maximum charge that can be placed on this capacitor?

✦ 20. What are the ratios of the resistances of (a) silver and (b) aluminum wire to the resistance of copper wire (R_{Ag}/R_{Cu} and R_{Al}/R_{Cu}) for wires of the same length and the same *mass* (not the same diameter)? (c) Which material is the best conductor, for wires of equal length and equal mass? The densities are: silver 10.1×10^3 kg/m³; copper 8.9×10^3 kg/m³; aluminum 2.7×10^3 kg/m³.

21. A parallel plate capacitor used in a flash for a camera must be able to store 32 J of energy when connected to 300 V. (Most electronic flashes actually use a 1.5- to 6.0-V battery, but increase the effective voltage using a dc–dc inverter.) (a) What should be the capacitance of this capacitor? (b) If this capacitor has an area of 9.0 m², and a distance between the plates of 1.1×10^{-6} m, what is the dielectric constant of the material between the plates? (The large effective area can be put into a small volume by rolling the capacitor tightly in a cylinder.) (c) Assuming the capacitor completely discharges to produce a flash in 4.0×10^{-3} s, what average power is dissipated in the flashbulb during this time? (d) If the distance between the plates of the capacitor could be reduced to half its value, how much energy would the capacitor store if charged to the same voltage?

22. Consider the camera flash in Problem 21. If the flash really discharges according to Eq. (18-26), then it takes an infinite amount of time to discharge. When Problem 21 assumes that the capacitor discharges in 4.0×10^{-3} s, we mean that the capacitor has almost no charge stored on it after that amount of time. Suppose that after 4.0×10^{-3} s the capacitor has only 1.0% of the original charge still on it. (a) What is the time constant of this RC circuit? (b) What is the resistance of the flashbulb in this case? (c) What is the maximum power dissipated in the flashbulb?

✦✦ 23. This problem illustrates the ideas behind the Millikan oil drop experiment—the first measurement of the electron charge. Millikan examined a fine spray of spherical oil droplets falling through air; the drops had picked up an electric charge as they were sprayed through an atomizer. He measured the terminal speed of a drop when there was no electric field and the electric field that kept the drop motionless between the plates of a capacitor. (a) With no electric field, the forces acting on the oil droplet were the gravitational force, the buoyant force, and the viscous drag. The droplets used were so tiny (a radius of about one thousandth of a millimeter) that they rapidly reached terminal velocity. Find the radius R of a drop in terms of the terminal velocity (v_t), the densities of the oil and of air (ρ_{oil} and ρ_{air}), the viscosity (η), and the gravitational field strength (*g*). [*Hint:* At terminal velocity, the net force on the drop is zero. Use Stokes's law, Eq. (9-16), and don't forget buoyancy.] (b) Find the charge *q* of a drop in terms of the electric field strength between the plates (*E*), the distance between the plates (*d*), the radius of the drop (*R*), the densities of the oil and of air (ρ_{oil} and ρ_{air}), and the gravitational field strength (*g*). [*Hint:* The net force is again zero. There is an electric force but no viscous force (since the drop is at rest).]

MCAT Review

The section that follows includes MCAT exam material and is reprinted with permission of the Association of American Medical Colleges (AAMC).

1. At a given temperature, the resistance of a wire to direct current depends only on the

    A. voltage applied across the wire.

    B. resistivity, length, and voltage.

    C. voltage, length, and cross-sectional area.

    D. resistivity, length, and cross-sectional area.

Refer to the two paragraphs about the holding tank for synthetic lubricating oil in the MCAT Review section for Chapters 13–15. Based on those paragraphs, answer the following two questions.

2. What electric current is required to run all of the heaters at maximum power output from a single 600-V power supply?

    A. 7.2 A

    B. 24.0 A

    C. 83.0 A

    D. 120.0 A

3. In another test, the 10 heaters are exchanged for 5 larger heaters that each use a current of 20 A from an 800-V power supply. What is the total power usage of the 5 new heaters?

    A. 16 kW

    B. 32 kW

    C. 80 kW

    D. 320 kW

Read the paragraph and then answer the following questions:

The diagram shows a small water heater that uses an electrical current to supply energy to heat water. A heating element, R_L, is immersed in the water and acts as a 1.0-Ω load resistor. A dc source is mounted on the outside of the water heater and is wired in parallel with a 2.0-Ω resistor (R_S) and the load resistor. When the water is being heated, the current source supplies a steady current (*I*) of 0.5 A to the circuit. The water heater has a heat capacity of *C* and holds 1.0×10^{-3} m^3 of water. The water has a mass of 1.0 kg. The entire system is thermally isolated and designed to

maintain an approximately constant temperature of 60°C. [*Note:* The specific heat of water (c_w) = 4.2×10^3 J/(kg·°C).]

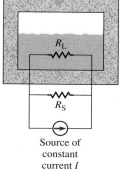

Source of constant current *I*

4. What is the voltage drop across R_L?

    A. 0.22 V

    B. 0.33 V

    C. 0.75 V

    D. 1.50 V

5. If the equipment outside the water heater is changed so that *I* is 1.2 A and R_S is 3.0 Ω, how much power will be dissipated in R_S?

    A. 0.27 W

    B. 0.40 W

    C. 1.08 W

    D. 4.32 W

6. As current flows through R_L, which of the following quantities does *not* increase?

    A. Entropy of the system

    B. Temperature of the system

    C. Total energy in the water

    D. Power dissipated in R_L

7. If the power source used for the water heater is a battery, which of the following best describes the energy transfers that take place when the current is flowing through the circuit in the water-heater system?

    A. Chemical to electrical to heat

    B. Chemical to heat to electrical

    C. Electrical to chemical to heat

    D. Electrical to heat to chemical

8. If the resistance of R_L increased as a function of time, which of the following quantities would also increase with time?

    A. Power dissipated in R_L

    B. Current through R_L

    C. Current through R_S

    D. Resistance of R_S

9. If a different current source caused R_L to dissipate power into the water at a rate of 1.0 W, how long would it take to increase the temperature of the water by 1.0°C? [*Note:* Assume that the heat used to heat the heating element and insulation is negligible.]

    A. 70 s

    B. 420 s

    C. 700 s

    D. 4200 s

Read the passage and then answer the following questions:

Electric power is generally transmitted to consumers by overhead wires. To reduce power loss due to heat, utility companies strive to reduce the magnitudes of both the current (I) through the wires and the resistance (R) of the wires.

A reduction in R requires the use of highly conductive materials and large wires. The size of wires is limited by the cost of materials and weight. The table lists the resistances and masses of 1000-m sections of copper wires of different diameters at two different temperatures.

Diameter (m)	Resistance per 10^3 m at 25°C (Ω)	Resistance per 10^3 m at 65°C (Ω)	Mass per 10^3 m (kg)
6.6×10^{-2}	7.2×10^{-3}	8.2×10^{-3}	2.4×10^{4}
2.9×10^{-2}	3.5×10^{-2}	4.1×10^{-2}	4.6×10^{3}
2.1×10^{-2}	7.1×10^{-2}	8.2×10^{-2}	2.3×10^{3}
9.5×10^{-3}	3.4×10^{-1}	3.8×10^{-1}	4.9×10^{2}

Safety and technical equipment considerations limit voltage. Because electricity is transmitted at high voltage levels for long-distance transmission, transformers are needed to lower the voltage to safer levels before entering residences.

10. If a residence uses 1.2×10^4 W at 120 V, how much current is required?

    A. 10 A

    B. 12 A

    C. 100 A

    D. 120 A

11. Based on the table, if the temperature changes from 25°C to 65°C in a 10^5-m section of 9.5×10^{-3}-m-diameter wire, approximately how much will the wire's resistance change?

    A. 0.04 Ω

    B. 0.4 Ω

    C. 4.0 Ω

    D. 40 Ω

12. How much power is lost to heat in a transmission line with a resistance of 3 Ω that carries 2 A?

    A. 1.5 W

    B. 6 W

    C. 12 W

    D. 18 W

13. In order to supply 10 residences with 10^4 W of power each over a grid that loses 5×10^3 W of power to heat, how much power is needed?

    A. 1.5×10^4 W

    B. 5.25×10^4 W

    C. 1.05×10^5 W

    D. 1.5×10^5 W

Magnetic Forces and Fields

Chapter 19

Some bacteria live in the mud at the bottom of the sea. As long as they are in the mud, all is well. Suppose that the mud gets stirred up, perhaps by a crustacean walking by. Now things are not so rosy. The bacteria cannot survive for long in the water, so it is imperative that they swim back down to the mud as soon as possible. The problem is that knowing which direction is down is not so easy. The mass density of the bacteria is almost identical to that of water, so the buoyant force prevents them from "feeling" the downward pull of gravity. Nevertheless, the bacteria are somehow able to swim in the correct direction to get back to the mud. How do they do it? (See p. 691 for the answer.)

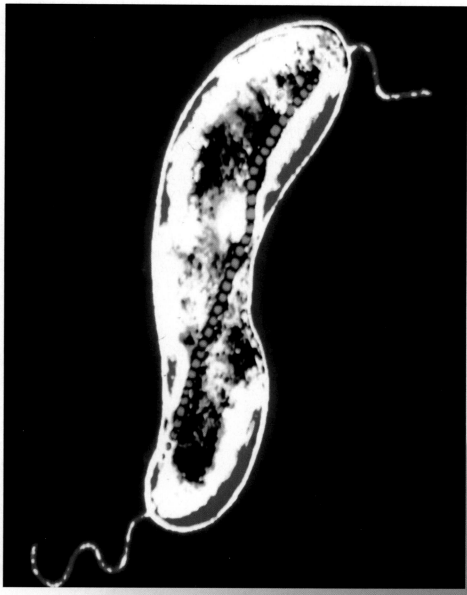

Electron micrograph of a magnetotactic bacterium

Concepts & Skills to Review

● sketching and interpreting electric field lines (Section 16.4)
● uniform circular motion; radial acceleration (Section 5.2)
● torque; lever arm (Section 8.2)
● relation between current and drift velocity (Section 18.3)

Working model of a spoon-shaped compass from the Han Dynasty (202 BCE to 220 CE). The spoon, made of lodestone (magnetite ore) rests on a bronze plate called a "heaven-plate" or diviner's board. The earliest Chinese compasses were used for prognostication; only much later were they used as navigation aids. The model was constructed by Susan Silverman.

● Symbol for magnetic field: $\vec{B}$

19.1   MAGNETIC FIELDS

Permanent Magnets

Permanent magnets have been known at least since the time of the ancient Greeks, about 2500 years ago. A naturally occurring iron ore called lodestone (now called magnetite) was mined in various places, including the region of modern-day Turkey called Magnesia. Some of the chunks of lodestone were permanent magnets; they exerted magnetic forces on each other and on iron and could be used to turn a piece of iron into a permanent magnet. In China, the magnetic compass was used as a navigational aid at least a thousand years ago—possibly much earlier. Not until 1820 was a connection between electricity and magnetism established, when Danish scientist Hans Christian Oersted (1777–1851) discovered that a compass needle is deflected by a nearby electric current.

Figure 19.1a shows a plate of glass lying on top of a bar magnet. Iron filings have been sprinkled on the glass and then the glass has been tapped to shake the filings a bit and allow them to move around. The filings have lined up with the **magnetic field** (symbol: $\vec{B}$) due to the bar magnet. Figure 19.1b shows a sketch of the magnetic field lines representing this magnetic field. As is true for electric field lines, the magnetic field lines represent both the magnitude and direction of the magnetic field vector. The magnetic field vector at any point is tangent to the field line and the magnitude of the field is proportional to the number of lines per unit area perpendicular to the lines.

Figure 19.1b may strike you as being similar to a sketch of the electric field lines for an electric dipole (Fig. 16.25). The similarity is not a coincidence; the bar magnet is one instance of a **magnetic dipole**. By *dipole* we mean *two opposite poles*. In an electric dipole, the electric poles are positive and negative electric charges. A magnetic dipole consists of two opposite magnetic poles. The end of the bar magnet where the field lines emerge is called the **north pole** and the end where the lines go back in is

Figure 19.1 (a) Photo of a bar magnet. Nearby iron filings line up with the magnetic field. (b) Sketch of the magnetic field lines due to the bar magnet. The magnetic field vectors are tangent to the field lines.

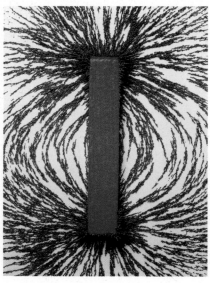

(a)

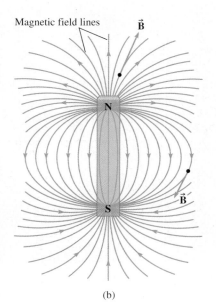

(b)

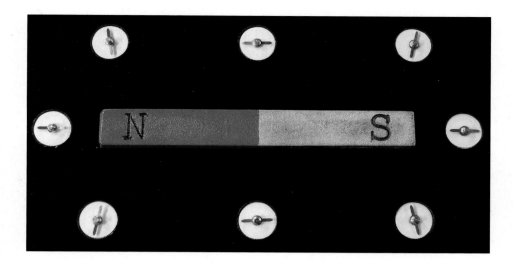

Figure 19.2 Each compass needle is aligned with the magnetic field due to the bar magnet. The "north" (red) end of each needle points in the direction of the magnetic field.

called the **south pole**. If two magnets are near each other, opposite poles (the north pole of one magnet and the south pole of the other) exert attractive forces on one another; like poles (two north poles or two south poles) repel each other.

The names *north pole* and *south pole* are derived from magnetic compasses. A compass is simply a small bar magnet that is free to rotate. Any magnetic dipole, including a compass needle, feels a torque that tends to line it up with an external magnetic field (Fig. 19.2). The north pole of the compass needle is the end that points in the direction of the magnetic field. In a compass, the bar magnet needle is mounted to minimize frictional and other torques so it can swing freely in response to a magnetic field.

Making the Connection:
magnetic compass

PHYSICS AT HOME

Obtain a flexible magnetic card. With scissors, cut a thin strip (about 2 mm wide) from one edge. Rub the back of the strip across the back of the remaining piece. Try both orientations (both parallel and perpendicular to the side from which the strip was cut). Repeat with a strip cut from an adjacent side of the card. Estimate the orientation and the size of the magnetized strips. (See Fig. 19.3b.)

Permanent magnets come in many shapes other than the bar magnet. Figure 19.3 shows some others, with the magnetic field lines sketched. Notice in Fig. 19.3a that if the pole faces are parallel and close together, the magnetic field between them is nearly uniform. A magnet need not have only two poles; it must have *at least* one north pole and *at least* one south pole. Some magnets are designed to have a large number of north and south poles. The flexible magnetic card (Fig. 19.3b), commonly found on refrigerator doors, is designed to have many poles, both north and south, on one side and no poles on the other. The magnetic field is strong near the side with the poles and weak near the other side; the card sticks to an iron surface (such as a refrigerator door) on one side but not on the other.

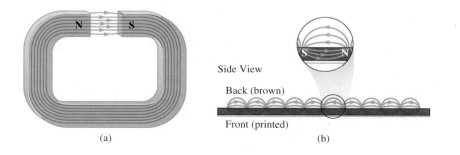

(a)   (b)

Figure 19.3 Two permanent magnets with their magnetic field lines. In (a), the magnetic field between the pole faces is nearly uniform. (b) A refrigerator magnet (shown here in a side view) has many poles.

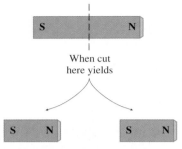

When cut
here yields

Figure 19.4 Sketch of a bar magnet that is subsequently cut in half. Each piece has both a north and a south pole.

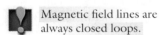

Magnetic field lines are always closed loops.

Just as like charges repel and unlike charges attract, like magnetic poles repel and unlike poles attract. However, there is an important difference between electricity and magnetism. Coulomb's law for electrical forces gives the force acting between two point charges—two electric *monopoles*. However, as far as we know, there are no *magnetic* monopoles—that is, there is no such thing as an isolated north pole or an isolated south pole. If you take a bar magnet and cut it in half, you do not obtain one piece with a north pole and another piece with a south pole. Both pieces are magnetic dipoles (Fig. 19.4). There have been theoretical predictions of the existence of magnetic monopoles, but years of experiments have yet to turn up a single one. If magnetic monopoles do exist in our universe, they must be extremely rare.

Magnetic Field Lines

Figure 19.1a may suggest that magnetic field lines begin on north poles and end on south poles, but they do not: *magnetic field lines are all closed loops*. If there are no magnetic monopoles, there is no place for the field lines to begin or end, so they *must* be closed loops. Contrast Fig. 19.1b with Fig. 16.25—the field lines for an electric dipole. The field line patterns are similar away from the dipole, but nearby and between the poles they are quite different. The electric field lines are not closed loops; they start on the positive charge and end on the negative charge.

Despite these differences between electric and magnetic field lines, the *interpretation* of magnetic field lines is exactly the same as for electric field lines:

Interpretation of Magnetic Field Lines

- The direction of the magnetic field vector at any point is *tangent to the field line* passing through that point and is in the direction indicated by arrows on the field line (as in Fig. 19.1b).
- The magnetic field is strong where field lines are close together and weak where they are far apart. More specifically, if you imagine a small surface perpendicular to the field lines, the magnitude of the magnetic field is proportional to the number of lines that cross the surface, divided by the area.

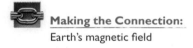

Making the Connection:
Earth's magnetic field

The Earth's Magnetic Field

Figure 19.5 shows field lines for the Earth's magnetic field. Near Earth's surface, the magnetic field is approximately that of a dipole, as if a bar magnet were buried at the center of the Earth. Farther away from Earth's surface, the dipole field is distorted by

Figure 19.5 Earth's magnetic field. The diagram shows the magnetic field lines in one plane. In general, the magnetic field at the surface has both horizontal and vertical components. The magnetic poles are the points where the magnetic field at the surface is purely vertical. The magnetic poles do not coincide with the geographic poles, which are the points at which the axis of rotation intersects the surface. Near the surface, the field is approximately that of a dipole, like that of the fictitious bar magnet shown. Note that the south pole of this bar magnet points toward the Arctic and the north pole points toward the Antarctic.

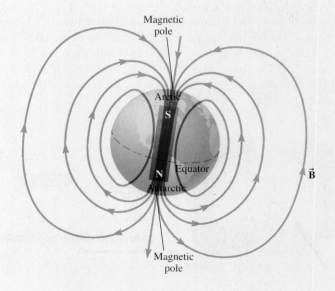

the solar wind—charged particles streaming from the Sun toward the Earth. As discussed in Section 19.8, moving charged particles create their own magnetic fields, so the solar wind has a magnetic field associated with it.

In most places on the surface, the Earth's magnetic field is not horizontal; it has a significant vertical component. The vertical component can be measured directly using a *dip meter*, which is just a compass mounted so that it can rotate in a vertical plane. In the northern hemisphere, the vertical component is downward, while in the southern hemisphere it is upward. In other words, magnetic field lines emerge from Earth's surface in the southern hemisphere and reenter in the northern hemisphere. A magnetic dipole that is free to rotate aligns itself with the magnetic field such that the north end of the dipole points in the direction of the field. Figure 19.2 shows a bar magnet with several compasses in the vicinity. Each compass needle points in the direction of the local magnetic field, which in this case is due to the magnet. A compass is normally used to detect the Earth's magnetic field. In a horizontally mounted compass, the needle is free to rotate only in a horizontal plane, so its north end points in the direction of the *horizontal component* of the Earth's field.

Note the orientation of the fictitious bar magnet in Fig. 19.5: the south pole of the magnet faces roughly toward geographic *north* and the north pole of the magnet faces roughly toward geographic *south.* The field lines emerge from Earth's surface in the southern hemisphere and return in the northern hemisphere.

The origin of the Earth's magnetic field is still under investigation. According to a leading theory, the field is created by electric currents in the molten iron and nickel of Earth's outer core, more than 3000 km below the surface. The Earth's magnetic field is slowly changing. In 1948, Canadian scientists discovered that the location of Earth's magnetic pole in the Arctic was about 250 km away from where it was found in 1831 by a British explorer. The magnetic poles move about 40 km per year. The magnetic poles have undergone a complete reversal in polarity (north becomes south and south becomes north) roughly 100 times in the past 5 million years. The most recent Geological Survey of Canada, completed in May 2001, located the north magnetic pole—the point on Earth's surface where the magnetic field points straight down—at 81°N latitude and 111°W longitude, about 1600 km south of the geographic north pole (the point where Earth's rotation axis intersects the surface, at 90°N latitude).

Magnetotactic Bacteria

Making the Connection:
magnetotactic bacteria

In the electron micrograph of the bacterium shown with the chapter opener, a line of crystals (stained orange) stands out. They are crystals of magnetite, the same iron oxide (Fe_3O_4) that was known to the ancient Greeks. The crystals are tiny permanent magnets that function essentially as compass needles. When the bacteria get stirred up into the water, their compass needles automatically rotate to line up with the magnetic field. As the bacteria swim along, they follow a magnetic field line. In the northern hemisphere, the north end of the "compass needle" faces forward. The bacteria swim in the direction of the magnetic field, which has a downward component, so they return to their home in the mud. Bacteria in the southern hemisphere have the south pole forward; they must swim opposite to the magnetic field since the field has an *upward* component. If some of these *magnetotactic* (*-tactic* = feeling or sensing) bacteria are brought from the southern hemisphere to the northern, or *vice versa*, they swim up instead of down!

There is evidence of magnetic navigation in several species of bacteria and also in some higher organisms. Experiments with homing pigeons, robins, and bees have shown that these organisms have some magnetic sense. On sunny days, they primarily use the Sun's location for navigation, but on overcast days they use the Earth's magnetic field. Permanently magnetized crystals, similar to those found in the mud bacteria, have been found in the brains of these organisms, but the mechanism by which they can sense the Earth's field and use it to navigate is not understood. Some experiments have shown that even humans may have some sense of the Earth's magnetic field, which is not out of the realm of possibility since tiny magnetite crystals have been found in the brain.

19.2 MAGNETIC FORCE ON A POINT CHARGE

Before we go into more detail on the magnetic forces and torques on a magnetic dipole, we need to start with the simpler case of the magnetic force on a point charge. In Chapter 16 we defined the electric field as the electric force per unit charge. A point charge q located where the electric field is $\vec{\mathbf{E}}$ experiences an electric force

$$\vec{\mathbf{F}}_E = q\vec{\mathbf{E}} \qquad \text{(16-4b)}$$

The electric force is either in the same direction as $\vec{\mathbf{E}}$ or in the opposite direction, depending on the sign of the point charge.

The magnetic force on a point charge is more complicated—it is *not* the charge times the magnetic field. The magnetic force *depends on the point charge's velocity* as well as on the magnetic field. If the point charge is at rest, there is no magnetic force. The magnitude and direction of the magnetic force depend on the direction and speed of the charge's motion. We have learned about other velocity-dependent forces, such as the drag force on an object moving through a fluid. Like drag forces, the magnetic force increases in magnitude with increasing velocity. However, the direction of the drag force is always opposite to the object's velocity, while the direction of the magnetic force on a charged particle is *perpendicular* to the velocity of the particle.

Imagine that a positive point charge q moves at velocity $\vec{\mathbf{v}}$ at a point where the magnetic field is $\vec{\mathbf{B}}$. The angle between $\vec{\mathbf{v}}$ and $\vec{\mathbf{B}}$ is θ (Fig. 19.6a). The magnitude of the magnetic force acting on the point charge is the product of

- The magnitude of the charge $|q|$,
- The magnitude of the field B, and
- The component of the velocity perpendicular to the field (Fig. 19.6b).

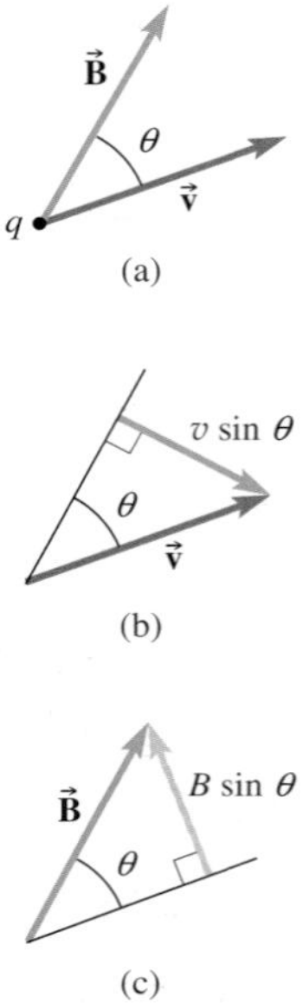

> **Magnitude of the magnetic force on a moving point charge:**
>
> $$F_B = |q|v_\perp B = |q|(v\sin\theta)B \qquad \text{(19-1a)}$$
>
> $$\text{(since } v_\perp = v\sin\theta\text{)}$$

Note that if the point charge is at rest ($v = 0$) or if its motion is along the same line as the magnetic field ($v_\perp = 0$), then the magnetic force is zero.

In some cases it is convenient to look at the factor $\sin\theta$ from a different point of view. If we associate the factor $\sin\theta$ with the magnetic field instead of with the velocity, then $B\sin\theta$ is the component of the magnetic field perpendicular to the velocity of the charged particle (Fig. 19.6c):

> $$F_B = |q|v(B\sin\theta) = |q|vB_\perp \qquad \text{(19-1b)}$$

From Eq. (19-1), the SI unit of magnetic field is

$$\frac{\text{force}}{\text{charge} \times \text{velocity}} = \frac{\text{N}}{\text{C}\cdot\text{m/s}} = \frac{\text{N}}{\text{A}\cdot\text{m}}$$

This combination of units is given the name tesla (symbol T) after Nikola Tesla (1856–1943), an American engineer who was born in Croatia.

$$1\ \text{T} = 1\ \frac{\text{N}}{\text{A}\cdot\text{m}} \qquad \text{(19-2)}$$

Cross Product

The direction and magnitude of the magnetic force depend on the vectors $\vec{\mathbf{v}}$ and $\vec{\mathbf{B}}$ in a special way that occurs often in physics and mathematics. The magnetic force can be written in terms of the **cross product** (or *vector product*) of $\vec{\mathbf{v}}$ and $\vec{\mathbf{B}}$. The cross product

 The magnetic force is velocity-dependent.

Figure 19.6 A positive charge moving in a magnetic field. (a) The particle's velocity vector $\vec{\mathbf{v}}$ and the magnetic field vector $\vec{\mathbf{B}}$ are drawn starting at the same point. θ is the angle between them. (b) The component of $\vec{\mathbf{v}}$ perpendicular to $\vec{\mathbf{B}}$ is $v\sin\theta$. (c) The component of $\vec{\mathbf{B}}$ perpendicular to $\vec{\mathbf{v}}$ is $B\sin\theta$.

of two vectors $\vec{a}$ and $\vec{b}$ is written $\vec{a} \times \vec{b}$. The magnitude of the cross product is the magnitude of one vector times the perpendicular component of the other; it doesn't matter which is which.

$$|\vec{a} \times \vec{b}| = |\vec{b} \times \vec{a}| = a_{\perp}b = ab_{\perp} = ab \sin \theta \qquad (19\text{-}3)$$

However, the order of the vectors *does* matter in determining the *direction* of the result. Switching the order reverses the direction of the product:

$$\vec{b} \times \vec{a} = -\vec{a} \times \vec{b} \qquad (19\text{-}4)$$

The cross product of two vectors $\vec{a}$ and $\vec{b}$ is a vector that is perpendicular to both $\vec{a}$ and $\vec{b}$. Note that $\vec{a}$ and $\vec{b}$ do not have to be perpendicular to one another. For any two vectors that are neither in the same direction nor in opposite directions, there are *two* directions perpendicular to both vectors. To choose between the two, we use a **right-hand rule**.

Using Right-Hand Rule I to Find the Direction of a Cross Product $\vec{a} \times \vec{b}$

1. Draw the vectors $\vec{a}$ and $\vec{b}$ starting from the same origin (Fig. 19.7a).
2. The cross product is in one of the two directions that are perpendicular to both $\vec{a}$ and $\vec{b}$. Determine these two directions.
3. Choose one of these two perpendicular directions to test. Place your right hand in a "karate chop" position with your palm at the origin, your fingertips pointing in the direction of $\vec{a}$, and your thumb in the direction you are testing (Fig. 19.7b).
4. Keeping the thumb and palm stationary, curl your fingers inward toward your palm until your fingertips point in the direction of $\vec{b}$ (Fig. 19.7c). If you can do it, sweeping your fingers through an angle less than 180°, then your thumb points in the direction of the cross product $\vec{a} \times \vec{b}$. If you can't do it because your fingers would have to sweep through an angle greater than 180°, then your thumb points in the direction *opposite* to $\vec{a} \times \vec{b}$.

Since magnetism is inherently three-dimensional, we often need to draw vectors that are perpendicular to the page. The symbol • (or ⊙) represents a vector arrow pointing out of the page; think of the tip of an arrow coming toward you. The symbol × (or ⊗) represents a vector pointing into the page; it suggests the tail feathers of an arrow moving away from you.

Direction of the Magnetic Force

The magnetic force on a charged particle can be written as the charge times the cross product of $\vec{v}$ and $\vec{B}$:

Magnetic force on a moving point charge:

$$\vec{F}_B = q\vec{v} \times \vec{B} \qquad (19\text{-}5)$$

Magnitude: $F_B = qvB \sin \theta$

Direction: use the right-hand rule to find $\vec{v} \times \vec{B}$, then reverse it if q is negative.

The direction of the magnetic force is not along the same line as the field (as is the case for the electric field); instead it is *perpendicular*. The force is also perpendicular to the charged particle's velocity. Therefore, if $\vec{v}$ and $\vec{B}$ lie in a plane, the magnetic force is always perpendicular to that plane; magnetism is inherently three-dimensional. A negatively charged particle feels a magnetic force in the direction *opposite* to $\vec{v} \times \vec{B}$; multiplying a *negative* scalar (q) by $\vec{v} \times \vec{B}$ reverses the direction of the magnetic force.

⬤ The cross product of two vectors is perpendicular to both vectors.

⬤ Vector symbols: • or ⊙ = out of the page; × or ⊗ = into the page

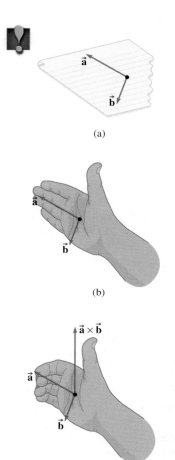

Figure 19.7 Using the right-hand rule to find the direction of a cross product. (a) First we draw the two vectors, $\vec{a}$ and $\vec{b}$, starting at the same point. (b) Initial hand position to test whether $\vec{a} \times \vec{b}$ is up. The thumb points up and the fingers point along $\vec{a}$. (c) The fingers are curled in through an angle < 180° until they point along $\vec{b}$. Therefore, $\vec{a} \times \vec{b}$ is up.

⬤ The magnetic force on a point charge is *perpendicular* to the magnetic field.

Problem-Solving Technique: Finding the Magnetic Force on a Point Charge

1. The magnetic force is zero if (a) the particle is not moving ($\vec{v} = 0$), (b) its velocity has no component perpendicular to the magnetic field ($v_\perp = 0$), or (c) the magnetic field is zero.
2. Otherwise, determine the angle θ between the velocity and magnetic field vectors when the two are drawn starting at the same point.
3. Find the magnitude of the force from $F_B = |q|vB \sin\theta$ [Eq. (19-1)], using the *magnitude* of the charge (since magnitudes of vectors are nonnegative).
4. Determine the direction of $\vec{v} \times \vec{B}$ using the right-hand rule. The magnetic force is in the direction of $\vec{v} \times \vec{B}$ if the charge is positive. If the charge is negative, the force is in the direction *opposite* to $\vec{v} \times \vec{B}$.

Because the magnetic force on a point charge is always perpendicular to the velocity, the magnetic force does no work. If no other forces act on the point charge, then its kinetic energy does not change. The magnetic force, acting alone, changes the *direction* of the velocity *but not the speed* (the magnitude of the velocity).

Conceptual Example 19.1

Deflection of Cosmic Rays

Cosmic rays are charged particles moving toward Earth at high speeds. The origin of the particles is not fully understood, but explosions of supernovae may produce a significant fraction of them. About $\frac{7}{8}$ of the particles are protons that move toward Earth with an average speed of about $\frac{2}{3}$ the speed of light. Suppose that a proton is moving straight down, directly toward the equator. (a) What is the direction of the magnetic force on the proton due to Earth's magnetic field? (b) Explain how the Earth's magnetic field shields us from bombardment by cosmic rays. (c) Where on Earth's surface is this shielding least effective?

Strategy and Solution (a) First we sketch the Earth's magnetic field lines and the velocity vector for the proton (Fig. 19.8). The field lines run from southern hemisphere to northern; high above the equator, the field is approximately horizontal (due north). To find the direction of the magnetic force, first we determine the two directions that are perpendicular to both $\vec{v}$ and $\vec{B}$; then we use the right-hand rule to determine which is the direction of $\vec{v} \times \vec{B}$. Figure 19.9 is a sketch of $\vec{v}$ and $\vec{B}$ in the *xy*-plane. The *x*-axis points away from the equator (up) and the *y*-axis points north. The two directions that are perpendicular to both vectors are perpendicular to the *xy*-plane: into the page and out of the page. Using the right-hand rule, if the thumb points out of the page, the fingers of the right hand would have to curl from $\vec{v}$ to $\vec{B}$ through an angle of 270°. Therefore, $\vec{v} \times \vec{B}$ is into the page (Fig. 19.10). Since $\vec{F}_B = q\vec{v} \times \vec{B}$ and q is positive, the magnetic force is into the page or east.

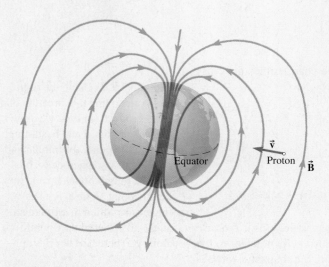

Figure 19.8

A sketch of the Earth, its magnetic field lines, and the velocity vector $\vec{v}$ of the proton.

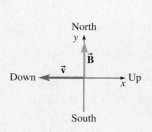

Figure 19.9

The vectors $\vec{v}$ and $\vec{B}$. The *y*-axis points north; the *x*-axis points away from the equator.

Continued on next page

Figure 19.10

The right-hand rule shows that $\vec{v} \times \vec{B}$ is into the page. With the thumb pointing into the page, the fingers sweep from $\vec{v}$ to $\vec{B}$ through an angle of 90°.

Conceptual Example 19.1 Continued

(b) Without the Earth's magnetic field, the proton would move straight down toward Earth's surface. The magnetic field deflects the particle sideways and keeps it from reaching the surface. Many fewer cosmic ray particles reach the surface than would do so if there were no magnetic field.

(c) Near the poles, the component of $\vec{v}$ perpendicular to the field ($v_\perp$) is a small fraction of v. Since the magnetic force is proportional to $v_\perp$, the deflecting force is much less effective near the poles.

 Discussion When finding the direction of the magnetic force (or any cross product), a good

sketch is essential. Since all three dimensions come into play, we must choose the two axes that lie in the plane of the sketch. In this example, both vectors $\vec{v}$ and $\vec{B}$ lie in the plane of the sketch, so we know that $\vec{F}_B$ is perpendicular to that plane.

Practice Problem 19.1   Acceleration of Cosmic Ray Particle

If $v = 6.0 \times 10^7$ m/s and $B = 6.0\ \mu$T, what is the magnitude of the magnetic force on the proton and the magnitude of the proton's acceleration?

Example 19.2

Magnetic Force on an Ion in the Air

At a certain place, the Earth's magnetic field has magnitude 0.50 mT. The field direction is 70.0° below the horizontal; its horizontal component points due north. (a) Find the magnetic force on an oxygen ion (O_2^-) moving due east at 250 m/s. (b) Compare the magnitude of the magnetic force to the ion's weight, 5.2×10^{-25} N, and to the electric force on it due to the Earth's fair-weather electric field (150 N/C downward).

Strategy Since there are two equivalent ways to find the magnitude of the magnetic force [Eq. (19-1)], we choose whichever seems most convenient. To find the direction of the force, first we determine the two directions that are perpendicular to both $\vec{v}$ and $\vec{B}$; then we use the right-hand rule to determine which one is the direction of $\vec{v} \times \vec{B}$. Since we are finding the force on a negatively charged particle, the direction of the magnetic force is *opposite* to the direction of $\vec{v} \times \vec{B}$. Note that the magnitude of the field is specified in *milli*teslas (1 mT = 10^{-3} T).

Solution (a) The ion is moving east; the field has northward and downward components, but no east-west component. Therefore, $\vec{v}$ and $\vec{B}$ are perpendicular; $\theta = 90°$ and $\sin \theta = 1$. The magnitude of the magnetic force is then

$F = |q|vB = (1.6 \times 10^{-19}\ \text{C}) \times 250\ \text{m/s} \times (5.0 \times 10^{-4}\ \text{T})$

$= 2.0 \times 10^{-20}$ N

Since $\vec{v}$ is east and the force must be perpendicular to $\vec{v}$, the force must lie in a plane perpendicular to the east/west axis. We draw the velocity and magnetic field vectors in this plane, using axes that run north/south and up/down (Fig. 19.11a, where east is out of the page). Since north is to the right in this sketch, the viewer looks westward; west is into the page and east is out of the

page. The force $\vec{F}$ must lie in this plane and be perpendicular to $\vec{B}$. There are two possible directions, shown with a dashed line in Fig. 19.11a. Now we try these two directions with the right-hand rule; the correct direction for $\vec{v} \times \vec{B}$ is shown in Fig. 19.11b. Since the ion is negatively charged, the magnetic force is in the direction opposite to $\vec{v} \times \vec{B}$; it is 20.0° below the horizontal, with its horizontal component pointing south.

(b) The electric force has magnitude

$$F_E = |q|E = (1.6 \times 10^{-19}\ \text{C}) \times 150\ \text{N/C} = 2.4 \times 10^{-17}\ \text{N}$$

The magnetic force on the ion is much stronger than the gravitational force and much weaker than the electric force.

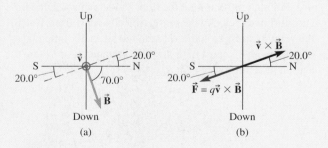

Figure 19.11

(a) The vectors $\vec{v}$ and $\vec{B}$, with $\vec{v}$ out of the page. West is into the page and east is out of the page. Since $\vec{F}$ is perpendicular to both $\vec{v}$ and $\vec{B}$, it must lie along the dashed line. (b) The direction for $\vec{v} \times \vec{B}$ given by the right-hand rule. Since the ion is negatively charged, the magnetic force direction is *opposite* $\vec{v} \times \vec{B}$.

Continued on next page

Example 19.2 Continued

Discussion   Again, a key to solving this sort of problem is drawing a convenient set of axes. If one of the two vectors $\vec{v}$ and $\vec{B}$ lies along a reference direction—a point of the compass, up or down, or along one of the *xyz*-axes—and the other does not, a good choice is to sketch axes in a plane *perpendicular* to that reference direction. In this case, $\vec{v}$ is in a reference direction (east) but $\vec{B}$ is not, so we sketch axes in a plane perpendicular to east.

Practice Problem 19.2   Magnetic Force on an Electron

Find the magnetic force on an *electron* moving straight up at 3.0×10^6 m/s in the same magnetic field. [*Hint:* The angle between $\vec{v}$ and $\vec{B}$ is *not* 90°.]

Example 19.3
Electron in a Magnetic Field

An electron moves with speed 2.0×10^6 m/s in a uniform magnetic field of 1.4 T directed due north. At one instant, the electron experiences an upward magnetic force of 1.6 $\times 10^{-13}$ N. In what direction is the electron moving at that instant? [*Hint:* If there is more than one possible answer, find all the possibilities.]

Strategy   This example is more complicated than Examples 19.1 and 19.2. We need to apply the magnetic force law again, but this time we must deduce the direction of the velocity from the directions of the force and field.

Solution   The magnetic force is always perpendicular to both the magnetic field and the particle's velocity. The force is upward, therefore the velocity must lie in a horizontal plane.

Figure 19.12 shows the magnetic field pointing north and a variety of possibilities for the velocity (all in the horizontal plane). The direction of the magnetic force is up, so the direction of $\vec{v} \times \vec{B}$ must be down since the charge is negative. Pointing the thumb of the right hand downward, the fingers curl in the clockwise sense. Since we curl from $\vec{v}$ to $\vec{B}$, the velocity must be somewhere in the left half of the plane; in other words, it must have a west component in addition to a north or south component.

The westward component is the component of $\vec{v}$ that is perpendicular to the field. Using the magnitude of the force, we can find the perpendicular component of the velocity:

$$F_\text{B} = |q|v_\perp B$$

$$v_\perp = \frac{F_\text{B}}{|q|B} = \frac{1.6 \times 10^{-13} \text{ N}}{1.6 \times 10^{-19} \text{ C} \times 1.4 \text{ T}} = 7.14 \times 10^5 \text{ m/s}$$

The velocity also has a component in the direction of the field that can be found using the Pythagorean theorem:

$$v^2 = v_\perp^2 + v_\parallel^2$$

$$v_\parallel = \pm \sqrt{v^2 - v_\perp^2} = \pm 1.87 \times 10^6 \text{ m/s}$$

The ± sign would seem to imply that $v_\parallel$ could either be a north or a south component. The two possibilities are shown in Fig. 19.13. Use of the right-hand rule confirms that *either* gives $\vec{v} \times \vec{B}$ in the correct direction.

Now we need to find the direction of $\vec{v}$ given its components. From Fig. 19.13,

$$\sin \theta = \frac{v_\perp}{v} = \frac{7.14 \times 10^5 \text{ m/s}}{2.0 \times 10^6 \text{ m/s}} = 0.357$$

$$\theta = 21° \text{ W of N or } 159° \text{ W of N}$$

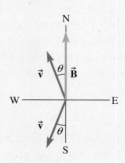

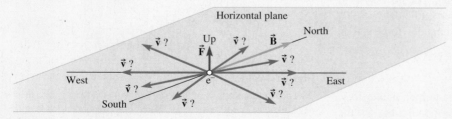

Figure 19.12

The velocity must be perpendicular to the force and thus in the plane shown. Various possibilities for the direction of $\vec{v}$ are considered. Only those in the west half of the plane give the correct direction for $\vec{v} \times \vec{B}$.

Figure 19.13

Two possibilities for the direction of $\vec{v}$.

Continued on next page

Example 19.3 Continued

Since 159° W of N is the same as 21° W of S, the direction of the velocity is either 21° W of N or 21° W of S.

Discussion   We *cannot* assume that $\vec{v}$ is perpendicular to $\vec{B}$. The magnetic force is always perpendicular to both $\vec{v}$ and $\vec{B}$, but there can be any angle between $\vec{v}$ and $\vec{B}$.

Practice Problem 19.3   Velocity Component Parallel to the Field

Suppose the electron moves with the same speed in the same magnetic field. If the magnetic force on the electron has magnitude 2.0×10^{-13} N, what is the component of the electron's velocity parallel to the magnetic field?

19.3   CHARGED PARTICLE MOVING PERPENDICULARLY TO A UNIFORM MAGNETIC FIELD

Using the magnetic force law and Newton's second law of motion, we can deduce the trajectory of a charged particle moving in a uniform magnetic field with no other forces acting. In this section, we discuss a case of particular interest: when the particle is initially moving perpendicularly to the magnetic field.

Figure 19.14a shows the magnetic force on a positively charged particle moving perpendicularly to a magnetic field. Since $v_\perp = v$, the magnitude of the force is

$$F = |q|vB \tag{19-6}$$

Since the force is perpendicular to the velocity, the particle changes direction but not speed. The force is also perpendicular to the field, so there is no acceleration component in the direction of $\vec{B}$. Thus, the particle's velocity remains perpendicular to $\vec{B}$. As the velocity changes direction, the magnetic force changes direction to stay perpendicular to both $\vec{v}$ and $\vec{B}$. The magnetic force acts as a steering force, curving the particle around in a trajectory of radius r at constant speed. The particle undergoes uniform circular motion, so its acceleration is directed radially inward and has magnitude v^2/r. From Newton's second law,

$$a_r = \frac{v^2}{r} = \frac{F}{m} = \frac{|q|vB}{m} \tag{19-7}$$

where m is the mass of the particle. Since the radius of the trajectory is constant—r depends only on q, v, B, and m, which are all constant—the particle moves in a circle at constant speed (Fig. 19.14b). Negative charges move in the opposite sense from positive charges in the same field (Fig. 19.14c).

Magnetic fields can cause charges to move along circular paths.

Bubble Chamber

The circular motion of charged particles in uniform magnetic fields has many applications. The *bubble chamber*, invented by American physicist Donald Glaser (1926–), is a particle detector that was used in high-energy physics experiments from the 1950s into the 1970s. The chamber is filled with liquid hydrogen and is immersed in a magnetic field.

Making the Connection:
bubble chamber

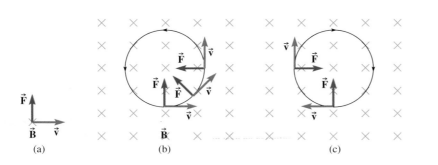

Figure 19.14 (a) Force on a positive charge moving to the right in a magnetic field that is into the page. (b) As the velocity changes direction, the magnetic force changes direction to stay perpendicular to both $\vec{v}$ and $\vec{B}$. The force is constant in magnitude, so the particle moves along the arc of a circle. (c) Motion of a negative charge in the same magnetic field.

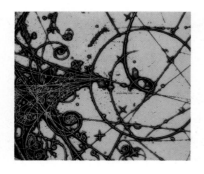

(a)

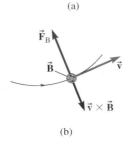

(b)

Figure 19.15 (a) Artistically enhanced tracks left by charged particles moving through the BEBC (Big European Bubble Chamber). The tracks are curved due to the presence of a magnetic field. The direction of curvature reveals the sign of the charge. (b) Analysis of the magnetic force on one particular particle. This particle must have a negative charge since the force is opposite in direction to $\vec{\mathbf{v}} \times \vec{\mathbf{B}}$.

Making the Connection:

mass spectrometer

When a charged particle moves through the liquid, it leaves a trail of bubbles. Figure 19.15a shows tracks made by particles in a bubble chamber. The magnetic field is out of the page. The magnetic force on any particle points toward the center of curvature of the particle's trajectory. Figure 19.15b shows the directions of $\vec{\mathbf{v}}$ and $\vec{\mathbf{B}}$ for one particle. Using the right-hand rule, $\vec{\mathbf{v}} \times \vec{\mathbf{B}}$ is in the direction shown in Fig. 19.15b. Since $\vec{\mathbf{v}} \times \vec{\mathbf{B}}$ points away from the center of curvature, which is the direction of $\vec{\mathbf{F}}$, the particle must have a negative charge. The magnetic force law lets us determine the sign of the charge on the particle.

Mass Spectrometer

The basic purpose of a *mass spectrometer* is to separate ions (charged atoms or molecules) by mass and measure the mass of each type of ion. Although originally devised to measure the masses of the products of nuclear reactions, mass spectrometers are now used by researchers in many different scientific fields and in medicine to identify what atoms or molecules are present in a sample and in what concentrations. Even ions present in minute concentrations can be isolated, making the mass spectrometer an essential tool in toxicology and in monitoring the environment for trace pollutants. Mass spectrometers are used in food production, petrochemical production, the electronics industry, and in the international monitoring of nuclear facilities. They are also an important tool for investigations of crime scenes, as several popular TV shows demonstrate weekly.

Today, many different types of mass spectrometer are in use. The oldest type, now called a magnetic-sector mass spectrometer, is based on the circular motion of a charged particle in a magnetic field. The atoms or molecules are first ionized so that they have a known electric charge. They are then accelerated by an electric field that can be varied to adjust their speeds. The particles then enter a region of uniform magnetic field $\vec{\mathbf{B}}$ oriented perpendicular to their velocities $\vec{\mathbf{v}}$ so that they move in circular arcs. From the charge, speed, magnetic field strength, and radius of the circular arc, we can determine the mass of the particle.

In some magnetic-sector spectrometers, the ions start at rest or at low speed and are accelerated through a fixed potential difference. If the ions all have the same charge, then they all have the *same kinetic energy* when they enter the magnetic field but, if they have different masses, their speeds are not all the same. Another possibility is to use a *velocity selector* (Section 19.5) to make sure that all ions, regardless of mass or charge, have the same *speed* when they enter the magnetic field. In the spectrometer of Example 19.4, ions of different masses travel in circular paths of different radii (Fig. 19.16a). In other spectrometers, only ions that travel along a path of *fixed radius* reach the detector; either the speed of the ions or the magnetic field is varied to select which ions move with the correct radius (Fig. 19.16b).

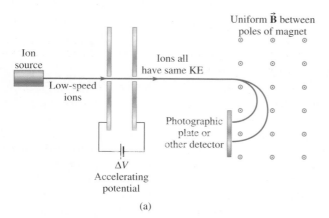

(a)

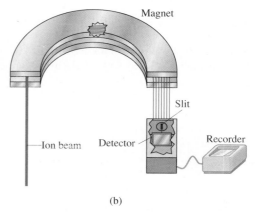

(b)

Figure 19.16 (a) A simplified diagram of a magnetic-sector mass spectrometer that accelerates ions through a fixed potential difference so that they all enter the magnetic field with the same kinetic energy. (b) A mass spectrometer in which ions travel around a path of fixed radius.

Example 19.4

Separation of Lithium Ions in a Mass Spectrometer

In a mass spectrometer, a beam of $^6Li^+$ and $^7Li^+$ ions passes through a velocity selector so that the ions all have the same velocity. The beam then enters a region of uniform magnetic field. If the radius of the orbit of the $^6Li^+$ ions is 8.4 cm, what is the radius of the orbit of the $^7Li^+$ ions?

Strategy   Much of the information in this problem is implicit. The charge of the $^6Li^+$ ions is the same as the charge of the $^7Li^+$ ions. The ions enter the magnetic field with the same speed. We do not know the magnitudes of the charge, velocity, or magnetic field, but they are the same for the two types of ion. With so many common quantities, a good strategy is to try to find the *ratio* between the radii for the two types of ion so that the common quantities cancel out.

Solution   From Appendix B we find the masses of $^6Li^+$ and $^7Li^+$:

$$m_6 = 6.015 \text{ u}$$

$$m_7 = 7.016 \text{ u}$$

We now apply Newton's second law to an ion moving in a circle. The acceleration is that of uniform circular motion:

$$a_\perp = \frac{v^2}{r} = \frac{F}{m} = \frac{|q|vB}{m} \qquad (1)$$

Since the charge q, the speed v, and the field B are the same for both types of ion, the radius must be directly proportional to the mass.

$$r \propto m$$

$$\frac{r_7}{r_6} = \frac{m_7}{m_6} = \frac{7.016 \text{ u}}{6.015 \text{ u}} = 1.166$$

$$r_7 = 8.4 \text{ cm} \times 1.166 = 9.8 \text{ cm}$$

Discussion   To solve this sort of problem, there aren't any new formulas to learn. We apply Newton's second law with the net force given by the magnetic force law ($\vec{F}_B = q\vec{v} \times \vec{B}$) and the magnitude of the radial acceleration being what it always is for uniform circular motion (v^2/r).

If the direct proportion between r and m is not apparent, we could proceed by solving (1) for the radius:

$$r = \frac{mv^2}{|q|vB}$$

Now, if we set up a ratio between r_7 and r_6, all quantities except the masses cancel, yielding

$$\frac{r_7}{r_6} = \frac{m_7}{m_6}$$

Practice Problem 19.4   Ion Speed

The magnetic field strength used in the mass spectrometer of Example 19.4 is 0.50 T. At what speed do the Li^+ ions move through the magnetic field? (Each ion has charge $q = +e$ and moves perpendicular to the field.)

Cyclotrons

Making the Connection:
medical uses of cyclotrons

Another device that was originally used in experimental physics but is now used frequently in the life sciences and medicine is the *cyclotron*, invented in 1929 by American physicist E. O. Lawrence (1901–1958). Figure 19.17 shows a schematic diagram of a proton cyclotron. The two hollow metal shells are called *dees* after their shape (like the letter "D"). An alternating potential difference is maintained between the dees to accelerate the protons. When the protons are inside one of the dees, there is no electric field acting on them; inside the conductor they are all at the same potential. However, the uniform magnetic field causes the protons to travel in a circular arc at constant speed. The potential difference alternates so that, whenever a proton reaches the gap between the dees, the dee toward which it moves is at a lower potential. Thus, the electric field between the dees gives the proton a little kick every time it crosses the gap. As the proton speed increases, the radius of its path increases. When protons reach the maximum radius of the dees, they are taken out of the cyclotron and the high-energy proton beam is used to bombard some target.

Figure 19.17 Schematic view of a cyclotron.

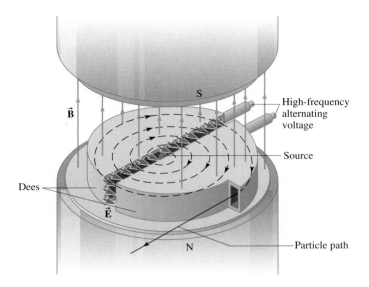

The fortunate coincidence that makes the cyclotron work is that, as the protons increase their speed and kinetic energy, the time it takes them to move around one complete circle stays constant (see Problems 25 and 26). As the speed increases, so does the distance they travel (the circumference of the circular path), and therefore the time for one revolution stays the same. The potential difference between the dees can then be made to alternate at this same frequency (the *cyclotron frequency*) so that the protons gain rather than lose kinetic energy each time they cross the gap.

In hospitals, cyclotrons produce some of the radioisotopes used in nuclear medicine. While nuclear reactors also produce medical radioisotopes, cyclotrons offer certain advantages. For one thing, a cyclotron is much easier to operate and is much smaller—typically 1 m or less in radius. A cyclotron can be located in or adjacent to a hospital so that short-lived radioisotopes can be produced as they are needed. It would be difficult to try to produce short-lived isotopes in a nuclear reactor and transport them to the hospital fast enough for them to be useful. Cyclotrons also tend to produce different kinds of isotopes than do nuclear reactors.

Another medical use of the cyclotron is *proton beam radiosurgery*, where the cyclotron's proton beam is used as a surgical tool (Fig. 19.18). Proton beam radiosurgery offers advantages over surgical and other radiological methods in the treatment of unusually shaped brain tumors. For one thing, doses to the surrounding tissue are much lower than with other forms of radiosurgery.

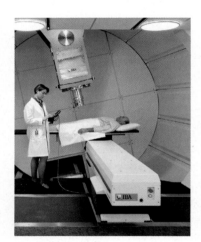

Figure 19.18 A patient is prepared for surgery at the Northeast Proton Therapy Center of Massachusetts General Hospital. The protons are accelerated by a cyclotron (not shown).

Example 19.5

Maximum Kinetic Energy in a Proton Cyclotron

A proton cyclotron uses a magnet that produces a 0.60-T field between its poles. The radius of the dees is 24 cm. What is the maximum possible kinetic energy of the protons accelerated by this cyclotron?

Strategy   As a proton's kinetic energy increases, so does the radius of its path in the dees. The maximum kinetic energy is therefore determined by the maximum radius.

Solution   While in the dees, the only force acting on the proton is magnetic. First we apply Newton's second law to a circular path.

$$F = |q|vB = \frac{mv^2}{r}$$

We can solve for v:

$$v = \frac{|q|Br}{m}$$

Continued on next page

Example 19.5 Continued

From v, we calculate the kinetic energy:

$$K = \frac{1}{2}mv^2 = \frac{1}{2}m\left(\frac{|q|Br}{m}\right)^2$$

For a proton, $q = +e$. The magnetic field strength is $B = 0.60$ T. For the maximum kinetic energy, we set the radius to its maximum value $r = 0.24$ m.

$$K = \frac{(qBr)^2}{2m} = \frac{(1.6 \times 10^{-19}\text{ C} \times 0.60\text{ T} \times 0.24\text{ m})^2}{2 \times 1.67 \times 10^{-27}\text{ kg}}$$

$$= 1.6 \times 10^{-13}\text{ J}$$

Discussion   Just as in Example 19.4 (the mass spectrometer), this cyclotron problem is solved using Newton's second law. Once again the net force on the moving charge is given by the magnetic force law and the radial acceleration has magnitude v^2/r for motion at constant speed along the arc of a circle.

Practice Problem 19.5   Increasing Kinetic Energy in a Proton Cyclotron

Using the same magnetic field, what would the radius of the dees have to be to accelerate the protons to a kinetic energy of 1.6×10^{-12} J (ten times the previous value)?

19.4   MOTION OF A CHARGED PARTICLE IN A UNIFORM MAGNETIC FIELD: GENERAL

What is the trajectory of a charged particle moving in a uniform magnetic field with no other forces acting? In Section 19.3, we saw that the trajectory is a circle *if* the velocity is perpendicular to the magnetic field. If $\vec{v}$ has no perpendicular component, the magnetic force is zero and the particle moves at constant velocity.

In general, the velocity may have components both perpendicular to and parallel to the magnetic field. The component parallel to the field is constant, since the magnetic force is always perpendicular to the field. The particle therefore moves along a *helical* path. The helix is formed by circular motion of the charge in a plane perpendicular to the field superimposed onto motion of the charge at constant speed along a field line (Fig. 19.19a).

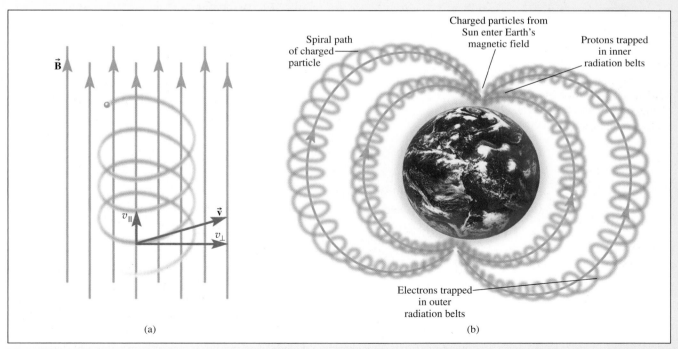

Figure 19.19 (a) Helical motion of a charged particle in a uniform magnetic field. (b) Charged particles spiral back and forth along field lines high in the atmosphere.

Even in nonuniform fields, charged particles tend to spiral around magnetic field lines. Above Earth's surface, charged particles from cosmic rays and the solar wind (charged particles streaming toward Earth from the Sun) are trapped by Earth's magnetic field. The particles spiral back and forth along magnetic field lines (Fig. 19.19b). Near the poles, the field lines are closer together, so the field is stronger. As the field strength increases, the radius of a spiraling particle's path gets smaller and smaller. As a result, there is a concentration of these particles near the poles. The particles collide with and ionize air molecules. When the ions recombine with electrons to form neutral atoms, visible light is emitted—the *aurora borealis* in the northern hemisphere and the *aurora australis* in the southern hemisphere. Aurorae also occur on Jupiter and Saturn, which have much stronger magnetic fields than does the Earth.

Making the Connection:
aurorae on Earth, Jupiter, and Saturn

19.5   A CHARGED PARTICLE IN CROSSED $\vec{E}$ AND $\vec{B}$ FIELDS

If a charged particle moves in a region of space where both electric and magnetic fields are present, then the electromagnetic force on the particle is the vector sum of the electric and magnetic forces:

$$\vec{F} = \vec{F}_E + \vec{F}_B \qquad (19\text{-}8)$$

🔵 The magnetic force is velocity-dependent, while the electric force is not.

A particularly important and useful case is when the electric and magnetic fields are perpendicular to each other and the velocity of a charged particle is perpendicular to both fields. Since the magnetic force is always perpendicular to both $\vec{v}$ and $\vec{B}$, it must be either in the same direction as the electric force or in the opposite direction. If the magnitudes of the two forces are the same and the directions are opposite, then there is zero net force on the charged particle (Fig. 19.20). For any particular combination of electric and magnetic fields, this balance of forces occurs only for one particular particle speed, since the magnetic force is velocity-dependent, while the electric force is not. The velocity that gives zero net force can be found from

$$\vec{F} = \vec{F}_E + \vec{F}_B = 0$$

$$q\vec{E} + q\vec{v} \times \vec{B} = 0$$

Dividing out the common factor of q,

$$\vec{E} + \vec{v} \times \vec{B} = 0 \qquad (19\text{-}9)$$

There is zero net force on the particle only if

$$v = \frac{E}{B} \qquad (19\text{-}10)$$

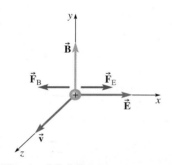

Figure 19.20 Positive point charge moving in crossed $\vec{E}$ and $\vec{B}$ fields. For the velocity direction shown, $\vec{F}_E + \vec{F}_B = 0$ if $v = E/B$.

and if the direction of $\vec{v}$ is correct. Since $\vec{E} = -\vec{v} \times \vec{B}$, it can be shown (see Conceptual Question 7) that the correct direction of $\vec{v}$ is the direction of $\vec{E} \times \vec{B}$.

Velocity Selector

A **velocity selector** uses crossed electric and magnetic fields to select a single velocity out of a beam of charged particles. Suppose a beam of ions is produced in the first stage of a mass spectrometer. The beam may contain ions moving at a range of different speeds. If the second stage of the mass spectrometer is a velocity selector (Fig. 19.21), only ions moving at a single speed $v = E/B$ pass through the velocity selector and into the third stage. The speed can be selected by adjusting the magnitudes of the electric and magnetic fields. For particles moving *faster* than the selected speed, the magnetic force is stronger than the electric force; fast particles curve out of the beam in the direction of the magnetic force. For particles moving *slower* than the selected speed, the magnetic force is weaker than the electric force; slow particles curve out of the beam in the direction of the electric force. The velocity selector ensures that only ions with speeds very near $v = E/B$ enter the magnetic sector of the mass spectrometer.

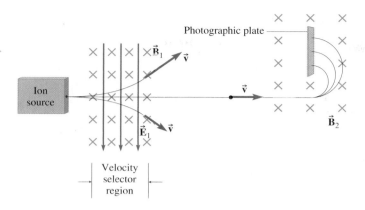

Figure 19.21 A mass spectrometer that uses a velocity selector to ensure that all ions enter the second magnetic field with the same speed. Both magnetic fields are into the page.

Example 19.6

Velocity Selector

A velocity selector is to be constructed to select ions moving to the right at 6.0 km/s. The electric field is 300.0 V/m into the page. What should be the magnitude and direction of the magnetic field?

Strategy   First, in a velocity selector, $\vec{E}$, $\vec{B}$, and $\vec{v}$ are mutually perpendicular. That allows only two possibilities for the direction of $\vec{B}$. Setting the magnetic force equal and opposite to the electric force determines which of the two directions is correct and gives the magnitude of $\vec{B}$. The magnitude of the magnetic field is chosen so that the electric and magnetic forces on a particle moving at the given speed are exactly opposite.

Solution   Since $\vec{v}$ is to the right and $\vec{E}$ is into the page, the magnetic field must either be up or down. The sign of the ions' charge is irrelevant—changing the charge from positive to negative would change the directions of *both* forces, leaving them still opposite to each other. For simplicity, then, we assume the charge to be positive.

The direction of the electric force on a positive charge is the same as the direction of the field, which here is into the page. Then we need a magnetic force that is out of the page. Using the right-hand rule to evaluate both possibilities for $\vec{B}$ (up and down), we find that $\vec{v} \times \vec{B}$ is out of the page if $\vec{B}$ is up (Fig. 19.22).

Figure 19.22
Directions of $\vec{E}$, $\vec{v}$, and $\vec{B}$.

The magnitudes of the forces must also be equal:

$$qE = qvB$$

$$B = \frac{E}{v} = \frac{300.0\ \text{V/m}}{6000\ \text{m/s}} = 0.050\ \text{T}$$

Discussion   Let's check the units; is a tesla really equal to $\frac{\text{V/m}}{\text{m/s}}$? From $\vec{F} = q\vec{v} \times \vec{B}$, we can reconstruct the tesla:

$$[B] = \text{T} = \left[\frac{F}{qv}\right] = \frac{\text{N}}{\text{C·m/s}}$$

Recall that two equivalent units for electric field are N/C = V/m. By substitution,

$$\text{T} = \frac{\text{V}}{\text{m}^2/\text{s}} = \frac{\text{V/m}}{\text{m/s}}$$

so the units check out.

Another check: for a velocity selector the correct direction of $\vec{v}$ is the direction of $\vec{E} \times \vec{B}$. The velocity is to the right. Using the right-hand rule, $\vec{E} \times \vec{B}$ is to the right if $\vec{B}$ is up.

Practice Problem 19.6   Deflection of a Particle Moving Too Fast

If a particle enters this velocity selector with a speed greater than 6.0 km/s, in what direction is it deflected out of the beam?

The velocity selector can be used to determine the charge-to-mass ratio q/m of a charged particle. First, the particle is accelerated from rest through a potential difference ΔV, converting electric potential energy into kinetic energy. The change in its electric potential energy is $\Delta U = q\,\Delta V$, so the charge acquires a kinetic energy

$$K = \tfrac{1}{2}mv^2 = -q\,\Delta V$$

Figure 19.23 Modern apparatus, similar in principle to the one used by Thomson, to find the charge-to-mass ratio of the electron. Electrons emitted from the cathode are accelerated toward the anode by the electric field between the two. Some of the electrons pass through the anode and then enter a velocity selector. The deflection of the electrons is viewed on the screen. The electric and magnetic fields in the velocity selector are adjusted until the electrons are not deflected.

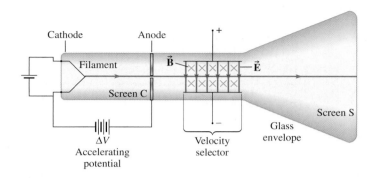

(K is positive regardless of the sign of q: a positive charge is accelerated by decreasing its potential, while a negative charge is accelerated by increasing its potential.) Now a velocity selector is used to determine the speed $v = E/B$, by adjusting the electric and magnetic fields until the particles pass straight through. The charge-to-mass ratio q/m can now be determined (see Problem 28). In 1897, British physicist J. J. Thomson (1856–1940) used this technique to show that "cathode rays" are charged particles. In a vacuum tube, he maintained two electrodes at a potential difference of a few thousand volts (Fig. 19.23) so that cathode rays were emitted by the negative electrode (the cathode). By measuring the charge-to-mass ratio, Thomson established that cathode rays are streams of negatively charged particles that all have the same charge-to-mass ratio—particles we now call *electrons*.

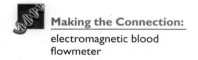

Making the Connection:

electromagnetic blood flowmeter

Electromagnetic Flowmeter

The principle of the velocity selector finds another application in the electromagnetic flowmeters used to measure the speed of blood flow through a major artery during cardiovascular surgery. Blood contains ions; the motion of the ions can be affected by a magnetic field. In an electromagnetic flowmeter, a magnetic field is applied perpendicular to the flow direction. The magnetic force on positive ions is toward one side of the artery, while the magnetic force on negative ions is toward the opposite side (Fig. 19.24a). This separation of charge, with positive charge on one side and negative charge on the other, produces an electric field across the artery (Fig. 19.24b). As the electric field builds up, it exerts a force on moving ions in a direction opposite to that of the magnetic field. In equilibrium, the two forces are equal in magnitude:

$$F_E = F_B$$

$$qE = qvB$$

$$E = vB$$

Figure 19.24 Principles behind the electromagnetic blood flowmeter. (a) When a magnetic field is applied perpendicular to the direction of blood flow, positive and negative ions are deflected toward opposite sides of the artery. (b) As the ions are deflected, an electric field develops across the artery. In equilibrium, the electric force on an ion due to this field is equal and opposite to the magnetic force; the ions move straight down the artery with an average velocity of magnitude $v = E/B$.

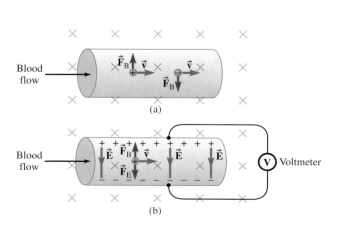

where v is the average speed of an ion, equal to the average speed of the blood flow. Thus, the flowmeter is just like a velocity selector, except that the ion speed determines the electric field instead of the other way around.

A voltmeter is attached to opposite sides of the artery to measure the potential difference. From the potential difference, we can calculate the electric field; from the electric field and magnetic field magnitudes, we can determine the speed of blood flow. A great advantage of the electromagnetic flowmeter is that it does not involve anything being inserted into the artery.

The Hall Effect

The **Hall effect** is similar to the electromagnetic flowmeter, but pertains to the moving charges in a current-carrying wire or other solid instead of to the moving ions in blood. A magnetic field perpendicular to the wire causes the moving charges to be deflected to one side. An electric field then exists across the wire. The potential difference (or **Hall voltage**) *across* the wire is measured and then used to calculate the electric field (or **Hall field**) across the wire. The drift velocity of the charges is then given by $v_D = E/B$. The Hall effect enables the measurement of the drift velocity and the determination of the sign of the charges. (The carriers in metals are generally electrons, but semiconductors may have positive or negative carriers or both.)

The Hall effect is also the principle behind the **Hall probe**, a common device used to measure magnetic fields. As shown in Example 19.7, the Hall voltage across a conducting strip is proportional to the magnetic field strength. A circuit causes a fixed current flow through the strip. The probe is then calibrated by measuring the Hall voltage caused by magnetic fields of known strength. Once calibrated, measurement of the Hall voltage enables a quick and accurate determination of magnetic field strengths.

Example 19.7

Hall Effect

A flat slab of semiconductor has thickness $t = 0.50$ mm, width $w = 1.0$ cm, and length $L = 30.0$ cm. A current $I = 2.0$ A flows along its length to the right (Fig. 19.25). A magnetic field $B = 0.25$ T is directed into the page, perpendicular to the flat surface of the slab. Assume that the carriers are electrons. There are 7.0×10^{24} mobile electrons per m³. (a) What is the magnitude of the Hall voltage across the slab? (b) Which edge (top or bottom) is at the higher potential?

Strategy   We need to find the drift velocity of the electrons from the relation between current and drift velocity. Since the Hall field is uniform, the Hall voltage is the Hall field times the width of the slab.

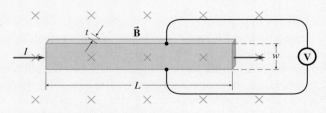

Figure 19.25

Measuring the Hall voltage.

Given: current $I = 2.0$ A, magnetic field $B = 0.25$ T, thickness $t = 0.50 \times 10^{-3}$ m, width $w = 0.010$ m, $n = 7.0 \times 10^{24}$ electrons/m³

Solution   (a) The drift velocity is related to the current:
$$I = neAv_D \qquad (18\text{-}3)$$
The area is the width times the thickness of the slab:
$$A = wt$$
Solving for the drift velocity,
$$v_D = \frac{I}{newt}$$

We find the Hall field by setting the magnitude of the magnetic force equal to the magnitude of the electric force caused by the Hall field across the slab:
$$F_E = eE_H = F_B = ev_D B$$
$$E_H = v_D B$$
The Hall voltage is
$$V_H = E_H w = B v_D w$$

Continued on next page

Example 19.7 Continued

Substituting the expression for drift velocity,

$$V_H = \frac{BIw}{newt} = \frac{BI}{net}$$

$$= \frac{0.25\ \text{T} \times 2.0\ \text{A}}{7.0 \times 10^{24}\ \text{m}^{-3} \times 1.6 \times 10^{-19}\ \text{C} \times 0.50 \times 10^{-3}\ \text{m}}$$

$$= 0.89\ \text{mV}$$

(b) Since the current flows to the right, the electrons actually move to the left. Figure 19.26a shows that the magnetic force on an electron moving to the left is upward. The magnetic force deflects electrons toward the top of the slab, leaving the bottom with a positive charge. An upward electric field is set up across the slab (Fig. 19.26b). Therefore, the bottom edge is at the higher potential.

Discussion   The width of the slab w does not appear in the final expression for the Hall voltage $V_H = BI/(net)$. Is it possible that the Hall voltage is independent of the width? If the slab were twice as wide, for instance, the same current means half the drift velocity v_D since the number of carriers per unit volume n and their charge magnitude e cannot change. With the carriers moving half as fast on average, the average magnetic force is half. Then in equilibrium, the electric force is half, which means the field is half. An electric field half as strong times a width twice as wide gives the same Hall voltage.

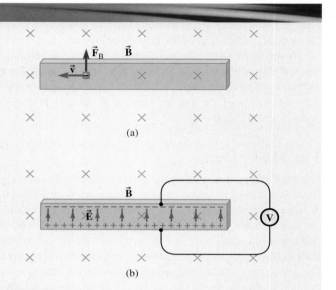

(a)

(b)

Figure 19.26

(a) Magnetic force on an electron moving to the left. (b) With electrons deflected toward the top of the slab, the top is negatively charged and the bottom is positively charged. The Hall field in this case is directed upward, from the positive charges to the negative charges.

Practice Problem 19.7   Holes as Carriers

If the carriers had been particles with charge $+e$ instead of electrons, with everything else the same, would the Hall voltage have been any different? Explain.

19.6   MAGNETIC FORCE ON A CURRENT-CARRYING WIRE

A wire carrying electric current has many moving charges in it. For a current-carrying wire in a magnetic field, the magnetic forces on the individual moving charges add up to produce a net magnetic force on the wire. Although the average force on one of the charges may be small, there are so many charges that the net magnetic force on the wire can be appreciable.

Say a straight wire segment of length L in a uniform magnetic field $\vec{B}$ carries a current I. The mobile carriers have charge q. The magnetic force on any one charge is

$$\vec{F} = q\vec{v} \times \vec{B}$$

where $\vec{v}$ is the instantaneous velocity of that charge. The net magnetic force on the wire is the vector sum of these forces. The sum isn't easy to carry out, since we don't know the instantaneous velocity of each of the charges. The charges move about in random directions at high speeds; their velocities suffer large changes when they collide with other particles. Instead of summing the instantaneous magnetic force on each charge, we can instead multiply the *average* magnetic force on each charge by the number of charges. Since each charge has the same average velocity—the drift velocity—each experiences the same average magnetic force $\vec{F}_{av}$.

$$\vec{F}_{av} = q\vec{v}_D \times \vec{B}$$

Then, if N is the total number of carriers in the wire, the total magnetic force on the wire is

$$\vec{\mathbf{F}} = Nq\vec{\mathbf{v}}_{\mathrm{D}} \times \vec{\mathbf{B}} \qquad (19\text{-}11)$$

Equation (19-11) can be rewritten in a more convenient way. Instead of having to figure out the number of carriers and the drift velocity, it is more convenient to have an expression that gives the magnetic force in terms of the current I. The current I is related to the drift velocity:

$$I = nqAv_{\mathrm{D}} \qquad (18\text{-}3)$$

Here n is the number of carriers *per unit volume*. If the length of the wire is L and the cross-sectional area is A, then

$$N = \text{number per unit volume} \times \text{volume} = nLA$$

By substitution, the magnetic force on the wire can be written

$$\vec{\mathbf{F}} = Nq\vec{\mathbf{v}}_{\mathrm{D}} \times \vec{\mathbf{B}} = nqAL\vec{\mathbf{v}}_{\mathrm{D}} \times \vec{\mathbf{B}}$$

Almost there! Since current is not a vector, we cannot substitute $\vec{\mathbf{I}} = nqA\vec{\mathbf{v}}_{\mathrm{D}}$. Therefore, we define a *length vector* $\vec{\mathbf{L}}$ to be a vector in the direction of the current with magnitude equal to the length of the wire (Fig. 19.27). Then $nqAL\vec{\mathbf{v}}_{\mathrm{D}} = I\vec{\mathbf{L}}$ and

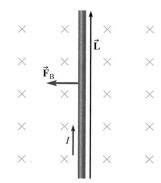

Figure 19.27 A current-carrying wire in a magnetic field experiences a magnetic force.

Magnetic force on a straight segment of current-carrying wire:

$$\vec{\mathbf{F}} = I\vec{\mathbf{L}} \times \vec{\mathbf{B}} \qquad (19\text{-}12a)$$

The current I times the cross product $\vec{\mathbf{L}} \times \vec{\mathbf{B}}$ gives the magnitude and direction of the force. The magnitude of the force is

$$F = IL_{\perp}B = ILB_{\perp} = ILB \sin \theta \qquad (19\text{-}12b)$$

The direction of the force is perpendicular to both $\vec{\mathbf{L}}$ and $\vec{\mathbf{B}}$. The same right-hand rule used for any cross product is used to choose between the two possibilities.

Problem-Solving Technique: Finding the Magnetic Force on a Straight Segment of Current-Carrying Wire

1. The magnetic force is zero if (a) the current in the wire is zero, (b) the wire is parallel to the magnetic field, or (c) the magnetic field is zero.
2. Otherwise, determine the angle θ between $\vec{\mathbf{L}}$ and $\vec{\mathbf{B}}$ when the two are drawn starting at the same point.
3. Find the magnitude of the force from Eq. (19-12b).
4. Determine the direction of $\vec{\mathbf{L}} \times \vec{\mathbf{B}}$ using the right-hand rule.

Example 19.8

Magnetic Force on a Power Line

A 125-m-long power line is horizontal and carries a current of 2500 A toward the south. The Earth's magnetic field at that location is 0.52 mT toward the north and inclined 62° below the horizontal (Fig. 19.28). What is the magnetic force on the power line? (Ignore any drooping of the wire; assume it's straight.)

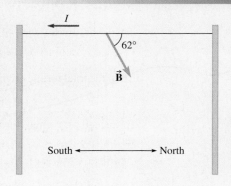

Figure 19.28
The wire and the magnetic field vector.

Continued on next page

Example 19.8 Continued

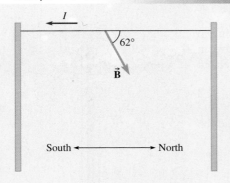

Figure 19.28 (repeated)
The wire and the magnetic field vector.

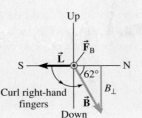

Figure 19.29
The vectors $\vec{L}$ and $\vec{B}$ sketched in a vertical plane. The cross product of the two must then be perpendicular to this plane—either east (out of the page) or west (into the page). The right-hand rule enables us to choose between the two possibilities.

Strategy   We are given all the quantities necessary to calculate the force:

$I = 2500$ A;

$\vec{L}$ has magnitude 125 m and direction south;

$\vec{B}$ has magnitude 0.52 mT. It has a downward component and a northward component.

We find the cross product $\vec{L} \times \vec{B}$ and then multiply by I.

Solution   The magnitude of the force is given by

$$F = IL_{\perp}B = ILB_{\perp}$$

The second form is more convenient here, since $\vec{L}$ is southward. The perpendicular component of $\vec{B}$ is the vertical component, which is $B \sin 62°$ (see Fig. 19.29). Then

$$F = ILB \sin 62° = 2500 \text{ A} \times 125 \text{ m} \times 5.2 \times 10^{-4} \text{ T} \times \sin 62°$$
$$= 140 \text{ N}$$

Figure 19.29 shows the vectors $\vec{L}$ and $\vec{B}$ sketched in the north/south–up/down plane. Since north is to the right, this is a view looking toward the west. The cross product $\vec{L} \times \vec{B}$ is out of the page by the right-hand rule. Therefore, the direction of the force is east.

Discussion   The hardest thing in this sort of problem is choosing a plane in which to sketch the vectors. Here we chose a plane in which we could draw both $\vec{L}$ and $\vec{B}$; then the cross product has to be perpendicular to this plane.

Practice Problem 19.8   Magnetic Force on a Current-Carrying Wire

A vertical wire carries 10.0 A of current upward. What is the direction of the magnetic force on the wire if the magnetic field is the same as in Example 19.8?

19.7   TORQUE ON A CURRENT LOOP

Consider a rectangular loop of wire carrying current I in a uniform magnetic field $\vec{B}$. In Fig. 19.30a, the field is parallel to sides 1 and 3 of the loop. There is no magnetic force on sides 1 and 3 since $\vec{L} \times \vec{B} = 0$ for each. The forces on sides 2 and 4 are equal in magnitude and opposite in direction. There is no net magnetic force on the loop, but the lines of action of the two forces are offset by a distance b, so there is a nonzero net torque. The torque tends to make the loop rotate about a central axis in the direction indicated in Fig. 19.30a. The magnitude of the magnetic force on sides 2 and 4 is

$$F = ILB = IaB$$

The lever arm for each of the two forces is $\frac{1}{2}b$, so the torque due to each is

$$\text{magnitude of force} \times \text{lever arm} = F \times \tfrac{1}{2}b = \tfrac{1}{2}IabB$$

Then the total torque on the loop is $\tau = IabB$. The area of the rectangular loop is $A = ab$, so

$$\tau = IAB$$

If, instead of a single turn, there are N turns forming a coil, then the magnetic torque on the coil is

$$\tau = NIAB \qquad\qquad (19\text{-}13a)$$

Equation (19-13a) holds for a planar loop or coil of *any* shape (see Problem 51).

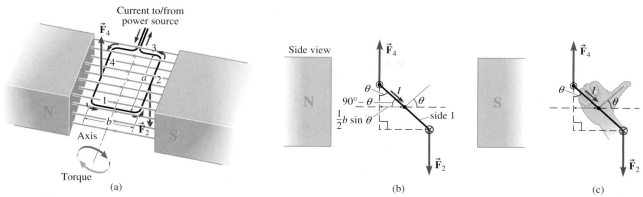

Figure 19.30 (a) A rectangular coil of wire in a uniform magnetic field. The current in the coil (counterclockwise as viewed from the top) causes a magnetic torque, which is clockwise as viewed from the front. (b) Side view of the same coil after it has been rotated in the field. The current in side 4 comes out of the page, along side 1 (diagonally down the page), and back into the page in side 2. The lever arms of the forces on sides 2 and 4 are now smaller: $\frac{1}{2}b \sin \theta$ instead of $\frac{1}{2}b$. The torque is then smaller by the same factor ($\sin \theta$). (c) Using the right-hand rule to choose the perpendicular direction from which θ is measured.

What if the field is not parallel to the plane of the coil? In Fig. 19.30b, the same loop has been rotated about the axis shown. The angle θ is the angle between the magnetic field and a line *perpendicular* to the current loop. Which perpendicular direction is determined by a right-hand rule: curl the fingers of your right hand in toward your palm, following the current in the loop, and your thumb indicates the direction of $\theta = 0$ (Fig. 19.30c). Before, when the field was in the plane of the loop, θ was 90°. For $\theta \neq 90°$, the magnetic forces on sides 1 and 3 are no longer zero, but they are equal and opposite and act along the same line of action, so they contribute neither to the net force nor to the net torque. The magnetic forces on sides 2 and 4 are the same as before, but now the lever arms are smaller by a factor of $\sin \theta$: instead of $\frac{1}{2}b$, the lever arms are now $\frac{1}{2}b \sin \theta$. Therefore,

Torque on a curent loop:

$$\tau = NIAB \sin \theta \qquad \qquad \text{(19-13b)}$$

The torque has maximum magnitude if the field is in the plane of the coil ($\theta = 90°$ or 270°). If $\theta = 0°$ or 180°, the field is perpendicular to the plane of the loop and the torque is zero. There are *two* positions of rotational equilibrium, but they are not equivalent. The position at $\theta = 180°$ is an *unstable* equilibrium, because at angles *near* 180° the torque tends to rotate the coil *away* from 180°. The position at $\theta = 0°$ is a *stable* equilibrium; the torque for angles *near* 0° makes the coil rotate back toward $\theta = 0°$ and thus tends to restore the equilibrium.

The torque on a current loop in a uniform magnetic field is analogous to the torque on an electric dipole in a uniform electric field (see Problem 50). This similarity is our first hint that

A current loop is a magnetic dipole.

The direction perpendicular to the loop chosen by the right-hand rule is the direction of the **magnetic dipole moment vector**. The dipole moment vector points from the dipole's south pole toward its north pole. (By comparison, the *electric* dipole moment vector points from the electric dipole's negative charge toward its positive charge.)

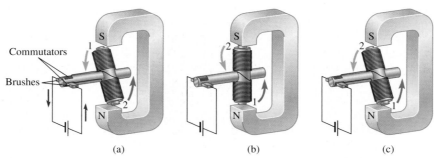

(a)   (b)   (c)

Figure 19.31 Simple dc motor. The two sides of the rotating coil are labeled 1 and 2. In position (a) the coil rotates away from unstable equilibrium. In position (b) brushes pass over the split in the commutator, interrupting the flow of current. If the current in the coil still flowed in the same direction as in (a), this would be stable equilibrium. When the coil turns a little farther, in position (c), the brushes reverse the direction of the current. Now the coil is pushed away from *unstable* equilibrium rather than pulled back toward stable equilibrium.

Making the Connection:

electric motor (dc)

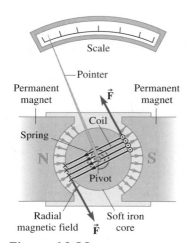

Figure 19.32 A galvanometer.

Making the Connection:

galvanometer

Electric Motor

In a simple dc motor, a coil of wire is free to rotate between the poles of a permanent magnet (Fig. 19.31). When current flows through the loop, the magnetic field exerts a torque on the loop. If the direction of the current in the coil doesn't change, then the coil just oscillates about the stable equilibrium orientation ($\theta = 0°$). To make a motor we need the coil to keep turning in the same direction. The trick used to make a dc motor is to automatically reverse the direction of the current as soon as the coil passes $\theta = 0°$. In effect, just as the coil goes through the stable equilibrium orientation, we reverse the current to make the coil's orientation an *unstable* equilibrium. Then, instead of pulling the coil backward toward the (stable) equilibrium, the torque keeps turning the coil in the same direction by pushing it *away from* (unstable) equilibrium.

To reverse the current, the source of current is connected to the coil of the motor by means of two brushes. The brushes make electric contact with the *commutator*, which rotates with the coil. The commutator is a split ring with each side connected to one end of the coil. Every time the brushes pass over the split (Fig. 19.31b), the current to the coil is reversed.

Galvanometer

The magnetic torque on a current loop is also the principle behind the operation of a galvanometer—a sensitive device used to measure current. A rectangular coil of wire is placed between the poles of a magnet (Fig. 19.32). The shape of the magnet's pole faces keeps the field perpendicular to the wires and constant in magnitude regardless of the angle of the coil, so the torque does not depend on the angle of the coil. A hairspring provides a restoring torque that is proportional to the angular displacement of the coil. When a current passes through the coil, the magnetic torque is proportional to the current. The coil rotates until the restoring torque due to the spring is equal in magnitude to the magnetic torque. Thus, the angular displacement of the coil is proportional to the current in the coil.

Conceptual Example 19.9

Force and Torque on a Galvanometer Coil

Show that (a) there is zero net magnetic force on the pivoted coil in the galvanometer of Fig. 19.32; (b) there is a net torque; and (c) the torque is in the correct direction to swing the pointer in the plane of the page. (d) Determine which direction the current in the coil must flow to swing

the pointer to the right. Assume that the magnetic field is radial and has uniform *magnitude* in the space between the magnet pole faces and the iron core and that the field is zero in the vicinity of the two sides of the coil that cross over the iron core.

Continued on next page

Strategy Since we do not know the direction of the current, we pick one arbitrarily; in part (d) we will find out whether the choice was correct. Only the two sides of the coil near the magnet pole faces experience magnetic forces, since the other two sides are in zero field.

Solution We choose the current in the side near the north pole to flow into the page. The current must then flow out of the page in the side of the coil near the south pole. In Fig. 19.32, the current directions are marked with symbols $\odot$ and $\times$, which also represent the directions of the $\vec{\mathbf{L}}$ vectors used to find the magnetic force. The magnetic field vectors are also shown. Note that, since the direction of the field is radial, the two magnetic vectors are the same (same direction *and* magnitude). The direction of the magnetic force on either side is given by

$$\vec{\mathbf{F}} = NI\vec{\mathbf{L}} \times \vec{\mathbf{B}}$$

where N stands for the number of turns of wire in the coil. The force vectors are shown on Fig. 19.32.

(a) Since the $\vec{\mathbf{B}}$ vectors are the same and the $\vec{\mathbf{L}}$ vectors are equal and opposite (same length but opposite direction), the forces are equal and opposite. Then the net magnetic force on the coil is zero. (b) The net torque is not zero because the lines of action of the forces are separated. (c) The forces make the pointer rotate counterclockwise in the plane of the page. (d) Since the meter shows positive current by rotating clockwise, we have chosen the wrong direction for the current. The leads of the galvanometer should be attached so that positive current makes the current in the coil flow in the direction opposite to the one we chose initially.

Discussion The galvanometer works because the torque is proportional to the current but independent of the orientation of the coil. In Eq. (19-13b), θ is the angle between the magnetic field and a line perpendicular to the coil. In the galvanometer, the magnetic field acting on the coil is always in the plane of the coil; in essence θ is a constant 90° even while the coil swings about the pivot.

Practice Problem 19.9   Torque on a Coil

Starting with the magnetic forces on the sides of the coil, show that the torque on the coil is $\tau = NIAB$, where A is the area of the coil.

Audio Speakers

In contrast to a coil in a uniform field, a coil of wire in a *radial* magnetic field may experience a nonzero net magnetic *force*. A coil in a radial field is the principle behind the operation of many audio speakers (Fig. 19.33a). An electric current passes through a coil of wire. The coil sits between the poles of a magnet shaped so that the magnetic field is radial (Fig. 19.33b). Even though the coil is not a straight wire, the field direction is such that the force on every part of the coil is in the same direction. Since the field is everywhere perpendicular to the wire, the magnetic force is $F = ILB$ where L is the *total* length of the wire in the coil. A spring-like mechanism exerts a linear restoring force on the coil so that when a magnetic force acts, the displacement of the coil is proportional to the magnetic force, which in turn is proportional to the current in the coil. Thus, the motion of the coil—and the motion of the attached cone—mirrors the current sent through the speaker by the amplifier.

Making the Connection:

audio speakers

19.8   MAGNETIC FIELD DUE TO AN ELECTRIC CURRENT

So far we have explored the magnetic forces acting on charged particles and current-carrying wires. We have not yet looked at *sources* of magnetic fields other than permanent magnets. It turns out that *any moving charged particle* creates a magnetic field. There is a certain symmetry about the situation:

- Moving charges experience magnetic forces and moving charges create magnetic fields;
- Charges at rest feel no magnetic forces and create no magnetic fields;
- Charges feel electric forces and create electric fields, whether moving or not.

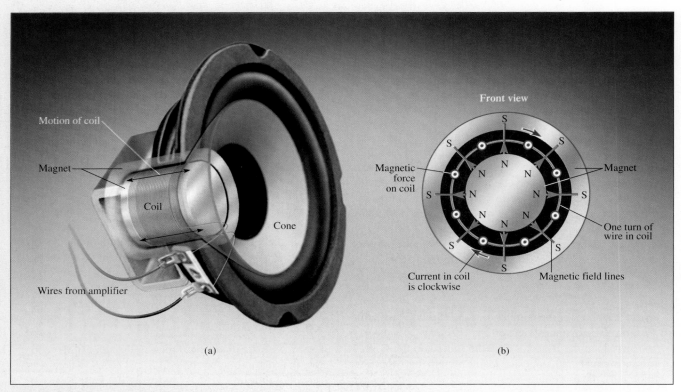

Figure 19.33 (a) Simplified sketch of a loudspeaker. A varying current from the amplifier flows through a coil. The magnetic force on the coil makes it and the attached cone move in and out. The motion of the cone displaces air in the vicinity and creates a sound wave. (b) A front view of the coil. The coil is sandwiched between cylindrical shaped poles of a magnet. The magnetic field is directed radially outward. (Compare to Fig. 19.32 to see how the radial magnetic fields and the coil orientations differ.) Applying $\vec{F} = I\vec{L} \times \vec{B}$ to any short length of the coil shows that, for the clockwise current shown here, the magnetic force is out of the page. (In the galvanometer, the net magnetic force on the coil is zero, but there is a nonzero net magnetic torque.)

Today we know that electricity and magnetism are closely intertwined. It may be surprising to learn that they were not known to be related until the nineteenth century. Hans Christian Oersted discovered in 1820 by happy accident that electric currents flowing in wires made nearby compass needles swing around. Oersted's discovery was the first evidence of a connection between electricity and magnetism.

The magnetic field due to a single moving charged particle is negligibly small in most situations. However, when an electric current flows in a wire, there are enormous numbers of moving charges. The magnetic field due to the wire is the sum of the magnetic fields due to each charge; the principle of superposition applies to magnetic fields just as it does to electric fields.

Magnetic Field due to a Long Straight Wire

Let us first consider the magnetic field due to a long, straight wire carrying a current I. What is the magnetic field at point P, a distance r from the wire? Point P is near the wire and far from its ends. Figure 19.34a is a photo of such a wire, passing through a glass plate on which iron filings have been sprinkled. The iron bits line up with the magnetic field due to the current in the wire. The photo suggests that the magnetic field lines are circles centered on the wire. Circular field lines are indeed the only possibility, given the symmetry of the situation. If the lines were any other shape, they would be farther from the wire in some directions than in others.

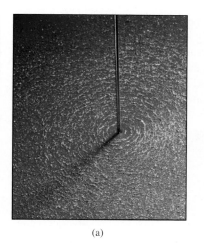
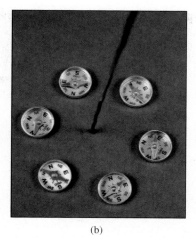

(a)   (b)   (c)

Figure 19.34 Magnetic field due to a long straight wire. (a) Photo of a long wire, with iron filings lining up with the magnetic field. (b) Compasses show the direction of the field. (c) Sketch illustrating how to use the right-hand rule to determine the direction of the field lines.

The iron filings do not tell us the direction of the field. By using compasses instead of iron filings (Fig. 19.34b), the direction of the field is revealed—it is the direction indicated by the north end of each compass. The field lines due to the wire are shown in Fig. 19.34c, where the current in the wire flows upward. A right-hand rule relates the current direction in the wire to the direction of the field around the wire:

Using Right-Hand Rule 2 to Find the Direction of the Magnetic Field due to a Long Straight Wire

1. Point the thumb of the right hand in the direction of the current in the wire.
2. Curl the fingers inward toward the palm; the direction that the fingers curl is the direction of the magnetic field lines around the wire (Fig. 19.34c).

The magnitude of the magnetic field at a distance r from the wire can be found using Ampère's law (Section 19.9; see Example 19.11):

Magnetic field due to a long straight wire:

$$B = \frac{\mu_0 I}{2\pi r} \qquad \text{(19-14)}$$

where I is the current in the wire and μ_0 is a universal constant known as the **permeability of free space**. The permeability plays a role in magnetism similar to the role of the permittivity (ϵ_0) in electricity. In SI units, the value of μ_0 is

$$\mu_0 = 4\pi \times 10^{-7} \frac{\text{T·m}}{\text{A}} \qquad \text{(exact, by definition)} \qquad \text{(19-15)}$$

Two parallel current-carrying wires that are close together exert magnetic forces on one another. The magnetic field of wire 1 causes a magnetic force on wire 2; the magnetic field of wire 2 causes a magnetic force on wire 1 (Fig. 19.35). From Newton's third law, we expect the forces on the wires to be equal and opposite. If the currents flow in the same direction, the force is attractive; if they flow in opposite directions, the force is repulsive (see Problem 62). Note that for current-carrying wires, "likes" (currents in the same direction) *attract* each other and "unlikes" (currents in opposite directions) *repel* each other.

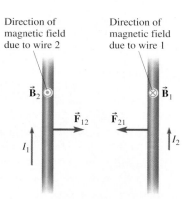

Direction of magnetic field due to wire 2   Direction of magnetic field due to wire 1

Figure 19.35 Two parallel wires exert magnetic forces on one another. The force on wire 1 due to wire 2's magnetic field is $\vec{F}_{12} = I_1 \vec{L}_1 \times \vec{B}_2$. Even if the currents are unequal, $\vec{F}_{21} = -\vec{F}_{12}$ (Newton's third law).

The constant μ_0 can be assigned an exact value because the magnetic forces on two parallel wires are used to *define* the ampere, which is an SI base unit. One ampere is the current in each of two long parallel wires 1 m apart such that each exerts a magnetic force on the other of exactly 2×10^{-7} N per meter of length. The ampere, not the coulomb, is chosen to be an SI base unit because it can be defined in terms of forces and lengths that can be measured accurately. The coulomb is then defined as 1 ampere-second.

Example 19.10

Magnetic Field due to Household Wiring

In household wiring, two long parallel wires are separated and surrounded by an insulator. The wires are a distance d apart and carry currents of magnitude I in opposite directions. (a) Find the magnetic field at a distance $r \gg d$ from the center of the wires (point P in Fig. 19.36). (b) Find the numerical value of B if $I = 5$ A, $d = 5$ mm, and $r = 1$ m and compare to the Earth's magnetic field strength at the surface ($\sim 5 \times 10^{-4}$ T).

Figure 19.36

The two wires are perpendicular to the plane of the page. They are marked to show that the current in the upper wire flows out of the page and the current in the lower wire flows into the page.

Strategy The magnetic field is the vector sum of the fields due to each of the wires. The fields due to the wires at P are equal in magnitude (since the currents and distances are the same), but the directions are not the same. Equation (19-14) gives the magnitude of the field due to either wire. Since the field lines due to a single long wire are circular, the direction of the field is tangent to a circle that passes through P and whose center is on the wire. The right-hand rule determines which of the two tangent directions is correct.

Solution (a) Since $r \gg d$, the distance from either wire to P is approximately r (see Fig. 19.37). Then the magnitude of the field at P due to either wire is

$$B \approx \frac{\mu_0 I}{2\pi r}$$

In Fig. 19.37, we draw radial lines from each wire to point P. The direction of the magnetic field due to a long wire is tangent to a circle and therefore perpendicular to a radius. Using the right-hand rule, the field directions are as shown in Fig. 19.37. The y-components of the two field vectors add to zero; the x-components are the same:

$$B_x = \frac{\mu_0 I}{2\pi r} \sin \theta$$

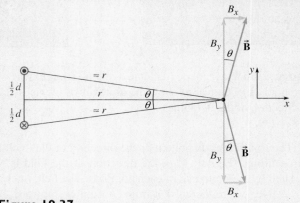

Figure 19.37

Field vectors due to each wire.

Since $r \gg d$,

$$\sin \theta = \frac{\text{opposite}}{\text{hypotenuse}} \approx \frac{\frac{1}{2}d}{r}$$

The total magnetic field due to the two wires is in the $+x$-direction and has magnitude

$$B_{\text{net}} = 2B_x = \frac{\mu_0 I d}{2\pi r^2}$$

(b) By substitution,

$$B = \frac{\mu_0}{2\pi} \times \frac{Id}{r^2} = 2 \times 10^{-7} \frac{\text{T·m}}{\text{A}} \times \frac{5\,\text{A} \times 0.005\,\text{m}}{(1\,\text{m})^2} = 5 \times 10^{-9}\,\text{T}$$

The field due to the wires is 10^{-5} times the Earth's field.

Discussion The field strength at P due to both wires is a factor of d/r times the field strength due to either wire alone. Since $d/r = 0.005$, the field strength due to both is only 0.5% of the field strength due to either one. The field due to the two wires decreases with distance proportional to $1/r^2$. It falls off much faster with distance than does the field due to a single wire, which is proportional to $1/r$. With equal currents flowing in opposite directions, we have a net current of zero. The only reason the field isn't zero is the small distance between the two wires.

Continued on next page

Example 19.10 Continued

Since the current in household wiring actually alternates at 60 Hz, so does the field. If 5.0 A is the maximum current, then 5×10^{-9} T is the maximum field strength.

Practice Problem 19.10   Field Midway Between Two Wires

Find the magnetic field at a point halfway between the two wires in terms of I and d.

Magnetic Field due to a Circular Current Loop

In Section 19.7, we saw the first clue that a loop of wire that carries current around in a complete circuit is a magnetic dipole. A second clue comes from the magnetic field produced by a circular loop of current. As for a straight wire, the magnetic field lines circulate around the wire, but for a circular current loop, the field lines are not circular. The field lines are more concentrated inside the current loop and less concentrated outside (Fig. 19.38a). The field lines emerge from one side of the current loop (the north pole) and reenter the other side (the south pole). Thus, the field due to a current loop is similar to the field of a short bar magnet.

The direction of the field lines is given by right-hand rule 3.

Using Right-Hand Rule 3 to Find the Direction of the Magnetic Field due to a Circular Loop of Current

Curl the fingers of your right hand inward toward the palm, following the current around the loop (Fig. 19.38b). Your thumb points in the direction of the magnetic field in the *interior* of the loop.

The magnitude of the magnetic field *at the center* of a circular loop (or coil) is given by

$$B = \frac{\mu_0 NI}{2r} \tag{19-16}$$

where N is the number of turns, I is the current, and r is the radius.

The magnetic fields due to coils of current-carrying wire are used in televisions and computer monitors to deflect the electron beam so that it lands on the screen in the desired spot.

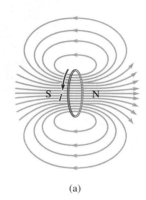

(a)

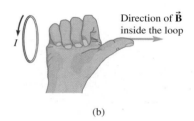

Direction of $\vec{\mathbf{B}}$ inside the loop

(b)

Figure 19.38 (a) Magnetic field lines due to a circular current loop. (b) Using right-hand rule 3 to determine the direction of the field inside the loop.

Magnetic Field due to a Solenoid

An important source of magnetic field is that due to a **solenoid** because the field inside a solenoid is nearly uniform. In magnetic resonance imaging (MRI), the patient is immersed in a strong magnetic field inside a solenoid.

To construct a solenoid with a circular cross section, wire is tightly wrapped in a cylindrical shape, forming a helix (Fig. 19.39a). We can think of the field as the superposition of the fields due to a large number of circular loops. If the loops are sufficiently close together, then the field lines go straight through one loop to the next, all the way down the solenoid. Having a large number of loops, one next to the other, straightens out the field lines. Figure 19.39b shows the magnetic field lines due to a solenoid. Inside the solenoid and away from the ends, the field is nearly uniform and parallel to the solenoid's axis as long as the solenoid is long compared to its radius. To find in which direction the field points along the axis, use right-hand rule 3 exactly as for the circular loop of current.

If a long solenoid has N turns of wire and length L, then the magnetic field strength inside is given by (see Problem 67)

Magnetic field strength inside an ideal solenoid:

$$B = \frac{\mu_0 NI}{L} = \mu_0 nI \tag{19-17}$$

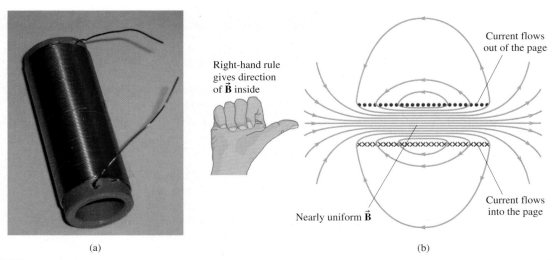

Figure 19.39 (a) A solenoid. (b) Magnetic field lines due to a solenoid. Each dot represents the wire crossing the plane of the page with current out of the page; each cross represents the wire crossing the plane of the page with current into the page.

In Eq. (19-17), I is the current in the wire and $n = N/L$ is the number of turns per unit length. Note that the field does *not* depend on the radius of the solenoid. The magnetic field near the ends is weaker and starts to bend outward; the field outside the solenoid is quite small—look how spread out the field lines are outside. A solenoid is one way to produce a nearly uniform magnetic field.

The similarity in the magnetic field lines due to a solenoid compared to those due to a bar magnet (Fig. 19.1b) suggested to André-Marie Ampère that the magnetic field of a permanent magnet might also be due to electric currents. The nature of these currents is explored in Section 19.10.

Magnetic Resonance Imaging

In magnetic resonance imaging (Fig. 19.40), the main solenoid is usually made with superconducting wire, which must be kept at low temperature (see Section 18.4). The main solenoid produces a strong, uniform magnetic field (typically 0.5–2 T). The nuclei of hydrogen atoms (protons) in the body act like tiny permanent magnets; a magnetic torque tends to make them line up with the magnetic field. A radio-frequency coil emits pulses of radio waves (rapidly varying electric and magnetic fields). If the radio wave has just the right frequency (the resonant frequency), the protons can absorb energy from the wave, which disturbs their magnetic alignment. When the protons flip back into alignment with the field, they emit radio wave signals of their own that can be detected by the radio-frequency coil.

The resonant frequency of the pulse that makes the protons flip depends on the total magnetic field due to the MRI machine and due to the neighboring atoms. Protons in different chemical environments have slightly different resonant frequencies. In order to image a slice of the body, three other coils create small (15 to 30-mT) magnetic fields that vary in the x-, y-, and z-directions. The magnetic fields of these coils are adjusted so that the protons are in resonance with the radio-frequency signal only in a single slice, a few mm thick, in any desired direction through the body.

19.9   AMPÈRE'S LAW

Ampère's law plays a role in magnetism similar to that of Gauss's law in electricity. Both relate the field to the source of the field. For the electric field, the source is charge. Gauss's law relates the net charge inside a closed surface to the flux of the electric field through that surface. The source of magnetic fields is current. Ampère's law must take a different form from Gauss's law: since magnetic field lines are always closed loops, the magnetic flux through a *closed surface* is always zero. (This fact is called *Gauss's law for magnetism* and is itself a fundamental law of electromagnetism.)

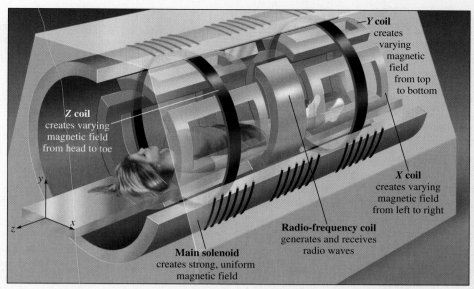

Figure 19.40 MRI apparatus.

Instead of a closed surface, Ampère's law concerns any closed *path* or *loop*. For Gauss's law we would find the flux: the perpendicular component of the electric field times the surface area. If $E_\perp$ is not the same everywhere, then we break the surface into pieces and sum up $E_\perp \Delta A$. For Ampère's law, we multiply the component of the magnetic field *parallel* to the path (or the tangential component at points along a closed curve) times the *length* of the path. Just as for flux, if the magnetic field component is not constant then we take parts of the path (each of length Δl) and sum up the product. This quantity is called the **circulation**.

$$\text{circulation} = \sum B_\parallel \Delta l \qquad (19\text{-}18)$$

Ampère's law relates the circulation of the field to the *net* current I that crosses the interior of the path.

Ampère's Law

$$\sum B_\parallel \Delta l = \mu_0 I \qquad (19\text{-}19)$$

There is a symmetry between Gauss's law and Ampère's law (Table 19.1).

Table 19.1

Gauss's Law	Ampère's Law
Electric field	Magnetic field (static only)
Applies to any closed *surface*	Applies to any closed *path*
Relates the electric field on the surface to the net *electric charge* inside the surface	Relates the magnetic field on the path to the net *current* cutting through interior of the path
Component of the electric field *perpendicular* to the surface ($E_\perp$)	Component of the magnetic field *parallel* to the path ($B_\parallel$)
Flux = perpendicular field component $\times$ *area* of surface	Circulation = parallel field component $\times$ *length* of path
$\sum E_\perp \Delta A$	$\sum B_\parallel \Delta l$
Flux = $1/\epsilon_0 \times$ net charge	Circulation = $\mu_0 \times$ net current
$\sum E_\perp \Delta A = \dfrac{1}{\epsilon_0} q$	$\sum B_\parallel \Delta l = \mu_0 I$

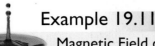

Example 19.11

Magnetic Field due to a Long Straight Wire

Use Ampère's law to show that the magnetic field due to a long straight wire is $B = \mu_0 I/(2\pi r)$.

Strategy   As with Gauss's law, the key is to exploit the symmetry of the situation. The field lines have to be circles around the wire, assuming the ends are far away. Choose a closed path around a circular field line (Fig. 19.41). The field is everywhere tangent to the field line and therefore tangent to the path; there is no perpendicular component. The field must also have the same magnitude at a uniform distance r from the wire.

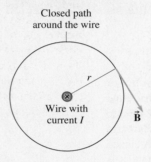

Closed path
around the wire

Wire with
current I

$\vec{\mathbf{B}}$

Figure 19.41

Applying Ampère's law to a long straight wire. A closed path is chosen to follow a circular magnetic field line; the magnetic field is then calculated from Ampère's law.

Solution   Since the field has no component perpendicular to the path, $B_\parallel = B$. Going around the circular path, B is constant, so

$$\text{circulation} = B \times 2\pi r = \mu_0 I$$

where I is the current in the wire. Solving for B,

$$B = \frac{\mu_0 I}{2\pi r}$$

Discussion   Ampère's law shows why the magnetic field of a long wire varies inversely as the distance from the wire. A circle of any radius r around the wire has a length that is proportional to r, while the current that cuts through the interior of the circle is always the same (I). So the field must be proportional to $1/r$.

Practice Problem 19.11   Circulation due to Three Wires

What is the circulation of the magnetic field for the path in Fig. 19.42?

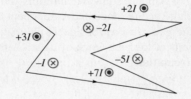

Figure 19.42

Six wires perpendicular to the page carry currents as indicated. A path is chosen to enclose three of the wires.

19.10   MAGNETIC MATERIALS

All materials are magnetic in the sense that they have magnetic properties. The magnetic properties of most substances are quite unremarkable, though. If a bar magnet is held near a piece of wood or aluminum or plastic, there is no noticeable interaction between the two. In common parlance, these substances might be called nonmagnetic. In reality, all substances experience *some* force when near a bar magnet. For most substances, the magnetic force is so weak that it is not noticed.

Substances that experience a noticeable force due to a nearby magnet are called **ferromagnetic** (*ferro-* in Latin refers to iron). Iron is a well-known ferromagnet; others include nickel, cobalt, and chromium dioxide (used to make chrome audiotapes). Ferromagnetic materials experience a magnetic force toward a region of stronger magnetic field. Refrigerator magnets stick because the refrigerator door is made of a ferromagnetic metal. When a permanent magnet is brought near, there is an attractive force on the door, and from Newton's third law there must also be an attractive force on the magnet. The surfaces of the magnet and the door are pulled together by magnetic forces. As a result, each exerts a surface contact force on the other; the component of the contact force parallel to the contact surface—the frictional force—holds the magnet up.

The so-called nonmagnetic substances can be divided into two groups. **Paramagnetic substances** are like the ferromagnets in that they are attracted toward regions of stronger magnetic field, though the force is *much* weaker. **Diamagnetic** substances are weakly repelled by a region of stronger field. All substances, including liquids and gases, are either ferromagnetic, paramagnetic, or diamagnetic.

Any substance, whether ferromagnetic, diamagnetic, or paramagnetic, contains a large number of tiny magnets: the electrons. The electrons are like little magnets in two ways. First, an electron's orbital motion around the nucleus makes it a tiny current loop and thus is a magnetic dipole. Second, an electron has an *intrinsic* magnetic dipole moment *independent of its motion*. The intrinsic magnetism of the electron is one of its fundamental properties, just like its electric charge and mass. (Other particles, such as protons and neutrons, also have intrinsic magnetic dipole moments.) The net magnetic dipole moment of an atom or molecule is the vector sum of the dipole moments of its constituent particles.

In most materials—paramagnets and diamagnets—the atomic dipoles are randomly oriented. Even when the material is immersed in a strong external magnetic field, the dipoles only have a slight tendency to line up with it. The torque that tends to make dipoles line up with the external magnetic field is overwhelmed by the thermal tendency for the dipoles to be *randomly* aligned, so there is only a slight degree of large-scale alignment. The magnetic field inside the material is nearly the same as the applied field; the dipoles have little effect in paramagnets and diamagnets.

Ferromagnetic materials have much stronger magnetic properties because there is an interaction—the explanation of which requires quantum physics—that keeps the magnetic dipoles aligned, even in the *absence* of an external magnetic field. A ferromagnetic material is divided up into regions called **domains** in which the atomic or molecular dipoles line up with each other. Even though each atom is a weak magnet by itself, when all of them have their dipoles aligned in the same direction within a domain, the domain can have a significant dipole moment.

The moments of different domains are not necessarily aligned with each other, however. Some may point one way and some another (Fig. 19.43a). When the net dipole moment of all the domains is zero, the material is unmagnetized. If the material is placed in an external magnetic field, two things happen. Atomic dipoles at domain boundaries can "defect" from one domain to an adjacent one by flipping their dipole moments. Thus, domains with their dipole moments aligned or nearly aligned with the external field grow in size and the others shrink. The other thing that happens is that domains can change their direction of orientation, with all the atomic dipoles flipping to a new direction. When the net dipole moment of all the domains is nonzero, the material is magnetized (Fig. 19.43b).

PHYSICS AT HOME

If a paper clip is placed in contact with a magnet, the paper clip becomes magnetized and can attract other paper clips. This phenomenon is easily observed in paper-clip containers with magnets that hold the paper clips upright for ease in pulling one out. The magnetized paper clips often drag out other paper clips as well (Fig. 19.44). Try it.

Once a ferromagnet is magnetized, it does not necessarily lose its magnetization when the external field is removed. It takes some energy to align the domains with the field; there is a kind of internal friction that must be overcome. If there is a lot of this internal friction, then the domains stay aligned even after the external field is removed. The material is then a permanent magnet. If there is relatively little of this internal friction, then there is little energy required to reorient the domains. This kind of ferromagnet does not make a good permanent magnet; when the external field is removed, it retains only a small fraction of its maximum magnetization.

At high temperature, the interaction that keeps the dipoles aligned within a domain is no longer able to do so. Without the alignment of dipoles, there are no longer any domains; the material becomes paramagnetic. The temperature at which this occurs for a particular ferromagnetic material is called the *Curie temperature* of that material [after Pierre Curie (1859–1906), the French physicist famous for studies of radioactive materials done with his wife, Marie Curie]. For iron, the Curie temperature is about 770°C.

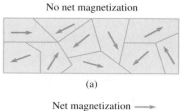
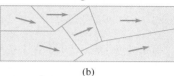

Figure 19.43 Domains within a ferromagnetic material are indicated by arrows indicating the direction of each domain's magnetic field. In (a), the domains are randomly oriented; the material is unmagnetized. In (b), the material is magnetized; the domains show a high degree of alignment to the right.

Figure 19.44 Each magnetized paper clip is capable of magnetizing another paper clip.

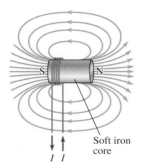

Figure 19.45 An electromagnet with field lines sketched.

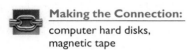

Electromagnets

An *electromagnet* is made by inserting a *soft iron* core into the interior of a solenoid. Soft iron does not retain a significant permanent magnetization when the solenoid's field is turned off—soft iron does not make a good permanent magnet. When current flows in the solenoid, magnetic dipoles in the iron tend to line up with the field due to the solenoid. The net effect is that the field inside the iron is intensified by a factor known as the **relative permeability** κ_B. The relative permeability is analogous in magnetism to the dielectric constant in electricity. However, the dielectric constant is the factor by which the electric field is *weakened*, while the relative permeability is the factor by which the magnetic field is *strengthened*. The relative permeability of a ferromagnet can be in the hundreds or even thousands—the intensification of the magnetic field is significant. Not only that, but in an electromagnet the strength and even direction of the magnetic field can be changed by changing the current in the solenoid. Figure 19.45 shows the field lines in an electromagnet. Notice that the iron core channels the field lines; the windings of the solenoid need not be at the business end of the electromagnet.

Magnetic Storage

The basic principles of magnetic storage are the same, whether applied to computer hard disks, removable disks, or magnetic tape used to store audio, video, or computer data. To record or write, an electromagnet called a *head* is used to magnetize ferromagnetic particles in a coating on the disk or tape surface (Fig. 19.46). The ferromagnetic particles retain their magnetization even after the head has moved away, so the data persists until it is erased or written over. Data can be erased if a tape or disk is brought close to a strong magnet.

Figure 19.46 A computer hard drive. Each platter has a magnetizable coating on each side. The spindle motor turns the platters at several thousand rpm. There is one read-write head on each surface of each platter.

MASTER THE CONCEPTS

- Magnetic field lines are interpreted just like electric field lines. The magnetic field at any point is tangent to the field line; the magnitude of the field is proportional to the number of lines per unit area perpendicular to the lines.

- Magnetic field lines are always closed loops because there are no magnetic monopoles.

- The smallest unit of magnetism is the magnetic dipole. Field lines emerge from the north pole and reenter at the south pole. A magnet can have more than two poles, but it must have at least one north pole and at least one south pole.

- The magnitude of the cross product of two vectors is the magnitude of one vector times the perpendicular component of the other:

$$|\vec{\mathbf{a}} \times \vec{\mathbf{b}}| = |\vec{\mathbf{b}} \times \vec{\mathbf{a}}| = a_\perp b = ab_\perp = ab \sin \theta \quad (19\text{-}3)$$

- The direction of the cross product is the direction perpendicular to both vectors that is chosen using right-hand rule 1 (see Fig. 19.7).

- The magnetic force on a charged particle is

$$\vec{\mathbf{F}}_B = q\vec{\mathbf{v}} \times \vec{\mathbf{B}} \quad (19\text{-}5)$$

MASTER THE CONCEPTS *continued*

If the charge is at rest ($v = 0$) or if its velocity has no component perpendicular to the magnetic field ($v_\perp = 0$), then the magnetic force is zero. The force is always perpendicular to the magnetic field and to the velocity of the particle.

$$\text{Magnitude: } F_B = qvB \sin \theta$$

Direction: use the right-hand rule to find $\vec{v} \times \vec{B}$, then reverse it if q is negative.

- The SI unit of magnetic field is the tesla:

$$1 \text{ T} = 1 \frac{\text{N}}{\text{A·m}} \qquad (19\text{-}2)$$

- If a charged particle moves at right angles to a uniform magnetic field, then its trajectory is a circle. If the velocity has a component parallel to the field as well as a component perpendicular to the field, then its trajectory is a helix.

- The magnetic force on a straight wire carrying current I is

$$\vec{F} = I\vec{L} \times \vec{B} \qquad (19\text{-}12\text{a})$$

where $\vec{L}$ is a vector whose magnitude is the length of the wire and whose direction is along the wire in the direction of the current.

- The magnetic torque on a planar current loop is

$$\tau = NIAB \sin \theta \qquad (19\text{-}13\text{b})$$

where θ is the angle between the magnetic field and the dipole moment vector of the loop. The direction

of the dipole moment is perpendicular to the loop as chosen using right-hand rule 1 (take the cross product of $\vec{L}$ for any side with $\vec{L}$ for the *next* side, going around in the same direction as the current).

- The magnetic field at a distance r from a long straight wire has magnitude

$$B = \frac{\mu_0 I}{2\pi r} \qquad (19\text{-}14)$$

The field lines are circles around the wire with the direction given by right-hand rule 2 (see Fig. 19.34c).

- The permeability of free space is

$$\mu_0 = 4\pi \times 10^{-7} \frac{\text{T·m}}{\text{A}} \qquad (19\text{-}15)$$

- The magnetic field inside a long tightly wound solenoid is uniform:

$$B = \frac{\mu_0 NI}{L} = \mu_0 nI \qquad (19\text{-}17)$$

Its direction is along the axis of the solenoid, as given by right-hand rule 3 (Fig. 19.38b).

- Ampère's law relates the circulation of the magnetic field around a closed path to the *net* current I that crosses the interior of the path.

$$\sum B_\parallel \Delta l = \mu_0 I \qquad (19\text{-}19)$$

- The magnetic properties of ferromagnetic materials are due to an interaction that keeps the magnetic dipoles aligned within regions called domains, even in the *absence* of an external magnetic field.

Conceptual Questions

1. The electric field is defined as the electric force per unit charge. Explain why the magnetic field *cannot* be defined as the magnetic force per unit charge.

2. A charged particle moves through a region of space at constant velocity. Ignore gravity. In the region, is it possible that there is (a) a magnetic field but no electric field? (b) an electric field but no magnetic field? (c) a magnetic field and an electric field? For each possibility, what must be true about the direction(s) of the field(s)?

3. Suppose that a horizontal electron beam is deflected to the right by a uniform magnetic field. What is the direction of the magnetic field? If there is more than one possibility, what can you say about the direction of the field?

4. A circular metal loop carries a current I as shown. The points are all in the plane of the page and the loop is perpendicular to the page. Sketch the loop, and draw vector arrows at the 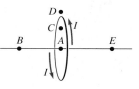 points A, B, C, D, and E to show the direction of the magnetic field at those points.

5. In a TV or computer monitor, a constant electric field accelerates the electrons to high speed; then a magnetic field is used to deflect the electrons to the side. Why can't a constant magnetic field be used to speed up the electrons?

6. A uniform magnetic field directed upward exists in some region of space. In what direction(s) could an electron be moving if its trajectory is (a) a straight line? (b) a circle? Assume that the electron is subject only to magnetic forces.

7. In a velocity selector, the electric and magnetic forces cancel if $\vec{E} + \vec{v} \times \vec{B} = 0$. Show that $\vec{v}$ must be in the same direction as $\vec{E} \times \vec{B}$. [*Hint:* Since $\vec{v}$ is perpendicular to both $\vec{E}$ and $\vec{B}$ in a velocity selector, there are only two possibilities for the direction of $\vec{v}$: the direction of $\vec{E} \times \vec{B}$ or the direction of $-\vec{E} \times \vec{B}$.]

8. Two ions with the same velocity and mass but different charges enter the magnetic field of a mass spectrometer. One is singly charged ($q = +e$) and the other is doubly charged ($q = +2e$). Is the radius of their circular paths the same? If not, which is larger? By what factor?

9. The mayor of a city proposes a new law to require that magnetic fields generated by the power lines running through the city be zero outside of the electric company's right of way. What would you say at a public discussion of the proposed law?

10. A horizontal wire that runs east-west carries a steady current to the east. A C-shaped magnet (see Fig. 19.3a) is placed so that the wire runs between the poles, with the north pole above the wire and the south pole below. What is the direction of the magnetic force on the wire between the poles?

11. The magnetic field due to a long straight wire carrying steady current is measured at two points, P and Q. Where is the wire and in what direction does the current flow?

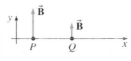

12. A circular loop of current carries a steady current. (a) Sketch the magnetic field lines in a plane perpendicular to the plane of the loop. (b) Which side of the loop is the north pole of the magnetic dipole and which is the south pole?

13. Computer speakers that are intended to be placed near a computer monitor are magnetically shielded—either they don't use magnets or they are designed so that their magnets produce only a small magnetic field nearby. Why is the shielding important? What might happen if an ordinary speaker (*not* intended for use near a monitor) is placed next to a computer monitor?

14. One iron nail does not necessarily attract another iron nail, although both are attracted by a magnet. Explain.

15. Two wires at right angles in a plane carry equal currents. At what points in the plane is the magnetic field zero?

16. If a magnet is held near the screen of a TV, computer monitor, or oscilloscope, the picture is distorted. [*Don't try this*—see part (b).] (a) Why is the picture distorted? (b) With a color TV or monitor, the distortion remains even after the magnet is removed. Explain. (A color CRT has a metal mask just behind the screen with holes to line up the electrons from different guns with the red, green, and blue phosphors. Of what kind of metal is the mask made?)

17. A metal bar is shown at two different times. The arrows represent the alignment of the dipoles within each magnetic domain. (a) What happened between t_1 and t_2 to cause the change? (b) Is the metal a paramagnet, diamagnet, or ferromagnet? Explain.

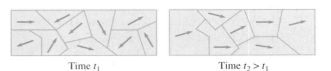

Time t_1 Time $t_2 > t_1$

18. Explain why a constant magnetic field does no work on a point charge moving through the field. Since the field does no work, what can we say about the speed of a point charge acted on only by a magnetic field?

19. Refer to the bubble chamber tracks in Fig. 19.15a. Suppose that particle 2 moves in a smaller circle than particle 1. Can we conclude that $|q_2| > |q_1|$? Explain.

20. The trajectory of a charged particle in a uniform magnetic field is a helix if $\vec{v}$ has components both parallel to and perpendicular to the field. Explain how the two other cases (circular motion for $v_{\parallel} = 0$ and straight line motion for $v_{\perp} = 0$) can each be considered to be special cases of helical motion.

Multiple-Choice Questions

Multiple-Choice Questions 1–4. In the figure, four point charges move in the directions indicated in the vicinity of a bar magnet. The magnet, charge positions, and velocity vectors all lie in the plane of this page. Answer choices:

   (a) ↑   (b) ↓   (c) ←   (d) →
   (e) × (into page)   (f) • (out of page)   (g) the force is zero

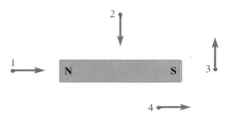

Multiple-Choice Questions 1–4

1. What is the direction of the magnetic force on charge 1 if $q_1 < 0$?

2. What is the direction of the magnetic force on charge 2 if $q_2 > 0$?

3. What is the direction of the magnetic force on charge 3 if $q_3 < 0$?

4. What is the direction of the magnetic force on charge 4 if $q_4 < 0$?

5. The magnetic force on a point charge in a magnetic field $\vec{\mathbf{B}}$ is largest, for a given speed, when it

   (a) moves in the direction of the magnetic field.
   (b) moves in the direction opposite to the magnetic field.
   (c) moves perpendicular to the magnetic field.
   (d) has velocity components both parallel to and perpendicular to the field.

Multiple-Choice Questions 6–9. A wire carries current as shown in the figure. Charged particles 1, 2, 3, and 4 move in the directions indicated. Answer choices for Questions 6–8:

   (a) ↑   (b) ↓
   (c) ←   (d) →
   (e) ×(into page)
   (f) ⊙ (out of page)
   (g) the force is zero

Multiple-Choice
Questions 6–9

6. What is the direction of the magnetic force on charge 1 if $q_1 < 0$?

7. What is the direction of the magnetic force on charge 2 if $q_2 > 0$?

8. What is the direction of the magnetic force on charge 3 if $q_3 < 0$?

9. If the magnetic forces on charges 1 and 4 are equal and their velocities are equal,

   (a) the charges have the same sign and $|q_1| > |q_4|$.
   (b) the charges have opposite signs and $|q_1| > |q_4|$.
   (c) the charges have the same sign and $|q_1| < |q_4|$.
   (d) the charges have opposite signs and $|q_1| < |q_4|$.
   (e) $q_1 = q_4$.   (f) $q_1 = -q_4$.

10. The magnetic field lines *inside* a bar magnet run in what direction?

   (a) from north pole to south pole
   (b) from south pole to north pole
   (c) from side to side
   (d) None of the above—there are no magnetic field lines *inside* a bar magnet.

11. The magnetic forces that two parallel wires with unequal currents flowing in opposite directions exert on each other are

   (a) attractive and unequal in magnitude.
   (b) repulsive and unequal in magnitude.
   (c) attractive and equal in magnitude.
   (d) repulsive and equal in magnitude.
   (e) both zero.
   (f) in the same direction and unequal in magnitude.
   (g) in the same direction and equal in magnitude.

12. What is the direction of the magnetic field at point P in the figure? (P is on the axis of the coil.)

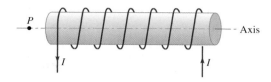

   (a) ↑   (b) ↓   (c) ←   (d) →
   (e) ×(into page)   (f) • (out of page)

Problems

Ⓒ   Combination conceptual/quantitative problem

🔬   Biological or medical application

No ✦   Easy to moderate difficulty level

✦   More challenging

✦✦   Most challenging

Blue # Detailed solution in the Student Solutions Manual

[1 2] Problems paired by concept

19.1 Magnetic Fields

Ⓒ 1. At which point in the diagram is the magnetic field strength (a) the smallest and (b) the largest? Explain.

2. Draw vector arrows to indicate the direction and relative magnitude of the magnetic field at each of the points A–F.

   Problems 1 and 2

3. Two identical bar magnets lie next to one another on a table. Sketch the magnetic field lines if the north poles are at the same end.

N	S
N	S

4. Two identical bar magnets lie next to one another on a table. Sketch the magnetic field lines if the north poles are at opposite ends.

N	S
S	N

5. Two identical bar magnets lie on a table along a straight line with their north poles facing each other. Sketch the magnetic field lines.

   | S | N | N | S |

6. Two identical bar magnets lie on a table along a straight line with opposite poles facing each other. Sketch the magnetic field lines.

   | N | S | N | S |

7. The magnetic forces on a magnetic dipole result in a torque that tends to make the dipole line up with the magnetic field. In this problem we show that the *electric forces* on an *electric dipole* result in a torque that tends to make the electric dipole line up with the electric field. (a) For each orientation of the dipole shown in

the diagram, sketch the electric forces and determine the direction of the torque—clockwise or counterclockwise—about an axis perpendicular to the page through the center of the dipole. (b) The torque always tends to make the dipole rotate toward what orientation?

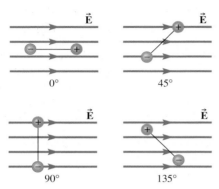

19.2 Magnetic Force on a Point Charge

8. Find the magnetic force exerted on an electron moving vertically upward at a speed of 2.0×10^7 m/s by a horizontal magnetic field of 0.50 T directed north.

9. A uniform magnetic field points north; its magnitude is 1.5 T. A proton with kinetic energy 8.0×10^{-13} J is moving vertically downward in this field. What is the magnetic force acting on it?

10. Find the magnetic force (magnitude and direction) on an electron moving at speed 8.0 $\times 10^5$ m/s for each of the directions shown. The magnetic field has magnitude $B = 0.40$ T.

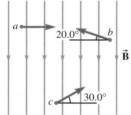

C 11. Electrons in a television's CRT are accelerated from rest by an electric field through a potential difference of 2.5 kV. In contrast to an oscilloscope, where the electron beam is deflected by an electric field, the beam is deflected by a magnetic field. (a) What is the speed of the electrons? (b) The beam is deflected by a perpendicular magnetic field of magnitude 0.80 T. What is the acceleration of the electrons while in the field? (c) What is the speed of the electrons after they travel 4.0 mm through the magnetic field? (d) What strength electric field would give the electrons the same magnitude acceleration as in (b)? (e) Why do we have to use an electric field in the first place to get the electrons up to speed? Why not use the large acceleration due to a magnetic field for that purpose?

12. A magnet produces a 0.30-T field between its poles, directed to the east. A dust particle with charge $q = -8.0 \times 10^{-18}$ C is moving straight down at 0.30 cm/s in this field. What is the magnitude and direction of the magnetic force on the dust particle?

✦ 13. An electron beam in vacuum moving at 1.8×10^7 m/s passes between the poles of an electromagnet. The diameter of the magnet pole faces is 2.4 cm and the field between them is 0.20×10^{-2} T. How far and in what direction is the beam deflected when it hits the screen, which is 25 cm past the magnet? [Hint: The electron velocity changes relatively little, so approximate the magnetic force as a constant force acting during a 2.4-cm displacement to the right.]

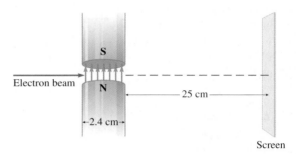

✦ 14. A positron ($q = +e$) moves at 5.0×10^7 m/s in a magnetic field of magnitude 0.47 T. The magnetic force on the positron has magnitude 2.3×10^{-12} N. (a) What is the component of the positron's velocity perpendicular to the magnetic field? (b) What is the component of the positron's velocity parallel to the magnetic field? (c) What is the angle between the velocity and the field?

✦ 15. An electron moves with speed 2.0×10^5 m/s in a 1.2-T uniform magnetic field. At one instant, the electron is moving due west and experiences an upward magnetic force of 3.2×10^{-14} N. What is the direction of the magnetic field? Be specific: give the angle(s) with respect to N, S, E, W, up, down. (If there is more than one possible answer, find all the possibilities.)

✦ 16. An electron moves with speed 2.0×10^5 m/s in a uniform magnetic field of 1.4 T, pointing south. At one instant, the electron experiences an upward magnetic force of 1.6×10^{-14} N. In what direction is the electron moving at that instant? Be specific: give the angle(s) with respect to N, S, E, W, up, down. (If there is more than one possible answer, find all the possibilities.)

17. At a certain point on the surface of the Earth in the southern hemisphere, the Earth's magnetic field has a magnitude of 5.0×10^{-5} T and points upward and toward the north at an angle of 55° above the horizontal. A cosmic ray muon with the same charge as an electron and a mass of 1.9×10^{-28} kg is moving directly down toward Earth's surface with a speed of 4.5×10^7 m/s. What is the magnitude and direction of the force on the muon?

19.3 Charged Particle Moving Perpendicularly to a Uniform Magnetic Field

18. The magnetic field in a cyclotron is 0.50 T. Find the magnitude of the magnetic force on a proton with velocity of 1.0×10^7 m/s in a plane perpendicular to the field.

19. When two particles travel through a region of uniform magnetic field pointing out of the plane of the paper, they follow the trajectories shown. What are the signs of the charges of each particle?

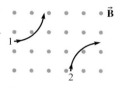

20. The magnetic field in a cyclotron is 0.50 T. What must be the radius of the vacuum chamber if the maximum proton velocity desired is 1.0×10^7 m/s?

21. A singly charged ion of unknown mass moves in a circle of radius 12.5 cm in a magnetic field of 1.2 T. The ion was accelerated through a potential difference of 7.0 kV before it entered the magnetic field. What is the mass of the ion?

22. Natural carbon consists of two different isotopes (excluding ^{14}C, which is present in only trace amounts). The isotopes have different masses, which is due to different numbers of neutrons in the nucleus; however, the number of protons is the same, and subsequently the chemical properties are the same. The most abundant isotope has an atomic mass of 12.0000 u. When natural carbon is placed in a mass spectrometer, two lines are formed on the photographic plate. The lines show that the more abundant isotope moved in a circle of radius 15.0 cm, while the rarer isotope moved in a circle of radius 15.6 cm. What is the atomic mass of the rarer isotope? (The ions are accelerated through the same potential difference before entering the magnetic field.)

23. After being accelerated through a potential difference of 5.0 kV, a singly charged carbon ion (^{12}C) moves in a circle of radius 21 cm in the magnetic field of a mass spectrometer. What is the magnitude of the field?

24. A sample containing carbon (atomic mass 12 u), oxygen (16 u), and an unknown element is placed in a mass spectrometer. The ions all have the same charge and are accelerated through the same potential difference before entering the magnetic field. The carbon and oxygen lines are separated by 2.250 cm on the photographic plate, and the unknown element makes a line between them that is 1.160 cm from the carbon line. (a) What is the mass of the unknown element? (b) Identify the element.

25. A sample containing sulfur (atomic mass 32 u), manganese (55 u), and an unknown element is placed in a mass spectrometer. The ions are accelerated through the same potential difference before entering the magnetic field. The sulfur and manganese lines are separated by 3.20 cm, and the unknown element makes a line between them that is 1.07 cm from the sulfur line. (a) What is the mass of the unknown element? (b) Identify the element.

26. In one type of mass spectrometer, ions having the *same velocity* move through a uniform magnetic field. The spectrometer is being used to distinguish ^{12}C and ^{14}C ions that have the same charge. The ^{12}C ions move in a circle of diameter 25 cm. (a) What is the diameter of the orbit of ^{14}C ions? (b) What is the ratio of the frequencies of revolution for the two types of ion? (c) Repeat parts (a) and (b) if the ions are given the same *kinetic energy* rather than the same velocity.

19.5 A Charged Particle in Crossed $\vec{E}$ and $\vec{B}$ Fields

27. Crossed electric and magnetic fields are established over a certain region. The magnetic field is 0.635 T vertically downward. The electric field is 2.68×10^6 V/m horizontally east. An electron, traveling horizontally northward, experiences zero net force from these fields and so continues moving in a straight line. What is the electron's speed?

28. A charged particle is accelerated from rest through a potential difference ΔV. The particle then passes straight through a velocity selector (field magnitudes E and B). Derive an expression for the charge-to-mass ratio (q/m) of the particle in terms of ΔV, E, and B.

29. A current $I = 40.0$ A flows through a strip of metal. An electromagnet is switched on so that there is a uniform magnetic field of magnitude 0.30 T directed into the page. (a) How would you hook up a voltmeter to measure the Hall voltage? Show how the voltmeter is connected on a sketch of the strip. (b) Assuming the carriers are electrons, which lead of your voltmeter is at the higher potential? Mark it with a "+" sign in your sketch. Explain briefly.

Problems 29–33

30. In Problem 29, if the width of the strip is 3.5 cm, the magnetic field is 0.43 T, and the Hall voltage is measured to be 7.2 µV, what is the drift velocity of the carriers in the strip?

31. In Problem 29, the width of the strip is 3.5 cm, the magnetic field is 0.43 T, the Hall voltage is measured to be 7.2 µV, the thickness of the strip is 0.24 mm, and the current in the wire is 54 A. What is the density of carriers (number of carriers per unit volume) in the strip?

32. The strip in the diagram is used as a Hall probe to measure magnetic fields. (a) What happens if the strip is not perpendicular to the field? Does the Hall probe still read the correct field strength? Explain. (b) What happens if the field is in the plane of the strip?

33. A strip of copper 2.0 cm wide carries a current $I = 30.0$ A to the right. The strip is in a magnetic field $B = 5.0$ T into the page. (a) What is the direction of the average magnetic force on the conduction electrons? (b) The Hall voltage is 20.0 µV. What is the drift velocity?

34. A proton is initially at rest and moves through three different regions as shown in the figure. In region 1, the proton accelerates across a potential difference of 3330 V. In region 2, there is a magnetic field of 1.20 T pointing out of the page and an electric field pointing perpendicular to the magnetic field and perpendicular to the proton's velocity. Finally, in region 3, there is no electric field, but just a 1.20-T magnetic field pointing out of the page. (a) What is the speed of the proton as it leaves region 1 and enters region 2? (b) If the proton travels in a straight line through region 2, what is the magnitude and direction of the electric field? (c) In region 3, will the proton follow path 1 or 2? (d) What will be the radius of the circular path the proton travels in region 3?

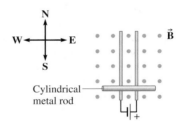

35. An electromagnetic flowmeter is used to measure blood flow rates during surgery. Blood containing Na^+ ions flows due south through an artery with a diameter of 0.40 cm. The artery is in a downward magnetic field of 0.25 T and develops a Hall voltage of 0.35 mV across its diameter. (a) What is the blood speed (in m/s)? (b) What is the flow rate (in m^3/s)? (c) The leads of a voltmeter are attached to diametrically opposed points on the artery to measure the Hall voltage. Which of the two leads is at the higher potential?

36. An electromagnetic flowmeter is used to measure blood flow rates during surgery. Blood containing ions (primarily Na^+) flows through an artery with a diameter of 0.50 cm. The artery is in a magnetic field of 0.35 T and develops a Hall voltage of 0.60 mV across its diameter. (a) What is the blood speed (in m/s)? (b) What is the flow rate (in m^3/s)? (c) If the magnetic field points west and the blood flow is north, is the top or bottom of the artery at the higher potential?

19.6 Magnetic Force on a Current-Carrying Wire

37. A straight wire segment of length 0.60 m carries a current of 18.0 A and is immersed in a uniform external magnetic field of magnitude 0.20 T. (a) What is the magnitude of the maximum possible magnetic force on the wire segment? (b) Explain why the given information enables you to calculate only the *maximum possible* force.

38. A straight wire segment of length 25 cm carries a current of 33.0 A and is immersed in a uniform external magnetic field. The magnetic force on the wire segment has magnitude 4.12 N. (a) What is the minimum possible magnitude of the magnetic field? (b) Explain why the given information enables you to calculate only the *minimum possible* field strength.

39. Parallel conducting tracks, separated by 2.0 cm, run north and south. There is a uniform magnetic field of 1.2 T pointing upward (out of the page). A 0.040-kg cylindrical metal rod is placed across the tracks and a battery is connected between the tracks, with its positive terminal connected to the east track. If the current through the rod is 3.0 A, find the magnitude and direction of the magnetic force on the rod.

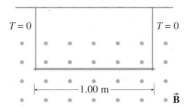

40. An electromagnetic rail gun can fire a projectile using a magnetic field and an electric current. Consider two conducting rails that are 0.500 m apart with a 50.0-g conducting rod connecting the two rails as in the figure with Problem 39. A magnetic field of magnitude 0.750 T is directed perpendicular to the plane of the rails and rod. A current of 2.00 A passes through the rod. (a) What direction is the force on the rod? (b) If there is no friction between the rails and the rod, how fast is the rod moving after it has traveled 8.00 m down the rails?

41. A straight, stiff wire of length 1.00 m and mass 25 g is suspended in a magnetic field $B = 0.75$ T. The wire is connected to an emf. How much current must flow in the wire and in what direction so that the wire is suspended and the tension in the supporting wires is zero?

42. A 20.0 cm × 30.0 cm rectangular loop of wire carries 1.0 A of current clockwise around the loop. (a) Find the magnetic force on each side of the loop if the magnetic field is 2.5 T out of the page. (b) What is the net magnetic force on the loop?

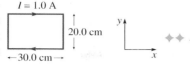

$I = 1.0$ A

20.0 cm

←30.0 cm→

Problems 42, 43, and 87

43. Repeat Problem 42 if the magnetic field is 2.5 T to the left (in the –x-direction).

✦ 44. A straight wire is aligned east-west in a region where the Earth's magnetic field has magnitude 0.48 mT and direction 72° below the horizontal, with the horizontal component directed due north. The wire carries a current I toward the west. The magnetic force on the wire per unit length of wire has magnitude 0.020 N/m. (a) What is the direction of the magnetic force on the wire? (b) What is the current I?

19.7 Torque on a Current Loop

45. In an electric motor, a circular coil with 100 turns of radius 2.0 cm can rotate between the poles of a magnet. When the current through the coil is 75 mA, the maximum torque that the motor can deliver is 0.0020 N·m. (a) What is the strength of the magnetic field? (b) Is the torque on the coil clockwise or counterclockwise as viewed from the front at the instant shown in the figure?

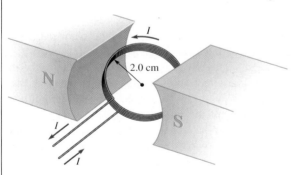

46. In an electric motor, a coil with 100 turns of radius 2.0 cm can rotate between the poles of a magnet. The magnetic field strength is 0.20 T. When the current through the coil is 50.0 mA, what is the maximum torque that the motor can deliver?

✦ 47. A certain fixed length L of wire carries a current I. (a) Show that if the wire is formed into a square coil, then the maximum torque in a given magnetic field B is developed when the coil has just one turn. (b) Show that the magnitude of this torque is $\tau = \frac{1}{16}L^2IB$.

48. A square loop of wire of side 3.0 cm carries 3.0 A of current. A uniform magnetic field of magnitude 0.67 T makes an angle of 37° with the plane of the loop.

(a) What is the magnitude of the torque on the loop? (b) What is the net magnetic force on the loop?

✦✦ 49. A square loop of wire with side 0.60 m carries a current of 9.0 A as shown in the figure. When there is no applied magnetic field, the plane of the loop is horizontal and the nonconducting, nonmagnetic spring (k = 550 N/m) is unstretched. A horizontal magnetic field of magnitude 1.3 T is now applied. At what angle θ is the wire loop's new equilibrium position? Assume the spring remains vertical because θ is small. [*Hint:* Set the sum of the torques from the spring and the magnetic field equal to 0.]

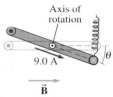

Axis of rotation

9.0 A

$\vec{\mathbf{B}}$

50. The torque on a loop of wire (a magnetic dipole) in a uniform magnetic field is $\tau = NIAB \sin \theta$, where θ is the angle between $\vec{\mathbf{B}}$ and a line perpendicular to the loop of wire. Suppose an *electric* dipole, consisting of two charges $\pm q$ a fixed distance d apart is in a uniform electric field $\vec{\mathbf{E}}$. (a) Show that the net electric force on the dipole is zero. (b) Let θ be the angle between $\vec{\mathbf{E}}$ and a line running from the negative to the positive charge. Show that the torque on the electric dipole is $\tau = qdE \sin \theta$ for all angles $-180° \leq \theta \leq 180°$. (Thus, for both electric and magnetic dipoles, the torque is the product of the *dipole moment* times the field strength times sin θ. The quantity qd is the electric dipole moment; the quantity NIA is the magnetic dipole moment.)

Ⓒ 51. Use the following method to show that the torque on an irregularly shaped planar loop is given by Eq. (19-13a). The irregular loop of current in part (a) of the figure carries current I. There is a perpendicular magnetic field B. To find the torque on the irregular loop, sum up the torques on each of the smaller loops shown in part (b) of the figure. The pairs of imaginary currents flowing across carry equal currents in opposite directions, so the magnetic forces on them would be equal and opposite; they would therefore contribute nothing to the net torque. Now generalize this argument to a loop of *any* shape. [*Hint:* Think of a curved loop as a series of tiny, straight, perpendicular segments.]

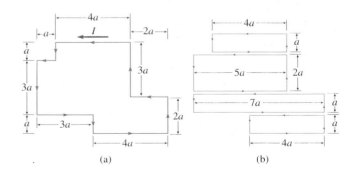

(a)   (b)

19.8 Magnetic Field due to an Electric Current

✦✦ 52. Two parallel long straight wires are suspended by strings of length $L = 1.2$ m. Each wire has mass per unit length 0.050 kg/m. When the wires each 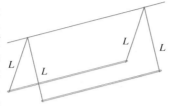 carry 50.0 A of current, the wires swing apart. (a) How far apart are the wires in equilibrium? (Assume that this distance is small compared to L.) [*Hint:* Use a small angle approximation.] (b) Are the wires carrying current in the same or opposite directions?

53. Imagine a long straight wire perpendicular to the page and carrying a current I into the page. Sketch some $\vec{B}$ field lines with arrowheads to indicate directions.

54. Two conducting wires perpendicular to the page are shown in cross section as gray dots in the figure. They each carry 10.0 A out of the page. What is the magnetic field at point P?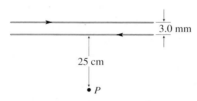

55. Two wires each carry 10.0 A of current (in *opposite directions*) and are 3.0 mm apart. (a) Calculate the magnetic field 25 cm away at point P, in the plane of the wires. (b) What is the magnetic field at the same point if the currents instead both run to the left?

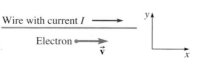

56. Point P is midway between two long, straight, parallel wires that run north-south in a horizontal plane. The distance between the wires is 1.0 cm. Each wire carries a current of 1.0 A toward the north. (a) Find the magnitude and direction of the magnetic field at point P. (b) Repeat the question if the current in the wire on the east side runs toward the south instead.

57. A long straight wire carries a current of 50.0 A. An electron, traveling at 1.0×10^7 m/s, is 5.0 cm from the wire. What force (magnitude and direction) acts on the electron if the electron's velocity is directed toward the wire?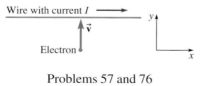

Problems 57 and 76

58. A long straight wire carries a current of 3.2 A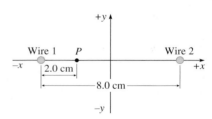

in the positive x-direction. An electron, traveling at 6.8×10^6 m/s in the positive x-direction, is 4.6 cm from the wire. What force acts on the electron?

ⓒ 59. Two long straight wires carry the same amount of current in the directions indicated. The wires cross each other in the plane of the paper. Rank points A, B, C, and D in order of decreasing field strength.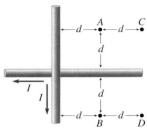

Problems 59 and 88

60. A solenoid of length 0.256 m and radius 2.0 cm has 244 turns of wire. What is the magnitude of the magnetic field well inside the solenoid when there is a current of 4.5 A in the wire?

61. Two long straight parallel wires separated by 8.0 cm carry currents of equal magnitude but heading in opposite directions. The wires are shown perpendicular to the plane of this page. Point P is 2.0 cm from wire 1, and the magnetic field at point P is 1.0×10^{-2} T directed in the $-y$-direction. Calculate the current in wire 1 and its direction.

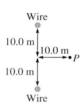

ⓒ 62. Two parallel wires in a horizontal plane carry currents I_1 and I_2 to the right. The wires each have length L and are separated by a distance d. (a) What are the magnitude and direction of the field due to wire 1 at the location of wire 2? (b) What are the magnitude and direction of the magnetic force on wire 2 due to this field? (c) What are the magnitude and direction of the field due to wire 2 at the location of wire 1? (d) What are the magnitude and direction of the magnetic force on wire 1 due to this field? (e) Do parallel currents in the same direction attract or repel? (f) What about parallel currents in opposite directions?

63. The derivation of Eq. (19-16) for the magnetic field at the center of a circular current loop, $B_{\text{loop}} = \mu_0 I/(2r)$, requires calculus. We can find an approximate value by arranging four long straight wires, each with current I, so they intersect to form a square loop with side $2r$. Find the magnetic field at the center of the square. Express your answer in terms of B_{loop}.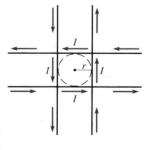

64. Two concentric circular wire loops in the same plane each carry a current. The larger loop has a current of 8.46 A circulating clockwise and has a radius of 6.20 cm. The smaller loop has a radius of 4.42 cm. What is the current in the smaller loop if the total magnetic field at the center of the system is zero? [See Eq. (19-16).]

19.9 Ampère's Law

65. A number of wires carry currents into or out of the page as indicated in the figure. (a) Using loop 1 for Ampère's law, what is the net current through the interior of the loop? (b) Repeat for loop 2.

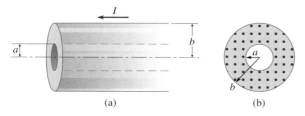

66. An infinitely long, thick cylindrical shell of inner radius a and outer radius b carries a current I uniformly distributed across a cross section of the shell. (a) On a sketch of a cross section of the shell, draw some magnetic field lines. The current flows out of the page. Consider all regions ($r \le a$, $a \le r \le b$, $b \le r$). (b) Find the magnetic field for $r > b$.

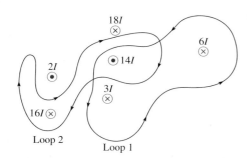

(a)   (b)

67. In this problem, use Ampère's law to show that the magnetic field inside a long solenoid is $B = \mu_0 nI$. Assume that the field inside the solenoid is uniform and parallel to the axis and that the field outside is zero. Choose a rectangular path for Ampère's law. (a) Write down $B_\parallel \Delta l$ for each of the four sides of the path, in terms of B, a, (the short side) and b (the long side). (b) Sum these to form the circulation. (c) Now, to find the current cutting through the path: each loop carries the same current I, and some number N of loops cut through the path, so the total current is NI. Rewrite N in terms of the number of turns per unit length (n) and the physical dimensions of the path. (d) Solve for B.

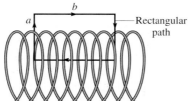

68. A toroid is like a solenoid that has been bent around in a circle until its ends meet. The field lines are circular, as shown in the figure. What is the magnitude of the magnetic field inside a toroid of N turns carrying current I? Apply Ampère's law, following a field line at a distance r from the center of the toroid. Work in terms of the total number of turns N, rather than the number of turns per unit length (why?). Is the field uniform, as it is for a long solenoid? Explain.

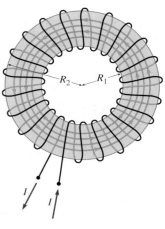

19.10 Magnetic Materials

69. A bar magnet is broken into two parts. If care is taken not to disturb the magnetic domains, what are the polarities of the new ends c and d respectively?

N   S   N c d S
(a)   (b)

70. The intrinsic magnetic dipole moment of the electron has magnitude 9.3×10^{-24} A·m². In other words, the electron acts as though it were a tiny current loop with $NIA = 9.3 \times 10^{-24}$ A·m². What is the maximum torque on an electron due to its intrinsic dipole moment in a 1.0-T magnetic field?

71. In a simple model, the electron in a hydrogen atom orbits the proton at a radius of 53 pm and at a constant speed of 2.2×10^6 m/s. The orbital motion of the electron gives it an orbital magnetic dipole moment. (a) What is the current I in this current loop? [Hint: How long does it take the electron to make one revolution?] (b) What is the orbital dipole moment IA? (c) Compare the orbital dipole moment to the intrinsic magnetic dipole moment of the electron (9.3×10^{-24} A·m²).

72. An electromagnet is made by inserting a soft iron core into a solenoid. The solenoid has 1800 turns, radius 2.0 cm, and length 15 cm. When 2.0 A of current flows through the solenoid, the magnetic field inside the iron core has magnitude 0.42 T. What is the relative permeability of the iron core?

73. The figure shows *hysteresis curves* for three different materials. A hysteresis curve is a plot of the magnetic field strength inside the material (B) as a function of the

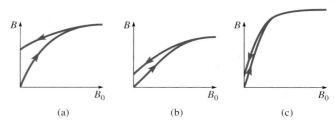

(a)   (b)   (c)

externally applied field (B_0). (a) Which material would make the best permanent magnet? Explain. (b) Which would make the best core for an electromagnet? Explain.

Comprehensive Problems

© 74. A compass is placed directly on top of a wire (needle not shown). The current in the wire flows to the right. Which way does the north end of the needle point? Explain. (Neglect the Earth's magnetic field.)

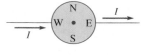

75. You want to build a cyclotron to accelerate protons to a speed of 3.0×10^7 m/s. The largest magnetic field strength you can attain is 1.5 T. What must be the minimum radius of the dees in your cyclotron? Show how your answer comes from Newton's second law.

76. A long straight wire carries a 4.70-A current in the positive x-direction. At a particular instant, an electron moving at 1.00×10^7 m/s in the positive y-direction is 0.120 m from the wire. Determine the magnetic force on the electron at this instant. See the figure with Problem 57.

77. A uniform magnetic field of 0.50 T is directed to the north. At some instant, a particle with charge +0.020 μC is moving with velocity 2.0 m/s in a direction 30° north of east. (a) What is the magnitude of the magnetic force on the charged particle? (b) What is the direction of the magnetic force?

78. Two identical long straight conducting wires with a mass per unit length of 25.0 g/m are resting parallel to each other on a table. The wires are separated by 2.5 mm and are carrying currents in opposite directions. (a) If the coefficient of static friction between the wires and the table is 0.035, what minimum current is necessary to make the wires start to move? (b) Do the wires move closer together or farther apart?

79. Two long insulated wires lie in the same horizontal plane. A current of 20.0 A flows toward the north in wire A and a current of 10.0 A flows toward the east in wire B. What is the magnitude and direction of the magnetic field at a point that is 5.00 cm above the point where the wires cross?

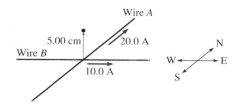

✦ 80. An electron moves in a circle of radius R in a uniform magnetic field $\vec{\mathbf{B}}$. The field is into the page. (a) Does the electron move clockwise or counterclockwise? (b) How

much time does the electron take to make one complete revolution? *Derive* an expression for the time, starting with the magnetic force on the electron. Your answer may include R, B, and any fundamental constants.

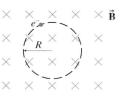

✦ 81. Prove that the time for one revolution of a charged particle moving perpendicular to a uniform magnetic field is independent of its speed. (This is the principle on which the cyclotron operates.) In doing so, write an expression that gives the period T (the time for one revolution) in terms of the mass of the particle, the charge of the particle, and the magnetic field strength.

82. (a) A proton moves with uniform circular motion in a magnetic field of magnitude 0.80 T. At what frequency f does it circulate? (b) Repeat for an electron.

83. The concentration of free electrons in silver is 5.85×10^{28} per m³. A strip of silver of thickness 0.050 mm and width 20.0 mm is placed in a magnetic field of 0.80 T. A current of 10.0 A is sent down the strip. (a) What is the drift velocity of the electrons? (b) What is the Hall voltage measured by the meter? (c) Which side of the voltmeter is at the higher potential?

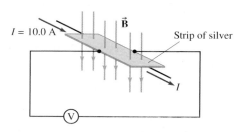

84. An electromagnetic flowmeter is to be used to measure blood speed. A magnetic field of 0.115 T is applied across an artery of inner diameter 3.80 mm. The Hall voltage is measured to be 88.0 μV. What is the average speed of the blood flowing in the artery?

✦ 85. In a carbon-dating experiment, a particular type of mass spectrometer is used to separate ^{14}C from ^{12}C. Carbon ions from a sample are first accelerated through a potential difference ΔV_1 between the charged accelerating plates. Then the ions enter a region of uniform vertical magnetic field $B = 0.20$ T. The ions pass between deflection plates spaced 1.0 cm apart. By adjusting the potential difference ΔV_2 between these plates, only one of the two isotopes (^{12}C or ^{14}C) is allowed to pass through to the next stage of the mass spectrometer. The distance from the entrance to the ion detector is a fixed 0.20 m. By suitably adjusting ΔV_1 and ΔV_2, the detector counts only one type of ion, so the relative abundances can be determined. (a) Are the ions positively or negatively charged? (b) Which of the accelerating plates (east or west) is positively charged? (c) Which of the deflection plates (north or south) is positively charged? (d) Find the correct values of ΔV_1 and ΔV_2 in order to count $^{12}C^+$ ions. (e) Find the correct values of ΔV_1 and ΔV_2 in order to count $^{14}C^+$ ions.

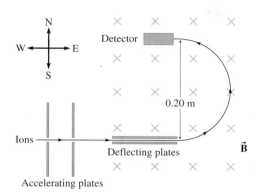

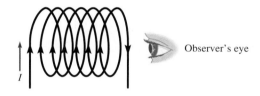

86. Sketch the magnetic field as it would appear inside the coil of wire to an observer, looking into the coil from the position shown.

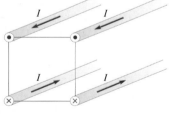

87. Repeat Problem 42 if the magnetic field is 2.5 T in the plane of the loop, 60.0° below the +x-axis.

88. In Problem 59, find the magnetic field at points C and D when $d = 3.3$ cm and $I = 6.50$ A.

89. Four long parallel wires pass through the four corners of a square. All four wires carry the same amount of current and the current directions are as indicated. (a) What is the direction of the magnetic field at the center of the square? (b) The current is 10.0 A in each wire and the square is 0.10 m on a side. What is the magnitude of the magnetic field?

90. A *current balance* is a device to measure magnetic forces. It is constructed from two parallel coils, each with an average radius of 12.5 cm. The lower coil rests on a balance; it has 20 turns and carries a constant current of 4.0 A. The upper coil, suspended 0.314 cm above the lower coil, has 50 turns and a current that can be varied. The reading of the balance changes as the magnetic force on the lower coil changes. What current is needed in the upper coil to exert a force of 1.0 N on the bottom coil? [*Hint:* Since the distance between the coils is small compared to the radius of the coils, approximate the setup as two long parallel straight wires.]

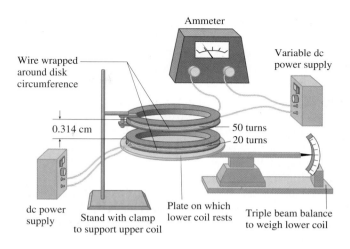

91. A rectangular loop of wire, carrying current $I_1 = 2.0$ mA, is next to a very long wire carrying a current $I_2 = 8.0$ A. (a) What is the direction of the magnetic force on each of the four sides of the rectangle due to the long wire's magnetic field? (b) Calculate the net magnetic force on the rectangular loop due to the long wire's magnetic field. [*Hint:* The long wire does *not* produce a uniform magnetic field.]

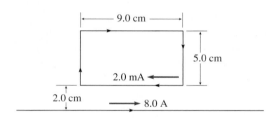

92. A strip of copper carries current in the +x-direction. There is an external magnetic field directed out of the page. What is the direction of the Hall electric field?

93. A bar magnet is held near the electron beam in an oscilloscope. The beam passes directly below the south pole of the magnet. In what direction will the beam move on the screen? (*Don't try this* with a color TV tube. There is a metal mask just behind the screen that separates the pixels for red, green, and blue. If you succeed in magnetizing the mask, the picture will be permanently distorted.)

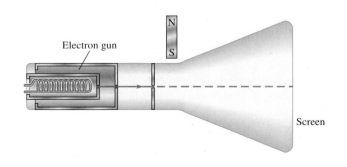

✦ 94. In a certain region of space, there is a uniform electric field $\vec{E} = 3.0 \times 10^4$ V/m directed due east and a uniform magnetic field $\vec{B} = 0.080$ T *also directed due east*. What is the electromagnetic force on an electron moving *due south* at 5.0×10^6 m/s?

95. The strength of the Earth's magnetic field, as measured on the surface, is approximately 6.0×10^{-5} T at the poles and 3.0×10^{-5} T at the equator. Suppose an alien from outer space were at the North Pole with a single loop of wire of the same circumference as his space helmet. The diameter of his helmet is 20.0 cm. The space invader wishes to cancel the Earth's magnetic field at his location. (a) What is the current required to produce a magnetic field (due to the current alone) at the center of his loop of the same size as that of the Earth's field at the North Pole? (b) In what direction does the current circulate in the loop, CW or CCW, as viewed from above, if it is to cancel the Earth's field?

96. A tangent galvanometer is an instrument, developed in the nineteenth century, designed to measure current based on the deflection of a compass needle. A coil of wire in a vertical plane is aligned in the magnetic north-south direction. A compass is placed in a horizontal plane at the center of the coil. When no current  flows, the compass needle points directly toward the north side of the coil. When a current is sent through the coil, the compass needle rotates through an angle θ. Derive an equation for θ in terms of the number of coil turns N, the coil radius r, the coil current I, and the horizontal component of Earth's field B_H. [*Hint:* The name of the instrument is a clue to the result.]

✦ 97. An early cyclotron at Cornell University was used from the 1930s to the 1950s to accelerate protons, which would then bombard various nuclei. The cyclotron used a large electromagnet with an iron yoke to produce a uniform magnetic field of 1.3 T over a region in the shape of a flat cylinder. Two hollow copper dees of inside radius 16 cm were located in a vacuum chamber in this region. (a) What is the frequency of oscillation necessary for the alternating voltage difference between the dees? (b) What is the kinetic energy of a proton by the time it reaches the outside of the dees? (c) What would be the equivalent voltage necessary to accelerate protons to this energy from rest in one step (say between parallel plates)? (d) If the potential difference between the dees has a magnitude of 10.0 kV each time the protons cross the gap, what is the minimum number of revolutions each proton has to make in the cyclotron?

Ⓒ 98. In a certain region of space, there is a uniform electric field $\vec{E} = 2.0 \times 10^4$ V/m to the east and a uniform mag-

netic field $\vec{B} = 0.0050$ T to the west. (a) What is the electromagnetic force on an electron moving north at 1.0×10^7 m/s? (b) With the electric and magnetic fields as specified, is there some velocity such that the net electromagnetic force on the electron would be zero? If so, give the magnitude and direction of that velocity. If not, explain briefly why not.

99. In the mass spectrometer of the diagram, neon ions ($q = +e$) come from the ion source and are accelerated through a potential difference V. The ions then pass through an aperture in a metal plate into a uniform magnetic field where they travel in semicircular paths until exiting into the detector. Neon ions having a mass of 20.0 u leave the field at a distance of 50.0 cm from the aperture. At what distance from the aperture do neon ions having a mass of 22.0 u leave the field?

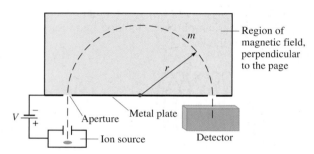

✦✦ 100. A proton moves in a helical path at speed $v = 4.0 \times 10^7$ m/s high in the atmosphere, where the Earth's magnetic field has magnitude $B = 1.0 \times 10^{-6}$ T. The proton's velocity makes an angle of 25° with the magnetic field. (a) Find the radius of the helix. [*Hint:* Use the perpendicular component of the velocity.] (b) Find the *pitch* of the helix—the distance between adjacent "coils." [*Hint:* Find the time for one revolution; then find how far the proton moves along a field line during that time interval.]

Answers to Practice Problems

19.1 5.8×10^{-17} N; 3.4×10^{10} m/s²

19.2 magnitude = 8.2×10^{-17} N, direction = east

19.3 $\pm 1.8 \times 10^6$ m/s

19.4 6.7×10^5 m/s

19.5 76 cm

19.6 out of the page (if the speed is too great, the magnetic force is larger than the electric force)

19.7 same magnitude Hall voltage, but opposite polarity: the top edge would be at the higher potential

19.8 west

19.9 (proof)

19.10 $\vec{B} = \dfrac{2\mu_0 I}{\pi d}$ in the +x-direction

19.11 $+4\mu_0 I$

Electromagnetic Induction

In many electric stoves, an electric current passes through the coiled heating elements. As electric energy is dissipated in the elements, they get hot. A different kind of electric stove—the induction stove—has an advantage over stoves with heating elements. If you touch the heating element of a traditional stove, you will burn your hand; a potholder carelessly left in contact with a hot coil may catch on fire. With an induction stove, the surface does not feel hot to the touch and the potholder does not catch fire. (*Caution:* Most stoves with flat stovetops are *not* induction stoves, so do not try this at home unless you are *certain*.) How can heat get to the food in a pot or pan if the stove surface is not hot? (See p. 751 for the answer.)

Concepts & Skills to Review

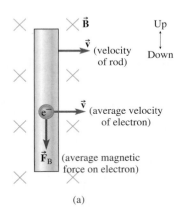

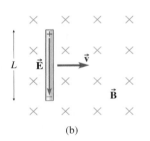

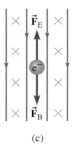

Figure 20.1 (a) An electron in a metal rod that is moving to the right with velocity $\vec{v}$. The magnetic field is into the page. The average magnetic force on the electron is $\vec{F}_B = -e\vec{v} \times \vec{B}$. (b) The magnetic force pushes electrons toward the bottom of the rod, leaving the top end positively charged. This separation of charge gives rise to an electric field in the rod. (c) In equilibrium, the sum of the electric and magnetic forces on the electron is zero.

20.1   MOTIONAL EMF

The only sources of electric energy (emf) we've discussed so far are batteries. The amount of electric energy that can be supplied by a battery before it needs to be recharged or replaced is limited. Most of the world's electric energy is produced by generators. In this section we study **motional emf**—the emf induced when a conductor is moved in a magnetic field. Motional emf is the principle behind the electric generator.

Imagine a metal rod of length L in a uniform magnetic field $\vec{B}$. When the rod is at rest, the conduction electrons move in random directions at high speeds, but their average velocity is zero. Since their average velocity is zero, the average magnetic force on the electrons is zero; therefore, the total magnetic force on the rod is zero. The magnetic field affects the motion of individual electrons, but the rod as a whole feels no net magnetic force.

Now imagine a vertical rod that is moving instead of being at rest. Figure 20.1a shows a uniform magnetic field into the page, the velocity $\vec{v}$ of the rod is to the right, and the rod is vertical—the field, velocity, and axis of the rod are mutually perpendicular. Now the electrons have a nonzero average velocity: it is $\vec{v}$, since the electrons are being carried to the right along with the rod. Then the average magnetic force on each conduction electron is

$$\vec{F}_B = -e\vec{v} \times \vec{B}$$

By the right-hand rule, the direction of this force is down (toward the lower end of the rod). The magnetic force causes electrons to accumulate at the lower end, giving it a negative charge and leaving positive charge at the upper end (Fig. 20.1b). This separation of charge by the magnetic field is similar to the Hall effect, but here the charges are moving due to the motion of the rod itself rather than due to a current flowing in a stationary rod.

As charge accumulates at the ends, an electric field develops in the rod, with field lines running from the positive to the negative charge. Eventually an equilibrium is reached: the electric field builds up until it causes a force equal and opposite to the magnetic force on electrons in the middle of the rod (Fig. 20.1c). Then there is no further accumulation of charge at the ends. Thus, in equilibrium,

$$\vec{F}_E = q\vec{E} = -\vec{F}_B = -(q\vec{v} \times \vec{B})$$

or

$$\vec{E} = -\vec{v} \times \vec{B}$$

just as for the Hall effect. Since $\vec{v}$ and $\vec{B}$ are perpendicular, $E = vB$. The potential difference between the ends is

$$\Delta V = EL = vBL \qquad (20\text{-}1a)$$

In this case, the direction of $\vec{E}$ is parallel to the rod. If it were not, then the potential difference between the ends is found using only the *component* of $\vec{E}$ parallel ($\parallel$) to the rod:

$$\Delta V = E_{\parallel}L \qquad (20\text{-}1b)$$

As long as the rod keeps moving at constant speed, the separation of charge is maintained. The moving rod acts like a battery that is not connected to a circuit; positive

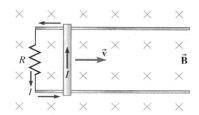

charge accumulates at one terminal and negative charge at the other, maintaining a constant potential difference. Now the important question: if we connect this rod to a circuit, does it act like a battery and cause current to flow?

Figure 20.2 shows the rod connected to a circuit. The rod slides on metal rails so that the circuit stays complete even as the rod continues to move. We assume the resistance R is large compared to the resistances of the rod and rails—in other words, the internal resistance of our source of emf (the moving rod) is negligibly small. The resistor R sees a potential difference ΔV across it, so current flows. The current tends to deplete the accumulated charge at the ends of the rod, but the magnetic force pumps more charge to maintain a constant potential difference. So the moving rod *does* act like a battery with an emf given by

Figure 20.2 When the rod is connected to a circuit with resistance R, current flows around the circuit.

Motional emf:

$$\mathscr{E} = vBL \qquad \qquad (20\text{-}2a)$$

More generally, if $\vec{\mathbf{E}}$ is not parallel to the rod, then

$$\mathscr{E} = (\vec{\mathbf{v}} \times \vec{\mathbf{B}})_{\parallel} L \qquad \qquad (20\text{-}2b)$$

A sliding rod would be a clumsy way to make a generator. No matter how long the rails are, the rod will eventually reach the end. In Section 20.2, we see that the principle of the motional emf can be applied to a *rotating coil* of wire instead of a sliding rod.

Where does the electric energy come from? The rod is acting like a battery, supplying electric energy that is dissipated in the resistor. How can energy be conserved? The key is to recognize that as soon as current flows through the rod, a magnetic force acts on the rod in the direction opposite to the velocity (Fig. 20.3). Left on its own, the rod would slow down as its kinetic energy gets transformed into electric energy. To maintain a constant emf, the rod must maintain a constant velocity, which can only happen if some other force pulls the rod. The work done by the force pulling the rod is the source of the electric energy (Problem 3).

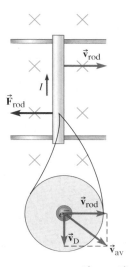

Figure 20.3 The magnetic force on the rod is $\vec{\mathbf{F}}_{\text{rod}} = I\vec{\mathbf{L}} \times \vec{\mathbf{B}}$ and is directed to the left, opposite the velocity of the rod ($\vec{\mathbf{v}}_{\text{rod}}$). The average velocity of an electron in the rod is $\vec{\mathbf{v}}_{\text{av}} = \vec{\mathbf{v}}_{\text{rod}} + \vec{\mathbf{v}}_{\text{D}}$; the electrons drift downward relative to the rod as the rod carries them to the right. The average magnetic force on an electron has two perpendicular components. One is $-e\vec{\mathbf{v}}_{\text{rod}} \times \vec{\mathbf{B}}$, which is directed downward and causes the electron to drift relative to the rod. The other is $-e\vec{\mathbf{v}}_{\text{D}} \times \vec{\mathbf{B}}$, which pulls the electron to the left side of the rod and, because each electron in turn pulls on the rest of the rod, contributes to the leftward magnetic force on the rod.

Example 20.1

Loop Moving Through a Magnetic Field

A square metal loop made of four rods of length L moves at constant velocity $\vec{v}$ (Fig. 20.4). The magnetic field in the central region has magnitude B; elsewhere the magnetic field is zero. The loop has resistance R. At each position 1–5, state the direction (CW or CCW) and the magnitude of the current in the loop.

Strategy   If current flows in the loop, it is due to the motional emf that pumps charge around. The vertical sides (a, c) have motional emfs as they move through the magnetic field, just as in Fig. 20.2. We need to look at the horizontal sides (b, d) to see whether they also give rise to motional emfs. Once we figure out the emf in each side, then we can determine whether they cooperate with each other—pumping charge around in the same direction—or tend to cancel each other.

Solution   The vertical sides (a, c) have motional emfs as they move through the region of magnetic field. The emf acts to pump current upward (toward the top end). The magnitude of the emf is

$$\mathcal{E} = vBL$$

For the horizontal sides (b, d), the average magnetic force on a current-carrying electron is $\vec{F}_{av} = -e\vec{v} \times \vec{B}$. Since the velocity is to the right and the field is into the page, the right-hand rule shows that the direction of the force is down, just as in sides a and c. However, now the magnetic force does not move charge along the length of the rod; the magnetic force instead moves charge across the diameter of the rod. An electric field then develops *across* the rod. In equilibrium, the magnetic and electric forces cancel, exactly as in the Hall effect. The magnetic force does not push charge along the length of the rod, so there is no motional emf in sides b and d.

In positions 1 and 5, the loop is completely out of the region of magnetic field. There is no motional emf in any of the sides; no current flows.

In position 2, there is a motional emf in side c only; side a is still outside the region of $\vec{B}$ field. The emf makes current flow upward in side c, and therefore counterclockwise in the loop. The magnitude of the current is

$$I = \frac{\mathcal{E}}{R} = \frac{vBL}{R}$$

In position 3, there are motional emfs in both sides a and c. Since the emfs in both sides push current toward the top of the loop, the net emf around the loop is zero—as if two identical batteries were connected as in Fig. 20.5. No current flows around the loop.

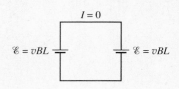

Figure 20.5
At position 3, the emfs induced in sides a and c can be represented with battery symbols in a circuit diagram.

In position 4, there is a motional emf only in side a, since side c has left the region of the $\vec{B}$ field. The emf makes current flow upward in side a, and therefore *clockwise* in the loop. The magnitude of the current is again

$$I = \frac{\mathcal{E}}{R} = \frac{vBL}{R}$$

  Discussion   Figure 20.5 illustrates a useful technique: it often helps to draw battery symbols to represent the directions of the induced emfs.

 Note that if the loop were *at rest* instead of moving to the right at constant velocity, there would be no motional emf at any of the positions 1–5. The motional emf does not arise simply because one of the vertical sides of the loop is immersed in magnetic field while the other is not; it arises because one side *moves through* a magnetic field while the other does not.

Conceptual Practice Problem 20.1   Loop of Different Metal

Suppose a loop made of a different metal but with identical size, shape, and velocity moved through the same magnetic field. Of these quantities, which would be different: the magnitudes of the emfs, the directions of the emfs, the magnitudes of the currents, or the directions of the currents?

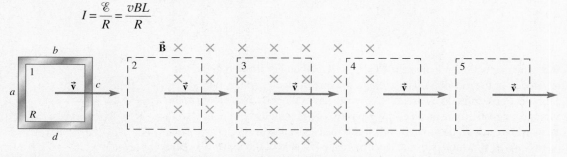

Figure 20.4   Loop moving into, through, and then out of a region of uniform magnetic field $\vec{B}$ perpendicular to the loop.

20.2   ELECTRIC GENERATORS

Making the Connection:
electric generators

For practical reasons, electric generators use coils of wire that rotate in a magnetic field rather than rods that slide on rails. The rotating coil is called an *armature*. A simple electric generator is shown in Fig. 20.6. The rectangular coil is mounted on a shaft that is turned by some external power source such as the turbine of a steam engine.

Let us begin with a single turn of wire—a rectangular loop—that rotates at a constant angular speed ω. The loop rotates in the space between the poles of a permanent magnet or an electromagnet that produces a nearly uniform field of magnitude B. Sides 2 and 4 are each of length L and are a distance r from the axis of rotation; the length of sides 1 and 3 is therefore $2r$ each.

Generators at Little Goose Dam in the state of Washington.

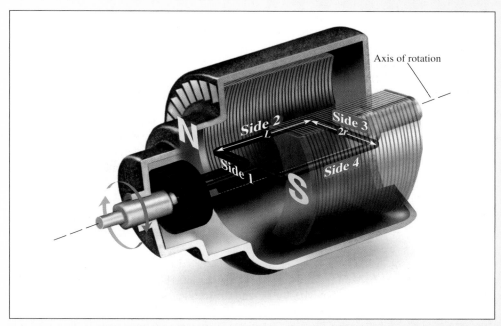

Figure 20.6 A simple ac generator, in which a rectangular loop or coil of wire rotates at constant angular speed between the poles of a permanent magnet or electromagnet. Emfs are induced in sides 2 and 4 of the loop due to their motion through the magnetic field as the loop rotates. (Sides 1 and 3 have zero induced emf.) A magnetic torque opposes the rotation of the coil, so an external torque must be applied to keep the loop rotating at constant angular velocity.

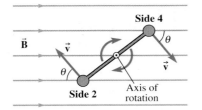

Side view

Figure 20.7 Side view of the rectangular loop, looking straight down the axis of rotation. The velocity vectors of sides 2 and 4 make an angle θ with the magnetic field.

None of the four sides of the loop moves perpendicularly to the magnetic field at all times, so we must generalize the results of Section 20.1. In Problem 7, you can verify that there is zero induced emf in sides 1 and 3, so we concentrate on sides 2 and 4. Since these two sides do not, in general, move perpendicularly to $\vec{\mathbf{B}}$, the magnitude of the average magnetic force on the electrons is reduced by a factor of $\sin \theta$, where θ is the angle between the velocity of the wire and the magnetic field (Fig. 20.7):

$$F_{av} = evB \sin \theta$$

The induced emf is then reduced by the same factor:

$$\mathscr{E} = vBL \sin \theta$$

Note that the induced emf is proportional to the component of the velocity perpendicular to $\vec{\mathbf{B}}$ ($v_\perp = v \sin \theta$). For a visual image, think of the induced emf as proportional to the *rate* at which the wire *cuts through magnetic field lines*. The component of the velocity *parallel* to $\vec{\mathbf{B}}$ moves the wire along the magnetic field lines, so it does not contribute to the rate at which the wire cuts through the field lines.

The loop turns at constant angular speed ω, so the speed of sides 2 and 4 is

$$v = \omega r$$

The angle θ changes at a constant rate ω. For simplicity, we choose $\theta = 0$ at $t = 0$, so that $\theta = \omega t$ and the emf $\mathscr{E}$ as a function of time t in each of sides 2 and 4 is

$$\mathscr{E}(t) = vBL \sin \theta = (\omega r)BL \sin \omega t$$

Sides 2 and 4 move in opposite directions, so current flows in opposite directions; in side 2, current flows into the page (as viewed in Fig. 20.7), while in side 4 it flows out of the page. *Both* sides tend to send current counterclockwise around the loop as viewed in Fig. 20.8. Therefore, the two emfs are connected with the negative "terminal" of one connected to the positive "terminal" of the other, and the *total* emf in the loop is the *sum* of the two:

$$\mathscr{E}(t) = 2\omega rBL \sin \omega t$$

The rectangular loop has sides L and $2r$, so the area of the loop is $A = 2rL$. Therefore, the total emf $\mathscr{E}$ as a function of time t is

$$\mathscr{E}(t) = \omega BA \sin \omega t \qquad\qquad \text{(20-3a)}$$

When written in terms of the area of the loop, Eq. (20-3a) is true for a planar loop of *any* shape. If the coil consists of N turns of wire (N identical loops), the emf is N times as great:

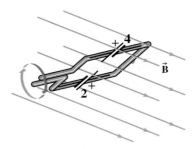

Figure 20.8 Battery symbols indicate the direction of the emfs in the rotating loop of wire.

Emf produced by an ac generator:

$$\mathscr{E}(t) = \omega NBA \sin \omega t \qquad\qquad \text{(20-3b)}$$

The emf produced by a generator is not constant; it is a sinusoidal function of time (Fig. 20.9). The maximum emf ($= \omega NBA$) is called the **amplitude** of the emf (just as in simple harmonic motion, where the maximum displacement is called the amplitude). Sinusoidal emfs are used in ac (alternating current) circuits. Household electric outlets in the United States and Canada provide an emf with an amplitude of approximately 170 V and a frequency $f = \omega/(2\pi) = 60$ Hz. In much of the rest of the world, the amplitude is about 310–340 V and the frequency is 50 Hz.

This energy does not come for free; work must be done to turn the generator shaft. As current flows in the coil, the magnetic force on sides 2 and 4 cause a torque in the direction opposing the coil's rotation (Problem 58). To keep the coil rotating at constant angular speed, an equal and oppositely directed torque must be applied to the shaft. In an ideal generator, this external torque would do work at exactly the same rate as electric energy is generated. In reality, some energy is dissipated by friction and by the electrical

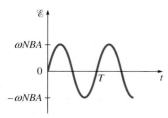

Figure 20.9 Generator-produced emf is a sinusoidal function of time.

resistance of the coil, among other things. Then the external torque does more work than the amount of electric energy generated. Since the rate at which electric energy is generated is

$$P = \mathcal{E}I$$

the external torque required to keep the generator rotating depends not only on the emf but also on the current it supplies. The current supplied depends on the *load*—the external circuit through which the current must flow.

In most power stations that supply our electricity, the work to turn the generator shaft is supplied by a steam engine. The steam engine is powered by burning coal, natural gas, or oil, or by a nuclear reactor. In a hydroelectric power plant, the gravitational potential energy of water is the energy source used to turn the generator shaft.

In electric and hybrid gas-electric cars, the drive train of the vehicle is connected to an electric generator when brakes are applied, which charges the batteries. Thus, instead of the kinetic energy of the vehicle being completely dissipated, much of it is stored in the batteries. This energy is used to propel the car after braking is finished.

The DC Generator

Note that the induced emf produced in an ac generator reverses direction twice per period. Mathematically, the sine functions in Eqs. (20-3) are positive half the time and negative half the time. When the generator is connected to a load, the current also reverses direction twice per period—which is why we call it alternating current.

What if the load requires a direct current (dc) instead? Then we need a dc generator, one in which the emf does *not* reverse direction. One way to make a dc generator is to equip the ac generator with a split-ring commutator and brushes, exactly as for the dc motor (Section 19.7). Just as the emf is about to change direction, the connections to the rotating loop are switched as the brushes pass over the gap in the split ring. The commutator effectively reverses the connections to the outside load so that the emf and current supplied maintain the same direction. The emf and current are *not* constant, though. The emf is described by

$$\mathcal{E}(t) = \omega NBA \left| \sin \omega t \right| \qquad (20\text{-}3c)$$

which is graphed in Fig. 20.10.

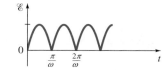

Figure 20.10 The emf in a dc generator as a function of time.

A simple dc *motor* can be used as a dc *generator*, and *vice versa*. When configured as a motor, an external source of electric energy such as a battery causes current to flow through the loop. The magnetic torque makes the motor rotate. In other words, the current is the input and the torque is the output. When configured as a generator, an external torque makes the loop rotate, the magnetic field induces an emf in the loop, and the emf makes current flow. Now the torque is the input and the current is the output. The conversion between mechanical energy and electric energy can proceed in either direction.

More sophisticated dc generators have many coils distributed evenly around the axis of rotation. The emf *in each coil* still varies sinusoidally, but each coil reaches its peak emf at a different time. As the commutator rotates, the brushes connect selectively to the coil that is nearest its peak emf. The output emf has only small fluctuations, which can be smoothed out by a circuit called a voltage regulator if necessary.

Example 20.2

A Bicycle Generator

A simple dc generator in contact with a bicycle's tire can be used to generate power for the headlight. The generator has 150 turns of wire in a circular coil of radius 1.8 cm. The magnetic field strength in the region of the coil is 0.20 T. When the generator supplies an emf of amplitude 4.2 V to the lightbulb, the lightbulb consumes an average power of 6.0 W and a maximum instantaneous

Continued on next page

Example 20.2 Continued

power of 12.0 W. (a) What is the rotational speed in rpm of the armature of the generator? (b) What is the average torque and maximum instantaneous torque that must be applied by the bicycle tire to the generator, assuming the generator to be ideal? (c) The radius of the tire is 32 cm and the radius of the shaft of the generator where it contacts the tire is 1.0 cm. At what linear speed must the bicycle move to supply an emf of amplitude 4.2 V?

Strategy   The amplitude is the maximum value of the time-dependent emf [Eq. (20-3c)]. To find the torques, two methods are possible. One is to find the current in the coil, then the torque on the coil due to the magnetic field. To keep the armature moving at a constant angular velocity, an equal magnitude but oppositely directed torque must be applied to it. Another method is to analyze the energy transfers. The external torque applied to the armature must do work at the same rate that electric energy is dissipated in the lightbulb. The second approach is easiest, especially since the problem states the power in the lightbulb. To find the linear speed of the bicycle, we set the tangential speeds of the tire and shaft equal (the shaft is "rolling" on the tire).

Solution   (a) The emf as a function of time is

$$\mathcal{E}(t) = \omega NBA \left| \sin \omega t \right| \qquad (20\text{-}3c)$$

The emf has its maximum value when $\sin \omega t = \pm 1$. Thus, the amplitude of the emf is

$$\mathcal{E}_m = \omega NBA$$

where $N = 150$, $A = \pi r^2$, and $B = 0.20$ T. Solving for the angular frequency,

$$\omega = \frac{\mathcal{E}_m}{NAB} = \frac{4.2 \text{ V}}{150 \times \pi \times (0.018 \text{ m})^2 \times 0.20 \text{ T}} = 137.5 \text{ rad/s}$$

A check of the units verifies that $1 \dfrac{\text{V}}{\text{T·m}^2} = 1 \text{ s}^{-1}$. The question asks for the number of rpm, so we convert the angular frequency to rev/min:

$$\omega = 137.5 \frac{\text{rad}}{\text{s}} \times \frac{1 \text{ rev}}{2\pi \text{ rad}} \times \frac{60 \text{ s}}{1 \text{ min}} = 1300 \text{ rpm}$$

(b) Assuming the generator to be ideal, the torque applied to the crank must do work at the same rate that electric energy is generated:

$$P = \frac{W}{\Delta t}$$

Since for a small angular displacement $\Delta \theta$ the work done is $W = \tau \Delta \theta$,

$$P = \tau \frac{\Delta \theta}{\Delta t} = \tau \omega$$

The average torque is then

$$\tau_{av} = \frac{P_{av}}{\omega} = \frac{6.0 \text{ W}}{137.5 \text{ rad/s}} = 0.044 \text{ N·m}$$

and the maximum torque is

$$\tau_m = \frac{P_m}{\omega} = \frac{12.0 \text{ W}}{137.5 \text{ rad/s}} = 0.087 \text{ N·m}$$

(c) The tangential speed of the generator shaft is

$$v_{tan} = \omega r = 137.5 \text{ rad/s} \times 0.018 \text{ m} = 2.5 \text{ m/s}$$

The tangential speed of the tire where it touches the generator shaft is the same, since the shaft rolls without slipping on the tire. Since the generator is almost at the outside edge of the tire, the tangential speed at the outer radius of the tire is approximately the same. Assuming that the bicycle rolls without slipping on the road, its linear speed is approximately 2.5 m/s.

Discussion   To check the result, we can find the maximum current in the coil and use it to find the maximum torque. The maximum current occurs when the power dissipated is maximum:

$$P_m = \mathcal{E}_m I_m$$

$$I_m = \frac{12.0 \text{ W}}{4.2 \text{ V}} = 2.86 \text{ A}$$

The magnetic torque on a current loop is

$$\tau = NIAB \sin \theta$$

where $\theta = \omega t$ is the angle between the magnetic field and the *normal* to the loop. At the position where the emf is maximum, $|\sin \theta| = 1$. Then

$$\tau_m = NI_m AB = 150 \times 2.86 \text{ A} \times \pi \times (0.018 \text{ m})^2 \times 0.20 \text{ T}$$

$$= 0.087 \text{ N·m}$$

Practice Problem 20.2   Riding More Slowly

What would the maximum power be if the bicycle moves half as fast? Assume that the resistance of the lightbulb does not change. Remember that the angular velocity affects the emf, which in turn affects the current. How does the power in the lightbulb depend on the bicycle's speed?

20.3   FARADAY'S LAW

In 1820, Hans Christian Oersted accidentally discovered that an electric current produces a magnetic field (Section 19.1). Soon after hearing the news of that discovery, the English scientist Michael Faraday (1791–1867) started experimenting with magnets and electric circuits in an attempt to do the reverse—use a magnetic field to produce an electric current. Faraday's brilliant experiments led to the development of the electric motor, the generator, and the transformer.

In 1831, Faraday discovered two ways to produce an induced emf. One is to move a conductor in a magnetic field. The other does *not* involve movement of the conductor. Instead, Faraday found that a changing magnetic field induces an emf in a conductor even if the conductor is stationary. The induced emf due to a changing $\vec{\mathbf{B}}$ field cannot be understood in terms of the magnetic force on the conduction electrons: if the conductor is stationary, the average velocity of the electrons is zero, and the average magnetic force is zero.

Consider a circular loop of wire between the poles of an electromagnet (Fig. 20.11). The loop is perpendicular to the magnetic field; field lines cross the interior of the loop. Since the strength of the magnetic field is related to the spacing of the field lines, if the strength of the field varies (by changing the current in the electromagnet), the number of field lines passing through the conducting loop changes. Faraday found that the emf induced in the loop is proportional to the *rate of change* of the number of field lines that cut through the interior of the loop.

We can formulate *Faraday's law* mathematically so that numbers of field lines are not involved. The magnitude of the magnetic field is proportional to the number of field lines *per unit cross-sectional area*:

$$B \propto \frac{\text{number of lines}}{\text{area}}$$

If a flat, open surface of area A is perpendicular to a uniform magnetic field of magnitude B, then the number of field lines that cross the surface is proportional to BA, since

$$\text{number of lines} = \frac{\text{number of lines}}{\text{area}} \times \text{area} \propto BA \qquad (20\text{-}4)$$

Equation (20-4) is correct only if the surface is perpendicular to the field. In general, the number of field lines crossing a surface is proportional to the *perpendicular component* of the field times the area:

$$\text{number of lines} \propto B_\perp A = BA \cos \theta$$

where θ is the angle between the magnetic field and the direction normal to the surface. The component of the magnetic field parallel to the surface $B_\parallel$ doesn't contribute to the number of lines crossing the surface; only $B_\perp$ does (see Fig. 20.12a). Equivalently, Fig. 20.12b shows that the number of lines crossing the surface area A is the same as the number crossing a surface of area $A \cos \theta$, which is perpendicular to the field.

The mathematical quantity that is proportional to the number of field lines cutting through a surface is called the **magnetic flux**. The symbol Φ (Greek capital phi) is used for flux; in Φ_B the subscript B indicates *magnetic* flux.

Magnetic flux through a flat surface of area A:

$$\Phi_B = B_\perp A = BA_\perp = BA \cos \theta \qquad (20\text{-}5)$$

(θ is the angle between $\vec{\mathbf{B}}$ and the *normal* to the surface)

The SI unit of magnetic flux is the weber (1 Wb = 1 T·m²).

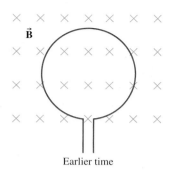

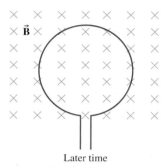

Figure 20.11 Circular loop in a magnetic field of increasing magnitude.

● The word *normal* means *perpendicular* in geometry. *The normal to the loop means the direction perpendicular to the plane of the loop.*

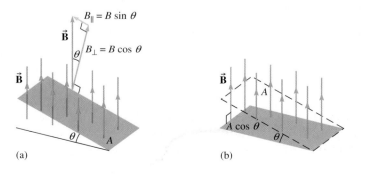

(a)   (b)

Figure 20.12 (a) The component of $\vec{\mathbf{B}}$ perpendicular to the surface of area A is $B \cos \theta$. (b) The projection of the area A onto a plane perpendicular to $\vec{\mathbf{B}}$ is $A \cos \theta$.

Faraday's law says that the magnitude of the induced emf around a loop is equal to the rate of change of the magnetic flux through the loop.

Faraday's Law

$$\mathscr{E} = -\frac{\Delta\Phi_B}{\Delta t} \qquad (20\text{-}6a)$$

Problem 15 asks you to verify the units of Eq. (20-6a). Faraday's law, if it is to give the *instantaneous* emf, must be taken in the limit of a very small time interval Δt. However, Faraday's law can be applied just as well to longer time intervals; then $\Delta\Phi_B/\Delta t$ represents the *average* rate of change of the flux, and $\mathscr{E}$ represents the *average* emf during that time interval.

The negative sign in Eq. (20-6a) concerns the sense of the induced emf around the loop (clockwise or counterclockwise). The interpretation of the sign depends on a formal definition of the emf direction that we do not use. Instead, in Section 20.4, we introduce *Lenz's law*, which gives the direction of the induced emf.

If, instead of a single loop of wire, we have a coil of N turns, then Eq. (20-6a) gives the emf induced in each turn; the total emf in the coil is then N times as great:

$$\mathscr{E} = -N\frac{\Delta\Phi_B}{\Delta t} \qquad (20\text{-}6b)$$

The quantity $N\Phi_B$ is called the total flux linkage through the coil.

Example 20.3

Induced Emf due to Changing Magnetic Field

A 40.0-turn coil of wire of radius 3.0 cm is placed between the poles of an electromagnet. The field increases from 0 to 0.75 T at a constant rate in a time interval of 225 s. What is the magnitude of the induced emf in the coil if (a) the field is perpendicular to the plane of the coil? (b) the field makes an angle of 30.0° with the plane of the coil?

Strategy   First we write an expression for the flux through the coil in terms of the field. The only thing changing is the strength of the field, so the rate of flux change is proportional to the rate of change of the field. Faraday's law gives the induced emf.

Solution   (a) The magnetic field is perpendicular to the coil, so the flux through one turn is

$$\Phi_B = BA$$

where B is the field strength and A is the area of the loop. Since the field increases at a constant rate, so does the flux. The rate of change of flux is then equal to the change in flux divided by the time interval. The flux changes at a constant rate, so the emf induced in the loop is constant.

By Faraday's law,

$$\mathscr{E} = -N\frac{\Delta\Phi_B}{\Delta t} = -N\frac{B_f A - 0}{\Delta t}$$

$$|\mathscr{E}| = 40.0 \times \frac{0.75\ \text{T} \times \pi \times (0.030\ \text{m})^2}{225\ \text{s}} = 3.77 \times 10^{-4}\ \text{V}$$

$$= 0.38\ \text{mV}$$

(b) In Eq. (20-5), θ is the angle between $\vec{\mathbf{B}}$ and the direction *normal* to the coil. If the field makes an angle of 30.0° with the plane of the coil, then it makes an angle

$$\theta = 90.0° - 30.0° = 60.0°$$

with the normal to the coil. The magnetic flux through one turn is

$$\Phi_B = BA\cos\theta$$

The induced emf is therefore,

$$|\mathscr{E}| = N\frac{\Delta\Phi_B}{\Delta t} = N\frac{B_f A\cos\theta - 0}{\Delta t} = 3.77 \times 10^{-4}\ \text{V} \times \cos 60.0°$$

$$= 0.19\ \text{mV}$$

Discussion   If the rate of change of the field were not constant, then 0.38 mV would be the *average* emf during that time interval. The instantaneous emf would be sometimes higher and sometimes lower.

Practice Problem 20.3   Using the Perpendicular Component of $\vec{\mathbf{B}}$

Draw a sketch that shows the coil, the direction normal to the coil, and the magnetic field lines. Find the component of $\vec{\mathbf{B}}$ in the normal direction. Now use $\Phi_B = B_\perp A$ to verify the answer to part (b).

Sinusoidal Emfs

Emfs that are sinusoidal (sine or cosine) functions of time, such as in Example 20.2, are common in ac generators, motors, and circuits. A sinusoidal emf is generated whenever the flux is a sinusoidal function of time. It can be shown (see Fig. 20.13 and Problem 19) that:

$$\text{If } \Phi(t) = \Phi_0 \sin \omega t, \text{ then } \frac{\Delta\Phi}{\Delta t} = \omega\Phi_0 \cos \omega t \quad \text{(for small } \Delta t\text{);} \qquad \textbf{(20-7a)}$$

$$\text{if } \Phi(t) = \Phi_0 \cos \omega t, \text{ then } \frac{\Delta\Phi}{\Delta t} = -\omega\Phi_0 \sin \omega t \quad \text{(for small } \Delta t\text{).} \qquad \textbf{(20-7b)}$$

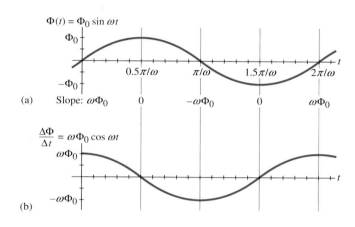

Figure 20.13 (a) A graph of a sinusoidal emf $\Phi(t) = \Phi_0 \sin \omega t$ as a function of time. (b) A graph of the slope $\Delta\Phi/\Delta t$—which represents the rate of change of $\Phi(t)$.

Example 20.4

Applying Faraday's Law to a Generator

The magnetic field between the poles of an electromagnet has constant magnitude B. A circular coil of wire immersed in this magnetic field has N turns and area A. An externally applied torque causes the coil to rotate with constant angular velocity ω about an axis perpendicular to the field (as in Fig. 20.6). Use Faraday's law to find the emf induced in the coil.

Strategy The magnetic field does not vary, but the orientation of the coil does. The number of field lines crossing through the coil depends on the angle that the field makes with the normal (the direction perpendicular to the coil). The changing magnetic flux induces an emf in the coil, according to Faraday's law.

Solution Let us choose $t = 0$ to be an instant when the field is perpendicular to the coil. At this instant, $\vec{\mathbf{B}}$ is parallel to the normal, so $\theta = 0$. At a later time $t > 0$, the coil has rotated through an angle $\Delta\theta = \omega t$. Thus, the angle that the field makes with the normal as a function of t is

$$\theta = \omega t$$

The flux through the coil is

$$\Phi = BA \cos \theta = BA \cos \omega t$$

To find the instantaneous emf, we need to know the instantaneous rate of change of the flux. Using Eq. (20-7b), where $\Phi_0 = BA$,

$$\frac{\Delta\Phi}{\Delta t} = -\omega BA \sin \omega t$$

From Faraday's law,

$$\mathscr{E} = -N\frac{\Delta\Phi}{\Delta t} = \omega NBA \sin \omega t$$

which is what we found in Section 20.2 [Eq. (20-3b)].

Discussion Equation (20-3b) was obtained using the magnetic force on the electrons in a rectangular loop to find the motional emfs in each side. It would be difficult to do the same for a *circular* loop or coil. Faraday's law is easier to use and shows clearly that the induced emf doesn't depend on the particular shape of the loop or coil, as long as it is flat. Only the area and number of turns are relevant.

Practice Problem 20.4 Rotating Coil Generator

In a rotating coil generator, the magnetic field between the poles of an electromagnet has magnitude 0.40 T. A circular coil between the poles has 120 turns and radius 4.0 cm. The coil rotates with *frequency* 5.0 Hz. Find the *maximum* emf induced in the coil.

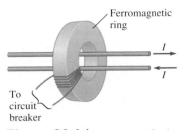

Figure 20.14 A ground fault interrupter.

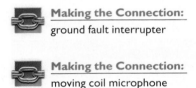

Figure 20.15 A moving coil microphone.

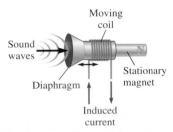
Making the Connection:
ground fault interrupter

Making the Connection:
moving coil microphone

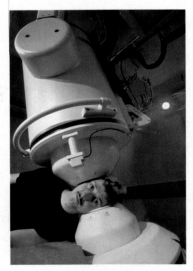

Figure 20.16 In magneto-encephalography, brain function can be observed in real time through non-invasive means. The two white cryostats seen here contain sensitive magnetic field detectors cooled by liquid helium.

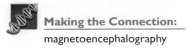
Making the Connection:

magnetoencephalography

Earlier in this section, we wrote Faraday's law to give the magnitude of the induced emf due to a changing magnetic field. But that's only part of the story. Faraday's law gives the induced emf due to a changing magnetic flux, *no matter what the reason for the flux change*. The flux change can occur for reasons other than a changing magnetic field. A conducting loop might be moving through regions where the field is not constant, or it can be rotating, or changing size or shape. In all of these cases, Faraday's law as already stated gives the correct emf, regardless of why the flux is changing. Recall that flux can be written

$$\Phi_B = BA \cos \theta \qquad (20\text{-}5)$$

Then the flux changes if the magnetic field strength (B) changes, or if the area of the loop (A) changes, or if the angle between the field and the normal changes.

Faraday's law says that, no matter what the reason for the change in flux, the induced emf is

$$\mathcal{E} = -N\frac{\Delta\Phi_B}{\Delta t} \qquad (20\text{-}6b)$$

The mobile charges in a moving conductor are pumped around due to the magnetic force on the charges. Since the conductor as a whole is moving, the mobile charges have a nonzero average velocity and therefore a nonzero average magnetic force. In the case of a changing magnetic field and a stationary conductor, the mobile charges aren't set into motion by the magnetic force—they have zero average velocity before current starts to flow. Exactly what *does* make current flow is considered in Section 20.8.

Technology Based on Electromagnetic Induction

An enormous amount of our technology depends on electromagnetic induction. There are so many applications of Faraday's law that it's hard to even begin a list. Certainly first on the list has to be the electric generator. Almost all of the electricity we use is produced by generators—either moving coil or moving field—that operate according to Faraday's law. Our entire system for distributing electricity is based on *transformers*, devices that use magnetic induction to change ac voltages (Section 20.6). Transformers raise voltages for transmission over long distances across power lines; transformers then reduce the voltages for safe use in homes and businesses. So our entire system for generating *and* distributing electricity depends on Faraday's law of induction.

A *ground fault interrupter* (GFI) is a device commonly used in ac electric outlets in bathrooms and other places where the risk of electric shock is great. In Fig. 20.14, the two wires that supply the outlet normally carry equal currents in opposite directions at all times. These ac currents reverse direction 120 times per second. If a person with wet hands accidentally comes into contact with part of the circuit, a current may flow to ground through the person instead of through the return wiring. Then the currents in the two wires are unequal. The magnetic field lines due to the unequal currents are channeled by a ferromagnetic ring through a coil. The flux through the coil reverses direction 120 times per second, so there is an induced emf in the coil, which trips a circuit breaker that disconnects the circuit from the power lines. GFIs are sensitive and fast, so they are a significant safety improvement over a simple circuit breaker.

Figure 20.15 is a simplified sketch of a moving coil microphone. The coil of wire is attached to a diaphragm that moves back and forth in response to sound waves in the air. The magnet is fixed in place. An induced emf appears in the coil due to the changing magnetic flux. In another common type of microphone, the magnet is attached to the diaphragm and the coil is fixed in place.

Faraday's law provides another way to detect currents that flow in the human body. In addition to measuring potential differences between points on the skin, we can measure the magnetic fields generated by these currents. Since the currents are small, the magnetic fields are weak, so sensitive detectors called SQUIDs (superconducting quantum interference devices) are used. When the currents change, changes in the magnetic field induce emfs in the SQUIDs. In a magnetoencephalogram, the induced emfs are measured at many points just outside the cranium (Fig. 20.16); then a computer calculates the location, magnitude, and direction of the currents in the brain that produce the field. Similarly, a magnetocardiogram detects the electric currents in the heart and surrounding nerves.

20.4   LENZ'S LAW

The directions of the induced emfs and currents caused by a changing magnetic flux can be determined using **Lenz's law**, named for the Baltic German physicist Heinrich Friedrich Emil Lenz (1804–1865):

Lenz's Law

The direction of the induced current in a loop always opposes the *change* in magnetic flux that induces the current.

Note that induced emfs and currents do not necessarily oppose the magnetic field or the magnetic flux; they oppose the *change* in the magnetic flux.

One way to apply Lenz's law is to look at the direction of the magnetic field produced by the induced current. The induced current around a loop produces its own magnetic field. This field may be weak compared to the external magnetic field. It cannot prevent the magnetic flux through the loop from changing, but its direction is always such that it "*tries*" to prevent the flux from changing. The magnetic field direction is related to the direction of the current by right-hand rule 2 (Section 19.8).

Lenz's law is really an expression of energy conservation. That connection is not easy to make in general, but in specific cases the connection can often be quite apparent (see Conceptual Example 20.5).

Conceptual Example 20.5

Faraday's and Lenz's Laws for the Moving Loop

Verify the emfs and currents calculated in Example 20.1 using Faraday's and Lenz's laws—that is, find the direction and magnitudes of the emfs and currents by looking at the changing magnetic flux through the loop.

Strategy   To apply Faraday's law, look for the reason why the flux is changing. In Example 20.1, a loop moves to the right at constant velocity into, through, and then out of a region of magnetic field. The magnitude and direction of the magnetic field within the region are not changing, nor is the area of the loop. What does change is the *portion* of that area that is immersed in the region of magnetic field.

Solution   At positions 1, 3, and 5, the flux is *not* changing even though the loop is moving. In each case, a small displacement of the loop causes no flux change.

The flux is zero at positions 1 and 5, and nonzero but constant at position 3. For these three positions, the induced emf is zero and so is the current.

If the loop were *at rest* at position 2, the magnetic flux would be constant. However, since the loop is moving into the region of field, the area of the loop through which magnetic field lines cross is increasing. Thus, the flux is increasing. According to Lenz's law, the direction of the induced current opposes the change in flux. Since the field is into the page, and the flux is increasing, the induced current flows in the direction that produces a magnetic field *out of* the page. By the right-hand rule, the current is counterclockwise.

At position 2, a length x of the loop is in the region of magnetic field. The area of the loop that is immersed in the field is Lx. The flux is then

$$\Phi_B = BA = BLx$$

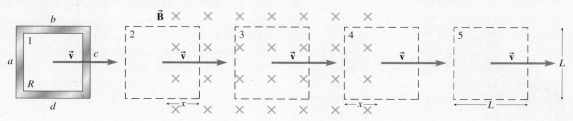

Continued on next page

Conceptual Example 20.5 Continued

Only x is changing. The rate of change of flux is

$$\frac{\Delta\Phi_B}{\Delta t} = BL\frac{\Delta x}{\Delta t} = BLv$$

Therefore,

$$|\mathscr{E}| = BLv$$

and

$$I = \frac{|\mathscr{E}|}{R} = \frac{BLv}{R}$$

At position 4, the flux is decreasing as the loop leaves the region of magnetic field. Once again, let a length x of the loop be immersed in the field. Just as at position 2,

$$\Phi_B = BLx$$

$$|\mathscr{E}| = \left|\frac{\Delta\Phi_B}{\Delta t}\right| = BL\left|\frac{\Delta x}{\Delta t}\right| = BLv$$

and

$$I = \frac{|\mathscr{E}|}{R} = \frac{BLv}{R}$$

This time the flux is *decreasing*. To oppose a *decrease*, the induced current makes a magnetic field in the *same* direction as the external field—into the page. Then the current must be clockwise.

The magnitudes and directions of the emfs and currents are exactly as found in Example 20.1.

Discussion   Another way to use Lenz's law to find the direction of the current is by looking at the magnetic force on the loop. The changing flux is due to the motion of the loop to the right. In order to oppose the change in flux, current flows in the loop in whatever direction gives a magnetic force to the *left*, to try to bring the loop to rest and stop the flux from changing. At position 2, the magnetic forces on sides b and d are equal and opposite; there is no magnetic force on side a since $B = 0$ there. Then there must be a magnetic force on side c to the left. From $\vec{F} = I\vec{L} \times \vec{B}$, the current in side c is up and thus flows counterclockwise in the loop. Similarly, at position 4, the current in side a is upward to give a magnetic force to the left.

The connection between Lenz's law and energy conservation is more apparent when looking at the force on the loop. When current flows in the loop, electric energy is dissipated at a rate $P = I^2R$. Where does this energy come from? If there is no external force pulling the loop to the right, the magnetic force slows down the loop; the dissipated energy comes from the kinetic energy of the loop. To keep the loop moving to the right at constant velocity while current is flowing, an external force must pull it to the right. The work done by the external force replenishes the loop's kinetic energy.

Practice Problem 20.5   The Magnetic Force on the Loop

(a) Find the magnetic force on the loop at positions 2 and 4 in terms of B, L, v, and R. (b) Verify that the rate at which an external force does work ($P = Fv$) to keep the loop moving at constant velocity is equal to the rate at which energy is dissipated in the loop ($P = I^2R$).

Conceptual Example 20.6

Lenz's Law for a Conducting Loop in a Changing Magnetic Field

A circular loop of wire moves toward a bar magnet at constant velocity (Fig. 20.17). The loop passes around the magnet and continues away from it on the other side. Use Lenz's law to find the direction of the current in the loop at positions 1 and 2.

Strategy   The magnetic flux through the loop is changing because the loop moves from weaker to stronger field (at position 1), and *vice versa* (at position 2). We can specify current directions as counterclockwise or clockwise as viewed from the left (with the loop moving away).

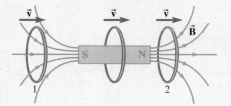

Figure 20.17

Conducting loop passing over a bar magnet.

Solution   At position 1, the magnetic field lines enter the magnet at the south pole, so the field lines cross the loop from left to right (Fig. 20.18a). Since the loop is moving closer to the magnet, the field is getting stronger; the number of field lines crossing the loop increases (Fig. 20.18b). The flux is therefore increasing. To oppose the increase, the current makes a magnetic field to the left (Fig. 20.18c).

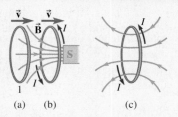

Figure 20.18

Loop moving toward magnet from position (a) to (b); (c) current induced in loop to produce a $\vec{B}$ field opposing the increasing strength of the nearing bar magnet.

Continued on next page

Conceptual Example 20.6 Continued

Figure 20.19

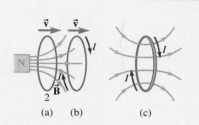

(a)   (b)   (c)

Loop moving away from magnet from position (a) to (b); (c) current induced in loop to produce a **B** field opposing the decreasing strength of the retreating bar magnet.

The right-hand rule gives the current direction to be counterclockwise as viewed from the left.

At position 2, the field lines still cross the loop from left to right (Fig. 20.19a), but now the field is getting weaker (Fig. 20.19b). The current must flow in the opposite direction—clockwise as viewed from the left (Fig. 20.19c).

Discussion There's almost always more than one way to apply Lenz's law. An alternative way to think about the situation is to remember the current loop is a magnetic dipole and we can think of it as a little bar magnet. At posi-

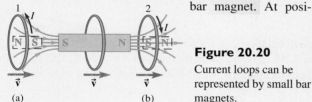

(a)   (b)

Figure 20.20

Current loops can be represented by small bar magnets.

tion 1, the current loop is repelled by the (real) bar magnet. The flux change is due to the motion of the loop toward the magnet; to oppose the change there should be a force pushing away. Then the poles of the current loop must be as in Fig. 20.20a; like poles repel. Point the thumb of the right hand in the direction of the north pole, and curl the fingers to find the current direction.

The same procedure can be used at position 2. Now the flux change is due to the loop moving away from the magnet, so to oppose the change in flux there must be a force attracting the loop toward the magnet (Fig. 20.20b).

Conceptual Practice Problem 20.6   Direction of Induced Emf in Coil

(a) In Fig. 20.21, just after the switch is closed, what is the direction of the magnetic field in the iron core? (b) In what direction does current flow through the resistor connected to coil 2? (c) If the switch remains closed, does current continue to flow in coil 2? Why or why not? (d) Make a drawing in which coils 1 and 2, just after the switch is closed, are replaced by equivalent little bar magnets.

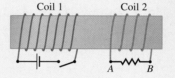

Coil 1   Coil 2

                    A B

Figure 20.21

Two coils wrapped about a common soft-iron core.

20.5   BACK EMF IN A MOTOR

If a generator and a motor are essentially the same device, is there an induced emf in the coil (or windings) of a motor? There must be, according to Faraday's law, since the magnetic flux through the coil changes as the coil rotates. By Lenz's law, this induced emf—called a **back emf**—opposes the flow of current in the coil, since it is the current that makes the coil rotate and thus causes the flux change. The magnitude of the back emf depends on the rate of change of the flux, so the back emf increases as the rotational speed of the coil increases.

Figure 20.22 shows a simple circuit model of the back emf in a dc motor. We assume that this motor has many coils (also called windings) at all different angles so that the torques, emfs, and currents are all constant. When the external emf is first applied, there is no back emf because the windings are not rotating. Then the current has a maximum value $I = \mathcal{E}_{ext}/R$. The faster the motor turns, the greater the back emf, and the smaller the current: $I = (\mathcal{E}_{ext} - \mathcal{E}_{back})/R$.

You may have noticed that when a large motor—as in a refrigerator or washing machine—first starts up, the room lights dim a bit. The motor draws a large current when it starts up because there is no back emf. The voltage drop across the wiring in the walls is proportional to the current flowing in them, so the voltage across lightbulbs and other loads on the circuit is reduced, causing a momentary "brown-out." As the motor comes up to speed, the current drawn is much smaller, so the brown-out ends.

If a motor is overloaded, so that it turns slowly or not at all, the current through the windings is large. Motors are designed to withstand such a large current only momentarily, as they start up; if the current is sustained at too high a level the motor "burns out"—the windings heat up enough to do damage to the motor.

Making the Connection:

back emf in a motor

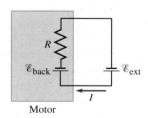

Motor

Figure 20.22 An external emf ($\mathcal{E}_{ext}$) is connected to a dc motor. The back emf ($\mathcal{E}_{back}$) is due to the changing flux through the windings. As the motor's rotational speed increases, the back emf increases and the current decreases.

● The current through a load that is connected to an emf is sometimes called the current *drawn* by the load.

Making the Connection:

transformers

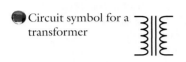

Circuit symbol for a transformer

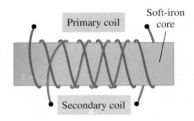

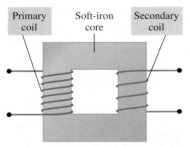

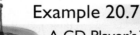

Figure 20.23 Two simple transformers. Each consists of two coils wound on a common soft-iron core so that nearly all the magnetic field lines produced by the primary coil pass through each turn of the secondary.

20.6   TRANSFORMERS

In the late nineteenth century, there were ferocious battles over what form of current should be used to supply electric power to homes and businesses. Thomas Edison was a proponent of direct current, while George Westinghouse, who owned the patents for the ac motor and generator invented by Nikola Tesla, was in favor of alternating current. Westinghouse won mainly because ac permits the use of transformers to change voltages and to transmit over long distances with less power loss than dc, as we see in this section.

Figure 20.23 shows two simple transformers. In each, two separate strands of insulated wire are wound around a soft-iron core. The magnetic field lines are guided through the iron, so the two coils enclose the same magnetic field lines. An alternating voltage is applied to the *primary* coil; the ac current in the primary causes a changing magnetic flux through the *secondary* coil.

If the primary coil has N_1 turns, an emf $\mathscr{E}_1$ is induced in the primary coil according to Faraday's law:

$$\mathscr{E}_1 = -N_1 \frac{\Delta \Phi_B}{\Delta t} \qquad (20\text{-}8a)$$

Here $\Delta\Phi_B/\Delta t$ is the rate of change of the flux through *each turn* of the primary. Ignoring resistance in the coil and other energy losses, the induced emf is equal to the ac voltage applied to the primary.

If the secondary coil has N_2 turns, then the emf induced in the secondary coil is

$$\mathscr{E}_2 = -N_2 \frac{\Delta \Phi_B}{\Delta t} \qquad (20\text{-}8b)$$

At any instant, the flux through each turn of the secondary is equal to the flux through each turn of the primary, so $\Delta\Phi_B/\Delta t$ is the same quantity in Eqs. (20-8a) and (20-8b). Eliminating $\Delta\Phi_B/\Delta t$ from the two equations, we find the ratio of the two emfs to be

$$\frac{\mathscr{E}_2}{\mathscr{E}_1} = \frac{N_2}{N_1} \qquad (20\text{-}9)$$

The output—the emf in the secondary—is N_2/N_1 times the input emf applied to the primary. The ratio N_2/N_1 is called the **turns ratio**. A transformer is often called a *step-up* or a *step-down* transformer, depending on whether the secondary emf is larger or smaller than the emf applied to the primary. The same transformer may often be used as a step-up or step-down transformer depending on which coil is used as the primary.

Current Ratio

In an *ideal transformer*, power losses in the transformer itself are negligible. Most transformers are very efficient, so neglecting power loss is usually reasonable. Then the rate at which energy is supplied to the primary is equal to the rate at which energy is supplied by the secondary ($P_1 = P_2$). Since power equals voltage times current, the ratio of the currents is the inverse of the ratio of the emfs:

$$\frac{I_2}{I_1} = \frac{\mathscr{E}_1}{\mathscr{E}_2} = \frac{N_1}{N_2} \qquad (20\text{-}10)$$

Example 20.7

A CD Player's Transformer

A transformer inside the power supply for a portable CD player has 500 turns in the primary coil. It supplies an emf of amplitude 6.8 V when plugged into the usual sinusoidal household emf of amplitude 170 V. (a) How many turns does the secondary coil have? (b) If the current drawn by the CD player has amplitude 1.50 A, what is the amplitude of the current in the primary?

Continued on next page

Example 20.7 Continued

Strategy The ratio of the emfs is the same as the turns ratio. We know the two emfs and the number of turns in the primary, so we can find the number of turns in the secondary. To find the current in the primary, we assume an ideal transformer. Then the currents in the two are inversely proportional to the emfs.

Solution (a) The turns ratio is equal to the emf ratio:

$$\frac{\mathscr{E}_2}{\mathscr{E}_1} = \frac{N_2}{N_1}$$

Solving for N_2 yields

$$N_2 = \frac{\mathscr{E}_2}{\mathscr{E}_1}N_1 = \frac{6.8 \text{ V}}{170 \text{ V}} \times 500 = 20 \text{ turns}$$

(b) The currents are inversely proportional to the emfs:

$$\frac{I_1}{I_2} = \frac{\mathscr{E}_2}{\mathscr{E}_1} = \frac{N_2}{N_1}$$

$$I_1 = \frac{\mathscr{E}_2}{\mathscr{E}_1}I_2 = \frac{6.8 \text{ V}}{170 \text{ V}} \times 1.50 \text{ A} = 0.060 \text{ A}$$

Discussion The most likely error would be to get the turns ratio upside down. Here we need a step-down trans-

former, so N_2 must be smaller than N_1. If the same transformer were hooked up backward, interchanging the primary and the secondary, then it would act as a step-up transformer. Instead of supplying 6.8 V to the CD player, it would supply

$$170 \text{ V} \times \frac{500}{20} = 4250 \text{ V}$$

We can check that the power input and the power output are equal:

$$P_1 = \mathscr{E}_1 I_1 = 170 \text{ V} \times 0.060 \text{ A} = 10.2 \text{ W}$$
$$P_2 = \mathscr{E}_2 I_2 = 6.8 \text{ V} \times 1.50 \text{ A} = 10.2 \text{ W}$$

(Since emfs and currents are sinusoidal, the instantaneous power is not constant. By multiplying the amplitudes of the current and emf, we calculate the *maximum* power.)

Practice Problem 20.7 An Ideal Transformer

An ideal transformer has five turns in the primary and two turns in the secondary. If the average power input to the primary is 10.0 W, what is the average power output of the secondary?

Transformers in the Distribution of Electricity

Making the Connection:
electric power distribution

Why is it so important to be able to transform voltages? The main reason is to minimize energy dissipation in power lines. Suppose that a power plant supplies a power P to a distant city. Since the power supplied is $P_S = I_S V_S$, where I_S and V_S are the current and voltage supplied to the load (the city), the plant can either supply a higher voltage and a smaller current, or a lower voltage and a larger current. If the power lines have total resistance R, the rate of energy dissipation in the power lines is $I_S^2 R$. Thus, to minimize energy dissipation in the power lines, we want as small a current as possible flowing through them, which means the potential differences must be large—hundreds of kilovolts in some cases. Transformers are used to raise the output emf of a generator to high voltages (Fig. 20.24). It would be unsafe to have such high voltages on household wiring, so the voltages are transformed back down before reaching the house.

Figure 20.24 Voltages are transformed in several stages. This step-up transformer raises the voltage from a generating station to 345 kV for transmission over long distances. Voltages are transformed back down in several stages. The last transformer in the series reduces the 3.4 kV on the local power lines to the 170 V used in the house.

20.7 EDDY CURRENTS

Whenever a conductor is subjected to a changing magnetic flux, the induced emf causes currents to flow. In a solid conductor, induced currents flow simultaneously along many different paths. These **eddy currents** are so named due to their resemblance to swirling eddies of current in air or in the rapids of a river. Though the pattern of current flow is complicated, we can still use Lenz's law to get a general idea of the direction of the current flow (clockwise or counterclockwise). We can also determine the qualitative effects of eddy current flow using energy conservation. Since they flow in a resistive medium, the eddy currents dissipate electric energy.

Conceptual Example 20.8
Eddy-Current Damping

A balance must have some damping mechanism. Without one, the balance arm would tend to oscillate for a long time before it settles down; determining the mass of an object would be a long, tedious process. A typical device used to damp out the oscillations is shown in Fig. 20.25.

A metal plate attached to the balance arm passes between the poles of a permanent magnet. (a) Explain the damping effect in terms of energy conservation. (b) Does the damping force depend on the speed of the plate?

Strategy   As portions of the metal plate move into or out of the magnetic field, the changing magnetic flux induces emfs. These induced emfs cause the flow of eddy currents. Lenz's law determines the direction of the eddy currents.

Solution   (a) As the plate moves between the magnet poles, parts of it move into the magnetic field while other parts move out of the field. Due to the changing magnetic flux, induced emfs cause eddy currents to flow. The eddy currents dissipate energy; the energy must come from the kinetic energy of the balance arm, pan, and object on the pan. As the currents flow, the kinetic energy of the balance decreases and it comes to rest much sooner than it would otherwise.

(b) If the plate is moving faster, the flux is changing faster. Faraday's law says that the induced emfs are proportional to the rate of change of the flux. Larger induced emfs cause larger currents to flow. The damping force is the magnetic force acting on the eddy currents. Therefore, the damping force is larger.

Discussion   Another way to approach part (a) is to use Lenz's law. The magnetic force acting on the eddy currents must oppose the flux change, so it must oppose the motion of the plate through the magnet. Slowing down the plate lessens the rate of flux change, while speeding up the plate would increase the rate of flux change—and increase the balance's kinetic energy, violating energy conservation.

Conceptual Practice Problem 20.8
Choosing a Core for a Transformer

In some transformers, the core around which wire is wrapped consists of parallel, insulated iron wires instead of solid iron (Fig. 20.26). Explain the advantage of using the insulated wires instead of the solid core. [*Hint:* Think about eddy currents. Why are eddy currents a disadvantage here?]

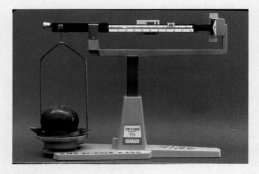

Figure 20.25
A balance. The damping mechanism is at the far right; as the balance arm oscillates, the metal plate moves between the poles of a magnet.

(a) Bundles of   (b) Solid soft-
    iron wires   iron core

Figure 20.26
Transformer cores.

PHYSICS AT HOME

If either the magnets or the metal plate are removed from a balance, it takes much longer for the oscillations of the balance arm to die out. If your instructor consents, test this on a laboratory balance. Usually a few screws need to be removed.

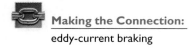

Making the Connection:
eddy-current braking

Eddy-Current Braking

The phenomenon described in Example 20.8 is called *eddy-current braking*. The eddy-current brake is ideal for a sensitive instrument such as a balance. The damping mechanism never wears out or needs adjustment and we are guaranteed that it exerts no force when the balance arm is not moving. Eddy-current brakes are also used with modern rail vehicles such as the maglev monorail, tramways, locomotives, passenger coaches, freight cars, and the latest high-speed maglev trains.

The damping force due to eddy currents automatically acts opposite to the motion; its magnitude is also larger when the speed is larger. The damping force is much like the viscous force on an object moving through a fluid (see Problem 32).

The Induction Stove

The induction stove discussed in the opening of this chapter operates via eddy currents. Under the cooking surface is an electromagnet that generates an oscillating magnetic field. When a metal pan is put on the stove, the emf causes currents to flow, and the energy dissipated by these currents is what heats the pan (Fig. 20.27). The pan must be made of metal; if a pan made of Pyrex glass is used, no currents flow and no heating occurs. For the same reason, there is no risk of starting a fire if a pot holder or sheet of paper is accidentally put on the induction stove. The cooking surface itself is a nonconductor; its temperature only rises to the extent that heat is conducted to it from the pan. The cooking surface therefore gets no hotter than the bottom of the pan.

20.8   INDUCED ELECTRIC FIELDS

When a conductor moves in a magnetic field, a motional emf arises due to the magnetic force on the mobile charges. Since the charges move along with the conductor, they have a nonzero average velocity. The magnetic force on these charges pushes them around the circuit if a complete circuit exists.

What causes the induced emf in a stationary conductor in a changing magnetic field? Now the conductor is at rest and the mobile charges have an average velocity of zero. The average magnetic force on them is then zero, so it cannot be the magnetic force that pushes the charges around the circuit. An **induced electric field**, created by the changing magnetic field, acts on the mobile charge in the conductor, pushing it around the circuit. The same force law ($\vec{\mathbf{F}} = q\vec{\mathbf{E}}$) applies to induced electric fields as to any other electric field.

The induced emf around a loop is the work done per unit charge on a charged particle that moves around the loop. Thus, an induced electric field does nonzero work on a charge that moves around a closed path, starting and ending at the same point. In other words, the induced electric field is nonconservative. The work done by the induced $\vec{\mathbf{E}}$ field *cannot* be described as the charge times the potential difference. The concept of potential depends on the electric field doing zero work on a charge moving around a closed path—only then can the potential have a unique value at each point in space. Table 20.1 summarizes the differences between conservative and nonconservative $\vec{\mathbf{E}}$ fields.

Making the Connection:
induction stove

Figure 20.27 The eddy currents induced in a metal pan on an induction stove.

Table 20.1

Comparison of Conservative and Nonconservative $\vec{\mathbf{E}}$ Fields

	Conservative $\vec{\mathbf{E}}$ Fields	Nonconservative (Induced) $\vec{\mathbf{E}}$ Fields
Source	Charges	Changing $\vec{\mathbf{B}}$ fields
Field lines	Start on positive charges and end on negative charges	Closed loops
Can be described by an electric potential?	Yes	No
Work done over a closed path	Always zero	Can be nonzero work over a closed path

Electromagnetic Fields

How can Faraday's law give the induced emf regardless of why the flux is changing—whether because of a changing magnetic field or because of a conductor moving in a magnetic field? A conductor that is moving in one frame of reference is at rest in another frame of reference (see Section 3.5). As we will see in Chapter 26, Einstein's theory of special relativity says that either reference frame is equally valid. In one frame, the induced emf is due to the motion of the conductor; in the other, the induced emf is due to a changing magnetic field.

The electric and magnetic fields are not really separate entities. They are intimately connected. Though it is advantageous in many circumstances to think of them as distinct fields, a more accurate view is to think of them as two aspects of the **electromagnetic field**. To use a loose analogy: a vector has different x- and y-components in different coordinate systems, but these components represent the same vector quantity. In the same way, the electromagnetic field has electric and magnetic parts (analogous to vector components) that depend on the frame of reference. A purely electric field in one frame of reference has both electric and magnetic "components" in another reference frame.

You may notice a missing symmetry. If a changing $\vec{\mathbf{B}}$ field is always accompanied by an induced $\vec{\mathbf{E}}$ field, what about the other way around? Does a changing electric field make an induced magnetic field? The answer to this important question—central to our understanding of light as an electromagnetic wave—is yes (Chapter 22).

20.9   MUTUAL- AND SELF-INDUCTANCE

Mutual-Inductance

Figure 20.28 shows two coils of wire. A power supply with variable emf causes current I_1 to flow in coil 1; the current produces magnetic field lines as shown. Some of these field lines cross through the turns of coil 2. If we adjust the power supply so that I_1 changes, the flux through coil 2 changes and an induced emf appears in coil 2. **Mutual-inductance**—when a changing current in one device causes an induced emf in another device—can occur between two circuit elements in the same circuit as well as between circuit elements in two different circuits. In either case, a changing current through one element induces an emf in the other. The effect is truly mutual: a changing current in coil 2 induces an emf in coil 1 as well.

At any point, the magnetic field due to coil 1 is proportional to I_1. For instance, if we double I_1, the magnetic field everywhere would be twice as large. The total flux linkage through coil 2 is proportional to the magnetic field, and therefore to the current I_1:

$$N_2\Phi_{21} \propto I_1$$

where the subscripts remind us that Φ_{21} stands for the total flux through coil 2 due to the field produced by coil 1. The constant of proportionality is called the *mutual-inductance* (M):

$$N_2\Phi_{21} = MI_1 \tag{20-11}$$

The mutual-inductance depends on the shape and size of the two circuit elements, their separation, and their relative orientation. It is exceedingly difficult to calculate mutual-inductances from the geometry of the two elements. In every case, the mutual-inductance M turns out to be the same regardless of whether we consider the flux linkage through coil 2 due to the current in coil 1 or *vice versa*:

$$M = \frac{N_2\Phi_{21}}{I_1} = \frac{N_1\Phi_{12}}{I_2} \tag{20-12}$$

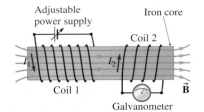

Figure 20.28 An induced emf appears in coil 2 due to the changing current in coil 1.

From Faraday's law, the induced emf in coil 2 is

$$\mathcal{E}_{21} = -N_2\frac{\Delta\Phi_{21}}{\Delta t} = -M\frac{\Delta I_1}{\Delta t} \qquad (20\text{-}13)$$

Similarly, the induced emf in coil 1 is

$$\mathcal{E}_{12} = -N_1\frac{\Delta\Phi_{21}}{\Delta t} = -M\frac{\Delta I_2}{\Delta t}$$

Recall that, to give the *instantaneous* emf, Faraday's law must be applied to a very short time interval. If Δt represents a longer time interval, then Faraday's law gives the *average* emf over that time interval.

From Eq. (20-13), we can find the SI units of M:

$$[M] = \frac{[\mathcal{E}]}{[\Delta I/\Delta t]} = \frac{\text{V}}{\text{A/s}} = \frac{\text{V}\cdot\text{s}}{\text{A}}$$

This combination of units is given the name henry (symbol: H) after Joseph Henry (1797–1878), the American scientist who was the first to wrap insulated wires around an iron core to make an electromagnet. Henry actually discovered induced emfs before Faraday, but Faraday published first.

Example 20.9

Mutual-Inductance

A circular loop of wire is placed near a solenoid (Fig. 20.29). When the current in the solenoid is 550 mA, the flux through the circular loop is 2.7×10^{-5} Wb. When the current in the solenoid changes at 6.0 A/s, the induced current in the circular loop is 0.36 mA. What is the resistance of the circular loop?

Strategy The mutual-inductance is the proportionality constant between the current in the solenoid and the flux through the loop. M is also the proportionality constant between the rate of change of current in the solenoid and the emf in the loop. From the induced emf and the induced current, we can find the resistance of the loop.

Solution The mutual-inductance is

$$M = \frac{N_1\Phi_{ls}}{I_s} = \frac{1\times2.7\times10^{-5}\ \text{Wb}}{0.550\ \text{A}} = 4.91\times10^{-5}\ \text{H}$$

The subscript "l" stands for "loop" and "s" stands for "solenoid." Then when the current in the solenoid changes at the rate $\Delta I_s/\Delta t = 6.0$ A/s, the induced emf in the loop is

$$|\mathcal{E}_{ls}| = M\left|\frac{\Delta I_s}{\Delta t}\right| = 4.91\times10^{-5}\ \frac{\text{V}\cdot\text{s}}{\text{A}}\times6.0\ \frac{\text{A}}{\text{s}} = 2.95\times10^{-4}\ \text{V}$$

The resistance of the loop is

$$R = \frac{|\mathcal{E}_{ls}|}{I} = \frac{0.295\ \text{mV}}{0.36\ \text{mA}} = 0.82\ \Omega$$

Discussion The mutual-inductance determines the induced emf in the loop for a given rate of change of current in the solenoid. How much current flows in the loop in response to the induced emf depends on the loop's electrical resistance. A loop with a much higher resistance would have the *same* emf, but a much smaller current would flow.

Figure 20.29

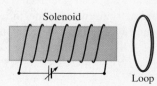

A changing current in the solenoid induces an emf in the loop; a changing current in the loop also induces an emf in the solenoid.

Practice Problem 20.9   Flux Through the Solenoid

If a 1.5-V power supply is connected to the loop, what would be the total magnetic flux through the solenoid due to the loop's magnetic field?

Self-Inductance

Henry was the first to suggest that a changing current in a coil induces an emf in the *same* coil as well as in other coils—an effect called **self-inductance**. When the current through the coil is changing, the changing magnetic flux inside the coil produces an

The circuit symbol for an inductor is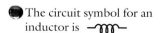

Figure 20.30 Inductors come in many sizes and shapes.

induced electric field that gives rise to an induced emf. When a coil, solenoid, toroid, or other circuit element is used in a circuit primarily for its self-inductance effects, it is often referred to as an **inductor**. *Self-inductance* is often shortened to *inductance*. A few inductors are shown in Fig. 20.30.

To calculate the self-inductance of coil 1 in Fig. 20.28, we follow the same steps that we used to find mutual-inductance. If a current I_1 flows in coil 1, then the total flux through coil 1 is proportional to I_1:

$$N_1 \Phi_{11} \propto I_1$$

The subscripts remind us that Φ stands for the total flux through coil 1 due to the current in coil 1. When the context is clearly one of self-inductance, we write simply $N\Phi \propto I$. The self-inductance L of the coil is defined as the constant of proportionality between self-flux and current:

Definition of self-inductance:

$$N\Phi = LI \tag{20-14}$$

The most common form of inductor is the solenoid. In Problem 38, the self-inductance L of a long air-core solenoid of n turns per unit length, length ℓ, and radius r is found to be

$$L = \mu_0 n^2 \pi r^2 \ell \tag{20-15a}$$

For a solenoid with $N = n\ell$ turns,

$$L = \frac{\mu_0 N^2 \pi r^2}{\ell} \tag{20-15b}$$

According to Faraday's law, the induced emf in coil 1 is then

$$\mathcal{E} = -N\frac{\Delta\Phi}{\Delta t} = -L\frac{\Delta I}{\Delta t} \tag{20-16}$$

The SI unit of self-inductance is the same as that of mutual-inductance: the henry.

The behavior of an inductor in a circuit can be summarized as current *stabilizer*. The inductor "likes" the current to be constant—it "tries" to maintain the status quo. If the current is constant, there is no induced emf; to the extent that we can neglect the resistance of its windings, the inductor acts like a short circuit. When the current is changing, the induced emf is proportional to the rate of change. According to Lenz's law, the direction of the emf opposes the change that produces it. If the current is increasing, the direction of the emf in the inductor pushes back as if to make it harder for the current to increase (Fig. 20.31a). If the current is decreasing, the direction of the emf in the inductor is forward, as if to help the current keep flowing (Fig. 20.31b).

An inductor stores energy in a magnetic field, just as a capacitor stores energy in an electric field. Suppose the current in an inductor increases at a constant rate from 0 to I in a time T. We let lowercase i stand for the instantaneous current at some time t between 0 and T, and let uppercase I stand for the *final* current. The instantaneous rate at which energy accumulates in the inductor is

$$P = \mathcal{E}i$$

Since current increases at a constant rate, the magnetic flux increases at a constant rate, so the induced emf is constant. Also, since the current increases at a constant rate, the average current is $I_{av} = I/2$. Then the *average* rate at which energy accumulates is

$$P_{av} = \mathcal{E}I_{av} = \tfrac{1}{2}\mathcal{E}I$$

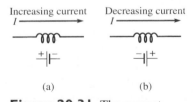

Increasing current   Decreasing current

(a)   (b)

Figure 20.31 The current through both these inductors flows to the right. In (a), the current is increasing; the induced emf in the inductor "tries" to prevent the increase. In (b), the current is decreasing; the induced emf in the inductor "tries" to prevent the decrease.

Using Eq. (20-16) for the emf, the average power is

$$P_{av} = \tfrac{1}{2} L \frac{\Delta i}{\Delta t} I$$

and the total energy stored in the inductor is

$$U = P_{av} T = \tfrac{1}{2} \left(L \frac{\Delta i}{\Delta t} \right) I T$$

Since the current changes at a constant rate, $\Delta i / \Delta t = I/T$. The total energy stored in the inductor is

Magnetic energy stored in an inductor:

$$U = \tfrac{1}{2} L I^2 \qquad\qquad (20\text{-}17)$$

Although to simplify the calculation we assumed that the current was increased from zero at a constant rate, Eq. (20-17) for the energy stored in an inductor depends only on the current I and not on how the current reached that value (see Problem 40).

Compare the energy stored in an inductor and the energy stored in a capacitor:

$$U_C = \tfrac{1}{2} C^{-1} Q^2 \qquad\qquad (17\text{-}18c)$$

The energy in the inductor is proportional to the square of the current, just as the energy in the capacitor is proportional to the square of the charge. We can use the inductor to find the magnetic energy density in a magnetic field, just as we found the energy density in an electric field using a capacitor. Consider a solenoid so long that we can neglect the magnetic energy stored in the field outside it. The inductance is

$$L = \mu_0 n^2 \pi r^2 \ell$$

where n is the number of turns per unit length, ℓ is the length of the solenoid, and r is its radius. The energy stored in the inductor when a current I flows is

$$U = \tfrac{1}{2} L I^2 = \tfrac{1}{2} \mu_0 n^2 \pi r^2 \ell I^2$$

The volume of space inside the solenoid is the length times the cross-sectional area:

$$\text{volume} = \pi r^2 \ell$$

Then the magnetic energy density—energy per unit volume—is

$$u_B = \frac{U}{\pi r^2 \ell} = \frac{1}{2} \mu_0 n^2 I^2$$

To express the energy density in terms of the magnetic field strength, recall that $B = \mu_0 n I$ [Eq. (19-17)] inside a long solenoid. Therefore,

Magnetic energy density:

$$u_B = \frac{1}{2\mu_0} B^2 \qquad\qquad (20\text{-}18)$$

Equation (20-18) is valid for more than the interior of an air-core solenoid; it gives the energy density for *any* magnetic field except for the field inside a ferromagnet. Both the magnetic energy density and the electric energy density are proportional to the square of the field strength: recall that the electric energy density is

$$u_E = \tfrac{1}{2} \kappa \epsilon_0 E^2 \qquad\qquad (17\text{-}19)$$

Example 20.10

Energy Stored in a Solenoid

An ideal air-core solenoid has radius 2.0 cm, length 12 cm, and 9000.0 turns. The solenoid carries a current of 2.0 A. (a) Find the magnetic field inside the solenoid. (b) How much energy is stored in the solenoid?

Strategy Since the solenoid is ideal, we ignore the nonuniformity in the magnetic field near the ends. We consider the magnetic field to be uniform in the entire volume inside. There are two ways to find the energy. We can either find the self-inductance and then use Eq. (20-17) for the energy stored in an inductor, or we can find the energy density [Eq. (20-18)] and multiply by the volume.

Given: $N = 9000.0$, $r = 0.020$ m, $\ell = 0.12$ m
Find: B, U_B

Solution (a) The magnetic field inside an ideal solenoid is

$$B = \mu_0 n I = \frac{\mu_0 N I}{\ell}$$

$$= \frac{4\pi \times 10^{-7} \text{ H/m} \times 9000.0 \times 2.0 \text{ A}}{0.12 \text{ m}} = 0.19 \text{ T}$$

(b) The magnetic energy density is

$$u_B = \frac{1}{2\mu_0} B^2 \qquad (20\text{-}18)$$

The total energy stored in the solenoid is

$$U_B = \frac{1}{2\mu_0} B^2 \times \pi r^2 \ell$$

since $\pi r^2 \ell$ is the volume of the interior of the solenoid. Substituting the expression for B yields

$$U_B = \frac{1}{2\mu_0} \left(\frac{\mu_0 N I}{\ell} \right)^2 \times \pi r^2 \ell$$

$$= \frac{\mu_0 N^2 I^2 \pi r^2}{2\ell}$$

Now we can substitute numerical values.

$$U_B = \frac{4\pi \times 10^{-7} \text{ H/m} \times 9000.0^2 \times (2.0 \text{ A})^2 \times \pi (0.020 \text{ m})^2}{2 \times 0.12 \text{ m}}$$

$$= 2.1 \text{ J}$$

Discussion Let's use the alternative method as a check. For a solenoid with N turns,

$$L = \frac{\mu_0 N^2 \pi r^2}{\ell} \qquad (20\text{-}15\text{b})$$

The magnetic energy stored in an inductor is

$$U_B = \frac{1}{2} L I^2 \qquad (20\text{-}17)$$

By substitution,

$$U_B = \frac{1}{2} \frac{\mu_0 N^2 \pi r^2}{\ell} I^2$$

which agrees with the expression found previously. We should also verify the units. Since $1 \text{ H} = \dfrac{1 \text{ V}}{\text{A/s}}$,

$$\frac{\text{H/m} \times \text{A}^2 \times \text{m}^2}{\text{m}} = \text{H} \times \text{A}^2 = \frac{\text{V} \times \text{A}^2}{\text{A/s}} = \text{V} \times \text{A} \times \text{s} = \text{V} \times \text{C} = \text{J}$$

Practice Problem 20.10   Power in an Inductor

Suppose the current in the inductor of Example 20.10 increases from 0 to 2.0 A during a time interval of 4.0 s. Calculate the average rate at which energy is stored in the inductor during this time interval. [*Hint:* Use one method to calculate the answer and another as a check.]

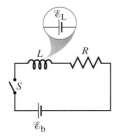

Figure 20.32 A dc circuit with an inductor L, a resistor R, and a switch S. When the current is changing, an emf is induced in the inductor (represented by a battery symbol above the inductor).

20.10 LR CIRCUITS

To get an idea of how inductors behave in circuits, let's first study them in dc circuits—that is, in circuits with batteries or other constant-voltage power supplies. Consider the **LR circuit** in Fig. 20.32. The inductor is assumed to be ideal: its windings have negligible resistance. At $t = 0$, the switch S is closed. What is the subsequent current in the circuit?

The current through the inductor just before the switch is closed is zero. As the switch is closed, the current is initially zero. An instantaneous change in current through an inductor would mean an instantaneous change in its stored energy, since $U \propto I^2$. An instantaneous change in energy means that energy is supplied in zero time. Since nothing can supply infinite power,

Current through an inductor must always change *continuously*, never instantaneously.

The initial current is zero, so there is no voltage drop across the resistor. The magnitude of the induced emf in the inductor ($\mathscr{E}_L$) is *initially* equal to the battery's emf ($\mathscr{E}_b$). Therefore, the current is rising at an initial rate given by

$$\frac{\Delta I}{\Delta t} = \frac{\mathscr{E}_b}{L}$$

As current builds up, the voltage drop across the resistor increases. Then the induced emf in the inductor ($\mathscr{E}_L$) gets smaller (Fig. 20.33) so that

$$(\mathscr{E}_b - \mathscr{E}_L) - IR = 0 \qquad (20\text{-}19a)$$

or

$$\mathscr{E}_b = \mathscr{E}_L + IR \qquad (20\text{-}19b)$$

Since the voltage across an *ideal* inductor is the induced emf, we can substitute $\mathscr{E}_L = L(\Delta I/\Delta t)$: [The minus sign has already been written explicitly in Eq. (20-19); $\mathscr{E}_L$ here stands for the *magnitude* of the emf.]

$$\mathscr{E}_b = L\frac{\Delta I}{\Delta t} + IR \qquad (20\text{-}20)$$

The battery emf is constant. Thus, as the current increases, the voltage drop across the resistor gets larger and the induced emf in the inductor gets smaller. Therefore, the *rate* at which the current increases gets smaller (Fig. 20.34).

After a very long time, the current reaches a stable value. Since the current is no longer changing, there is no voltage drop across the inductor, so $\mathscr{E}_b = I_f R$ or

$$I_f = \frac{\mathscr{E}_b}{R}$$

The equation for the current as a function of time $I(t)$ is an exponential function, similar to the charge on a charging capacitor:

$$I(t) = I_f(1 - e^{-t/\tau}) \qquad (20\text{-}21)$$

The time constant τ for this circuit must be some combination of L, R, and $\mathscr{E}$. Dimensional analysis (Problem 56) shows that τ must be some dimensionless constant times L/R. It can be proved with calculus that the dimensionless constant is 1:

Time constant, *LR* circuit:

$$\tau = \frac{L}{R} \qquad (20\text{-}22)$$

The induced emf as a function of time is

$$\mathscr{E}_L(t) = \mathscr{E}_b - IR = \mathscr{E}_b - \frac{\mathscr{E}_b}{R}(1 - e^{-t/\tau})R = \mathscr{E}_b e^{-t/\tau} \qquad (20\text{-}23)$$

The *LR* circuit in which the current is initially zero is analogous to the charging *RC* circuit. In both cases, the device starts with no stored energy and gains energy after the switch is closed. In charging a capacitor, the *voltage* eventually reaches a nonzero equilibrium value, while for the inductor the *current* reaches a nonzero equilibrium value. Compare the graphs of Fig. 18.35 with those of Figs. 20.33 and 20.34; current and voltage have switched places.

What about an *LR* circuit analogous to the discharging *RC* circuit? That is, once a steady current is flowing through an inductor, and energy is stored in the inductor, how can we stop the current and reclaim the stored energy? Simply opening the switch in Fig. 20.32 would *not* be a good way to do it. The attempt to suddenly stop the current would induce a *huge* emf in the inductor. Most likely, sparks would complete the circuit across the open switch, allowing the current to die out more gradually. Sparking generally isn't good for the health of the switch, though.

A better way to stop the current is shown in Fig. 20.35. Initially switch S_1 is closed and a current $I_0 = \mathscr{E}_b/R_1$ is flowing through the inductor (Fig. 20.35a). Switch S_2 is closed and then S_1 is immediately opened at $t = 0$. Since the current through the inductor

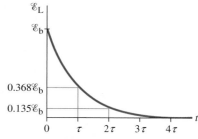

Figure 20.33 The voltage drop across the inductor as the current builds up.

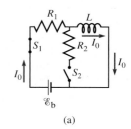

Figure 20.34 The current in the circuit as a function of time.

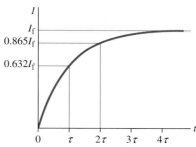

(a)

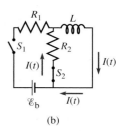

(b)

Figure 20.35 A circuit that allows the current in the inductor circuit to be safely stopped. (a) Initially switch 1 is closed and switch 2 is open. (b) At $t = 0$, switch 2 is closed and then switch 1 immediately opened.

Table 20.2

Comparison of *RC* and *LR* Circuits

	Capacitor	Inductor
Voltage is proportional to	Charge	Rate of change of current
Can change discontinuously	Current	Voltage
Cannot change discontinuously	Voltage	Current
Energy stored (U) is proportional to	V^2	I^2
When $V = 0$ and $I \neq 0$	$U = 0$	$U = $ maximum
When $I = 0$ and $V \neq 0$	$U = $ maximum	$U = 0$
Energy stored (U) is proportional to	E^2	B^2
Time constant =	RC	L/R
"Charging" circuit	$I(t) \propto e^{-t/\tau}$	$I(t) \propto (1 - e^{-t/\tau})$
	$V_C(t) \propto (1 - e^{-t/\tau})$	$V_L(t) = \mathscr{E}_L(t) \propto e^{-t/\tau}$
"Discharging" circuit	$I(t) \propto e^{-t/\tau}$	$I(t) \propto e^{-t/\tau}$
	$V_C(t) \propto e^{-t/\tau}$	$V_L(t) = \mathscr{E}_L(t) \propto e^{-t/\tau}$

can only change continuously, the current flows as shown in Fig. 20.35b. At $t = 0$, the current is $I_0 = \mathscr{E}_b/R_1$. The current gradually dies out as the energy stored in the inductor is dissipated in resistor R_2. The current as a function of time is a decaying exponential:

$$I(t) = I_0 e^{-t/\tau} \tag{20-24}$$

where

$$\tau = \frac{L}{R_2}$$

The voltages across the inductor and resistor can be found from the loop rule and Ohm's law. Table 20.2 organizes what we know about *RC* and *LR* circuits.

Example 20.11

Switching on a Large Electromagnet

A large electromagnet has an inductance $L = 15$ H. The resistance of the windings is $R = 8.2\ \Omega$. Treat the electromagnet as an ideal inductor in series with a resistor (as in Fig. 20.32). When a switch is closed, a 24-V dc power supply is connected to the electromagnet. (a) What is the ultimate current through the windings of the electromagnet? (b) How long after closing the switch does it take for the current to reach 99.0% of its final value?

Strategy   When the current reaches its final value, there is no induced emf. The ideal inductor in Fig. 20.32 therefore has no potential difference across it. Then the entire voltage of the power source is across the resistor. The current follows an exponential curve as it builds to its final value. When it is at 99.0% of its final value, it has 1.0% left to go.

Solution   (a) After the switch has been closed for many time constants, the current reaches a steady value. When the current is no longer changing, there is no induced emf. Therefore, the entire 24 V of the power supply is dropped across the resistor:

$$\mathscr{E}_b = \mathscr{E}_L + IR$$

when $\mathscr{E}_L = 0$, $I_f = \dfrac{\mathscr{E}_b}{R} = \dfrac{24\text{ V}}{8.2\ \Omega} = 2.9$ A

(b) The factor $e^{-t/\tau}$ represents the fraction of the current yet to build up. When the current reaches 99.0% of its final value,

$$1 - e^{-t/\tau} = 0.990$$

or

$$e^{-t/\tau} = 0.010$$

There is 1.0% yet to go. To solve for t, first take the natural log (ln) of both sides to get t out of the exponent:

$$\ln(e^{-t/\tau}) = -t/\tau = \ln 0.010 = -4.61$$

Now solve for t:

$$t = -\tau \ln 0.010 = -\frac{L}{R}\ln 0.010 = -\frac{15\text{ H}}{8.2\ \Omega} \times (-4.61) = 8.4 \text{ s}$$

It takes 8.4 s for the current to build up to 99.0% of its final value.

Continued on next page

Example 20.11 Continued

Discussion A slightly different approach is to write the current as a function of time:

$$I(t) = \frac{\mathscr{E}_b}{R}(1 - e^{-t/\tau}) = I_f(1 - e^{-t/\tau})$$

We are looking for the time t at which $I = 99.0\%$ of 2.9 A or $I/I_f = 0.990$. Then

$$0.990 = 1 - e^{-t/\tau} \quad \text{or} \quad e^{-t/\tau} = 0.010$$

as before.

Practice Problem 20.11   Switching Off the Electromagnet

When the electromagnet is to be turned off, it is connected to a 50.0-Ω resistor, as in Fig. 20.36, to allow the current to decrease gradually. How long after the switch is opened does it take for the current to decrease to 0.1 A?

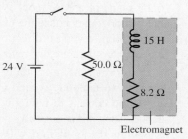

Figure 20.36
Practice Problem 20.11.

MASTER THE CONCEPTS

- A conductor moving through a magnetic field develops a motional emf given by

$$\mathscr{E} = vBL \tag{20-2a}$$

  if both $\vec{\mathbf{v}}$ and $\vec{\mathbf{B}}$ are perpendicular to the rod.

- The emf due to an ac generator with one planar coil of wire turning in a uniform magnetic field is sinusoidal and has amplitude ωNBA:

$$\mathscr{E}(t) = \omega NBA \sin \omega t \tag{20-3b}$$

  Here ω is the angular speed of the coil, A is its area, and N is the number of turns.

- Magnetic flux through a planar surface:

$$\Phi_B = B_\perp A = BA_\perp = BA \cos \theta \tag{20-5}$$

  (θ is the angle between $\vec{\mathbf{B}}$ and the *normal*)

  The magnetic flux is proportional to the number of magnetic field lines that cut through a surface. The SI unit of magnetic flux is the weber (1 Wb = 1 T·m^2).

- Faraday's law gives the induced emf whenever there is a changing magnetic flux, regardless of the reason the flux is changing:

$$\mathscr{E} = -N\frac{\Delta\Phi_B}{\Delta t} \tag{20-6b}$$

- Lenz's law: the direction of an induced emf or an induced current *opposes* the *change* that caused it.

- The back emf in a motor increases as the rotational speed increases.

- For an ideal transformer,

$$\frac{\mathscr{E}_2}{\mathscr{E}_1} = \frac{N_2}{N_1} = \frac{I_1}{I_2} \tag{20-9, 10}$$

  The ratio N_2/N_1 is called the turns ratio. There is no energy loss in an ideal transformer, so the power input is equal to the power output.

- Whenever a solid conductor is subjected to a changing magnetic flux, the induced emf causes eddy currents to flow simultaneously along many different paths. Eddy currents dissipate energy.

- A changing magnetic field gives rise to an induced electric field. The induced emf is the circulation of the induced electric field.

- A changing current in one circuit element induces an emf in another circuit element. The mutual-inductance is the constant of proportionality between the rate of change of the current and the induced emf.

$$M = \frac{N_2\Phi_{21}}{I_1} = \frac{N_1\Phi_{12}}{I_2} \tag{20-12}$$

$$\mathscr{E}_{21} = -N_2\frac{\Delta\Phi_{21}}{\Delta t} = -M\frac{\Delta I_1}{\Delta t} \tag{20-13}$$

- Self-inductance is when a changing current induces an emf in the same device:

$$N\Phi = LI \tag{20-14}$$

$$\mathscr{E} = -L\frac{\Delta I}{\Delta t} \tag{20-16}$$

- The energy stored in an inductor is

$$U = \tfrac{1}{2}LI^2 \tag{20-17}$$

- The energy density (energy per unit volume) in a magnetic field is

$$u_B = \frac{1}{2\mu_0}B^2 \tag{20-18}$$

- Current through an inductor must always change *continuously*, never instantaneously. In an *LR* circuit, the time constant is

$$\tau = \frac{L}{R} \tag{20-22}$$

  The current in an *LR* circuit is

$$\text{If } I_0 = 0, \quad I(t) = I_f(1 - e^{-t/\tau}) \tag{20-21}$$

$$\text{If } I_f = 0, \quad I(t) = I_0 e^{-t/\tau} \tag{20-24}$$

Conceptual Questions

1. A vertical magnetic field is perpendicular to the horizontal plane of a wire loop. When the loop is rotated about a horizontal axis in the plane, the current induced in the loop reverses direction twice per rotation. Explain why there are *two* reversals for *one* rotation.

2. A transformer is essentially a mutual-inductance device. Two coils are wound around an iron core; an alternating current in one coil induces an emf in the second. The core is normally made of either laminated iron—thin sheets of iron with an insulating material between them—or of a bundle of parallel insulated iron wires. Why not just make it of solid iron?

3. A certain amount of energy must be supplied to increase the current through an inductor from 0 mA to 10 mA. Does it take the same amount of energy, more, or less to increase the current from 10 mA to 20 mA?

4. Suppose you were to connect the primary coil of a transformer to a dc battery. Is there an emf induced in the secondary coil? If so, why do we not use transformers with dc sources?

5. A metal plate is attached to the end of a rod and positioned so that it can swing into and out of a perpendicular magnetic field pointing out of the plane of the paper as shown. In position 1, the plate is just swinging into the field; in position 2, the plate is swinging out of the field. Does an induced eddy current circulate clockwise or counterclockwise in the metal plate when it is in (a) position 1 and (b) position 2? (c) Will the induced eddy currents act as a braking force to stop the pendulum motion? Explain.

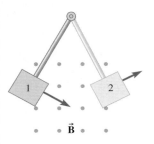

6. Magnetic induction is the principle behind the operation of mechanical speedometers used in automobiles and bicycles. In the drawing, a simplified version of the speedometer, a metal disk is free to spin about the vertical axis passing through its center. Suspended above the disk is a horseshoe magnet. (a) If the horseshoe magnet is connected to the drive shaft of the vehicle so that it rotates about a vertical axis, what happens to the disk? [*Hint:* Think about eddy currents and Lenz's law.]

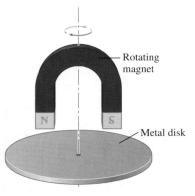

Rotating magnet

Metal disk

(b) Instead of being free to rotate, the disk is restrained by a hairspring. The hairspring exerts a restoring torque on the disk proportional to its angular displacement from equilibrium. When the horseshoe magnet rotates, what happens to the disk? A pointer attached to the disk indicates the speed of the vehicle. How does the angular *position* of the pointer depend on the angular *speed* of the magnet?

7. Wires that carry telephone signals are twisted. The twisting reduces the noise on the line from nearby electric devices that produce changing currents. How does the twisting reduce noise pickup?

8. In an MRI the patient must be immersed in a strong magnetic field. Why is the magnetic field turned on gradually rather than suddenly?

9. The magnetic flux through a flat surface is known. The area of the surface is also known. Is that information enough to calculate the average magnetic field on the surface? Explain.

10. Would a ground fault interrupter work if the circuit used dc current instead of ac? Explain.

11. In the study of thermodynamics, we thought of a refrigerator as a reversed heat engine. (a) Explain how a generator is a reversed electric motor. (b) What kind of device is a reversed loudspeaker?

12. Two identical circular coils of wire are separated by a fixed center-to-center distance. Describe the orientation of the coils that would (a) maximize or (b) minimize their mutual-inductance.

13. (a) Explain why a transformer works for ac but not for dc. (b) Explain why a transformer designed to be connected to an emf of amplitude 170 V would be damaged if connected to a dc emf of 170 V.

14. Credit cards have a magnetic strip that encodes information about the credit card account. Why do devices that read the magnetic strip often include the instruction to swipe the card rapidly? Why can't the magnetic strip be read if the card is swiped too slowly?

15. Think of an example that illustrates why an "anti-Lenz" law would violate the conservation of energy. (The "anti-Lenz" law is: The direction of induced emfs and currents always *reinforces* the *change* that produces them.)

16. A 2-m-long copper pipe is held vertically. When a marble is dropped down the pipe, it falls through in about 0.7 s. A magnet of similar size and shape dropped down the pipe takes *much* longer. Why?

17. An electric mixer is being used to mix up some cake batter. What happens to the motor if the batter is too thick, so the beaters are turning slowly?

18. A circular loop of wire can be used as an antenna to sense the changing magnetic fields in an electromagnetic wave

(such as a radio transmission). What is the advantage of using a coil with many turns rather than a single loop?

19. Some low-cost tape recorders do not have a separate microphone. Instead, the speaker is used as a microphone when recording. Explain how this works.

20. High-voltage power lines run along the edge of a farmer's field. Describe how the farmer might be able to steal electric power without making any electrical connection to the power line. (Yes, it works. Yes, it has been done. Yes, it is illegal.)

Multiple-Choice Questions

1. An electric current is induced in a conducting loop by all but one of these processes. Which one does *not* produce an induced current?
   (a) rotating the loop so that it cuts across magnetic field lines
   (b) placing the loop so that its area is perpendicular to a changing magnetic field
   (c) moving the loop parallel to uniform magnetic field lines
   (d) expanding the area of the loop while it is perpendicular to a uniform magnetic field

2. A split-ring commutator is used in a dc generator to
   (a) rotate a loop so that it cuts through magnetic flux.
   (b) reverse the connections to an armature so that the current periodically reverses direction.
   (c) reverse the connections to an armature so that the current does not reverse direction.
   (d) prevent a coil from rotating when the magnetic field is changing.

3. Suppose the switch in Fig. 20.21 has been closed for a long time but is suddenly opened at $t = t_0$. Which of these graphs best represents the current in coil 2 as a function of time? I_2 is positive if it flows from A to B through the resistor.

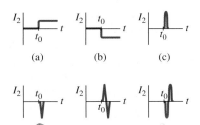

4. The current in the long wire is decreasing. What is the direction of the current induced in the conducting loop below the wire?

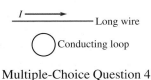

Multiple-Choice Question 4 and Problems 12 and 13

(a) counterclockwise   (b) clockwise
(c) CCW or CW depending on the shape of the loop
(d) No current is induced.

5. In a bicycle speedometer, a bar magnet is attached to the spokes of the wheel and a coil is attached to the frame so that the north pole of the magnet moves past it once for every revolution of the wheel. As the magnet moves past the coil, a pulse of current is induced in the coil. A computer then measures the time between pulses and computes the bicycle's speed. The figure shows the magnet about to move past the coil. Which of the graphs shows the resulting current pulse? Take current counterclockwise in part (a) of the figure to be positive.

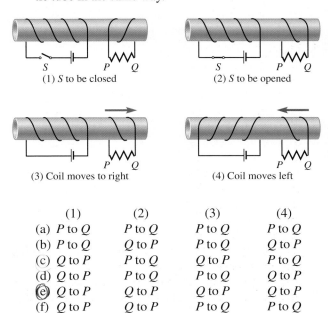

6. For each of the experiments (1, 2, 3, 4) shown, in what direction does current flow *through the resistor*? Note that the wires are not always wrapped around the plastic tube in the same way.

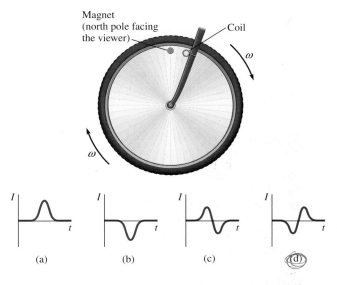

	(1)	(2)	(3)	(4)
(a)	P to Q	P to Q	P to Q	P to Q
(b)	P to Q	Q to P	P to Q	Q to P
(c)	Q to P	P to Q	Q to P	P to Q
(d)	Q to P	P to Q	P to Q	Q to P
(e)	Q to P	Q to P	Q to P	Q to P
(f)	Q to P	Q to P	P to Q	P to Q

7. The figure shows a region of uniform magnetic field out of the page. Outside the region, the magnetic field is zero. Some rectangular wire loops move as indicated. Which of the loops would feel a magnetic force directed to the right?

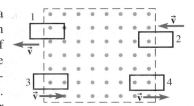

(a) 1   (b) 2   (c) 3   (d) 4
(e) 1 and 2 (f) 2 and 4 (g) 3 and 4 (h) none of them

8. In a moving coil microphone, the induced emf in the coil at any instant depends mainly on

(a) the displacement of the coil.
(b) the velocity of the coil.
(c) the acceleration of the coil.

9. A moving magnet microphone is similar to a moving coil microphone (Fig. 20.15) except that the coil is stationary and the magnet is attached to the diaphragm, which moves in response to sound waves in the air. If, in response to a sound wave, the magnet moves according to $x(t) = A \sin \omega t$, the induced emf in the coil would be (approximately) proportional to which of these?

(a) $\sin \omega t$ (b) $\cos \omega t$ (c) $\sin 2\omega t$ (d) $\cos 2\omega t$

10. An airplane is flying due east. The Earth's magnetic field has a downward vertical component and a horizontal component due north. Which point on the plane's exterior accumulates positive charge due to the motional emf?

(a) the nose (the point farthest east)
(b) the tail (the point farthest west)
(c) the tip of the left wing (the point farthest north)
(d) the tip of the right wing (the point farthest south)

Problems

 Combination conceptual/quantitative problem

 Biological or medical application

No ✦ Easy to moderate difficulty level

✦ More challenging

✦✦ Most challenging

Blue # Detailed solution in the Student Solutions Manual

[1 2] Problems paired by concept

20.1 Motional Emf; 20.2 Electric Generators

1. In Fig. 20.2, a metal rod of length L moves to the right at speed v. (a) What is the current in the rod, in terms of v, B, L, and R? (b) In what direction does the current flow? (c) What is the direction of the magnetic force on the rod? (d) What is the magnitude of the magnetic force on the rod (in terms of v, B, L, and R)?

2. Suppose that the current were to flow in the direction *opposite* to that found in Problem 1. (a) In what direc-

tion would the magnetic force on the rod be? (b) In the absence of an external force, what would happen to the rod's kinetic energy? (c) Why is this not possible? Returning to the correct direction of the current, sketch a rough graph of the kinetic energy of the rod as a function of time.

3. To maintain a constant emf, the moving rod of Fig. 20.2 must maintain a constant velocity. In order to maintain a constant velocity, some external force must pull it to the right. (a) What is the magnitude of the external force required, in terms of v, B, L, and R? (See Problem 1.) (b) At what rate does this force do work on the rod? (c) What is the power dissipated in the resistor? (d) Overall, is energy conserved? Explain.

4. In Fig. 20.2, what would the magnitude (in terms of v, L, R, and B) and direction (CW or CCW) of the current be if the direction of the magnetic field were: (a) into the page; (b) to the right (in the plane of the page); (c) up (in the plane of the page); (d) such that it has components both out of the page and to the right, with a 20.0° angle between the field and the plane of the page?

5. A 15.0-g conducting rod of length 1.30 m is free to slide downward between two vertical rails without friction. The rails are connected to an 8.00-Ω resistor, and the entire apparatus is placed in a 0.450-T uniform magnetic field. Ignore the resistance of the rod and rails. (a) What is the terminal velocity of the rod? (b) At this terminal velocity, compare the magnitude of the change in gravitational potential energy per second with the power dissipated in the resistor.

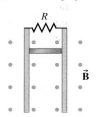

6. A solid metal cylinder of mass m rolls down parallel metal rails spaced a distance L apart with a constant acceleration of magnitude a_0 [part (a) of figure]. The rails are inclined at an angle θ to the horizontal. Now the rails are connected electrically at the top and immersed in a magnetic field of magnitude B that is perpendicular to the plane of the rails [part (b) of figure]. (a) As it rolls down the rails, in what direction does current flow in the cylinder? (b) What direction is the magnetic force on the cylinder? (c) Instead of rolling at constant acceleration, the cylinder now approaches a terminal speed v_t. What is v_t in terms of L, m, R, a_0, θ, and B? R is the total electrical resistance of the circuit consisting of the cylinder, rails, and wire; assume R is constant (that is, the resistances of the rails themselves are negligible).

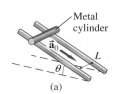
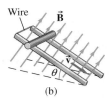

(a)   (b)

7. In Fig. 20.6, side 3 of the rectangular coil in the electric generator rotates about the axis at constant angular speed ω. The figure with this problem shows side 3 by itself.

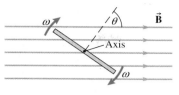

(a) First consider the right half of side 3. Although the speed of the wire differs depending on the distance from the axis, the direction is the same for the entire right half. Use the magnetic force law to find the direction of the force on electrons in the right half of the wire. (b) Does the magnetic force tend to push electrons along the wire, either toward or away from the axis? (c) Is there an induced emf along the *length* of this half of the wire? (d) Generalize your answers to the left side of wire 3 and the two sides of wire 1. What is the net emf due to these two sides of the coil?

8. A square loop of wire of side 2.3 cm and electrical resistance 79 Ω is near a long straight wire that carries a current of 6.8 A in the direction indicated.

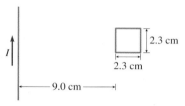

The long wire and loop both lie in the plane of the page. The left side of the loop is 9.0 cm from the wire. (a) If the loop is at rest, what is the induced emf in the loop? What are the magnitude and direction of the induced current in the loop? What are the magnitude and direction of the magnetic force on the loop? (b) Repeat if the loop is moving to the right at a constant speed of 45 cm/s. (c) In (b), find the electric power dissipated in the loop and show that it is equal to the rate at which an external force, pulling the loop to keep its speed constant, does work.

9. A solid copper disk of radius R rotates at angular velocity ω in a perpendicular magnetic field B. The figure shows the disk rotating clockwise and the magnetic field into the page.

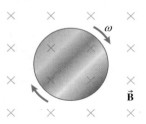

(a) Is the charge that accumulates on the edge of the disk positive or negative? Explain. (b) What is the potential difference between the center of the disk and the edge? [*Hint:* Think of the disk as a large number of thin wedge-shaped rods. The center of such a rod is at rest, and the outer edge moves at speed $v = \omega R$. The rod moves through a perpendicular magnetic field at an *average* speed of $\frac{1}{2}\omega R$.]

20.3 Faraday's Law; 20.4 Lenz's Law

10. A horizontal desk surface measures 1.3 m × 1.0 m. If the Earth's magnetic field has magnitude 0.44 mT and is directed 65° below the horizontal, what is the magnetic flux through the desk surface?

11. A square loop of wire, 0.75 m on each side, has one edge along the positive z-axis and is tilted toward the y-z plane at an angle of 30.0° with respect to the horizontal (x-z plane). There is a uniform magnetic field of 0.32 T pointing in the positive x-axis direction.

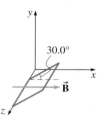

(a) What is the flux through the loop? (b) If the angle increases to 60°, what is the new flux through the loop? (c) While the angle is being increased,which direction will current flow through the top side of the loop?

12. A long straight wire carrying a steady current is in the plane of a circular loop of wire. See the figure with Multiple-Choice Question 4. (a) If the loop is moved closer to the wire, what direction does the induced current in the loop flow? (b) At one instant, the induced emf in the loop is 3.5 mV. What is the rate of change of the magnetic flux through the loop at that instant? Express your answer in T·m²/s.

13. A long straight wire carrying a current I is in the plane of a circular loop of wire. See the figure with Multiple-Choice Question 4. The current I is decreasing. Both the loop and the wire are held in place by external forces. The loop has resistance 24 Ω. (a) In what direction does the induced current in the loop flow? (b) In what direction is the external force holding the loop in place? (c) At one instant, the induced current in the loop is 84 mA. What is the rate of change of the magnetic flux through the loop at that instant in Wb/s?

14. A circular conducting coil with radius 3.40 cm is placed in a uniform magnetic field of 0.880 T with the plane of the coil perpendicular to the magnetic field. The coil is rotated 180° about the axis in 0.222 s. (a) What is the average induced emf in the coil during this rotation?

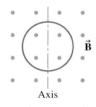

(b) If the coil is made of copper with a diameter of 0.900 mm, what is the average current that flows through the coil during the rotation?

15. Verify that, in SI units, $\Delta\Phi_B/\Delta t$ can be measured in volts—in other words, that 1 Wb/s = 1 V.

16. The component of the external magnetic field along the central axis of a 50-turn coil of radius 5.0 cm increases from 0 to 1.8 T in 3.6 s. (a) If the resistance of the coil is 2.8 Ω, what is the magnitude of the induced current in the coil? (b) What is the direction of the current if the axial component of the field points away from the viewer?

17. In the figure, switch S is initially open. It is closed, and then opened again a few seconds later. (a) In what direction does current flow through the ammeter when

switch S is closed? (b) In what direction does current flow when switch S is then opened? (c) Sketch a qualitative graph of the current through the ammeter as a function of time. Take the current to be positive to the right.

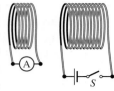

18. Another example of motional emf is a rod attached at one end and rotating in a plane perpendicular to a uniform magnetic field. We can analyze this motional emf using Faraday's law. (a) Consider the area that the rod sweeps out in each revolution and find the magnitude of the emf in terms of the angular frequency ω, the length of the rod R, and the strength of the uniform magnetic field B. (b) Write the emf magnitude in terms of the speed v of the tip of the rod and compare this with motional emf magnitude of a rod moving at constant velocity perpendicular to a uniform magnetic field.

19. (a) For a particle moving in simple harmonic motion, the position can be written $x(t) = x_m \cos \omega t$. What is the velocity $v_x(t)$ as a function of time for this particle? (b) Using the small-angle approximation for the sine function, find the slope of the graph of $\Phi(t) = \Phi_0 \sin \omega t$ at $t = 0$. Does your result agree with the value of $\Delta\Phi/\Delta t = \omega\Phi_0 \cos \omega t$ at $t = 0$?

20. Two loops of wire are next to each other in the same plane. (a) If the switch S is closed, does current flow in loop 2? If so, in what direction? (b) Does the current in loop 2 flow for only a brief moment, or does it continue? (c) Is there a magnetic force on loop 2? If so, in what direction? (d) Is there a magnetic force on loop 1? If so, in what direction?

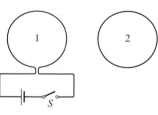

20.5 Back Emf in a Motor

21. A dc motor has coils with a resistance of 16 Ω and is connected to an emf of 120.0 V. When the motor operates at full speed, the back emf is 72 V. (a) What is the current in the motor when it first starts up? (b) What is the current when the motor is at full speed? (c) If the current is 4.0 A with the motor operating at less than full speed, what is the back emf at that time?

22. Tim is using a cordless electric weed trimmer with a dc motor to cut the long weeds in his back yard. The trimmer generates a back emf of 18.00 V when it is connected to an emf of 24.0 V dc. The total electrical resistance of the electric motor is 8.00 Ω. (a) How much

current flows through the motor when it is running smoothly? (b) Suddenly the string of the trimmer gets wrapped around a pole in the ground and the motor quits spinning. What is the current through the motor when there is no back emf? What should Tim do?

✦ 23. A dc motor is connected to a constant emf of 12.0 V. The resistance of its windings is 2.0 Ω. At normal operating speed, the motor delivers 6.0 W of mechanical power. (a) What is the initial current drawn by the motor when it is first started up? (b) What current does it draw at normal operating speed? (c) What is the back emf induced in the windings at normal speed?

20.6 Transformers

24. A step-down transformer has 4000 turns on the primary and 200 turns on the secondary. If the primary voltage amplitude is 2.2 kV, what is the secondary voltage amplitude?

25. A step-down transformer has a turns ratio of 1/100. An ac voltage of amplitude 170 V is applied to the primary. If the primary current amplitude is 1.0 mA, what is the secondary current amplitude?

26. A doorbell uses a transformer to deliver an amplitude of 8.5 V when it is connected to a 170-V amplitude line. If there are 50 turns on the secondary, (a) what is the turns ratio? (b) How many turns does the primary have?

27. The primary coil of a transformer has 250 turns; the secondary coil has 1000 turns. An alternating current is sent through the primary coil. The emf in the primary is of amplitude 16 V. What is the emf amplitude in the secondary?

28. When the emf for the primary of a transformer is of amplitude 5.00 V, the secondary emf is 10.0 V in amplitude. What is the transformer turns ratio (N_2/N_1)?

29. A transformer with a primary coil of 1000 turns is used to step up the standard 170-V amplitude line voltage to a 220-V amplitude. How many turns are required in the secondary coil?

30. A transformer with 1800 turns on the primary and 300 turns on the secondary is used in an electric slot car racing set to reduce the input voltage amplitude of 170 V from the wall output. The current in the secondary coil is of amplitude 3.2 A. What is the voltage amplitude across the secondary coil and the current amplitude in the primary coil?

31. A transformer for an answering machine takes an ac voltage of amplitude 170 V as its input and supplies a 7.8-V amplitude to the answering machine. The primary has 300 turns. (a) How many turns does the secondary have? (b) When idle, the answering machine uses a maximum power of 5.0 W. What is the amplitude of the current drawn from the 170-V line?

20.7 Eddy Currents

32. A 2-m-long copper pipe is held vertically. When a marble is dropped down the pipe, it falls through in about 0.7 s. A magnet of similar size and shape takes *much* longer to fall through the pipe. (a) As the magnet is falling through the pipe with its north pole below its south pole, what direction do currents flow around the pipe above the magnet? Below the magnet (CW or CCW as viewed from the top)? (b) Sketch a graph of the speed of the magnet as a function of time. [*Hint:* What would the graph look like for a marble falling through honey?]

33. In Problem 32, the pipe is suspended from a spring scale. The weight of the pipe is 12.0 N; the weight of the marble and magnet are each 0.3 N. Sketch graphs to show the reading of the spring scale as a function of time for the fall of the marble and again for the fall of the magnet. Label the vertical axis with numerical values.

20.9 Mutual- and Self-Inductance

34. A solenoid is made of 300.0 turns of wire, wrapped around a hollow cylinder of radius 1.2 cm and length 6.0 cm. What is the self-inductance of the solenoid?

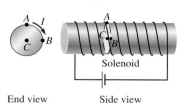

End view   Side view

35. A solenoid of length 2.8 cm and diameter 0.75 cm is wound with 160 turns per cm. When the current through the solenoid is 0.20 A, what is the magnetic flux through *one* of the windings of the solenoid?

36. If the current in the solenoid in Problem 35 is decreasing at a rate of 35.0 A/s, what is the induced emf (a) in one of the windings? (b) in the entire solenoid?

37. An ideal solenoid has length ℓ. If the windings are compressed so that the length of the solenoid is reduced to $0.50\,\ell$, what happens to the inductance of the solenoid?

38. In this problem, you derive the expression for the self-inductance of a long solenoid [Eq. (20-15a)]. The solenoid has n turns per unit length, length ℓ, and radius r. Assume that the current flowing in the solenoid is I. (a) Write an expression for the magnetic field inside the solenoid in terms of n, ℓ, r, I, and universal constants. (b) Assume that all of the field lines cut through each turn of the solenoid. In other words, assume the field is uniform right out to the ends of the solenoid—a good approximation if the solenoid is tightly wound and sufficiently long. Write an expression for the magnetic flux through one turn. (c) What is the total flux linkage through all turns of the solenoid? (d) Use the definition of self-inductance [Eq. (20-14)] to find the self-inductance of the solenoid.

39. Compare the electric energy that can be stored in a capacitor to the magnetic energy that can be stored in an inductor of the same size (that is, the same volume). For the capacitor, assume that air is between the plates; the maximum electric field is then the breakdown strength of air, about 3 MV/m. The maximum magnetic field attainable in an ordinary solenoid with an air core is on the order of 10 T.

40. In Section 20.9, in order to find the energy stored in an inductor, we assumed that the current was increased from zero at a constant rate. In this problem, you will prove that the energy stored in an inductor is $U_L = \frac{1}{2}LI^2$—that is, it only depends on the current I and not on the previous time-dependence of the current. (a) If the current in the inductor increases from i to $i + \Delta i$ in a very short time Δt, show that the energy added to the inductor is $\Delta U = Li\,\Delta i$. [*Hint:* Start with $\Delta U = P\,\Delta t$.] (b) Show that, on a graph of Li versus i, for any small current interval Δi, the energy added to the inductor can be interpreted as the area under the graph for that interval. (c) Now show that the energy stored in the inductor when a current I flows is $U = \frac{1}{2}LI^2$.

41. The current in a 0.080-H solenoid increases from 20.0 mA to 160.0 mA in 7.0 s. Find the average emf in the solenoid during that time interval.

42. Calculate the equivalent inductance L_{eq} of two ideal inductors, L_1 and L_2, connected in series in a circuit. Assume that their mutual-inductance is negligible. [*Hint:* Imagine replacing the two inductors with a single equivalent inductor L_{eq}. How is the emf in the series equivalent related to the emfs in the two inductors? What about the currents?]

43. Calculate the equivalent inductance L_{eq} of two ideal inductors, L_1 and L_2, connected in parallel in a circuit. Assume that their mutual-inductance is negligible. [*Hint:* Imagine replacing the two inductors with a single equivalent inductor L_{eq}. How is the emf in the parallel equivalent related to the emfs in the two inductors? What about the currents?]

20.10 *LR* Circuits

44. A 5.0-mH inductor and a 10.0-Ω resistor are connected in series with a 6.0-V dc battery. (a) What is the voltage across the resistor immediately after the switch is closed? (b) What is the voltage across the resistor after the switch has been closed for a long time? (c) What is the current in the inductor after the switch has been closed for a long time?

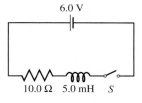

45. In a circuit, a parallel combination of a 10.0-Ω resistor and a 7.0-mH inductor is connected in series with a 5.0-Ω

resistor, a 6.0-V dc battery, and a switch. (a) What are the voltages across the 5.0-Ω resistor and the 10.0-Ω resistor, respectively, immediately after the

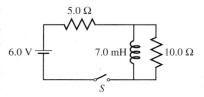

Problems 45 and 46

switch is closed? (b) What are the voltages across the 5.0-Ω resistor and the 10.0-Ω resistor, respectively, after the switch has been closed for a long time? (c) What is the current in the 7.0-mH inductor after the switch has been closed for a long time?

46. Refer to Problem 45. After the switch has been closed for a very long time, it is opened. What are the voltages across (a) the 5.0-Ω resistor and (b) the 10.0-Ω resistor immediately after the switch is opened?

47. In the circuit, switch S is opened at t = 0 after having been closed for a long time. (a) How much energy is stored in the inductor at t = 0? (b) What is the instantaneous rate of change of the inductor's energy at t = 0? (c) What is the *average* rate of change of the inductor's energy between t = 0.0 and t = 1.0 s? (d) How long does it take for the current in the inductor to reach 0.0010 times its initial value?

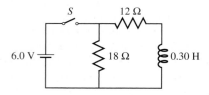

48. In the circuit for this problem, after the switch has been closed for a long time, it is opened. How long does it take for the energy stored in the inductor to decrease to 0.10 times its initial value?

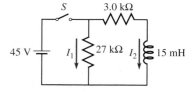

Problems 48 and 49

49. No currents flow in the circuit before the switch is closed. Consider all circuit elements to be ideal. (a) At the instant the switch is closed, what are the values of the currents I_1 and I_2, the potential differences across the resistors, the power supplied by the battery, and the induced emf in the inductor? (b) After the switch has been closed for a long time, what are the values of the currents I_1 and I_2, the potential differences across the

resistors, the power supplied by the battery, and the induced emf in the inductor?

50. A 0.30-H inductor and a 200.0-Ω resistor are connected in series to a 9.0-V battery. (a) What is the maximum current that flows in the circuit? (b) How long after connecting the battery does the current reach half its maximum value? (c) When the current is half its maximum value, find the energy stored in the inductor, the rate at which energy is being stored in the inductor, and the rate at which energy is dissipated in the resistor. (d) Redo parts (a) and (b) if, instead of being negligibly small, the internal resistances of the inductor and battery are 75 Ω and 20.0 Ω, respectively.

51. A coil has an inductance of 0.15 H and a resistance of 33 Ω. The coil is connected to a 6.0-V battery. After a long time elapses, the current in the coil is no longer changing. (a) What is the current in the coil? (b) What is the energy stored in the coil? (c) What is the rate of energy dissipation in the coil? (d) What is the induced emf in the coil?

52. A coil of wire is connected to an ideal 6.00-V battery at t = 0. At t = 10.0 ms, the current in the coil is 204 mA. One minute later, the current is 273 mA. Find the resistance and inductance of the coil. [*Hint:* Sketch I(t).]

53. A 0.67-mH inductor and a 130-Ω resistor are placed in series with a 24-V battery. (a) How long will it take for the current to reach 67% of its maximum value? (b) What is the maximum energy stored in the inductor? (c) How long will it take for the energy stored in the inductor to reach 67% of its maximum value? Comment on how this compares to the answer in part (a).

54. The windings of an electromagnet have inductance L = 8.0 H and resistance R = 2.0 Ω. A 100.0-V dc power supply is connected to the windings by closing switch S_2. (a) What is the current in the windings? (b) The electromagnet is to be shut off.

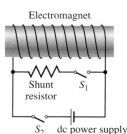

Electromagnet

Before disconnecting the power supply by opening switch S_2, a shunt resistor with resistance 20.0 Ω is connected in parallel across the windings. Why is the shunt resistor needed? Why must it be connected *before* the power supply is disconnected? (c) What is the maximum power dissipated in the shunt resistor? The shunt resistor must be chosen so that it can handle at least this much power without damage. (d) When the power supply is disconnected by opening switch S_2, how long does it take for the current in the windings to drop to 0.10 A? (e) Would a larger shunt resistor dissipate the energy stored in the electromagnet faster? Explain.

55. A coil has an inductance of 0.15 H and a resistance of 33 Ω. The coil is connected to a 6.0-V ideal battery.

When the current reaches half its maximum value: (a) At what *rate* is magnetic energy being stored in the inductor? (b) At what rate is energy being dissipated? (c) What is the total power that the battery supplies?

56. The time constant τ for an *LR* circuit must be some combination of *L*, *R*, and $\mathcal{E}$. (a) Write the units of each of these three quantities in terms of V, A, and s. (b) Show that the only combination that has units of seconds is *L/R*.

Comprehensive Problems

57. Switch S_2 has been closed for a long time. (a) If switch S_1 is closed, will a current flow in the left-hand coil? If so, what direction will it flow across the ammeter? (b) After some time, switch S_1 is opened again while switch S_2 remains closed. Will a current flow in the left coil? If so, what direction will it flow across the ammeter?

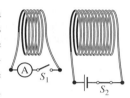

58. In the ac generator of Fig. 20.6, the emf produced is $\mathcal{E}(t) = \omega BA \sin \omega t$. If the generator is connected to a load of resistance *R*, then the current that flows is

$$I(t) = \frac{\omega BA}{R} \sin \omega t$$

(a) Find the magnetic forces on sides 2 and 4 at the instant shown in Fig. 20.7. (Remember that $\theta = \omega t$.) (b) Why do the magnetic forces on sides 1 and 3 not cause a torque about the axis of rotation? (c) From the magnetic forces found in (a), calculate the torque on the loop about its axis of rotation at the instant shown in Fig. 20.7. (d) In the absence of other torques, would the magnetic torque make the loop increase or decrease its angular velocity? Explain.

59. A *flip coil* is a device used to measure a magnetic field. A coil of radius *r*, *N* turns, and electrical resistance *R* is initially perpendicular to a magnetic field of magnitude *B*. The coil is connected to a special kind of galvanometer that measures the total charge *Q* that flows through it. To measure the field, the flip coil is rapidly flipped upside down. (a) What is the change in magnetic flux through the coil in one flip? (b) If the time interval during which the coil is flipped is Δt, what is the average induced emf in the coil? (c) What is the average current that flows through the galvanometer? (d) What is the total charge *Q* in terms of *r*, *N*, *R*, and *B*?

60. A 100-turn coil with a radius of 10.0 cm is mounted so the coil's axis can be oriented in any horizontal direction. Initially the axis is oriented so the magnetic flux from Earth's field is maximized. If the coil's axis is rotated through 90.0° in 0.080 s, an emf of 0.687 mV is induced in the coil. (a) What is the magnitude of the horizontal component of Earth's magnetic field at this location? (b) If the coil is moved to another place on Earth and the measurement is repeated, will the result be the same?

61. A bar magnet is initially far from a circular loop of wire. The magnet is moved at constant speed along the axis of the loop. It moves toward the loop, proceeds to pass through it, and then continues until it is far away on the right side of the loop. Sketch a qualitative graph of the current in the loop as a function of the position of the bar magnet. Take the current to be positive when it is counterclockwise as viewed from the left.

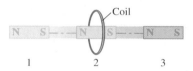

62. A bar magnet approaches a coil [part (a) of figure]. (a) In which direction does current flow through the galvanometer as the magnet approaches? (b) In part (b) of the figure, the magnet is initially at rest inside the coil. It is then pulled out from the left side. In which direction does current flow through the galvanometer as the magnet is pulled away? (c) In both situations, how does the magnitude of the current depend on the number of turns in the coil? (The resistance of the coil is negligible compared to the resistance of the galvanometer.) (d) How does the current depend on the speed of the magnet? (e) How does the magnitude of the current change if two such magnets were used, held together with the north poles together and the south poles together? (f) How does the magnitude of the current change if two such magnets were used, held together with the *opposite* poles together? (g) Would the experiment give similar results if the magnet remains stationary and the coil moves instead?

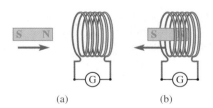

(a)   (b)

63. A circular metal ring is suspended above a solenoid. The magnetic field due to the solenoid is shown. The current in the solenoid is increasing. (a) What is the direction of the current in the ring? (b) The flux through the ring is proportional to the current in the solenoid. When the current in the solenoid is 12.0 A,

the magnetic flux through the ring is 0.40 Wb. When the current increases at a rate of 240 A/s, what is the induced emf in the ring? (c) Is there a net magnetic force on the ring? If so, in what direction? (d) If the ring is cooled by immersing it in liquid nitrogen, what happens to its electrical resistance, the induced current, and the magnetic force? The change in size of the ring is negligible. (With a sufficiently strong magnetic field, the ring can be made to shoot up high into the air.)

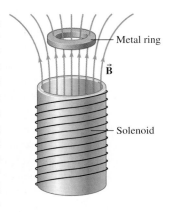
Metal ring
$\vec{B}$
Solenoid

64. The strings of an electric guitar are made of ferromagnetic metal. The pickup consists of two components. A magnet causes the part of the string near it to be magnetized. The vibrations of the string near the pickup coil produce an induced emf in the coil. The electrical signal in the coil is then amplified and used to drive the speakers. In the figure, the string is moving away from the coil. What is the direction of the induced current in the coil?

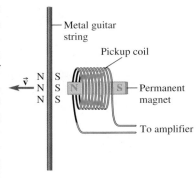
Metal guitar string
Pickup coil
$\vec{v}$
Permanent magnet
To amplifier

65. A toroid has a square cross section of side a. The toroid has N turns and radius R. The toroid is narrow ($a \ll R$) so that the magnetic field inside the toroid can be considered to be uniform in magnitude. What is the self-inductance of the toroid?

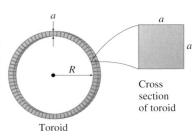
a
a
a
R
Cross section of toroid
Toroid

66. An ideal toroid has N turns and self-inductance L. A single turn of wire is wrapped around the toroid [see part (a) of the figure]. (a) What is the mutual-inductance between the toroid

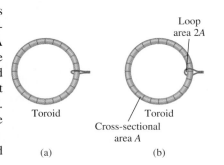
Loop area $2A$
Toroid
Toroid
Cross-sectional area A
(a)
(b)

and the single turn of wire? (b) What would the mutual-inductance be if the turn of wire had an area twice as large as the cross-sectional area of the toroid [see part (b) of the figure]?

67. Two solenoids, of N_1 and N_2 turns respectively, are wound on the same form. They have the same length L and radius r. (a) What is the mutual-inductance of these two solenoids? (b) If an ac current

$$I_1(t) = I_m \sin \omega t$$

flows in solenoid 1 (N_1 turns), write an expression for the total flux through solenoid 2. (c) What is the maximum induced emf in solenoid 2? [Hint: Refer to Eq. (20-7).]

✦ 68. An ideal inductor of inductance L is connected to an ac power supply, which provides an emf $\mathcal{E}(t) = \mathcal{E}_m \sin \omega t$. (a) Write an expression for the current in the inductor as a function of time. [Hint: See Eq. (20-7).] (b) What is the ratio of the maximum emf to the maximum current? This ratio is called the *reactance*. (c) Do the maximum emf and maximum current occur at the same time? If not, how much time separates them?

69. Suppose you wanted to use the Earth's magnetic field to make an ac generator at a location where the magnitude of the field is 0.50 mT. Your coil has 1000.0 turns and a radius of 5.0 cm. At what angular velocity would you have to rotate it in order to generate an emf of amplitude 1.0 V?

70. A uniform magnetic field of magnitude 0.29 T makes an angle of 13° with the plane of a circular loop of wire. The loop has radius 1.85 cm. What is the magnetic flux through the loop?

71. A solenoid is 8.5 cm long, 1.6 cm in diameter, and has 350 turns. When the current through the solenoid is 65 mA, what is the magnetic flux through one turn of the solenoid?

72. An airplane is flying due north at 180 m/s. The Earth's magnetic field has a northward component of 0.30 mT and an upward component of 0.38 mT. (a) If the wingspan (distance between the wingtips) is 46 m, what is the motional emf between the wingtips? (b) Which wingtip is positively charged?

✦ 73. Repeat Problem 72 if the plane flies 30.0° west of south at 180 m/s instead.

74. How much energy due to the Earth's magnetic field is present in 1.0 m³ of space near Earth's surface, at a place where the field has magnitude 0.45 mT?

75. The largest constant magnetic field achieved in the laboratory is about 40 T. (a) What is the magnetic energy density due to this field? (b) What magnitude electric field would have an equal energy density?

76. A TV tube requires a 20.0-kV-amplitude power supply. (a) What is the turns ratio of the transformer that raises the 170-V-amplitude household voltage to 20.0 kV?

(b) If the tube draws 82 W of power, find the currents in the primary and secondary windings. Assume an ideal transformer.

✦ 77. The magnetic field between the poles of an electromagnet is 2.6 T. A coil of wire is placed in this region so that the field is parallel to the axis of the coil. The coil has electrical resistance 25 Ω, radius 1.8 cm, and length 12.0 cm. When the current supply to the electromagnet is shut off, the total charge that flows through the coil is 9.0 mC. How many turns are there in the coil?

78. The alternator in an automobile generates an emf of amplitude 12.6 V when the engine idles at 1200 rpm. What is the amplitude of the emf when the car is being driven on the highway with the engine at 2800 rpm?

79. The outside of an ideal solenoid (N_1 turns, length L, radius r) is wound with a coil of wire with N_2 turns. (a) What is the mutual-inductance? (b) If the current in the solenoid is changing at a rate $\Delta I_1/\Delta t$, what is the magnitude of the induced emf in the coil?

✦ 80. An ideal solenoid (N_1 turns, length L_1, radius r_1) is placed inside another ideal solenoid (N_2 turns, length $L_2 > L_1$, radius $r_2 > r_1$) such that the axes of the two coincide. (a) What is the mutual-inductance? (b) If the current in the outer solenoid is changing at a rate $\Delta I_2/\Delta t$, what is the magnitude of the induced emf in the inner solenoid?

Ⓒ 81. A standard ammeter must be inserted in series into the circuit (Section 18.9). An *induction ammeter* has the great advantage of being able to measure currents without making any electrical connection to the circuit. An iron ring is hinged so that it can be snapped around a wire. A coil is wrapped around the iron ring; the ammeter uses the induced emf in the coil to determine the current flowing in the wire. (a) Does the induction ammeter work equally well for ac and dc currents? Explain. (b) Can the induction ammeter be placed

around both wires connected to an appliance to measure the current drawn by the appliance? Explain.

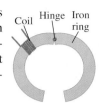 

Answers to Practice Problems

20.1 only the magnitudes of the currents

20.2 3.0 W. The power is proportional to the bicycle's speed *squared*.

20.3 $B_\perp = B \cos 60.0°$

20.4 7.6 V

20.5 (a) $F = B^2L^2v/R$ to the left at position 2 and position 4; (b) $P = B^2L^2v^2/R$

20.6 (a) to the left; (b) from A to B through the resistor; (c) no; current only flows in coil 2 while the flux is *changing*. When the magnetic field due to coil 1 is constant, no current flows in coil 2. (d)

N	S		S	N
Coil 1			Coil 2	

20.7 10.0 W

20.8 In a solid core, eddy currents would flow around the axis of the core. The insulation between wires prevents these eddy currents from flowing. Since energy is dissipated by eddy currents, their existence reduces the efficiency of the transformer.

20.9 9.0×10^{-5} Wb

20.10 0.53 W

20.11 0.9 s

Alternating Current

Look closely at the overhead power lines that supply electricity to a house. Why are there three cables—aren't two sufficient to make a complete circuit? Do the three cables correspond to the three prongs of an electrical outlet? (See p. 774 for the answer.)

**Concepts &
Skills to
Review**

- resistance; Ohm's law; power (Sections 18.4 and 18.8)
- emf and current (Sections 18.1 and 18.2)
- period, frequency, angular frequency (Section 10.6)
- capacitance and inductance (Sections 17.5 and 20.9)
- vector addition (Sections 2.2 and 2.4; Appendix A.8)
- resonance (Section 10.10)

21.1   SINUSOIDAL CURRENTS AND VOLTAGES; RESISTORS IN AC CIRCUITS

In an alternating current (ac) circuit, currents and emfs periodically change direction. An ac power supply periodically reverses the polarity of its emf. The sinusoidally varying emf due to an ac generator (also called an ac source) can be written (Fig. 21.1a)

$$\mathcal{E}(t) = \mathcal{E}_m \sin \omega t$$

The emf varies continuously between $+\mathcal{E}_m$ and $-\mathcal{E}_m$; $\mathcal{E}_m$ is called the **amplitude** (or **peak** value) of the emf. In a circuit with a sinusoidal emf connected to a resistor (Fig. 21.1b), the potential difference across the resistor is equal to $\mathcal{E}(t)$, by Kirchhoff's loop rule. Then the current $i(t)$ varies sinusoidally with amplitude $I = \mathcal{E}_m/R$:

$$i(t) = \frac{\mathcal{E}(t)}{R} = \frac{\mathcal{E}_m}{R} \sin \omega t = I \sin \omega t$$

 It is important to distinguish the time-dependent quantities from their amplitudes. Note that lowercase i stands for the instantaneous current, while capital I stands for the amplitude of the current. We use this convention for all time-dependent quantities in this chapter except for emf: $\mathcal{E}$ is the instantaneous emf and $\mathcal{E}_m$ ("m" for *maximum*) is the amplitude of the emf.

As simple as it may appear, the circuit of Fig. 21.1 has many applications. Electric heating elements found in toasters, hair dryers, electric baseboard heaters, electric stoves, and electric ovens are just resistors connected to an ac source. So is an incandescent lightbulb: the filament is a resistor whose temperature rises due to energy dissipation until it is hot enough to radiate a significant amount of visible light.

The definitions of period, frequency, and angular frequency used in ac circuits are the same as for simple harmonic motion. The time T for one complete cycle is the period. The frequency f is the inverse of the period:

$$\text{cycles per second} = \frac{1}{\text{seconds per cycle}}$$

$$f = \frac{1}{T}$$

Since there are 2π radians in one complete cycle, the angular frequency in radians is

$$\omega = 2\pi f$$

Figure 21.1 (a) A sinusoidal emf as a function of time. (b) The emf connected to a resistor, indicating the direction of the current and the polarity of the emf during the first half of the cycle ($0 < t < \frac{1}{2}T$). (c) The same circuit, indicating the direction of current and the polarity of the emf during the second half of the cycle ($\frac{1}{2}T < t < T$).

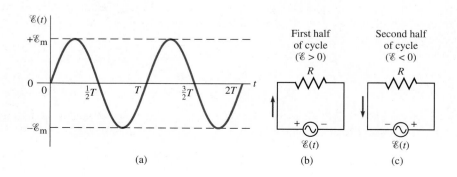

In SI units the period is measured in seconds, the frequency is measured in hertz (Hz), and the angular frequency is measured in rad/s. The usual voltage at a wall outlet in a home in the United States has an amplitude of about 170 V and a frequency of 60 Hz.

Power Dissipated in a Resistor

The instantaneous power dissipated by a resistor in an ac circuit is

$$p(t) = i(t)v(t) = I \sin \omega t \times V \sin \omega t = IV \sin^2 \omega t \tag{21-1}$$

where $i(t)$ and $v(t)$ represent the current through and potential difference across the resistor, respectively. Since $v = ir$, the power can also be written as

$$p = I^2 R \sin^2 \omega t = \frac{V^2}{R} \sin^2 \omega t$$

Figure 21.2 shows the instantaneous power delivered to a resistor in an ac circuit; it varies from 0 to a maximum of IV. Since the sine function *squared* is always nonnegative, the power is always nonnegative. The direction of *energy* flow is always the same—energy is dissipated in the resistor—no matter what the direction of the *current*.

The maximum power is given by the product of the peak current and the peak voltage (IV). We are usually more concerned with average power than with instantaneous power, since the instantaneous power varies rapidly. In a toaster or lightbulb, the fluctuations in instantaneous power are so fast that we usually don't notice them. The average power is IV times the average value of $\sin^2 \omega t$, which is 1/2 (see Problem 11).

Average power dissipated by a resistor:

$$P_{av} = \tfrac{1}{2}IV = \tfrac{1}{2}I^2 R \tag{21-2}$$

What dc current I_{dc} would dissipate energy at the same average rate as an ac current of amplitude I? Clearly $I_{dc} < I$ since I is the maximum current. To find I_{dc}, we set the average powers (through the same resistance) equal:

$$P_{av} = I_{dc}^2 R = \tfrac{1}{2}I^2 R$$

Solving for I_{dc} yields

$$I_{dc} = \sqrt{\tfrac{1}{2}I^2}$$

This effective dc current is called the **root mean square** (**rms**) current because it is the square *root* of the *mean* (average) of the *square* of the ac current:

$$i^2(t) = I^2 \sin^2 \omega t$$

$$\text{average of } i^2 = \text{average of } (I^2 \sin^2 \omega t) = I^2 \times \tfrac{1}{2}$$

$$I_{rms} = \sqrt{\text{average of } i^2} = \frac{1}{\sqrt{2}} I$$

Thus, the rms current is equal to the peak current divided by $\sqrt{2}$. Similarly, the rms values of sinusoidal emfs and potential differences are also equal to the peak values divided by $\sqrt{2}$.

$$\text{rms} = \frac{1}{\sqrt{2}} \times \text{amplitude} \tag{21-3}$$

Rms values have the advantage that they can be treated like dc values for finding the average power dissipated in a resistor:

$$P_{av} = I_{rms} V_{rms} = I_{rms}^2 R = \frac{V_{rms}^2}{R} \tag{21-4}$$

Remember that *power dissipated* means *the rate at which energy is dissipated.*

Circuit symbol for an ac generator (source of sinusoidal emf)

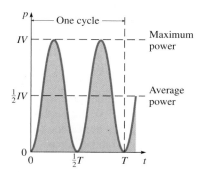

Figure 21.2 Power p dissipated by a resistor in an ac circuit as a function of time during one cycle. The area under the graph of $p(t)$ represents the energy dissipated. The *average* power is $IV/2$.

Meters designed to measure ac voltages and currents are usually calibrated to read rms values instead of peak values. In the United States, most electrical outlets supply an ac voltage of approximately 120 V rms; the peak voltage is 120 V × √2 = 170 V. Electrical devices are usually labeled with rms values. For instance, if a hair dryer is labeled "120 V, 10 A," both quantities are rms values; the hair dryer then consumes an average power of 120 V × 10 A = 1200 W.

Example 21.1

Resistance of a 100-W Lightbulb

A 100-W lightbulb is designed to be connected to an ac voltage of 120 V (rms). (a) What is the resistance of the lightbulb filament at normal operating temperature? (b) Find the rms and peak currents through the filament. (c) When the cold filament is initially connected to the circuit by flipping a switch, is the average power larger or smaller than 100 W?

Strategy   The *average* power dissipated by the filament is 100 W. Since the rms voltage across the bulb is 120 V, if we connected the bulb to a *dc* power supply of 120 V, it would dissipate a constant 100 W.

Solution   (a) Average power and rms voltage are related by

$$P_{av} = \frac{V_{rms}^2}{R} \qquad (21\text{-}4)$$

We solve for R:

$$R = \frac{V_{rms}^2}{P_{av}} = \frac{(120\ \text{V})^2}{100\ \text{W}} = 144\ \Omega$$

(b) Average power is rms voltage times rms current:

$$P_{av} = I_{rms}V_{rms}$$

We can solve for the rms current:

$$I_{rms} = \frac{P_{av}}{V_{rms}} = \frac{100\ \text{W}}{120\ \text{V}} = 0.833\ \text{A}$$

The amplitude of the current is a factor of √2 larger.

$$I = \sqrt{2}\, I_{rms} = 1.18\ \text{A}$$

(c) For metals, resistance increases with increasing temperature. When the filament is cold, its resistance is smaller. Since it is connected to the same voltage, the current is larger and the average power dissipated is larger.

Discussion   Check: The power dissipated can also be found from peak values:

$$P_{av} = \tfrac{1}{2}IV = \tfrac{1}{2}(1.18\ \text{A} \times 170\ \text{V}) = 100\ \text{W}$$

Another check: the amplitudes should be related by Ohm's law.

$$V = IR = 1.18\ \text{A} \times 144\ \Omega = 170\ \text{V}$$

Practice Problem 21.1   European Wall Outlet

The rms voltage at a wall outlet in Europe is 220 V. Suppose a space heater draws an rms current of 12.0 A. What are the amplitudes of the voltage and current? What are the peak power and the average power dissipated in the heating element? What is the resistance of the heating element?

Making the Connection:
household wiring

21.2   ELECTRICITY IN THE HOME

In a North American home, most electrical outlets supply an rms voltage of 110–120 V at a frequency of 60 Hz. However, some appliances with heavy demands—such as electric heaters, water heaters, stoves, and large air conditioners—are supplied with 220–240 V rms. At twice the voltage amplitude, they only need to draw half as much current for the same power to be delivered, reducing energy dissipation in the wiring (and the need for extra thick wires).

Local power lines are at voltages of several kilovolts. Step-down transformers reduce the voltage to 120/240 V rms. You can see these transformers wherever the power lines run on poles above the ground; they are the metal cans mounted to some of the poles (Fig. 21.3). The transformer has a center tap—a connection to the middle of the secondary coil; the voltage across the entire secondary coil is 240 V rms, but the voltage between the center tap and either end is only 120 V rms. The center tap is grounded at the

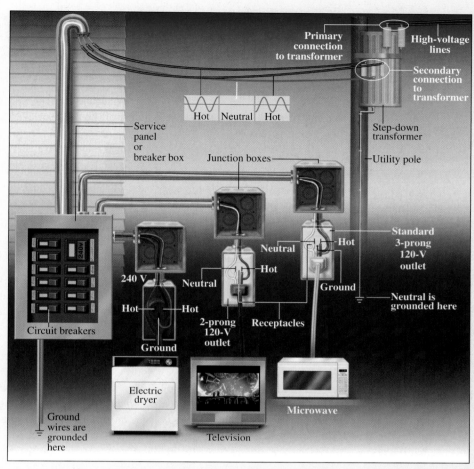

Figure 21.3 Electrical wiring in a North American home.

transformer and runs to a building by a cable that is often uninsulated. There it is connected to the *neutral* wire (which usually has white insulation) in every 120-V circuit in the building.

The other two connections from the transformer run to the building by insulated cables and are called *hot*. The hot wires in an outlet box usually have either black or red insulation. Relative to the neutral wire, each of the hot wires is at 120 V rms, but the two are 180° out of phase with each other. Half of the 120-V circuits in the building are connected to one of the hot cables and half to the other. Appliances needing to be supplied with 240 V are connected to both hot cables; they have no connection to the neutral cable.

Older 120-V outlets have only two prongs: hot and neutral. The slot for the neutral prong is slightly larger than the hot; a *polarized* plug can only be connected one way, preventing the hot and neutral connections from being interchanged. This safety feature is now superseded in devices that use the third prong on modern outlets. The third prong is connected directly to ground through its own set of wires (usually uninsulated or with green insulation)—it is not connected to the neutral wires. The metal case of most electrical appliances is connected to ground as a safety measure. If something goes wrong with the wiring inside the appliance so that the case becomes electrically connected to the hot wire, the third prong provides a low-resistance path for the current to flow to ground; the large current trips a circuit breaker or fuse. Without the ground connection, the case of the appliance would be at 120 V rms with respect to ground; someone touching the case could get a shock by providing a conducting path to ground.

21.3   CAPACITORS IN AC CIRCUITS

Figure 21.4a shows a capacitor connected to an ac source. The ac source pumps charge as needed to keep the voltage across the capacitor equal to the voltage of the source. Since the charge on the capacitor is proportional to the voltage v,

$$q(t) = Cv(t)$$

The current is proportional to the *rate of change* of the voltage $\Delta v/\Delta t$:

$$i(t) = \frac{\Delta q}{\Delta t} = C\frac{\Delta v}{\Delta t} \tag{21-5}$$

The time interval Δt must be small for i to represent the instantaneous current.

Figure 21.4b shows the voltage $v(t)$ and current $i(t)$ as functions of time for the capacitor. Note some important points:

- The current is maximum when the voltage is zero.
- The voltage is maximum when the current is zero.
- The capacitor repeatedly charges and discharges.

The voltage and the current are both sinusoidal functions of time with the same frequency, but they are out of phase: the current starts at its maximum positive value but the voltage reaches its maximum positive value $\frac{1}{4}$ cycle later. The voltage stays a quarter cycle behind the current at all times. The period T is the time for one complete cycle of a sinusoidal function; one cycle corresponds to 360° since

$$\omega T = 2\pi\,\text{rad} = 360°$$

● Current leads voltage by 90° in a capacitor in an ac circuit.

For $\frac{1}{4}$ cycle, $\frac{1}{4}\omega T = \pi/2$ rad = 90°. Thus, we say that the voltage and current are $\frac{1}{4}$ cycle out of phase or 90° out of phase. The current *leads* the capacitor voltage by a phase constant of 90°; equivalently, the voltage *lags* the current by the same phase angle.

If the voltage across the capacitor is given by

$$v(t) = V \sin \omega t$$

then the current varies in time as

$$i(t) = I \sin (\omega t + \pi/2)$$

We add the $\pi/2$ radians to the argument of the sine function to give the current a head start of $\pi/2$ rad. (We use radians rather than degrees since angular frequency ω is generally expressed in rad/s.)

Figure 21.4 (a) An ac generator connected to a capacitor. (b) One complete cycle of the current and voltage for a capacitor connected to an ac source as a function of time. Signs are chosen so that positive current (to the right) gives the capacitor a positive charge (left plate positive).

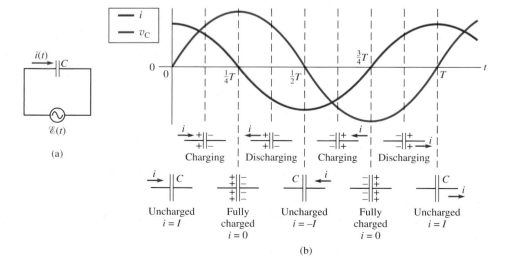

In the general expression

$$i = I \sin (\omega t + \phi)$$

the angle ϕ is called the **phase constant**, which, for the case of the current in the capacitive circuit, is $\phi = \pi/2$. A sine function shifted $\pi/2$ radians ahead is a cosine function, as can be seen in Fig. 21.4; that is,

$$\sin (\omega t + \pi/2) = \cos \omega t$$

so

$$i(t) = I \cos \omega t$$

The amplitude of the current I is proportional to the voltage amplitude V. A larger voltage means that more charge needs to be pumped onto the capacitor; to pump more charge in the same amount of time requires a larger current. We write the proportionality as

$$V_C = IX_C \qquad\qquad (21\text{-}6)$$

where the quantity X_C is called the **reactance** of the capacitor. Compare Eq. (21-6) to Ohm's law for a resistor ($v = iR$); reactance must have the same SI unit as resistance (ohms). We have written Eq. (21-6) in terms of the amplitudes (V, I), but it applies equally well if *both* V and I are rms values (since both are smaller by the same factor, $\sqrt{2}$).

By analogy with Ohm's law, we can think of the reactance as the "effective resistance" of the capacitor. The reactance determines how much current flows; the capacitor reacts in a way to impede the flow of current. A larger reactance means a smaller current, just as a larger resistance means a smaller current.

There are, however, important differences between reactance and resistance. A resistor dissipates energy, but an ideal capacitor does *not;* the average power dissipated by an ideal capacitor is zero, not $I_{rms}^2 X_C$. Note also that Eq. (21-6) relates only the *amplitudes* of the current and voltage. Since the current and voltage in a capacitor are 90° out of phase, it does *not* apply to the instantaneous values:

$$v(t) \neq i(t)X_C$$

For a resistor, on the other hand, the current and voltage are *in phase* (phase difference of zero); it *is* true for a resistor that $v(t) = i(t)R$.

Another difference is that reactance depends on frequency. Recall from Chapter 20 that

$$\text{If } \Phi(t) = \Phi_0 \sin \omega t, \text{ then } \frac{\Delta \Phi}{\Delta t} = \omega \Phi_0 \cos \omega t \quad \text{(for small } \Delta t); \qquad (20\text{-}7a)$$

$$\text{if } \Phi(t) = \Phi_0 \cos \omega t, \text{ then } \frac{\Delta \Phi}{\Delta t} = -\omega \Phi_0 \sin \omega t \quad \text{(for small } \Delta t). \qquad (20\text{-}7b)$$

These are general mathematical relationships giving the rates of change of sinusoidal functions. We have seen the same relationships in simple harmonic motion: if the position of a particle is

$$x(t) = A \sin \omega t$$

then its velocity, the rate of change of position, is

$$v_x(t) = \frac{\Delta x}{\Delta t} = \omega A \cos \omega t \qquad\qquad (10\text{-}25b)$$

For a capacitor in an ac circuit, if the charge as a function of time is

$$q(t) = Q \sin \omega t$$

then the current (the rate of change of the charge on the capacitor) must be

$$i(t) = \frac{\Delta q}{\Delta t} = \omega Q \cos \omega t$$

 Reactance: ratio of voltage amplitude to current amplitude for a capacitor or inductor

Therefore, the peak current is

$$I = \omega Q$$

Since $Q = CV$, we can find the reactance:

$$X_C = \frac{V}{I} = \frac{V}{\omega Q} = \frac{V}{\omega CV}$$

⬤ Reactance of a capacitor

$$X_C = \frac{1}{\omega C} \qquad\qquad (21\text{-}7)$$

The reactance is inversely proportional to the capacitance and to the angular frequency. To understand why, let us focus on the first quarter of a cycle ($0 \le t \le T/4$) in Fig. 21.4b. During this quarter cycle, a total charge $Q = CV$ flows onto the capacitor plates since the capacitor goes from being uncharged to fully charged. For a larger value of C, a proportionately larger charge must be put on the capacitor to reach a potential difference of V; to put more charge on in the same amount of time ($T/4$), the current must be larger. Thus, when the capacitance is larger, the reactance must be lower because more current flows for a given ac voltage amplitude.

The reactance is also inversely proportional to the frequency. For a higher frequency, the time available to charge the capacitor ($T/4$) is shorter. For a given voltage amplitude, a larger current must flow to achieve the same maximum voltage in a shorter amount of time. Thus, the reactance is smaller for a higher frequency.

At very high frequencies, the reactance approaches zero. The capacitor no longer impedes the flow of current; ac current flows in the circuit as if there were a conducting wire short-circuiting the capacitor. For the other limiting case, very low frequencies, the reactance approaches infinity. At a very low frequency, the applied voltage changes slowly; the current stops as soon as the capacitor is charged to a voltage equal to the applied voltage.

Example 21.2

Capacitive Reactance for Two Frequencies

(a) Find the capacitive reactance and the rms current for a 4.00-μF capacitor when it is connected to an ac source of 12.0 V rms at 60.0 Hz. (b) Find the reactance and current when the frequency is changed to 15.0 Hz while the rms voltage remains at 12.0 V.

Strategy The reactance is the proportionality constant between the rms values of the voltage across and current through the capacitor. The capacitive reactance is given by Eq. (21-7). Frequencies in Hz are given; we need *angular* frequencies to calculate the reactance.

Solution (a) Angular frequency is

$$\omega = 2\pi f$$

Then the reactance is

$$X_C = \frac{1}{2\pi f C}$$

$$= \frac{1}{2\pi \times 60.0 \text{ Hz} \times 4.00 \times 10^{-6} \text{ F}} = 663\ \Omega$$

The rms current is

$$I_{\text{rms}} = \frac{V_{\text{rms}}}{X_C} = \frac{12.0 \text{ V}}{663\ \Omega} = 18.1 \text{ mA}$$

(b) We could redo the calculation in the same way. An alternative is to note that the frequency is multiplied by a factor $\frac{15}{60} = \frac{1}{4}$. Since reactance is *inversely* proportional to frequency,

$$X_C = 4 \times 663\ \Omega = 2650\ \Omega$$

A larger reactance means a smaller current:

$$I_{\text{rms}} = \tfrac{1}{4} \times \frac{12.0 \text{ V}}{663\ \Omega} = 4.52 \text{ mA}$$

Discussion When the frequency is increased, the reactance decreases and the current increases. As we see in Section 21.7, capacitors can be used in circuits to filter out low frequencies because at lower frequency, less current flows. When a PA system makes a humming sound (60-Hz hum), a capacitor can be inserted between the amplifier and the speaker to block much of the 60-Hz noise while letting the higher frequencies pass through.

Continued on next page

Example 21.2 Continued

Practice Problem 21.2   Capacitive Reactance and rms Current for a New Frequency

Find the capacitive reactance and the rms current for a 4.00-μF capacitor when it is connected to an ac source of 220.0 V rms and 4.00 Hz.

Power

Figure 21.5 shows a graph of the instantaneous power $p(t) = v(t)i(t)$ for a capacitor superimposed on graphs of the current and voltage. The 90° ($\pi/2$ rad) phase difference between current and voltage has implications for the power in the circuit. During the first quarter cycle ($0 \leq t \leq T/4$), both the voltage and the current are positive. The power is positive: the generator is delivering energy to the capacitor to charge it. During the second quarter cycle ($T/4 \leq t \leq T/2$), the current is negative while the voltage remains positive. The power is negative; as the capacitor discharges, energy is returned to the generator from the capacitor.

The power continues to alternate between positive and negative as the capacitor stores and then returns electrical energy. The average power is zero since all the energy stored is given back and none of it is dissipated.

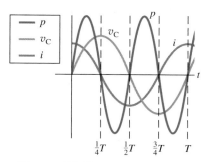

Figure 21.5 Current, voltage, and power for a capacitor in an ac circuit.

● The average power is zero for an ideal capacitor in an ac circuit.

21.4   INDUCTORS IN AC CIRCUITS

An inductor in an ac circuit develops an induced emf that opposes changes in the current, according to Faraday's law [Eq. (20-6)]. We use the same sign convention as for the capacitor: the current i through the inductor in Fig. 21.6a is positive when it flows to the right and the voltage across the inductor v_L is positive if the left side is at a higher potential than the right side. If current flows in the positive direction and is *increasing*, the induced emf *opposes the increase* (Fig. 21.6b) and v_L is positive. If current flows in the positive direction and is *decreasing*, the induced emf *opposes the decrease* (Fig. 21.6c) and v_L is negative. Since in the first case $\Delta i/\Delta t$ is positive and in the second case $\Delta i/\Delta t$ is negative, the voltage has the correct sign if we write

$$v_L = L\frac{\Delta i}{\Delta t} \tag{21-8}$$

In Problem 32 you can verify that Eq. (21-8) also gives the correct sign when current flows to the left.

The voltage amplitude across the inductor is proportional to the amplitude of the current. The constant of proportionality is called the **reactance** of the inductor (X_L):

$$V_L = IX_L \tag{21-9}$$

As for the capacitive reactance, the inductive reactance X_L has units of ohms. As in Eq. (21-6), V and I in Eq. (21-9) can be *either* amplitudes *or* rms values, but be careful not to mix amplitude and rms in the same equation.

In Problem 30 you can show, using reasoning similar to that used for the capacitor, that the reactance of an inductor is

$$X_L = \omega L \tag{21-10}$$

Note that the inductive reactance is directly proportional to the inductance L and to the angular frequency ω, in contrast to the capacitive reactance, which is *inversely* proportional to the angular frequency and to the capacitance. The induced emf in the inductor always acts to oppose changes in the current. At higher frequency, the more rapid changes in current are opposed by a greater induced emf in the inductor. Thus, the ratio

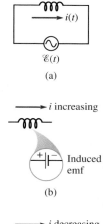

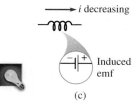

Figure 21.6 (a) An inductor connected to an ac source. (b) and (c) The potential difference across the inductor for current flowing to the right depends on whether the current is increasing or decreasing.

● Reactance of an inductor

Figure 21.7 Current and potential difference across an inductor in an ac circuit. Note that when the current is maximum or minimum, its instantaneous rate of change—represented by its slope—is zero, so $v_L = 0$. On the other hand, when the current is zero, it is changing the fastest, so v_L has its maximum magnitude.

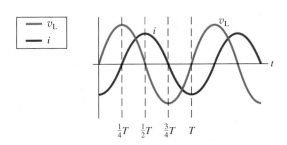

 Current lags voltage across an inductor in an ac circuit.

of the amplitude of the induced emf to the amplitude of the current—the reactance—is greater at higher frequency.

Figure 21.7 shows the potential difference across the inductor and the current through the inductor as functions of time. We assume an ideal inductor—one with no resistance in its windings. Since $v_L = L \, \Delta i/\Delta t$, the graph of $v_L(t)$ is proportional to the *slope* of the graph of $i(t)$ at any time t. The voltage and current are out of phase by $\frac{1}{4}$ cycle, but this time the current *lags* the voltage by 90° ($\pi/2$ rad); current reaches its maximum $\frac{1}{4}$ cycle *after* the voltage reaches a maximum. A mnemonic device for remembering what leads and what lags is that the letter c (for *current*) appears in the second half of the word *indu̲c̲tor* (current *lags* inductor voltage) and at the *beginning* of the word *c̲apacitor* (current *leads* capacitor voltage).

In Fig. 21.7, the voltage across the inductor can be written

$$v_L(t) = V \sin \omega t$$

The current is

$$i(t) = -I \cos \omega t = I \sin (\omega t - \pi/2)$$

where we have used the trigonometric identity $-\cos \omega t = \sin (\omega t - \pi/2)$. We see explicitly that the current lags behind the voltage from the phase constant $\phi = -\pi/2$.

Power

The average power is zero for an *ideal* inductor in an ac circuit.

As for the capacitor, the 90° phase difference between current and voltage means that the average power is zero. No energy is dissipated in an *ideal* inductor (one with no resistance). The generator alternately sends energy to the inductor and receives energy back from the inductor.

Example 21.3

Inductor in a Radio Tuning Circuit

A 0.56-μH inductor is used as part of the tuning circuit in a radio. Assume the inductor is ideal. (a) Find the reactance of the inductor at a frequency of 90.9 MHz. (b) Find the amplitude of the current through the inductor if the voltage amplitude is 0.27 V. (c) Find the capacitance of a capacitor that has the same reactance at 90.9 MHz.

Strategy   The reactance of an inductor is the product of angular frequency and inductance. The reactance in ohms is the ratio of the voltage amplitude to the amplitude of the current. For the capacitor, the reactance is $1/(\omega C)$.

Solution   (a) The reactance of the inductor is

$$X_L = \omega L = 2\pi f L$$
$$= 2\pi \times 90.9 \text{ MHz} \times 0.56 \text{ μH} = 320 \text{ Ω}$$

(b) The amplitude of the current is

$$I = \frac{V}{X_L}$$
$$= \frac{0.27 \text{ V}}{320 \text{ Ω}} = 0.84 \text{ mA}$$

Continued on next page

Example 21.3 Continued

(c) We set the two reactances equal ($X_L = X_C$) and solve for C:

$$\omega L = \frac{1}{\omega C}$$

$$C = \frac{1}{\omega^2 L} = \frac{1}{4\pi^2 \times (90.9 \times 10^6 \text{ Hz})^2 \times 0.56 \times 10^{-6} \text{ H}}$$

$$= 5.5 \text{ pF}$$

Discussion   We can check by calculating the reactance of the capacitor:

$$X_C = \frac{1}{\omega C} = \frac{1}{2\pi \times 90.9 \times 10^6 \text{ Hz} \times 5.5 \times 10^{-12} \text{ F}} = 320 \ \Omega$$

In Section 21.6 we study tuning circuits in more detail.

Practice Problem 21.3   Reactance and rms Current

Find the inductive reactance and the rms current for a 3.00-mH inductor when it is connected to an ac source of 10.0 mV (rms) at a frequency of 60.0 kHz.

21.5   *RLC* SERIES CIRCUITS

Figure 21.8a shows an *RLC* series circuit. Kirchhoff's junction rule tells us that the instantaneous current through each element is the same, since there are no junctions. The loop rule requires the sum of the instantaneous voltage drops across the three elements to equal the applied ac voltage:

$$\mathcal{E}(t) = v_L(t) + v_R(t) + v_C(t) \tag{21-11}$$

The three voltages are sinusoidal functions of time with the same frequency but different phase constants.

Suppose that we choose to write the current with a phase constant of zero. The voltage across the resistor is in phase with the current, so it also has a phase constant of zero (see Fig. 21.8b). The voltage across the inductor leads the current by 90°, so it has a phase constant of $+\pi/2$. The voltage across the capacitor lags the current by 90°, so it has a phase constant of $-\pi/2$.

$$\mathcal{E}(t) = \mathcal{E}_m \sin(\omega t + \phi) = V_L \sin\left(\omega t + \frac{\pi}{2}\right) + V_R \sin \omega t + V_C \sin\left(\omega t - \frac{\pi}{2}\right) \tag{21-12}$$

We could simplify this sum using trigonometric identities, but there is an easier method. We can represent each sinusoidal voltage by a vector-like object called a **phasor**. The magnitude of the phasor represents the amplitude of the voltage; the angle of the phasor represents the phase constant of the voltage. We can then add phasors the same way we add vectors. (See Problem 49 for insight into why the phasor method works.) Although we draw them like vectors and *add like vectors*, they are not vectors in the usual sense. A phasor is not a quantity with a direction in space, like real vectors such as acceleration, momentum, or magnetic field.

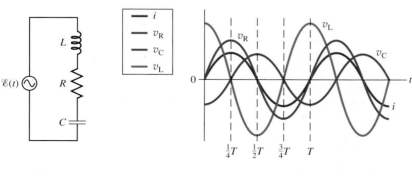

(a)   (b)

Figure 21.8 (a) An *RLC* series circuit. (b) The voltages across the circuit elements and the current as functions of time. The current is in phase with v_R, leads v_C by 90°, and lags v_L by 90°.

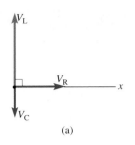

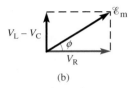

(a)

(b)

Figure 21.9 (a) Phasor representation of the voltages. (b) The phase angle ϕ between the source emf and the voltage across the resistor (which is in phase with the current).

Figure 21.9a shows three phasors representing the voltages $v_L(t)$, $v_R(t)$, and $v_C(t)$. An angle counterclockwise from the +x-axis represents a positive phase constant. First we add the phasors representing $v_L(t)$ and $v_C(t)$, which are in opposite directions. Then we add the sum of these two to the phasor that represents $v_R(t)$ (Fig. 21.9b). The vector sum represents $\mathscr{E}(t)$. The amplitude of $\mathscr{E}(t)$ is the length of the sum; from the Pythagorean theorem,

$$\mathscr{E}_m = \sqrt{V_R^2 + (V_L - V_C)^2} \tag{21-13}$$

Each of the voltage amplitudes on the right side of Eq. (21-13) can be rewritten as the amplitude of the current times a reactance or resistance:

$$\mathscr{E}_m = \sqrt{(IR)^2 + (IX_L - IX_C)^2}$$

Factoring out the current yields

$$\mathscr{E}_m = I \sqrt{R^2 + (X_L - X_C)^2}$$

Thus, the amplitude of the ac source voltage is proportional to the amplitude of the current. The constant of proportionality is called the **impedance** Z of the circuit.

$$\mathscr{E}_m = IZ \tag{21-14a}$$

$$Z = \sqrt{R^2 + (X_L - X_C)^2} \tag{21-14b}$$

Impedance is measured in ohms.

From Fig. 21.9b, the source voltage $\mathscr{E}(t)$ leads $v_R(t)$—and the current $i(t)$—by a phase angle ϕ where

$$\tan \phi = \frac{V_L - V_C}{V_R} = \frac{IX_L - IX_C}{IR} = \frac{X_L - X_C}{R} \tag{21-15}$$

We have assumed $X_L > X_C$ in Figs. 21.8 and 21.9. If $X_L < X_C$, the phase angle ϕ is negative, which means that the source voltage *lags* the current. Figure 21.9b also implies that

$$\cos \phi = \frac{V_R}{\mathscr{E}_m} = \frac{IR}{IZ} = \frac{R}{Z} \tag{21-16}$$

If one or two of the elements R, L, and C are not present in a circuit, the foregoing analysis is still valid. Since there is no potential difference across a missing element, we simply set the resistance or reactance of the missing element(s) to zero. For instance, since an inductor is made by coiling a long length of wire, it usually has an appreciable resistance. We can model a real inductor as an ideal inductor in series with a resistor. The impedance of the inductor is found by setting $X_C = 0$ in Eq. (21-14b).

Example 21.4

An *RLC* Series Circuit

In an *RLC* circuit, the following three elements are connected in series: a resistor of 40.0 Ω, a 22.0-mH inductor, and a 0.400-μF capacitor. The ac source has a peak voltage of 0.100 V and an angular frequency of 1.00×10^4 rad/s. (a) Find the amplitude of the current. (b) Find the phase angle between the current and the ac source. Which leads? (c) Find the peak voltages across each of the circuit elements.

Strategy The impedance is the ratio of the source voltage amplitude to the amplitude of the current. By

finding the reactances of the inductor and capacitor, we can find the impedance and then solve for the amplitude of the current. The reactances also enable us to calculate the phase constant ϕ. If ϕ is positive, the source voltage leads the current; if ϕ is negative, the source voltage lags the current. The peak voltage across any element is equal to the peak current times the reactance or resistance of that element.

Continued on next page

Example 21.4 Continued

Solution   (a) The inductive reactance is

$$X_L = \omega L = 1.00 \times 10^4 \text{ rad/s} \times 22.0 \times 10^{-3} \text{ H} = 220 \ \Omega$$

The capacitive reactance is

$$X_C = \frac{1}{\omega C} = \frac{1}{1.00 \times 10^4 \text{ rad/s} \times 0.400 \times 10^{-6} \text{ F}} = 250 \ \Omega$$

Then the impedance of the circuit is

$$Z = \sqrt{R^2 + X^2} = \sqrt{(40.0 \ \Omega)^2 + (-30 \ \Omega)^2} = 50 \ \Omega$$

For a source voltage amplitude $V = 0.100$ V, the amplitude of the current is

$$I = \frac{V}{Z} = \frac{0.100 \text{ V}}{50 \ \Omega} = 2.0 \text{ mA}$$

(b) The phase angle ϕ is

$$\phi = \tan^{-1} \frac{X_L - X_C}{R} = \tan^{-1} \frac{-30 \ \Omega}{40.0 \ \Omega} = -0.64 \text{ rad} = -37°$$

Since $X_L < X_C$, the phase angle ϕ is negative, which means that the source voltage *lags* the current.

(c) The voltage amplitude across the inductor is

$$V_L = IX_L = 2.0 \text{ mA} \times 220 \ \Omega = 440 \text{ mV}$$

For the capacitor and resistor,

$$V_C = IX_C = 2.0 \text{ mA} \times 250 \ \Omega = 500 \text{ mV}$$

and

$$V_R = IR = 2.0 \text{ mA} \times 40.0 \ \Omega = 80 \text{ mV}$$

Discussion   Since the voltage phasors in Fig. 21.9 are each proportional to *I*, we can divide each by *I* to form a phasor diagram where the phasors represent reactances or resistances (Fig. 21.10). Such a phasor diagram can be used to find the impedance of the circuit and the phase constant, instead of using Eqs. (21-14b) and (21-15).

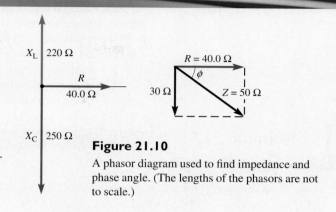

Figure 21.10

A phasor diagram used to find impedance and phase angle. (The lengths of the phasors are not to scale.)

 Note that the sum of the voltage amplitudes across the three circuit elements is not the same as the source voltage amplitude:

$$100 \text{ mV} \neq 440 \text{ mV} + 80 \text{ mV} + 500 \text{ mV}$$

The voltage amplitudes across the inductor and capacitor are each *larger* than the source voltage amplitude. The voltage amplitudes are *maximum* values; since the voltages are not in phase with each other, they do not attain their maximum values at the same instant of time. What is true is that the sum of the *instantaneous* potential differences across the three elements at any given time is equal to the instantaneous source voltage at the same time [Eq. (21-12)].

Practice Problem 21.4   Instantaneous Voltages

If the current in this same circuit is written as $i(t) = I \sin \omega t$, what would be the corresponding expressions for $v_C(t)$, $v_L(t)$, $v_R(t)$, and $\mathscr{E}(t)$? (The main task is to get the phase constants correct.) Using these expressions, show that at $t = 80.0$ μs, $v_C(t) + v_L(t) + v_R(t) = \mathscr{E}(t)$. (The loop rule is true at *any* time t; we just verify it at one particular time.)

Power Factor

No power is dissipated in an ideal capacitor or an ideal inductor; the power is dissipated only in the resistance of the circuit (including the resistances of the wires of the circuit and the windings of the inductor):

$$P_{av} = I_{rms} V_{R,rms} \tag{21-4}$$

We want to rewrite the average power in terms of the rms source voltage.

$$\frac{V_{R,rms}}{\mathscr{E}_{rms}} = \frac{I_{rms} R}{I_{rms} Z} = \frac{R}{Z}$$

From Eq. (21-16), $R/Z = \cos \phi$. Therefore,

$$V_{R,rms} = \mathscr{E}_{rms} \cos \phi$$

and

$$P_{av} = I_{rms} \mathscr{E}_{rms} \cos \phi \tag{21-17}$$

The factor cos ϕ in Eq. (21-17) is called the **power factor**. When there is only resistance and no reactance in the circuit, $\phi = 0$ and cos $\phi = 1$; then $P_{av} = I_{rms}\mathcal{E}_{rms}$. When there is only capacitance or inductance in the circuit, $\phi = \pm 90°$ and cos $\phi = 0$, so that $P_{av} = 0$. Many electrical devices contain appreciable inductance or capacitance; the load they present to the source voltage is not purely a resistance. In particular, any device with a transformer has some inductance due to the windings. The label on an electrical device sometimes includes a quantity with units of V·A and a smaller quantity with units of W. The former is the product $I_{rms}\mathcal{E}_{rms}$; the latter is the average power consumed.

Example 21.5

Laptop Power Supply

A power supply for a laptop computer is labeled as follows: "45 W AC Adapter. AC input: 1.0 A max, 120 V, 60.0 Hz." A simplified circuit model for the power supply is a resistor R and an ideal inductor L in series with an ideal ac emf. The inductor represents primarily the inductance of the windings of the transformer; the resistor represents primarily the load presented by the laptop computer. Find the values of L and R when the power supply draws the maximum rms current of 1.0 A.

Strategy First we sketch the circuit (Fig. 21.11). The next step is to identify the quantities given in the problem, taking care to distinguish rms quantities from amplitudes and average power from $I_{rms}\mathcal{E}_{rms}$. Since power is dissipated in the resistor but not in the inductor, we can find the resistance from the average power. Then we can use the power factor to find L. We assume no capacitance in the circuit, which means we can set $X_C = 0$.

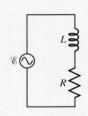

Figure 21.11

A circuit diagram for the power supply.

Solution The problem tells us that the maximum rms current is $I_{rms} = 1.0$ A. The rms source voltage is $\mathcal{E}_{rms} = 120$ V. The frequency is $f = 60.0$ Hz. The average power is 45 W when the power supply draws 1.0 A rms; the average power is smaller when the current drawn is smaller. Then

$$\mathcal{E}_{rms}I_{rms} = 120 \text{ V} \times 1.0 \text{ A} = 120 \text{ V·A}$$

Note that the average power is less than $I_{rms}\mathcal{E}_{rms}$; it can never be greater than $I_{rms}\mathcal{E}_{rms}$ since cos $\phi \le 1$.

Since power is dissipated only in the resistor,

$$P_{av} = I_{rms}^2 R$$

The resistance is therefore

$$R = \frac{P_{av}}{I_{rms}^2} = \frac{45 \text{ W}}{(1.0 \text{ A})^2} = 45 \text{ }\Omega$$

The ratio of the average power to $I_{rms}\mathcal{E}_{rms}$ gives the power factor:

$$\frac{\mathcal{E}_{rms}I_{rms} \cos \phi}{\mathcal{E}_{rms}I_{rms}} = \cos \phi = \frac{45 \text{ W}}{120 \text{ V·A}} = 0.375$$

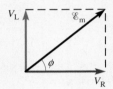

Figure 21.12

Phasor addition of the voltages across the inductor and resistor.

The phase angle is $\phi = \cos^{-1} 0.375 = 68.0°$. From the phasor diagram of Fig. 21.12,

$$\tan \phi = \frac{V_L}{V_R} = \frac{IX_L}{IR} = \frac{X_L}{R}$$

Solving for X_L,

$$X_L = R \tan \phi = (45 \text{ }\Omega) \tan 68.0° = 111.4 \text{ }\Omega = \omega L$$

Now we can solve for L:

$$L = \frac{X_L}{\omega} = \frac{111.4 \text{ }\Omega}{2\pi \times 60.0 \text{ Hz}} = 0.30 \text{ H}$$

Discussion Check: cos ϕ should be equal to R/Z.

$$\frac{R}{Z} = \frac{R}{\sqrt{R^2 + X_L^2}} = \frac{45 \text{ }\Omega}{\sqrt{(45 \text{ }\Omega)^2 + (111.4 \text{ }\Omega)^2}} = 0.375$$

which agrees with cos $\phi = 0.375$.

Practice Problem 21.5   A More Typical Current Draw

The adapter rarely draws the maximum rms current of 1.0 A. Suppose that, more typically, the adapter draws an rms current of 0.25 A. What is the average power? Use the same simplified circuit model with the same value of L but a *different* value of R. [*Hint:* Begin by finding the impedance $Z = \sqrt{R^2 + X_L^2}$.]

PHYSICS AT HOME

Find an electrical device that has a label with two numerical ratings, one in V·A and one in W. The windings of a transformer have significant inductance, so try something with an external transformer (inside the power supply) or an internal transformer (such as a desktop computer). The windings of motors also have inductance, so something with a motor is also a good choice. Calculate the power factor for the device. Now find a device that has little reactance compared to its resistance, such as a heater or a lightbulb. Why is there no numerical rating in V·A?

21.6   RESONANCE IN AN *RLC* CIRCUIT

Suppose an *RLC* circuit is connected to an ac source with a fixed amplitude but variable frequency. The impedance depends on frequency, so the amplitude of the current depends on frequency. Figure 21.13 shows three graphs (called **resonance curves**) of the amplitude of the current $I = \mathscr{E}_m/Z$ as a function of angular frequency for a circuit with $L = 1.0$ H, $C = 1.0$ μF, and $\mathscr{E}_m = 100$ V. Three different resistors were used: 200 Ω, 500 Ω, and 1000 Ω.

The shape of these graphs is determined by the frequency dependence of the inductive and capacitive reactances (Fig. 21.14). At low frequencies, the reactance of the capacitor $X_C = 1/(\omega C)$ is much greater than either R or X_L, so $Z \approx X_C$. At high frequencies, the reactance of the inductor $X_L = \omega L$ is much greater than either R or X_C, so $Z \approx X_L$. At extreme frequencies, either high or low, the impedance is larger and the amplitude of the current is therefore small.

The impedance of the circuit is

$$Z = \sqrt{R^2 + (X_L - X_C)^2} \qquad\qquad \textbf{(21-14b)}$$

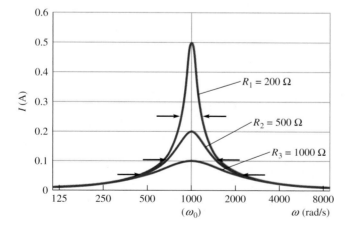

Figure 21.13 The amplitude of the current *I* as a function of angular frequency ω for three different resistances in a series *RLC* circuit. The widths of each peak at half-maximum current are indicated. The horizontal scale is logarithmic.

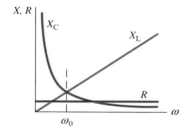

Figure 21.14 Frequency dependence of the inductive and capacitive reactances and of the resistance as a function of frequency.

Since R is constant, the minimum impedance $Z = R$ occurs at an angular frequency ω_0—called the **resonant** angular frequency—for which the reactances of the inductor and capacitor are equal so that $X_L - X_C = 0$.

$$X_L = X_C$$

$$\omega_0 L = \frac{1}{\omega_0 C}$$

Solving for ω_0,

Resonant angular frequency of RLC circuit

$$\omega_0 = \frac{1}{\sqrt{LC}} \qquad (21\text{-}18)$$

Note that the resonant frequency of a circuit depends only on the values of the inductance and the capacitance, not on the resistance. In Fig. 21.13, the maximum current occurs at the resonant frequency for any value of R. However, the value of the maximum current depends on R since $Z = R$ at resonance. The resonance peak is higher for a smaller resistance. If we measure the width of a resonance peak where the amplitude of the current has half its maximum value, we see that the resonance peaks get narrower with decreasing resistance.

Resonance in an RLC circuit is analogous to resonance in mechanical oscillations (see Section 10.10). Just as a mass-spring system has a single resonant frequency, determined by the spring constant and the mass, the RLC circuit has a single resonant frequency, determined by the capacitance and the inductance. When either system is driven externally—by a sinusoidal applied force for the mass-spring or by a sinusoidal applied emf for the circuit—the amplitude of the system's response is greatest when driven at the resonant frequency. In both systems, energy is being converted back and forth between two forms. For the mass-spring, the two forms are kinetic and elastic potential energy; for the RLC circuit, the two forms are electric energy stored in the capacitor and magnetic energy stored in the inductor. The resistor in the RLC circuit fills the role of friction in a mass-spring system: dissipating energy.

A sharp resonance peak enables the tuning circuit in a TV or radio to select one out of many different frequencies being broadcast. With one type of tuner, common in old radios, the tuning knob adjusts the capacitance by rotating one set of parallel plates relative to a fixed set so that the area of overlap is varied (Fig. 21.15). By changing the capacitance, the resonant frequency can be varied. The tuning circuit is driven by a mixture of many different frequencies coming from the antenna, but only frequencies very near the resonance frequency produce a significant response in the tuning circuit.

Figure 21.15 The variable capacitor inside an old radio. The radio is tuned to a particular resonant frequency by adjusting the capacitance. This is done by rotating the knob which increases the overlap of the plates of the capacitor.

Example 21.6

A Tuner for a Radio

A radio tuner has a 400.0-Ω resistor, a 0.50-mH inductor, and a variable capacitor connected in series. Suppose the capacitor is adjusted to 72.0 pF. (a) Find the resonant frequency for the circuit. (b) Find the reactances of the inductor and capacitor at the resonant frequency. (c) The applied emf at the resonant frequency coming in from the antenna is 20.0 mV (rms). Find the rms current in the tuning circuit. (d) Find the rms voltages across each of the circuit elements.

Strategy The resonant frequency can be found from the values of the capacitance and the inductance. The reactances at the resonant frequency must be equal. To find the current in the circuit, we note that the impedance

is equal to the resistance since the circuit is in resonance. The rms current is the ratio of the rms voltage to the impedance. The rms voltage across a circuit element is the rms current times the element's reactance or resistance.

Solution   (a) The resonant angular frequency is given by

$$\omega_0 = \frac{1}{\sqrt{LC}}$$

$$= \frac{1}{\sqrt{0.50 \times 10^{-3} \text{ H} \times 72.0 \times 10^{-12} \text{ F}}}$$

$$= 5.27 \times 10^6 \text{ rad/s}$$

Continued on next page

Example 21.6 Continued

The resonant frequency in Hz is

$$f_0 = \frac{\omega_0}{2\pi} = 840 \text{ kHz}$$

(b) The reactances are

$$X_L = \omega L = 5.27 \times 10^6 \text{ rad/s} \times 0.50 \times 10^{-3} \text{ H} = 2.6 \text{ k}\Omega$$

and

$$X_C = \frac{1}{\omega C} = \frac{1}{5.27 \times 10^6 \text{ rad/s} \times 72.0 \times 10^{-12} \text{ F}} = 2.6 \text{ k}\Omega$$

They are equal, as expected.

(c) At the resonant frequency, the impedance is equal to the resistance.

$$Z = R = 400.0 \ \Omega$$

The rms current is

$$I_{rms} = \frac{\mathscr{E}_{rms}}{Z} = \frac{20.0 \text{ mV}}{400.0 \ \Omega} = 0.0500 \text{ mA}$$

(d) The rms voltages are

$$V_{L\text{-}rms} = I_{rms}X_L = 0.0500 \text{ mA} \times 2.6 \times 10^3 \ \Omega = 130 \text{ mV}$$

$$V_{C\text{-}rms} = I_{rms}X_C = 0.0500 \text{ mA} \times 2.6 \times 10^3 \ \Omega = 130 \text{ mV}$$

$$V_{R\text{-}rms} = I_{rms}R = 0.0500 \text{ mA} \times 400.0 \ \Omega = 20.0 \text{ mV}$$

Discussion The resonant frequency of 840 kHz is a reasonable result since it lies in the AM radio band (530 kHz–1700 kHz).

The rms voltages across the inductor and across the capacitor are equal at resonance, but the instantaneous voltages are opposite in phase (a phase difference of π rad or 180°), so the sum of the potential difference across the two is always zero. In a phasor diagram, the phasors for v_L and v_C are opposite in direction and equal in length, so they add to zero. Then the voltage across the resistor is equal to the applied emf in both amplitude and phase.

Practice Problem 21.6 Tuning the Radio to a Different Station

Find the capacitance required to tune to a station broadcasting at 1420 kHz.

21.7 CONVERTING AC TO DC; FILTERS

Diodes

A *diode* is a circuit component that allows current to flow much more easily in one direction than in the other. An *ideal* diode has zero resistance for current in one direction, so that the current flows without any voltage drop across the diode, and infinite resistance for current in the other direction, so that no current flows. The circuit symbol for a diode has an arrowhead to indicate the direction of allowed current.

The circuit in Fig. 21.16a is called a *half-wave rectifier*. If the input is a sinusoidal emf, the output (the voltage across the resistor) is as shown in Fig. 21.16b. The output signal can be smoothed out by a capacitor (Fig. 21.16c). The capacitor charges up when

Making the Connection:
diodes and rectifiers

The circuit symbol for a diode is ⇥⊢. The arrow indicates the direction of current flow.

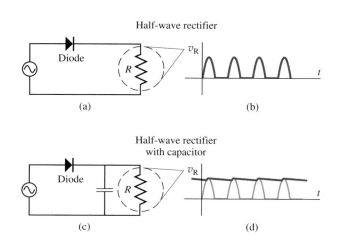

Figure 21.16 (a) A half-wave rectifier. (b) The voltage across the resistor. When the input voltage is negative, the output voltage v_R is zero, so the negative half of the "wave" has been cut off. (c) A capacitor inserted to smooth the output voltage. (d) The dark graph line shows the voltage across the resistor, assuming the RC time constant is much larger than the period of the sinusoidal input voltage. The light graph line shows what the output would have been without the capacitor.

Figure 21.17 (a) Output of a full-wave rectifier. (b) This ac adapter from a portable CD player contains a transformer (labeled "CK-62") to reduce the amplitude of the ac source voltage. The two red diodes serve as a full-wave rectifier circuit and the capacitor (labeled "470 μF") smooths out the ripples. The output is a nearly constant dc voltage.

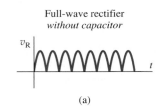

Full-wave rectifier
without capacitor

(a)

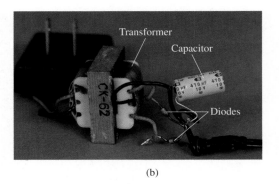

(b)

current flows through the diode; when the source voltage starts to drop and then changes polarity, the capacitor discharges through the resistor. (The capacitor cannot discharge through the diode because that would send current the wrong way through the diode.) The discharge keeps the voltage v_R up. By making the RC time constant ($\tau = RC$) long enough, the discharge through the resistor can be made to continue until the source voltage turns positive again (Fig. 21.16d).

Circuits involving more than one diode can be arranged to make a *full-wave rectifier*. The output of a full-wave rectifier (without a capacitor to smooth it) is shown in Fig. 21.17a. Circuits like these are found inside the ac adapter used with devices such as portable CD players, radios, and laptop computers (Fig. 21.17b). Many other devices have circuits to do ac-to-dc conversion inside of them.

Filters

Low-pass RC filter

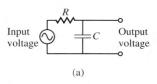

(a)

High-pass RC filter

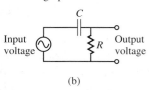

(b)

Figure 21.18 Two RC filters: (a) low-pass and (b) high-pass.

The capacitor in Fig. 21.16c serves as a *filter*. Figure 21.18 shows two *RC filters* commonly used in circuits. Figure 21.18a is a *low-pass filter*. For a high-frequency ac signal, the capacitor serves as a low reactance path to ground ($X_C \ll R$); the voltage across the resistor is much larger than the voltage across the capacitor, so the voltage across the output terminals is a small fraction of the input voltage. For a low-frequency signal, $X_C \gg R$, so the output voltage is nearly as great as the input voltage. For a signal consisting of a mixture of frequencies, the high frequencies are "filtered out" while the low frequencies "pass through."

The *high-pass filter* of Fig. 21.18b does just the opposite. Suppose a circuit connected to the input terminals supplies a mixture of a dc potential difference plus ac voltages at a range of frequencies. The reactance of the capacitor is large at low frequencies, so most of the voltage drop for low frequencies occurs across the capacitor; most of the high-frequency voltage drop occurs across the resistor and thus across the output terminals.

Combinations of capacitors and inductors are also used as filters. For both RC and LC filters, there is a gradual transition between frequencies that are blocked and frequencies that pass through. The frequency range where the transition occurs can be selected by choosing the values of R and C (or L and C).

Making the Connection:

crossover networks for
audio tweeters and woofers

Crossover Networks

In a speaker used with an audio system, there are often two vibrating cones (the *drivers*) producing the sounds. The *woofer* produces the low-frequency sounds, while the *tweeter* produces the high-frequency sounds. A *crossover network* (Fig. 21.19a) separates the signal from the amplifier, sending the low frequencies to the woofer and the high frequencies to the tweeter. Figure 21.19b shows the relative amplitude of each current as a function of frequency. The crossover point is the frequency at which the current is evenly divided, half going to the woofer and half to the tweeter (see Problems 60 and 61).

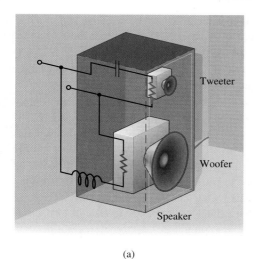

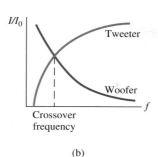

(a)   (b)

Figure 21.19 (a) Two speaker drivers are connected to an amplifier by a crossover network. (b) The amplitude of the current I going to each of the drivers expressed as a fraction of the input amplitude I_0, graphed as a function of frequency.

MASTER THE CONCEPTS

- In the equation

$$v = V \sin (\omega t + \phi)$$

the lowercase letter (v) represents the instantaneous voltage while the uppercase letter (V) represents the *amplitude* (peak value) of the voltage. The quantity ϕ is called the *phase constant*.

- The *rms value* of a sinusoidal quantity is $1/\sqrt{2}$ times the amplitude.

- *Reactances* (X_C, X_L) and *impedance* (Z) are generalizations of the concept of resistance and are measured in ohms. The amplitude of the voltage across a circuit element or combination of elements is equal to the amplitude of the current through the element(s) times the reactance or impedance of the element(s). Except for a resistor, there is a phase difference between the voltage and current:

	Amplitude	Phase
Resistor	$V_R = IR$	v_R, i are in phase
Capacitor	$V_C = IX_C$ $X_C = 1/(\omega C)$	i leads v_C by $90°$
Inductor	$V_L = IX_L$ $X_L = \omega L$	v_L leads i by $90°$
RLC series circuit	$\mathscr{E}_m = IZ$ $Z = \sqrt{R^2 + (X_L - X_C)^2}$	$\mathscr{E}$ leads/lags i by $\phi = \tan^{-1} \dfrac{X_L - X_C}{R}$

- The average power dissipated in a resistor is

$$P_{av} = I_{rms} V_{rms} = I_{rms}^2 R = \frac{V_{rms}^2}{R} \qquad (21\text{-}4)$$

The average power dissipated in an ideal capacitor or ideal inductor is zero.

- The average power dissipated in a series *RLC* circuit can be written

$$P_{av} = I_{rms} \mathscr{E}_{rms} \cos \phi \qquad (21\text{-}17)$$

where ϕ is the phase difference between $i(t)$ and $\mathscr{E}(t)$. The *power factor* $\cos \phi$ is equal to R/Z.

- To add sinusoidal voltages, we can represent each voltage by a vector-like object called a *phasor*. The magnitude of the phasor represents the amplitude of the voltage; the angle of the phasor represents the phase constant of the voltage. We can then add phasors the same way we add vectors.

- The angular frequency at which *resonance* occurs in a series *RLC* circuit is

$$\omega_0 = \frac{1}{\sqrt{LC}} \qquad (21\text{-}18)$$

At resonance, the current amplitude has its maximum value, the capacitive reactance is equal to the inductive reactance, and the impedance is equal to the resistance. If the resistance in the circuit is small, the resonance curve (the graph of current amplitude as a function of frequency) has a sharp peak. By adjusting the resonant frequency, such a circuit can be used to select a narrow range of frequencies from a signal consisting of a broad range of frequencies, as in radio or TV broadcasting.

- An *ideal* diode has zero resistance for current in one direction, so that the current flows without any voltage drop across the diode, and infinite resistance for current in the other direction, so that no current flows. Diodes can be used to convert ac to dc.

- Capacitors and inductors can be used to make filters to selectively remove unwanted high or low frequencies from an electrical signal.

Conceptual Questions

1. Explain why there is a phase difference between the current in an ac circuit and the potential difference across a capacitor in the same circuit.

2. Electric power is distributed long distances over transmission lines by using high ac voltages and therefore small ac currents. What is the advantage of using high voltages instead of safer low voltages?

3. Explain the differences between average current, rms current, and peak current in an ac circuit.

4. The United States and Canada use 120 V rms as the standard household voltage, while most of the rest of the world uses 240 V rms for the household standard. What are the advantages and disadvantages of the two systems?

5. Some electrical appliances are able to operate equally well with either dc or ac voltage sources, while other appliances require one type of source or the other and cannot run on both. Explain and give a few examples of each type of appliance.

6. For an ideal inductor in an ac circuit, explain why the voltage across the inductor must be zero when the current is maximum.

7. For a capacitor in an ac circuit, explain why the current must be zero when the voltage across the capacitor is maximum.

8. An electric heater is plugged into an ac outlet. Since the ac current changes polarity, there is no net movement of electrons through the heating element; the electrons just tend to oscillate back and forth. How, then, does the heating element heat up? Don't we need to send electrons *through* the element? Explain.

9. An electrical appliance is rated 120 V, 5 A, 500 W. The first two are rms values; the third is the average power consumption. Why is the power not 600 W ($= 120$ V $\times$ 5 A)?

10. How does adjusting the tuning knob on a radio tune in different stations?

11. A circuit has a resistor and an unknown component in series with a 12-V (rms) sinusoidal ac source. The current in the circuit decreases by 20% when the frequency decreases from 240 Hz to 160 Hz. What is the second component in the circuit? Explain your reasoning.

12. What happens if a 40-W lightbulb, designed to be connected to an ac voltage with amplitude 170 V and frequency 60 Hz, is instead connected to a 170-V dc power supply? Explain. What dc voltage would make the lightbulb burn with the same brightness as the 170 V peak 60-Hz ac?

13. How can the lights in a home be dimmed using a coil of wire and a soft-iron core?

14. Explain what is meant by a *phase difference*. Sketch graphs of $i(t)$ and $v_C(t)$, given that the current leads the voltage by $\pi/2$ radians.

15. What does it mean if the power factor is 1? What does it mean if it is zero?

16. A circuit has a resistor and an unknown component in series with a 12-V (rms) sinusoidal ac source. The current in the circuit decreases by 25% when the frequency increases from 150 Hz to 250 Hz. What is the second component in the circuit? Explain your reasoning.

17. Suppose you buy a 120-W lightbulb in Europe (where the rms voltage is 240 V). What happens if you bring it back to the United States (where the rms voltage is 120 V) and plug it in?

Multiple-Choice Questions

1. Graphs (1, 2) could represent:

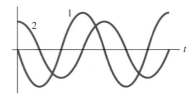

(a) the (1-voltage, 2-current) for a capacitor in an ac circuit.
(b) the (1-current, 2-voltage) for a capacitor in an ac circuit.
(c) the (1-voltage, 2-current) for a resistor in an ac circuit.
(d) the (1-current, 2-voltage) for a resistor in an ac circuit.
(e) the (1-voltage, 2-current) for an inductor in an ac circuit.
(f) the (1-current, 2-voltage) for an inductor in an ac circuit.
(g) either (a) or (e).   (h) either (a) or (f).
(i) either (b) or (e).   (j) either (b) or (f).

2. For a capacitor in an ac circuit, how much energy is stored in the capacitor at the instant when current is zero?
(a) zero   (b) maximum
(c) half of the maximum amount
(d) $1/\sqrt{2} \times$ the maximum amount
(e) impossible to answer without being given the phase angle

3. For an ideal inductor in an ac circuit, how much energy is stored in the inductor at the instant when current is zero?
(a) zero   (b) maximum
(c) half of the maximum amount
(d) $1/\sqrt{2} \times$ the maximum amount
(e) impossible to tell without being given the phase angle

4. For an ideal inductor in an ac circuit, the current through the inductor

(a) is in phase with the induced emf.
(b) leads the induced emf by 90°.
(c) leads the induced emf by an angle less than 90°.
(d) lags the induced emf by 90°.
(e) lags the induced emf by an angle less than 90°.

5. A capacitor is connected to the terminals of a variable frequency oscillator. The peak voltage of the source is kept fixed while the frequency is increased. Which statement is true?

(a) The rms current through the capacitor increases.
(b) The rms current through the capacitor decreases.
(c) The phase relation between the current and source voltage changes.
(d) The current stops flowing when the frequency change is large enough.

6. A voltage of $v(t) = (120 \text{ V}) \sin [(302 \text{ rad/s})t]$ is produced by an ac generator. What is the rms voltage and the frequency of the source?

(a) 170 V and 213 Hz   (b) 20 V and 427 Hz
(c) 60 V and 150 Hz   (d) 85 V and 48 Hz

7. An ac source is connected to a series combination of a resistor, capacitor, and an inductor. Which statement is correct?

(a) The current in the capacitor leads the current in the inductor by 180°.
(b) The current in the inductor leads the current in the capacitor by 180°.
(c) The current in the capacitor and the current in the resistor are in phase.
(d) The voltage across the capacitor and the voltage across the resistor are in phase.

8. A series *RLC* circuit is connected to an ac generator. When the generator frequency varies (but the peak emf is constant), the average power is:

(a) a minimum when $|X_L - X_C| = R$.
(b) a minimum when $X_C = X_L$.
(c) equal to $I_{rms}^2 R$ only at the resonant frequency.
(d) equal to $I_{rms}^2 R$ at all frequencies.

The graphs show the peak current as a function of frequency for various circuit elements placed in the diagrammed circuit. The amplitude of the generator emf is constant, independent of the frequency.

Multiple-Choice Questions 9 and 10

9. Which graph is correct if the circuit element is a capacitor?

10. Which graph is correct if the circuit element is a resistor?

Problems

© Combination conceptual/quantitative problem
🐾 Biological or medical application
No ✦ Easy to moderate difficulty level
✦ More challenging
✦✦ Most challenging
Blue # Detailed solution in the Student Solutions Manual
[1 2] Problems paired by concept

21.1 Sinusoidal Currents and Voltages; Resistors in ac Circuits; 21.2 Electricity in the Home

1. A lightbulb is connected to a 120-V (rms), 60-Hz source. How many times per second does the current reverse direction?

2. A European outlet supplies 220 V (rms) at 50 Hz. How many times per second is the magnitude of the voltage equal to 220 V?

3. A 1500-W heater runs on 120 V rms. What is the peak current through the heater?

4. A circuit breaker trips when the rms current exceeds 20.0 A. How many 100.0-W lightbulbs can run on this circuit without tripping the breaker? (The voltage is 120 V rms.)

5. A 1500-W electric hair dryer is designed to work in the United States, where the ac voltage is 120 V rms. What power is dissipated in the hair dryer when it is plugged into a 240-V rms socket in Europe? What may happen to the hair dryer in this case?

6. A 4.0-kW heater is designed to be connected to a 120-V rms source. What is the power dissipated by the heater if it is instead connected to a 120-V dc source?

7. (a) What rms current is drawn by a 4200-W electric room heater when running on 120 V rms? (b) What is the power dissipation by the heater if the voltage drops to 105 V rms during a brown-out? Assume the resistance stays the same.

8. A television set draws an rms current of 2.50 A from a 60-Hz power line. Find (a) the average current, (b) the average of the square of the current, and (c) the amplitude of the current.

9. The instantaneous sinusoidal emf from an ac generator with an rms emf of 4.0 V oscillates between what values?

10. A hair dryer has a power rating of 1200 W at 120 V rms. Assume the hair dryer circuit contains only resistance.

(a) What is the resistance of the heating element?
(b) What is the rms current drawn by the hair dryer?
(c) What is the maximum instantaneous power that the resistance must withstand?

✦ 11. Show that over one complete cycle, the average value of a sine function squared is $\frac{1}{2}$. [*Hint:* Use the following trigonometric identities: $\sin^2 a + \cos^2 a = 1$; $\cos 2a = \cos^2 a - \sin^2 a$.]

© 12. The diagram shows a simplified household circuit. Resistor R_1 = 240.0 Ω represents a lightbulb; resistor R_2 = 12.0 Ω represents a hair dryer. The resistors r = 0.50 Ω (each) represent the resistance of the wiring in the walls.

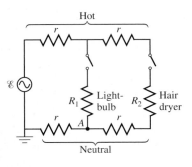

Assume that the generator supplies a constant 120.0 V rms. (a) If the lightbulb is on and the hair dryer is off, find the rms voltage across the lightbulb and the power dissipated by the lightbulb. (b) If both the lightbulb and the hair dryer are on, find the rms voltage across the lightbulb, the power dissipated by the lightbulb, and the rms voltage between point A and ground. (c) Explain why lights sometimes dim when an appliance is turned on. (d) Explain why the neutral and ground wires in a junction box are not at the same potential even though they are both grounded.

21.3 Capacitors in ac Circuits

13. A variable capacitor with negligible resistance is connected to an ac voltage source. How does the current in the circuit change if the capacitance is increased by a factor of 3.0 and the driving frequency is increased by a factor of 2.0?

14. At what frequency is the reactance of a 6.0-μF capacitor equal to 1.0 kΩ?

15. A 0.400-μF capacitor is connected across the terminals of a variable frequency oscillator. (a) What is the frequency when the reactance is 6.63 kΩ? (b) Find the reactance for half of that same frequency.

16. A 0.250-μF capacitor is connected to a 220-V rms ac source at 50.0 Hz. (a) Find the reactance of the capacitor. (b) What is the rms current through the capacitor?

17. A capacitor is connected across the terminals of a 115-V rms, 60.0-Hz generator. For what capacitance is the rms current 2.3 mA?

18. Show, from $X_C = 1/(\omega C)$, that the units of capacitive reactance are ohms.

19. A parallel plate capacitor has two plates, each of area 3.0 $\times 10^{-4}$ m^2, separated by 3.5 $\times 10^{-4}$ m. The space between the plates is filled with a dielectric. When the capacitor

is connected to a source of 120 V rms at 8.0 kHz, an rms current of 1.5 $\times 10^{-4}$ A is measured. (a) What is the capacitive reactance? (b) What is the dielectric constant of the material between the plates of the capacitor?

© 20. A capacitor (capacitance = C) is connected to an ac power supply with peak voltage V and angular frequency ω. (a) During a quarter-cycle when the capacitor goes from being uncharged to fully charged, what is the *average* current (in terms of C, V, and ω)? [*Hint:* $i_{av} = \Delta Q/\Delta t$.] (b) What is the rms current? (c) Explain why the average and rms currents are not the same.

21. Three capacitors (2.0 μF, 3.0 μF, 6.0 μF) are connected in series to an ac voltage source with amplitude 12.0 V and frequency 6.3 kHz. (a) What are the peak voltages across each capacitor? (b) What is the peak current that flows in the circuit?

22. A capacitor and a resistor are connected in parallel across an ac source. The reactance of the capacitor is equal to the resistance of the resistor. Assuming that $i_C(t)$ = $I \sin \omega t$, sketch graphs of $i_C(t)$ and $i_R(t)$ on the same axes.

21.4 Inductors in ac Circuits

23. A variable inductor with negligible resistance is connected to an ac voltage source. How does the current in the inductor change if the inductance is increased by a factor of 3.0 and the driving frequency is increased by a factor of 2.0?

24. At what frequency is the reactance of a 20.0-mH inductor equal to 18.8 Ω?

25. What is the reactance of an air-core solenoid of length 8.0 cm, radius 1.0 cm, and 240 turns at a frequency of 15.0 kHz?

26. A solenoid with a radius of 8.0 $\times 10^{-3}$ m and 200 turns/cm is used as an inductor in a circuit. When the solenoid is connected to a source of 15 V rms at 22 kHz, an rms current of 3.5 $\times 10^{-2}$ A is measured. Assume the resistance of the solenoid is negligible. (a) What is the inductive reactance? (b) What is the length of the solenoid?

27. A 4.00-mH inductor is connected to an ac voltage source of 151.0 V rms. If the rms current in the circuit is 0.820 A, what is the frequency of the source?

28. Two ideal inductors (0.10 H, 0.50 H) are connected in series to an ac voltage source with amplitude 5.0 V and frequency 126 Hz. (a) What are the peak voltages across each inductor? (b) What is the peak current that flows in the circuit?

© 29. Suppose that an ideal capacitor and an ideal inductor are connected in series in an ac circuit. (a) What is the phase difference between $v_C(t)$ and $v_L(t)$? [*Hint:* Since they are in series, the same current $i(t)$ flows through both.] (b) If the rms voltages across the capacitor and inductor are 5.0 V and 1.0 V, respectively, what would an ac voltmeter (which reads rms voltages) connected across the series combination read?

30. The voltage across an inductor and the current through the inductor are related by $v_L = L\,\Delta i/\Delta t$. Suppose that $i(t) = I \sin \omega t$. (a) Write an expression for $v_L(t)$. [*Hint:* Use one of the relationships of Eq. (20-7).] (b) From your expression for $v_L(t)$, show that the reactance of the inductor is $X_L = \omega L$. (c) Sketch graphs of $i(t)$ and $v_L(t)$ on the same axes. What is the phase difference? Which one leads?

31. Make a figure analogous to Fig. 21.4 for an ideal *inductor* in an ac circuit. Start by assuming that the voltage across an ideal inductor is $v_L(t) = V_L \sin \omega t$. Make a graph showing one cycle of $v_L(t)$ and $i(t)$ on the same axes. Then, at each of the times $t = 0, \frac{1}{8}T, \frac{2}{8}T, \ldots, T$, indicate the direction of the current (or that it is zero), whether the current is increasing, decreasing, or (instantaneously) not changing, and the direction of the induced emf in the inductor (or that it is zero).

32. Suppose that current flows to the *left* through the inductor in Fig. 21.6a so that i is negative. (a) If the current is increasing in magnitude, what is the sign of $\Delta i/\Delta t$? (b) In what direction is the induced emf that opposes the increase in current? (c) Show that Eq. (21-8) gives the correct sign for v_L. [*Hint:* v_L is positive if the left side of the inductor is at a higher potential than the right side.] (d) Repeat these three questions if the current flows to the left through the inductor and is *decreasing* in magnitude.

21.5 *RLC* Series Circuits

33. A 25.0-mH inductor, with internal resistance of 25.0 Ω, is connected to a 110-V rms source. If the average power dissipated in the circuit is 50.0 W, what is the frequency? (Model the inductor as an ideal inductor in series with a resistor.)

34. An inductor has an impedance of 30.0 Ω and a resistance of 20.0 Ω at a frequency of 50.0 Hz. What is the inductance? (Model the inductor as an ideal inductor in series with a resistor.)

35. A 6.20-mH inductor is one of the elements in a simple *RLC* series circuit. When this circuit is connected to a 1.60-kHz sinusoidal source with an rms voltage of 960.0 V, an rms current of 2.50 A lags behind the voltage by 52.0°. (a) What is the impedance of this circuit? (b) What is the resistance of this circuit? (c) What is the average power dissipated in this circuit?

36. A 0.48-μF capacitor is connected in series to a 5.00-kΩ resistor and an ac source of voltage amplitude 2.0 V. (a) At $f = 120$ Hz, what are the voltage amplitudes across the capacitor and across the resistor? (b) Do the voltage amplitudes add to give the amplitude of the source voltage (i.e., does $V_R + V_C = 2.0$ V)? Explain. (c) Draw a phasor diagram to show the addition of the voltages.

37. A series combination of a 22.0-mH inductor and a 145.0-Ω resistor are connected across the output termi-

nals of an ac generator with peak voltage 1.20 kV. (a) At $f = 1250$ Hz, what are the voltage amplitudes across the inductor and across the resistor? (b) Do the voltage amplitudes add to give the source voltage (i.e., does $V_R + V_L = 1.20$ kV)? Explain. (c) Draw a phasor diagram to show the addition of the voltages.

38. A series combination of a resistor and a capacitor are connected to a 110-V rms, 60.0-Hz ac source. If the capacitance is 0.80 μF and the rms current in the circuit is 28.4 mA, what is the resistance?

39. A 300.0-Ω resistor and a 2.5-μF capacitor are connected in series across the terminals of a sinusoidal emf with a frequency of 159 Hz. The inductance of the circuit is negligible. What is the impedance of the circuit?

40. A series *RLC* circuit has a 0.20-mF capacitor, a 13-mH inductor, and a 10.0-Ω resistor, and is connected to an ac source with amplitude 9.0 V and frequency 60 Hz. (a) Calculate the voltage amplitudes V_L, V_C, V_R, and the phase angle. (b) Draw the phasor diagram for the voltages of this circuit.

41. A 3.3-kΩ resistor is in series with a 2.0-μF capacitor in an ac circuit. The rms voltages across the two are the same. (a) What is the frequency? (b) Would each of the rms voltages be half of the rms voltage of the source? If not, what fraction of the source voltage are they? (In other words, $V_R/\mathscr{E}_m = V_C/\mathscr{E}_m = ?$) [*Hint:* Draw a phasor diagram.] (c) What is the phase angle between the source voltage and the current? Which leads? (d) What is the impedance of the circuit?

42. A 150-Ω resistor is in series with a 0.75-H inductor in an ac circuit. The rms voltages across the two are the same. (a) What is the frequency? (b) Would each of the rms voltages be half of the rms voltage of the source? If not, what fraction of the source voltage are they? (In other words, $V_R/\mathscr{E}_m = V_L/\mathscr{E}_m = ?$) (c) What is the phase angle between the source voltage and the current? Which leads? (d) What is the impedance of the circuit?

43. (a) Find the power factor for the *RLC* series circuit of Example 21.4. (b) What is the average power delivered to each element (R, L, C)?

44. A computer draws an rms current of 2.80 A at an rms voltage of 120 V. The average power consumption is 240 W. (a) What is the power factor? (b) What is the phase difference between the voltage and current?

45. An *RLC* series circuit is connected to an ac power supply with a 12-V amplitude and a frequency of 2.5 kHz. If $R = 220$ Ω, $C = 8.0$ μF, and $L = 0.15$ mH, what is the average power dissipated?

46. An ac circuit has a single resistor, capacitor, and inductor in series. The circuit uses 100 W of power and draws a maximum rms current of 2.0 A when operating at 60 Hz and 120 V rms. The capacitive reactance is 0.50 times the inductive reactance. (a) Find the phase

angle. (b) Find the values of the resistor, the inductor, and the capacitor.

✦ 47. A series circuit with a resistor and a capacitor has a time constant of 0.25 ms. The circuit has an impedance of 350 Ω at a frequency of 1250 Hz. What are the capacitance and the resistance?

✦ 48. (a) What is the reactance of a 10.0-mH inductor at the frequency $f = 250.0$ Hz? (b) What is the impedance of a series combination of the 10.0-mH inductor and a 10.0-Ω resistor at 250.0 Hz? (c) What is the maximum current through the same circuit when the ac voltage source has a peak value of 1.00 V? (d) By what angle does the current lag the voltage in the circuit?

49. Suppose that two sinusoidal voltages at the same frequency are added:

$$V_1 \sin \omega t + V_2 \sin (\omega t + \phi_2) = V \sin (\omega t + \phi)$$

A phasor representation is shown in the diagram. (a) Substitute $t = 0$ into the equation. Interpret the result by referring to the phasor diagram. (b) Substitute $t = \pi/(2\omega)$ and simplify using the trigonometric identity $\sin (\theta + \pi/2) = \cos \theta$. Interpret the result by referring to the phasor diagram.

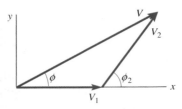

50. An ac circuit contains a 12.5-Ω resistor, a 5.00-μF capacitor, and a 3.60-mH inductor connected in series to an ac generator with an output voltage of 50.0 V (peak) and frequency of 1.59 kHz. Find the impedance, the power factor, and the phase difference between the source voltage and current for this circuit.

21.6 Resonance in an RLC Circuit

51. The FM radio band is broadcast between 88 MHz and 108 MHz. What range of capacitors must be used to tune in these signals if an inductor of 3.00 μH is used?

52. An RLC series circuit is built with a variable capacitor. How does the resonant frequency of the circuit change when the area of the capacitor is increased by a factor of 2?

53. Repeat Problem 40 for an operating frequency of 98.7 Hz. (a) What is the phase angle for this circuit? (b) Draw the phasor diagram. (c) What is the resonant frequency for this circuit?

54. An RLC series circuit has a resistance of $R = 325$ Ω, an inductance $L = 0.300$ mH, and a capacitance $C = 33.0$ nF. (a) What is the resonant frequency? (b) If the capacitor breaks down for peak voltages in excess of 7.0×10^2 V, what is the maximum source voltage amplitude when the circuit is operated at the resonant frequency?

55. An RLC series circuit has $L = 0.300$ H and $C = 6.00$ μF. The source has a peak voltage of 440 V. (a) What is the

angular resonant frequency? (b) When the source is set at the resonant frequency, the peak current in the circuit is 0.560 A. What is the resistance in the circuit? (c) What are the peak voltages across the resistor, the inductor, and the capacitor at the resonant frequency?

Ⓒ 56. A series RLC circuit has $R = 500.0$ Ω, $L = 35.0$ mH, and $C = 87.0$ pF. What is the impedance of the circuit at resonance? Explain.

57. In an RLC series circuit, these three elements are connected in series: a resistor of 60.0 Ω, a 40.0-mH inductor, and a 0.0500-F capacitor. The series elements are connected across the terminals of an ac oscillator with an rms voltage of 10.0 V. Find the resonant frequency for the circuit.

58. Finola has a circuit with a 4.00-kΩ resistor, a 0.750-H inductor, and a capacitor of unknown value connected in series to a 440.0-Hz ac source. With an oscilloscope, she measures the phase angle to be 25.0°. (a) What is the value of the unknown capacitor? (b) Finola has several capacitors on hand and would like to use one to tune the circuit to maximum power. Should she connect a second capacitor in parallel across the first capacitor or in series in the circuit? Explain. (c) What value capacitor does she need for maximum power?

21.7 Converting ac to dc; Filters

59. An RC filter is shown. The filter resistance R is variable between 180 Ω and 2200 Ω and the filter capacitance is $C = 0.086$ μF. At what frequency is the output amplitude equal to $1/\sqrt{2}$ times the input amplitude if $R =$ (a) 180 Ω? (b) 2200 Ω? (c) Is this a low-pass or high-pass filter? Explain.

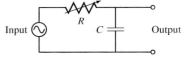

60. In the crossover network of the figure, the crossover frequency is found to be 252 Hz. The capacitance is $C = 560$ μF. Assume the inductor to be ideal. (a) What is the impedance of the tweeter branch (the capacitor in series with the 8.0-Ω resistance of the tweeter) at the crossover frequency? (b) What is the impedance of the woofer branch at the crossover frequency? [Hint: The current amplitudes in the two branches are the same.] (c) Find L. (d) Derive an equation for the crossover frequency f_{co} in terms of L and C.

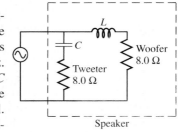

Problems 60 and 61

61. In the crossover network of Problem 60, the inductance L is 1.20 mH. The capacitor is variable; its capacitance can be adjusted to set the crossover point according to

the frequency response of the woofer and tweeter. What should the capacitance be set to for a crossover point of 180 Hz? [*Hint:* At the crossover point, the currents are equal in amplitude.]

✦✦ 62. The circuit shown has a source voltage of 440 V rms, resistance $R = 250\ \Omega$, inductance $L = 0.800$ H, and capacitance $C = 2.22\ \mu$F. (a) Find the angular frequency ω_0 for resonance in this circuit. (b) Draw a phasor diagram for the circuit at resonance. (c) Find these rms voltages measured between various points in the circuit: V_{ab}, V_{bc}, V_{cd}, V_{bd}, and V_{ad}. (d) The resistor is replaced with one of $R = 125\ \Omega$. Now what is the angular frequency for resonance? (e) What is the rms current in the circuit operated at resonance with the new resistor?

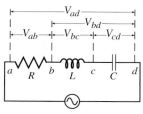

Comprehensive Problems

63. For a particular *RLC* series circuit, the capacitive reactance is 12.0 Ω, the inductive reactance is 23.0 Ω, and the maximum voltage across the 25.0-Ω resistor is 8.00 V. (a) What is the impedance of the circuit? (b) What is the maximum voltage across this circuit?

64. The phasor diagram for a particular *RLC* series circuit is shown in the figure. If the circuit has a resistance of 100 Ω and is driven at a frequency of 60 Hz, find (a) the current amplitude, (b) the capacitance, and (c) the inductance.

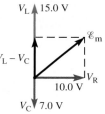

© 65. A portable heater is connected to a 60-Hz ac outlet. How many times per second is the instantaneous power a maximum?

66. What is the rms voltage of the oscilloscope trace of the figure, assuming that the signal is sinusoidal? The central horizontal line represents zero volts. The oscilloscope voltage knob has been clicked into its calibrated position.

Volts/DIV

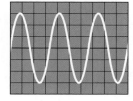

67. A certain circuit has a 25-Ω resistor and one other component in series with a 12-V (rms) sinusoidal ac source. The rms current in the circuit is 0.317 A when the frequency is 150 Hz and increases by 25.0% when the frequency increases to 250 Hz. (a) What is the second component in the circuit? (b) What is the current at

250 Hz? (c) What is the numerical value of the second component?

© 68. A 22-kV power line that is 10.0 km long supplies the electrical energy to a small town at an average rate of 6.0 MW. (a) If a pair of aluminum cables of diameter 9.2 cm are used, what is the average power dissipated in the transmission line? (b) Why is aluminum used rather than a better conductor such as copper or silver?

⬛ 69. An x-ray machine uses 240 kV rms at 60.0 mA rms when it is operating. If the power source is a 420-V rms line, (a) what must be the turns ratio of the transformer? (b) What is the rms current in the primary? (c) What is the average power used by the x-ray tube?

70. A coil with an internal resistance of 120 Ω and inductance of 12.0 H is connected to a 60.0-Hz, 110-V rms line. (a) What is the impedance of the coil? (b) Calculate the current in the coil.

71. The field coils used in an ac motor are designed to have a resistance of 0.45 Ω and an impedance of 35.0 Ω. What inductance is required if the frequency of the ac source is (a) 60.0 Hz? and (b) 0.20 kHz?

72. A capacitor is rated at 0.025 μF. How much rms current flows when the capacitor is connected to a 110-V rms, 60.0-Hz line?

73. A capacitor to be used in a radio is to have a reactance of 6.20 Ω at a frequency of 520 Hz. What is the capacitance?

✦ 74. (a) What is the reactance of a 5.00-μF capacitor at the frequencies $f = 12.0$ Hz and 1.50 kHz? (b) What is the impedance of a series combination of the 5.00-μF capacitor and a 2.00-kΩ resistor at the same two frequencies? (c) What is the maximum current through the circuit of part (b) when the ac source has a peak voltage of 2.00 V? (d) For each of the two frequencies, does the current lead or lag the voltage? By what angle?

75. An alternator supplies a peak current of 4.68 A to a coil with a negligibly small internal resistance. The voltage of the alternator is 420-V peak at 60.0 Hz. When a capacitor of 38.0 μF is placed in series with the coil, the power factor is found to be 1.00. Find (a) the inductive reactance of the coil and (b) the inductance of the coil.

76. At what frequency does the maximum current flow through a series *RLC* circuit containing a resistance of 4.50 Ω, an inductance of 440 mH, and a capacitance of 520 pF?

77. What is the rms current flowing in a 4.50-kW motor connected to a 220-V rms line when (a) the power factor is 1.00 and (b) when it is 0.80?

✦ 78. A 40.0-mH inductor, with internal resistance of 30.0 Ω, is connected to an ac source

$$\mathcal{E}(t) = (286\ \text{V}) \sin\left[(390\ \text{rad/s})t\right]$$

(a) What is the impedance of the inductor in the circuit? (b) What are the peak and rms voltages across the inductor (including the internal resistance)? (c) What is the peak current in the circuit? (d) What is the average power dissipated in the circuit? (e) Write an expression for the current through the inductor as a function of time.

✦ 79. In an *RLC* circuit, these three elements are connected in series: a resistor of 20.0 Ω, a 35.0-mH inductor, and a 50.0-μF capacitor. The ac source of the circuit has an rms voltage of 100.0 V and an angular frequency of 1.0×10^3 rad/s. Find (a) the reactances of the capacitor and inductor, (b) the impedance, (c) the rms current, (d) the current amplitude, (e) the phase angle, and (f) the rms voltages across each of the circuit elements. (g) Does the current lead or lag the voltage? (h) Draw a phasor diagram.

80. A variable capacitor is connected in series to an inductor with negligible internal resistance and of inductance 2.4×10^{-4} H. The combination is used as a tuner for a radio. If the lowest frequency to be tuned in is 0.52 MHz, what is the maximum capacitance required?

✦ 81. An *RLC* series circuit is connected to a 240-V rms power supply at a frequency of 2.50 kHz. The elements in the circuit have the following values: $R = 12.0$ Ω, $C = 0.26$ μF, and $L = 15.2$ mH. (a) What is the impedance of the circuit? (b) What is the rms current? (c) What is the phase angle? (d) Does the current lead or lag the voltage? (e) What are the rms voltages across each circuit element?

82. A large coil used as an electromagnet has a resistance of $R = 450$ Ω and an inductance of $L = 2.47$ H. The coil is connected to an ac source with a voltage amplitude of 2.0 kV and a frequency of 9.55 Hz. (a) What is the power factor? (b) What is the impedance of the circuit? (c) What is the peak current in the circuit? (d) What is the average power delivered to the electromagnet by the source?

🄒 83. An ac series circuit containing a capacitor, inductor, and resistance is found to have a current of amplitude 0.50 A for a source voltage of amplitude 10.0 V at an angular frequency of 200.0 rad/s. The total resistance in the circuit is 15.0 Ω. (a) What are the power factor and the phase angle for the circuit? (b) Can you determine whether the current leads or lags the source voltage? Explain.

84. A generator supplies an average power of 12 MW through a transmission line that has a resistance of 10.0 Ω. What is the power loss in the transmission line if the rms line voltage $\mathscr{E}_{rms}$ is (a) 15 kV and (b) 110 kV? What percentage of the total

power supplied by the generator is lost in the transmission line in each case?

🄒 85. (a) Calculate the rms current drawn by the load in the figure with Problem 84 if $\mathscr{E}_{rms} = 250$ kV and the average power supplied by the generator is 12 MW. (b) Suppose that the average power supplied by the generator is still 12 MW, but the load is not purely resistive; rather, the load has a power factor of 0.86. What is the rms current drawn? (c) Why would the power company want to charge more in the second case, even though the average power is the same?

🄒 86. Transformers are often rated in terms of kilovolt-amps. A pole on a residential street has a transformer rated at 35 kV·A to serve four homes on the street. (a) If each home has a fuse that limits the incoming current to 60 A rms at 220 V rms, find the maximum load in kV·A on the transformer. (b) Is the rating of the transformer adequate? (c) Explain why the transformer rating is given in kV·A rather than in kW.

🄒 87. A variable inductor can be placed in series with a lightbulb to act as a dimmer. (a) What inductance would reduce the current through a 100-W lightbulb to 75% of its maximum value? Assume a 120-V rms, 60-Hz source. (b) Could a variable resistor be used in place of the variable inductor to reduce the current? Why is the inductor a much better choice for a dimmer?

Answers to Practice Problems

21.1 $V = 310$ V; $I = 17.0$ A; $P_{max} = 5300$ W; $P_{av} = 2600$ W; $R = 18$ Ω

21.2 9950 Ω; 22.1 mA

21.3 1.13 kΩ; 8.84 μA

21.4 $v_C(t) = (500$ mV$)$ sin $(\omega t - \pi/2)$, $v_L(t) = (440$ mV$)$ sin $(\omega t + \pi/2)$, $v_R(t) = (80$ mV$)$ sin ωt, and $\mathscr{E}(t) = (100$ mV$)$ sin $(\omega t - 0.64)$.
At $t = 80.0$ μs, $\omega t = 0.800$ rad.
$v_C(t) = (500$ mV$)$ sin $(-0.771$ rad$) = -350$ mV,
$v_L(t) = (440$ mV$)$ sin $(2.371$ rad$) = +310$ mV,
$v_R(t) = (80$ mV$)$ sin $(0.80$ rad$) = +57$ mV,
and $\mathscr{E}(t) = (100$ mV$)$ sin $(0.16$ rad$) = +16$ mV.
$v_C + v_L + v_R = +17$ mV (discrepancy comes from roundoff error)

21.5 29 W

21.6 25 pF

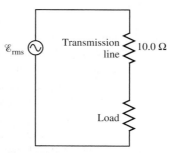

Problems 84 and 85

REVIEW AND SYNTHESIS: CHAPTERS 19–21

Review Exercises

1. A solenoid with 8500 turns per meter has radius 65 cm. The current in the solenoid is 25.0 A. A circular loop of wire with 100 turns and radius 8.00 cm is put inside the solenoid. The current in the circular loop is 2.20 A. What is the maximum possible magnetic torque on the loop? What orientation does the loop have if the magnetic torque has its maximum value?

2. Two long, straight wires, each with a current of 5.0 A, are placed on two corners of an equilateral triangle with sides of length 3.2 cm as shown. One of the wires has a current into the page and one has a current out of the page. (a) What is the magnetic field at the third corner of the triangle? (b) A proton has a velocity of 1.8×10^7 m/s out of the page when it crosses the plane of the page at the third corner of the triangle. What is the magnetic force on the proton at that point due to the two wires?

3. Two long, straight wires, each with a current of 12.0 A, are placed on two corners of an equilateral triangle with sides of length 2.50 cm as shown. Both of the wires have a current into the page. (a) What is the magnetic field at the third corner of the triangle? (b) Another wire is placed at the third corner, parallel to the other two wires. Which direction should current flow in the third wire so that the force on it is in the +y-direction. (c) If the third wire has a linear mass density of 0.150 g/m, what current should it have so that the magnetic force on the wire is equal in magnitude to the gravitational force, and the third wire can "hover" above the other two?

4. A loop of wire is connected to a battery and a variable resistor as shown. Two other loops of wire, B and C, are placed inside the large loop and outside the large loop, respectively. As the resistance in the variable resistor is increased, are there currents induced in the loops B and C? If so, do the currents circulate CW or CCW?

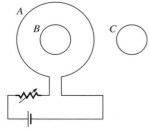

5. A cosmic ray muon with the same charge as an electron and a mass of 1.9×10^{-28} kg is moving toward the ground at an angle of 25° from the vertical with a speed of 7.0×10^7 m/s. As it crosses point P, the muon is at a horizontal distance of 85.0 cm from a high-voltage power line. At that moment, the power line has a current of 16.0 A. What is the magnitude and direction of the force on the muon at the point P in the diagram?

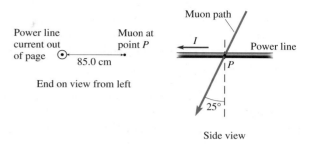

6. A variable capacitor is connected to an ac source. The rms current in the circuit is I_i. If the frequency of the source is reduced by a factor of 2.0 while the overlapping area of the capacitor plates is increased by a factor of 3.0, what will be the new rms current in the circuit? The resistance in the circuit is negligible.

7. Power lines carry electricity to your house at high voltage. This problem investigates the reason for that. Suppose a power plant produces 800 kW of power and wants to send that power for many miles over a copper wire with a total resistance of 12 Ω. (a) If the power is sent at a voltage of 120 V rms as used in houses in the United States, how much current flows through the copper wires? [*Hint:* The 12-Ω resistance of the wires is in series with the load in the house, and the 120-V rms voltage is connected across the series combination.] (b) What is the power dissipated due to the resistance of the copper wires? (c) If transformers are used so that the power is sent across the copper wires at 48 kV rms, how much current flows through the wires? (d) What is the power dissipated due to the resistance of the wires at this current? What percent of the total power output of the plant is this? (e) Although a series of transformers step the voltage down to the 120 V used for household voltage, assume you are using a single transformer to do the job. If the single transformer has 10,000 primary turns, how many secondary turns should it have?

8. A square loop of wire is made up of 50 turns of wire, 45 cm on each side. The loop is immersed in a 1.4-T magnetic field perpendicular to the plane of the loop. The loop of wire has little resistance but it is connected to two resistors in parallel as shown. (a) When the loop of wire is rotated by 180°, how much charge flows through the circuit? (b) How much charge goes through the 5.0-Ω resistor?

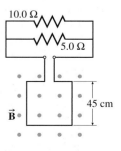

9. A circular loop of wire is placed near a long current carrying wire, as shown. Explain what happens while the loop is moved in each of the three directions shown. Does current flow? If so, is it CW or CCW? In what direction does a magnetic force act on the loop, if any?

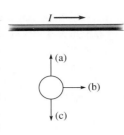

10. You are working as an electrical engineer designing transformers for transmitting power from a generating station producing 2.5×10^6 W to a city 120 km away. The power will be carried on two transmission lines to complete a circuit, each line constructed out of copper with a radius of 5.0 cm. (a) What is the total resistance of the transmission lines? (b) If the power is transmitted at 1200 V rms, find the average power dissipated in the wires. [*Hint:* See Section 20.2.] (c) The rms voltage is increased from 1200 V by a factor of 150 using a transformer with a primary coil of 1000 turns. How many turns are in the secondary coil? (d) What is the new rms current in the transmission lines after the voltage is stepped up with the transformer? (e) How much average power is dissipated in the transmission lines when using the transformer?

11. An electromagnetic rail gun can fire a projectile using a magnetic field and an electric current. Consider two conducting rails that are 0.500 m apart with a 50.0-g conducting projectile that slides along the two rails. A magnetic field of 0.750 T is directed perpendicular to the plane of the rails and points upward. A constant current of 2.00 A passes through the projectile. (a) What direction is the force on the projectile? (b) If the coefficient of kinetic friction between the rails and the projectile is 0.350, how fast is the projectile moving after it has traveled 8.00 m down the rails? (c) As the projectile slides down the rails, does the applied emf have to increase, decrease, or stay the same to maintain a constant current?

12. An air-filled parallel plate capacitor is used in a simple series *RLC* circuit along with a 0.650-H inductor. At a frequency of 220 Hz, the power output is found to be less than the maximum possible power output. After the space between the plates is filled with a dielectric with $\kappa = 5.50$, the circuit dissipates the maximum possible power. (a) What is the capacitance of the air-filled capacitor? (b) What was the resonant frequency of this circuit *before* inserting the dielectric?

13. (a) When the resistance of an *RLC* series circuit that is at resonance is doubled, what happens to the power dissipated? (b) Now consider an *RLC* series circuit that is not at resonance. For this circuit, the initial resistance and impedance are related by $R = X_C = X_L/2$. Determine how the power output changes when the resistance doubles for this circuit.

14. An *RLC* circuit has a resistance of 10.0 Ω, an inductance of 15.0 mH, and a capacitance of 350 μF. By what factor does the impedance of this circuit change when the frequency at which it is driven changes from 60 Hz to 120 Hz? Does the impedance increase or decrease?

15. An *RLC* circuit has a resistance of 255 Ω, an inductance of 146 mH, and a capacitance of 877 nF. (a) What is the resonant frequency of this circuit? (b) If this circuit is connected to a sinusoidal generator with a frequency 0.50 times the resonant frequency and a maximum voltage of 480 V, which will lead, the current or the voltage? (c) What is the phase angle of this circuit? (d) What is the rms current in this circuit? (e) How much average power is dissipated in this circuit? (f) What is the maximum voltage across each circuit element?

16. A variable inductor is connected to a voltage source whose frequency can vary. The rms current is I_i. If the inductance is increased by a factor of 3.0 and the frequency is reduced by a factor of 2.0, what will be the new rms current in the circuit? The resistance in the circuit is negligible.

17. Kieran measures the magnetic field of an electron beam. The beam strength is such that 1.40×10^{11} electrons pass a point every 1.30 μs. What magnetic field strength does Kieran measure at a distance of 2.00 cm from the beam center?

18. We wish to use a mass spectrometer to measure the mass m of the $^{238}U^+$ ion. Assume a source of $^{238}U^+$ ions exists and that the ions initially move slowly. We want the ions to move at a high speed v in the mass spectrometer. (a) To accelerate the ions to speed v, we use the electric field between the plates of a capacitor, as shown. If the plates have area A and are a distance d apart, what should the charge on the plates be? Indicate which plate is positive and which negative. (Answer in terms of v, A, d, m, and universal constants.) (b) The ions now have speeds roughly equal to v, but because their initial speeds varied somewhat, there is a spread. We want to select ions with speeds very close to v and reject the rest. To do so, we pass the beam of ions

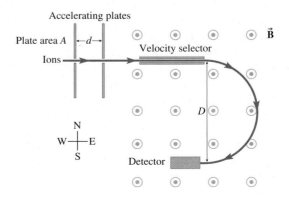

through a velocity selector. In the selector, there is a uniform magnetic field out of the page with magnitude B. What are the magnitude and direction of the electric field in the selector? (Answer in terms of v, m, B, and universal constants.) (c) Sketch the trajectory of ions that enter the velocity selector with speeds less than v. (d) Some of the ions now enter the mass spectrometer. The magnetic field is the same as in part (b), but there is no electric field. The ions are detected when the detector is a distance D from the entry point of the ions. Find the mass of the ions. (Answer in terms of v, B, D, and universal constants.

MCAT Review

The section that follows includes MCAT exam material and is reprinted with permission of the Association of American Medical Colleges (AAMC).

Read the paragraph and then answer the following questions.

An electromagnetic railgun is a device that can fire projectiles using electromagnetic energy instead of chemical energy. A schematic of a typical railgun is shown in the figure.

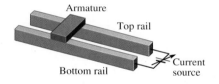

Figure 1 Schematic of a railgun

The operation of the railgun is simple. Current flows from the current source into the top rail, through a movable, conducting armature into the bottom rail, then back to the current source. The current in the two rails produces a magnetic field directly proportional to the amount of current. This field produces a force on the charges moving through the movable armature. The force pushes the armature and the projectile along the rails.

The force is proportional to the square of the current running through the railgun. For a given current, the force and the magnetic field will be constant along the entire length of the railgun. The detectors placed outside the railgun give off a signal when the projectile passes them. This information can be used to determine the exit speed v_i and kinetic energy of the projectile. The projectile mass, rail current, and exit speed for four different trials are listed in the table.

Projectile Mass (kg)	Rail Current (A)	Exit Speed (km/s)
0.01	10.0	2.0
0.01	15.0	3.0
0.02	10.0	1.4
0.04	10.0	1.0

1. Which of the following diagrams best represents the magnetic field created by the rail currents in the region between the rails?

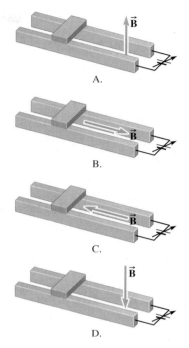

2. For a given mass, if the current were decreased by a factor of 2, the new exit speed v would be equal to
   A. $2v_i$
   B. $\sqrt{2}v_i$
   C. $v_i/\sqrt{2}$
   D. $v_i/2$

3. Lengthening the rails would increase the exit speed because of
   A. an increased rail resistance.
   B. a stronger magnetic field between the rails.
   C. a larger force on the armature.
   D. a longer distance over which the force is present.

4. What change made to the railgun would reduce power consumption without lowering the exit speeds?
   A. Lowering the rail current
   B. Lowering the rail resistivity
   C. Lowering the rail cross-sectional area
   D. Reducing the magnetic field strength

5. If a projectile with a mass of 0.10 kg accelerates from a resting position to a speed of 10.0 m/s in 2.0 s, what will be the average power supplied by the railgun to the projectile?
   A. 0.5 W
   B. 2.5 W
   C. 5.0 W
   D. 10.0 W

6. A projectile with a mass of 0.08 kg that is propelled by a rail current of 20.0 A will have approximately what exit speed?

A. 0.7 km/s

B. 1.0 km/s

C. 1.4 km/s

D. 2.0 km/s

Refer to the three paragraphs about power being transmitted to consumers by utility companies in the MCAT Review section for Chapters 16–18. Based on those paragraphs, answer the following two questions.

7. When delivering a constant amount of power, why does the power lost to heat decrease as the transmission-line voltage increases?

A. Increasing the voltage decreases the required current.

B. Increasing the voltage increases the required current.

C. Increasing the voltage decreases the required resistance.

D. Increasing the voltage increases the required resistance.

8. Which of the following figures best illustrates the direction of the magnetic field ($\vec{B}$) associated with a section of wire carrying a current?

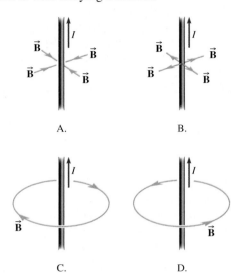

Electromagnetic Waves

Bees use the position of the Sun in the sky to navigate and find their way back to their hives. This is remarkable in itself—since the Sun moves across the sky during the day, the bees navigate with respect to a moving reference point rather than a fixed reference point. Even if the bees are kept in the dark for part of the day, they still navigate with reference to the Sun; they compensate for the motion of the Sun during the time they were in the dark. They must have some sort of internal clock that enables them to keep track of the Sun's motion.

What do they do when the Sun's position is obscured by clouds? Experiments have shown that the bees can still navigate as long as there is a patch of blue sky. How is this possible? (See p. 827 for the answer.)

Concepts & Skills to Review

- simple harmonic motion (Section 10.5)
- energy transport by waves; transverse waves; amplitude, frequency, wavelength, wavenumber, and angular frequency; equations for waves (Sections 11.1–11.5)
- Ampère's and Faraday's laws (Sections 19.9 and 20.3)
- dipoles (Sections 16.4 and 19.1)
- thermal radiation (Section 14.8)
- Doppler effect (Section 12.8)
- relative velocity (Section 3.5)

● EM waves are produced only by *accelerating* charges.

22.1   ACCELERATING CHARGES PRODUCE ELECTROMAGNETIC WAVES

In our study of electromagnetism so far, we have considered the electric and magnetic fields due to charges whose accelerations are small. A point charge at rest gives rise to an electric field only. A charge moving at constant velocity gives rise to both electric and magnetic fields. Charges at rest or moving at constant velocity do not generate **electromagnetic waves**—waves that consist of oscillating electric and magnetic fields. Electromagnetic (EM) waves are produced only by charges that *accelerate*. EM waves, also called **electromagnetic radiation**, consist of oscillating electric and magnetic fields that travel away from the accelerating charges.

A brief acceleration of a charged particle causes a brief EM wave pulse. To create an EM wave that lasts longer than a pulse, the charge must continue to accelerate. Let's consider two point charges $\pm q$ that move in simple harmonic motion along the same line with the same amplitude and frequency but half a cycle out of phase. What do the electric and magnetic fields due to this oscillating electric dipole look like? Figure 22.1 shows the electric field due to a *static* electric dipole. The static dipole produces no magnetic field (because the charges are at rest) and emits no EM radiation (because the charges have zero acceleration at all times).

The oscillating electric dipole consists of *moving* charges and therefore generates a magnetic field as well as an electric field. However, the fields don't just look like oscillating versions of the fields of static electric and magnetic dipoles. The charges accelerate and therefore they emit EM radiation. Let's try to develop a visual idea of how the radiation comes about.

The oscillating fields affect each other. The magnetic field is not constant, since the current is changing. According to Faraday's law of induction, a changing magnetic field induces an electric field. The electric field of the oscillating dipole at any instant is therefore different from the electric field of a static dipole. Faraday's law liberates the electric field lines: they do not have to start and end on the source charges. Instead, they can be closed loops far from the oscillating dipole.

According to Ampère's law as we have stated it, the magnetic field lines must enclose the current that is their source. However, Scottish physicist James Clerk Maxwell (1831–1879) was puzzled by a lack of symmetry in the laws of electromagnetism. If a changing magnetic field gives rise to an electric field, might not a changing electric field give rise to a magnetic field? The answer turns out to be yes. A changing electric field does give rise to a magnetic field. The magnetic field lines need not enclose a current; they can circulate around electric field lines, which extend far from the oscillating dipole.

Figure 22.2 shows the electric and magnetic field lines due to an *oscillating* dipole. With changing electric fields as a source of magnetic fields, the field lines (both electric and magnetic) can break free of the dipole, form closed loops, and travel away from the dipole as an electromagnetic wave. The electric and magnetic fields sustain each other as the wave travels outward. Although the fields do diminish in strength, they do so much less rapidly than if the field lines were tied to the dipole. Since changing electric fields are a source of magnetic fields, a wave consisting of just an oscillating electric

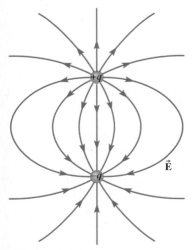

Figure 22.1 Electric field lines due to an electric dipole at rest.

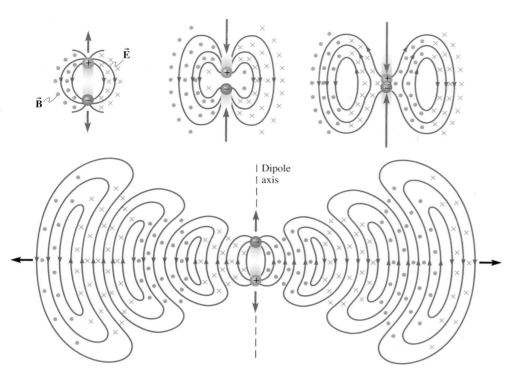

Dipole axis

Figure 22.2 Electric and magnetic field lines due to an oscillating dipole. The loops are electric field lines in the plane of the page. The dots and crosses are magnetic field lines crossing the plane of the page; the magnetic field lines are all closed loops. The field lines break free of the dipole and travel away from it as an electromagnetic wave.

field without an oscillating magnetic field is impossible. Since changing magnetic fields are a source of electric fields, a wave consisting of just an oscillating magnetic field without an oscillating electric field is also impossible.

> There are no electric waves or magnetic waves; there are only electromagnetic waves.

Figure 22.2 illustrates that the fields far from an oscillating dipole are strongest—field lines are closest together—in directions perpendicular to the dipole axis and weakest along the axis.

22.2 MAXWELL'S EQUATIONS

The Ampère-Maxwell Law

Here is an example to show that a changing electric field *must* give rise to a magnetic field. Imagine a long straight wire of radius R carrying a constant current I. At one point, the wire has a tiny gap (Fig. 22.3). The surfaces of the gap act as a capacitor; as current flows, the left surface accumulates positive charge at a rate $\Delta q/\Delta t = I$ and the right surface accumulates negative charge at the same rate. Ampère's law says that the circulation of $\vec{\mathbf{B}}$ around a loop must equal μ_0 times the current that crosses the interior of the loop. Applying Ampère's law to circular loop 1 gives the usual result for the magnetic field near a long, straight wire. However, the interior of circular loop 2 has *no current cutting through it*. Could the magnetic field at points just outside the gap be zero, no matter how tiny the gap?

Maxwell recognized that, although no current cuts through the interior of loop 2, there is a *changing electric flux* through it. The surface cuts through the electric field lines between the capacitor plates; as more and more charge accumulates on the plates, the field is getting stronger, and therefore the electric flux is increasing. The electric field in the gap is

$$E = \frac{\sigma}{\epsilon_0} = \frac{q}{\epsilon_0 A} = \frac{q}{\epsilon_0 \pi R^2} \qquad (17\text{-}13)$$

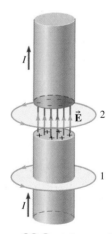

Figure 22.3 A long cylindrical wire carrying a constant current I has a small gap. The faces of the gap act as capacitor plates and charge accumulates on them. Two circular loops, one around the wire and one around the gap, are used in Ampère's law. No current cuts through the interior of loop 2, but electric field lines in the gap do cut through it. As the electric field in the gap increases in magnitude, the electric flux through the interior of loop 2 increases.

The rate of change of the electric flux is

$$\frac{\Delta \Phi_E}{\Delta t} = \frac{\Delta E \times \pi R^2}{\Delta t} = \frac{\Delta q}{\epsilon_0 \pi R^2} \times \frac{\pi R^2}{\Delta t} = \frac{I}{\epsilon_0}$$

The rate of change of the flux is proportional to the current! Maxwell recognized that the contradiction is resolved if Ampère's law is modified as

Ampère-Maxwell Law

$$\sum B_{\parallel} \Delta l = \mu_0 \left(I + \epsilon_0 \frac{\Delta \Phi_E}{\Delta t} \right) \tag{22-1}$$

Using this modified form of Ampère's law, the magnetic field at a point on loop 2 is the same as the magnetic field at the corresponding point on loop 1.

The Ampère-Maxwell law [Eq. (22-1)] says that changing electric fields as well as currents are sources of magnetic fields. Magnetic field lines are still always closed loops, but the loops do not have to surround currents; they can surround changing electric fields as well.

Maxwell's Equations

Maxwell modified Ampère's law and then used it with the three other basic laws of electromagnetism to show that electromagnetic waves exist and to derive their properties. In honor of this achievement, the four laws are collectively called **Maxwell's equations**. They are

1. **Gauss's law** [Eqs. (16-7) and (16-8)]: If an electric field line is not a closed loop, it can only start and stop on electric charges. Electric charges produce electric fields.
2. **Gauss's law for magnetism**: Magnetic field lines are always closed loops since there are no magnetic charges (*monopoles*). The magnetic flux *through a closed surface* (or the net number of field lines leaving the surface) is zero.

$$\Phi_B = \sum B_{\perp} A = 0 \tag{22-2}$$

3. **Faraday's law** [Eq. (20-6)]: Changing magnetic fields are another source of electric fields.
4. **The Ampère-Maxwell law** [Eq. (22-1)]: Both currents and changing electric fields are sources of magnetic fields.

22.3   ANTENNAS

As we saw in Section 22.1, an electric dipole that oscillates back and forth produces oscillating electric and magnetic fields that then travel away from the charge as EM waves. The **electric dipole antenna** generates EM waves in this way. It consists of two metal rods lined up as if they were a single long rod (Fig. 22.4). The rods are fed from the center with an oscillating current. For half of a cycle, the current flows upward; the top of the antenna acquires a positive charge and the bottom acquires an equal negative charge. Thus, an electric dipole is produced. When the current reverses direction, these accumulated charges diminish and then reverse direction so that the top of the antenna becomes negatively charged and the bottom becomes positively charged. The result of feeding an alternating current to the antenna is an oscillating electric dipole.

The field lines for the EM wave emitted by an electric dipole antenna are similar to the field lines for an oscillating electric dipole (Fig. 22.2). From the field lines, some of the properties of EM waves can be observed:

•   For equal distances from the antenna, the amplitudes of the fields are smallest along the antenna's axis (in the $\pm y$-direction in Fig. 22.4) and largest in directions perpendicular to the antenna (in any direction perpendicular to the y-axis in Fig. 22.4).

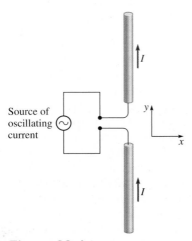

Figure 22.4 Current in an electric dipole antenna.

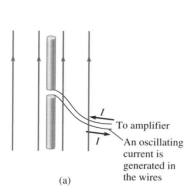

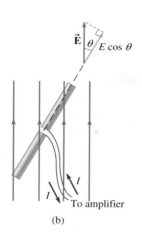

(a)

(b)

Figure 22.5 (a) The $\vec{E}$ field of an EM wave makes an oscillating current flow in an electric dipole antenna. (The magnetic field lines are omitted for clarity.) (b) The current in the antenna is smaller when it is not aligned with the electric field. Only the component of $\vec{E}$ parallel to the antenna accelerates electrons along the antenna's length.

- In directions perpendicular to the antenna, the electric field is parallel to the antenna's axis. In other directions, $\vec{E}$ is *not* parallel to the antenna's axis, but is perpendicular to the *direction of propagation* of the wave—that is, perpendicular to the direction that energy travels from the antenna to the observation point.
- The magnetic field is perpendicular to both the electric field and to the direction of propagation.

An electric dipole antenna can be used as a receiver or detector of EM waves as well. In Fig. 22.5a, an EM wave travels past an electric dipole antenna. The electric field of the wave acts on free electrons in the antenna, causing an oscillating current. This current can then be amplified and the signal processed to decode the radio or TV transmission. The antenna is most effective if it is aligned with the electric field of the wave. If it is not, then only the component of $\vec{E}$ parallel to the antenna acts to cause the oscillating current. The emf and the oscillating current are reduced by a factor of $\cos\theta$, where θ is the angle between $\vec{E}$ and the antenna (Fig. 22.5b). If the antenna is perpendicular to the $\vec{E}$ field, no oscillating current results.

Making the Connection:

radio/TV antennas

An electric dipole antenna used as a receiver should be aligned with the electric field of the wave.

Example 22.1

Electric Dipole Antenna

An electric dipole antenna at the origin has length 84 cm. It is used as a receiver for an EM wave traveling in the $+z$-direction. The electric field of the wave is always in the $\pm y$-direction and varies sinusoidally with time. The electric field in the vicinity of the antenna is

$$E_y(t) = E_m \cos \omega t; \quad E_x = E_z = 0$$

where the amplitude—the maximum magnitude—of the electric field is $E_m = 3.2$ V/m. (a) How should the antenna be oriented for best reception? (b) What is the emf in the antenna if it is oriented properly?

Strategy For maximum amplitude, the antenna must be oriented so that the full electric field can drive current along the length of the antenna. The emf is defined as the work done by the electric field per unit charge.

Solution (a) We want the electric field of the wave to push free electrons along the antenna's length with a force directed along the length of the antenna. The elec-

tric field is always in the $\pm y$-direction, so the antenna should be oriented along the y-axis.

(b) The work done by the electric field E as it moves a charge q along the length of the antenna is

$$W = F_y \Delta y = qEL$$

The emf is the work per unit charge:

$$\mathcal{E} = \frac{W}{q} = EL$$

The emf varies with time because the electric field oscillates. The emf as a function of time is

$$\mathcal{E}(t) = EL = E_m L \cos \omega t$$

Therefore, it is a sinusoidally varying emf with the same frequency as the wave. The amplitude of the emf is

$$\mathcal{E}_m = E_m L = 3.2 \text{ V/m} \times 0.84 \text{ m} = 2.7 \text{ V}$$

Continued on next page

Example 22.1 Continued

Discussion   The oscillating electric field has the same amplitude and phase at every point on the antenna. As a result, the emf is proportional to the length of the antenna. If the antenna is so long that the phase of the electric field varies with position along the antenna, then the emf is no longer proportional to the length of the antenna and may even start to decrease with additional length.

Practice Problem 22.1   Location of Transmitting Antenna

(a) If the wave in Example 22.1 is transmitted from a distant electric dipole antenna, where is the transmitting antenna located relative to the receiving antenna? (Answer in terms of *xyz* coordinates.) (b) Write an equation for the electric field components as a function of position and time.

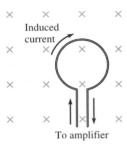

Figure 22.6 A loop of wire serves as a magnetic dipole antenna. As the magnetic field of the wave changes, the magnetic flux through the loop changes, causing an induced current in the loop. (The electric field lines are omitted for clarity.)

A magnetic dipole antenna used as a receiver should be aligned so the magnetic field of the wave is perpendicular to the plane of the antenna.

TV broadcasts in the United States and some other countries are transmitted from electric dipole antennas oriented horizontally. Thus, for best reception, a rooftop antenna should be oriented horizontally and with the antenna perpendicular to the direction to the transmitter. (Most rooftop antennas consist of several parallel pairs of metal rods; only one of these is actually the antenna, connected with wires to the TV set. The other rods help amplify the signal and make the antenna more directional.) In other countries, both the transmitting and receiving antennas are oriented vertically. Should you live where it is necessary to put up a rooftop antenna, it pays to know which convention is used in your area of the world.

Another kind of transmitting antenna is the **magnetic dipole antenna**. Recall that a loop of current is a magnetic dipole. (The right-hand rule establishes the direction of the north pole of the dipole: if the fingers of the right hand are curled around the loop in the direction of the current, the thumb points "north.") To make an oscillating magnetic dipole, we feed an alternating current into a loop or coil of wire. When the current reverses directions, the north and south poles of the magnetic dipole are interchanged.

If we consider the antenna axis to be the direction perpendicular to the coil, then the three observations made for the electric dipole antenna still hold, if we just substitute *magnetic* for *electric* and *vice versa*.

The magnetic dipole antenna works as a receiver as well (Fig. 22.6). The oscillating magnetic field of the wave causes a changing magnetic flux through the antenna. According to Faraday's law, an induced emf is present that makes an alternating current flow in the antenna. To maximize the rate of change of flux, the magnetic field should be perpendicular to the plane of the antenna.

Antennas can generate only EM waves with long wavelengths and low frequencies. It isn't practical to use an antenna to generate EM waves with short wavelengths and high frequencies such as visible light; the frequency at which the current would have to alternate to generate such waves is far too high to be achieved in an antenna, while the antenna itself cannot be made short enough. (To be most effective, the length of an antenna should not be larger than half the wavelength.)

Problem-Solving Strategy: Antennas

- Electric dipole antenna (rod): antenna axis is along the rod.
- Magnetic dipole antenna (loop): antenna axis is perpendicular to the loop.
- Used as a transmitter, a dipole antenna radiates most strongly in directions perpendicular to its axis. In these directions, the wave's electric field is parallel to the antenna axis if transmitted by an electric dipole antenna and the wave's magnetic field is parallel to the antenna axis if transmitted by a magnetic dipole antenna.
- An antenna does not radiate in the two directions along its axis.
- For maximum sensitivity when used as a receiver, the axis of an electric dipole antenna should be aligned with the electric field of the wave and the axis of a magnetic dipole antenna should be aligned with the magnetic field of the wave.

22.4   THE ELECTROMAGNETIC SPECTRUM

EM waves can exist at every frequency, without restriction. The properties of EM waves and their interactions with matter depend on the frequency of the wave. The **electromagnetic spectrum**—the range of frequencies (and wavelengths)—is traditionally divided into six or seven named regions (Fig. 22.7). The names persist partly for historical reasons—the regions were discovered at different times—and partly because the EM radiation of different regions interacts with matter in different ways. The boundaries between the regions are fuzzy and somewhat arbitrary. Throughout this section, the wavelengths given are those *in vacuum*; EM waves in vacuum or in air travel at a speed of 3.00×10^8 m/s.

Visible Light

Visible light is the part of the spectrum that can be detected by the human eye. This seems like a pretty cut-and-dried definition, but actually the sensitivity of the eye falls off gradually at both ends of the visible spectrum. Just as the range of frequencies of sound that can be heard varies from person to person, so does the range of frequencies of light that can be seen. For an average range we take frequencies of 430 THz (1 THz = 10^{12} Hz) to 750 THz, corresponding to wavelengths in vacuum of 700–400 nm. Light containing a mixture of all the wavelengths in the visible range appears white. White light can be separated by a prism into the colors red (700–620 nm), orange (620–600 nm), yellow (600–580 nm), green (580–490 nm), blue (490–450 nm), and violet (450–400 nm). Red has the lowest frequency (longest wavelength) and violet has the highest frequency (shortest wavelength).

It is not a coincidence that the human eye evolved to be most sensitive to the range of EM waves that are most intense in sunlight (see Fig. 22.8). However, other animals have visible ranges that differ from that of humans; the range is often well suited to the particular needs of the animal.

Lightbulbs, fire, the Sun, and fireflies are some *sources* of visible light. Most of the things we see are *not* sources of light; we see them by the light they *reflect*. When light strikes an object, some may be absorbed, some may be transmitted through the object,

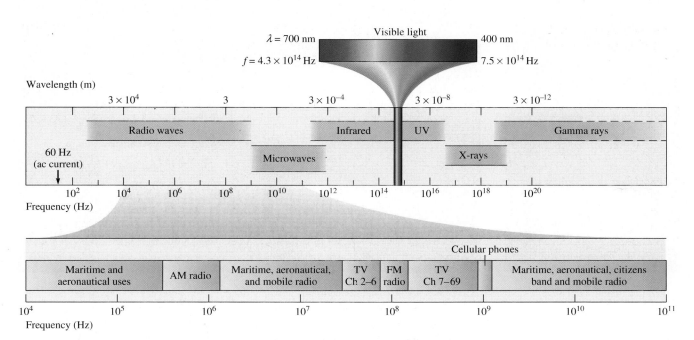

Figure 22.7 Regions of the EM spectrum. Note that the wavelength and frequency scales are logarithmic.

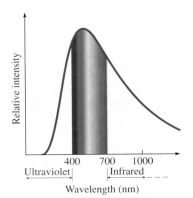

Figure 22.8 Graph of relative intensity (average power per unit area) of sunlight above Earth's atmosphere as a function of wavelength.

and some may be reflected. The relative amounts of absorption, transmission, and reflection usually differ for different wavelengths. A lemon appears yellow because it reflects much of the incident yellow light and absorbs most of the other spectral colors.

The wavelengths of visible light are small on an everyday scale but large compared to atoms. The diameter of an average-sized atom—and the distance between atoms in solids and liquids—is about 0.2 nm. Thus, the wavelengths of visible light are 2000–4000 times larger than the size of an atom.

Infrared

After visible light, the first parts of the EM spectrum to be discovered were those on either side of the visible: infrared and ultraviolet (discovered in 1800 and 1801, respectively). The prefix *infra-* means *below*; **infrared** radiation (IR) is lower in frequency than visible light. IR extends from the low-frequency (red) edge of the visible to a frequency of about 300 GHz ($\lambda = 1$ mm). The astronomer William Herschel (1738–1822) discovered IR in 1800 while studying the temperature rise caused by the light emerging from a prism. He discovered that the thermometer reading was highest for levels just *outside* the illuminated region, adjacent to the red end of the spectrum. Since the radiation was not *visible*, Herschel deduced that there must be some invisible radiation beyond the red.

The thermal radiation given off by objects near room temperature is primarily infrared (Fig. 22.9), with the peak of the radiated IR at a wavelength of about 0.01 mm = 10 μm. At higher temperatures, the power radiated increases as the wavelength of peak radiation decreases. A roaring wood stove with a surface temperature of 500°F has an absolute temperature about 1.8 times room temperature (530 K); it radiates about 11 times more power than when at room temperature since $P \propto T^4$ [Stefan's law, Eq. (14-17)]. Nevertheless, the peak is still in the infrared. The wavelength of peak radiation is about 5.5 μm = 5500 nm since $\lambda_{max} \propto 1/T$ [Wien's law, Eq. (14-18)]. If the stove gets even hotter, its radiation is still mostly IR but glows red as it starts to radiate significantly in the red part of the visible spectrum. (Call the fire department!) Even the filament of a lightbulb ($T \approx 3000$ K) radiates much more IR than it does visible. The *peak* of the Sun's thermal radiation is in the visible; nevertheless about half the energy reaching us from the Sun is IR.

Making the Connection:

thermograms

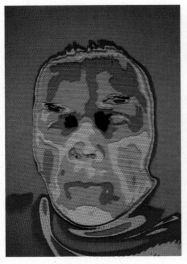

(a)

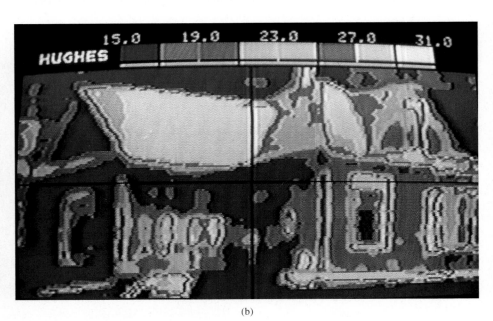

(b)

Figure 22.9 (a) False-color thermogram of a man's head. The red areas show regions of pain from a headache; these areas are warmer, so they give off more infrared radiation. (b) False-color thermogram of a house in winter, showing that most of the heat escapes through the roof. The scale shows that the blue areas are the coolest, while the pink areas are the warmest. Note that some heat escapes around the window frame, while the window itself is cool due to double-pane glass.

(a)   (b)

Figure 22.10 (a) The large star coral (*Montastraea cavernosa*) is dull brown when illuminated by white light. (b) When illuminated with an ultraviolet source, the coral absorbs UV and emits visible light that appears bright yellow. A small sponge (bottom right corner) looks bright red in white light due to selective reflection. It appears black when illuminated with UV because it does not fluoresce.

Ultraviolet

The prefix *ultra-* means *above*; **ultraviolet** (UV) radiation is higher in frequency than visible light. UV ranges in wavelength from the shortest visible wavelength (about 380 nm) down to about 10 nm. There is plenty of UV in the Sun's radiation; its effects on human skin include tanning, sunburn, formation of vitamin D, and melanoma. Water vapor transmits much of the Sun's UV, so tanning and sunburn can occur on overcast days. On the other hand, ordinary glass absorbs most UV. Black lights emit UV; certain *fluorescent* materials—such as the coating on the inside of the glass tube in a fluorescent light—can absorb UV and then emit visible light (Fig. 22.10).

Making the Connection:
fluorescence

Radio Waves

After IR and UV were identified, most of the nineteenth century passed before any of the outlying regions of the EM spectrum were discovered. The lowest frequencies (up to about 1 GHz) and longest wavelengths (down to about 0.3 m) are called **radio waves**. Radio waves were discovered in 1888 by Heinrich Hertz. AM and FM radio, VHF and UHF TV broadcasts, and ham radio operators occupy assigned frequency bands within the radio wave part of the spectrum.

Microwaves

Microwaves are the part of the EM spectrum lying between radio waves and IR, with vacuum wavelengths roughly from 1 mm to 30 cm. Microwaves are used in communications (cell phones and satellite TV) and in radar. After the development of radar in World War II, the search for peacetime uses of microwaves resulted in the development of the microwave oven.

A microwave oven (Fig 22.11) immerses food in microwaves with a wavelength in vacuum of about 12 cm. Water is a good absorber of microwaves because the water molecule is polar. An electric dipole in an electric field feels a torque that tends to align the dipole with the field, since the positive and negative charges are pulled in opposite directions. As a result of the rapidly oscillating electric field of the microwaves ($f = 2.5$ GHz), the water molecules rotate back and forth; the energy of this rotation then spreads throughout the food.

In the early 1960s, Arno Penzias and Robert Wilson were having trouble with their radio telescope; they were plagued by noise in the microwave part of the spectrum.

Making the Connection:
microwave ovens

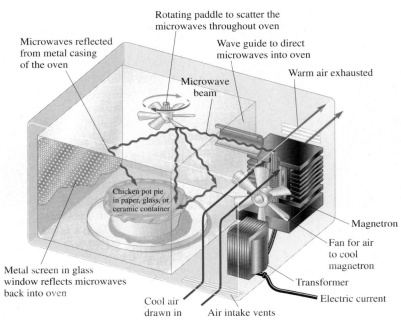

Figure 22.11 A microwave oven. The microwaves are produced in a *magnetron,* a resonant cavity that produces the oscillating currents that give rise to microwaves at the desired frequency. Since metals reflect microwaves well, a metal waveguide directs the microwaves toward the rotating metal stirrer, which reflects the microwaves in many different directions to distribute them throughout the oven. (This reflective property is one reason why metal containers and aluminum foil should generally not be used in a microwave oven; no microwaves could reach the food inside the container or foil.) The oven cavity is enclosed by metal to reflect microwaves back in and minimize the amount leaking out of the oven. The sheet of metal in the door has small holes so we can see inside, but since the holes are much smaller than the wavelength of the microwaves, the sheet still reflects microwaves.

Making the Connection:

cosmic microwave
background radiation

Subsequent investigation led them to discover that the entire universe is bathed in microwaves that correspond to blackbody radiation at a temperature of 2.7 K (peak wavelength about 1 mm). This *cosmic microwave background radiation* is left over from the origin of the universe—a huge explosion called the *Big Bang*.

X-Rays and Gamma Rays

Higher in frequency and shorter in wavelength than UV are **x-rays** and **gamma rays**, which were discovered in 1895 and 1900, respectively. The two names are still used, based on the source of the waves, mostly for historical reasons. There is considerable overlap in the frequencies of the EM waves generated by these two methods, so today the distinction is somewhat arbitrary.

X-rays were unexpectedly discovered by Wilhelm Konrad Röntgen (1845–1923) when he accelerated electrons to high energies and smashed them into a target. The large deceleration of the electrons as they come to rest in the target produces the x-rays. Röntgen received the first Nobel Prize in physics for the discovery of x-rays.

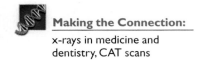

Making the Connection:

x-rays in medicine and
dentistry, CAT scans

Most diagnostic x-rays used in medicine and dentistry have wavelengths between 10 and 60 pm (1 pm = 10^{-12} m). In a conventional x-ray, film records the amount of x-ray radiation that passes through the tissue. Computer-assisted tomography (CAT or CT scan) allows a cross-sectional image of the body. An x-ray source is rotated around the body in a plane and a computer measures the x-ray transmission at many different angles. Using this information, the computer constructs an image of that slice of the body (Fig. 22.12).

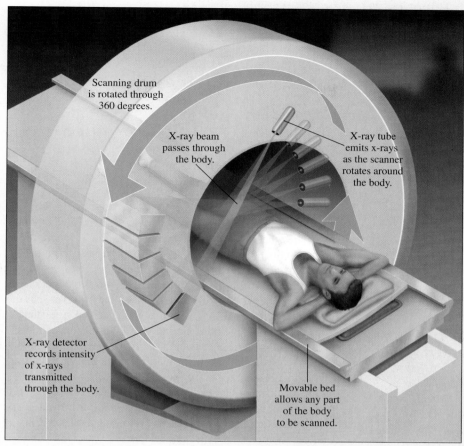

Figure 22.12 Apparatus used for a CAT scan.

Within the figure:
- Scanning drum is rotated through 360 degrees.
- X-ray beam passes through the body.
- X-ray tube emits x-rays as the scanner rotates around the body.
- X-ray detector records intensity of x-rays transmitted through the body.
- Movable bed allows any part of the body to be scanned.

Gamma rays were first observed in the decay of radioactive nuclei on Earth. Pulsars, neutron stars, black holes, and explosions of supernovae are sources of gamma rays that travel toward Earth, but—fortunately for us—gamma rays are absorbed by the atmosphere. Only when detectors were placed high in the atmosphere and above it by using balloons and satellites did the science of gamma-ray astronomy develop. In the late 1960s, scientists first observed bursts of gamma rays from deep space that last for times ranging from a fraction of a second to a few minutes; these bursts occur about once a day. A gamma-ray burst can emit more energy in 10 s than the Sun will emit in its entire lifetime. The source of the gamma-ray bursts is still under investigation.

22.5   SPEED OF EM WAVES IN VACUUM AND IN MATTER

Light travels so fast that it is not obvious that it takes any time at all to go from one place to another. Since high-precision electronic instruments were not available, early measurements of the speed of light had to be cleverly designed. In 1849, French scientist Armand Hippolyte Louis Fizeau (1819–1896) measured the speed of visible light to be approximately 3×10^8 m/s. Fizeau's experiment used a notched wheel (Fig. 22.13). When the apparatus is correctly aligned, a beam of light passes through one of the notches in the wheel, travels a long distance (over 8 km) to a mirror, reflects, and passes back through the same notch to the observer. When the wheel is made to rotate, the notch

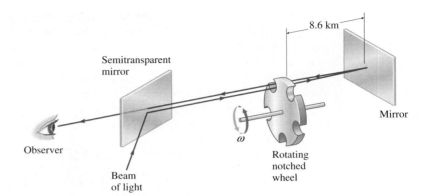

Figure 22.13 The apparatus used by Fizeau in 1849 to measure the speed of light.

moves out of position and the reflected beam is interrupted by the wheel. As the angular velocity of the wheel is increased, it reaches a value ω where the next notch moves into position just in time to allow the reflected beam to pass through. The observer can see the reflected beam for an integral multiple of ω, since any of the equally spaced notches allow the reflected beam to pass through. The speed of light can be determined from a measurement of the angular velocities at which the observer sees the reflected beam.

In Chapters 11 and 12 we saw that the speed of a mechanical wave depends on properties of the wave medium. Sound travels faster through steel than it does through water and faster through water than through air. In every case, the wave speed depended on two characteristics of the wave medium: one that characterizes the restoring force and another that characterizes the inertia.

Unlike mechanical waves, electromagnetic waves can travel through vacuum; they do not require a material medium. Light reaches Earth from galaxies billions of light-years away, traveling the vast distances between galaxies without problem; but a sound wave can't even travel a few meters between two astronauts on a space walk, since there is no air or other medium to sustain a sound wave's pressure variations. What, then, determines the speed of light in vacuum?

Looking back at the laws that describe electric and magnetic fields, we find two universal constants. One of them is the permittivity of free space ϵ_0, found in Coulomb's law and Gauss's law; it is associated with the electric field. The second is the permeability of free space μ_0, found in Ampère's law; it is associated with the magnetic field. Since these are the only two quantities that can determine the speed of light in vacuum, there must be a combination of them that has the dimensions of speed.

The values of these constants in SI units are

$$\epsilon_0 = 8.85 \times 10^{-12}\ \frac{\text{C}^2}{\text{N} \cdot \text{m}^2}$$

and

$$\mu_0 = 4\pi \times 10^{-7}\ \frac{\text{T} \cdot \text{m}}{\text{A}}$$

The tesla can be written in terms of other SI units. Using $\vec{\mathbf{F}} = q\vec{\mathbf{v}} \times \vec{\mathbf{B}}$ as a guide,

$$1\ \text{T} = 1\ \frac{\text{N}}{\text{C} \cdot \text{m/s}}$$

Multiplying $\epsilon_0 \times \mu_0$ gives

$$\epsilon_0 \mu_0 = 8.85 \times 10^{-12}\ \frac{\cancel{\text{C}}^2}{\text{N} \cdot \text{m}^2} \times 4\pi \times 10^{-7}\ \frac{\text{N} \cdot \cancel{\text{m}}}{\cancel{\text{C}} \cdot (\cancel{\text{m}}/\text{s}) \cdot (\cancel{\text{C}}/\text{s})}$$

$$= 1.11 \times 10^{-17}\ \frac{\text{s}^2}{\text{m}^2}$$

To end up with m/s, we need to take the reciprocal of the square root:

$$\frac{1}{\sqrt{\epsilon_0 \mu_0}} = 3.00 \times 10^8\ \text{m/s}$$

The dimensional analysis done here leaves the possibility of a multiplying factor such as $\frac{1}{2}$ or $\sqrt{\pi}$. In the mid-nineteenth century, Scottish physicist James Clerk Maxwell proved mathematically that an electromagnetic wave—a wave consisting of oscillating electric and magnetic fields propagating through space—could exist in vacuum. Starting from Maxwell's equations (Section 22.2), he derived the *wave equation*, an equation of a special mathematical form that describes wave propagation for *any* kind of wave. In the place of the wave speed appeared $(\epsilon_0 \mu_0)^{-1/2}$. Using the values of ϵ_0 and μ_0 that had been measured in 1856, Maxwell showed that electromagnetic waves in vacuum travel at 3.00×10^8 m/s—very close to what Fizeau measured. Maxwell's derivation was the first evidence that light is an electromagnetic wave.

The speed of electromagnetic waves in vacuum is represented by the symbol c (for the Latin *celeritas*, "speed").

Speed of electromagnetic waves in vacuum:

$$c = \frac{1}{\sqrt{\epsilon_0 \mu_0}} = 3.00 \times 10^8 \text{ m/s} \qquad \qquad \text{(22-3)}$$

While c is usually called *the speed of light*, it is the speed of *any* electromagnetic wave in vacuum, regardless of frequency or wavelength, not just the speed for frequencies visible to humans.

Example 22.2

Light Travel Time from a "Nearby" Supernova

A supernova is an exploding star; a supernova is billions of times brighter than an ordinary star. Most supernovae occur in distant galaxies and cannot be observed with the naked eye. The last two supernovae visible to the naked eye occurred in 1604 and 1987. Supernova SN1987a (Fig. 22.14) occurred 1.6×10^{21} m from Earth. *When* did the explosion occur?

Strategy   The light from the supernova travels at speed c. The time that it takes light to travel a distance 1.6×10^{21} m tells us how long ago the explosion occurred.

Figure 22.14
Photo of the sky after light from Supernova SN1987a reached Earth.

Solution   The time for light to travel a distance d at speed c is

$$\Delta t = \frac{d}{c} = \frac{1.6 \times 10^{21} \text{ m}}{3.00 \times 10^8 \text{ m/s}} = 5.33 \times 10^{12} \text{ s}$$

To get a better idea how long that is, we convert seconds to years:

$$5.33 \times 10^{12} \text{ s} \times \frac{1 \text{ yr}}{3.156 \times 10^7 \text{ s}} = 170{,}000 \text{ yr}$$

Discussion   When we look at the stars, the light we see was radiated by the stars long ago. By looking at distant galaxies, astronomers get a glimpse of the universe in the past. Beyond the Sun, the closest star to Earth is about 4 ly (light-years) away, which means that it takes light 4 yr to reach us from that star. The most distant galaxies observed are at a distance of over 10^{10} ly; looking at them, we see over 10 billion yr into the past.

Practice Problem 22.2   A Light-Year

A light-year is the distance traveled by light (in vacuum) in one Earth year. Find the conversion factor from light-years to meters.

Speed of Light in Matter

● The speed of an EM wave through matter is less than c.

When an EM wave travels through a material medium, it travels at a speed v that is less than c. For example, visible light travels through glass at speeds between about 1.6×10^8 m/s and 2.0×10^8 m/s, depending on the type of glass and the frequency of the light. Instead of specifying the speed, it is common to specify the **index of refraction** n:

Index of refraction:

$$n = \frac{c}{v} \tag{22-4}$$

Refraction refers to the bending of a wave as it passes from one medium to another; we study refraction in detail in Section 23.3. Since the index of refraction is a ratio of two speeds, it is a dimensionless number. For glass in which light travels at 2.0×10^8 m/s, the index of refraction is

$$n = \frac{3.0 \times 10^8 \text{ m/s}}{2.0 \times 10^8 \text{ m/s}} = 1.5$$

The speed of light in air (at 1 atm) is only slightly less than c; the index of refraction of air is 1.0003. Most of the time this 0.03% difference is not important, so we can use c as the speed of light in air. The speed of visible light in an optically transparent medium is less than c, so the index of refraction is greater than 1.

When an EM wave passes from one medium to another, the frequency and wavelength cannot both remain unchanged since

$$v = f\lambda$$

● A wave passing from one medium into another changes wavelength but retains the same frequency.

As is the case with mechanical waves, it is the wavelength that changes; the frequency remains the same. The incoming wave (with frequency f) causes charges in the atoms at the boundary to oscillate with the same frequency f, just as for the charges in an antenna. The oscillating charges at the boundary radiate an EM wave at that same frequency into the second medium. Therefore, the electric and magnetic fields in the second medium *must* oscillate at the same frequency as the fields in the first medium. In just the same way, if a transverse wave of frequency f traveling down a string reaches a point at which an abrupt change in wave speed occurs, the incident wave makes that point oscillate up and down at the same frequency f as any other point on the string. The oscillation of that point sends a wave of the same frequency to the other side of the string. Since the wave speed has changed but the frequency is the same, the wavelength has changed as well.

We sometimes need to find the wavelength λ of an EM wave in a medium of index n, given its wavelength λ_0 in vacuum. Since the frequencies are equal,

$$f = \frac{c}{\lambda_0} = \frac{v}{\lambda}$$

Solving for λ gives

$$\lambda = \frac{v}{c}\lambda_0 = \frac{\lambda_0}{n} \tag{22-5}$$

Since $n > 1$, the wavelength is shorter than the wavelength in vacuum. The wave travels more slowly in the medium than in vacuum; since the wavelength is the distance traveled by the wave in one period $T = 1/f$, the wavelength in the medium is shorter.

If blue light of wavelength $\lambda_0 = 480$ nm enters glass that has an index of refraction of 1.5, it is still visible light, even though its wavelength in glass is 320 nm; it has not been transformed into UV radiation. When the light enters the eye, it has the same frequency and wavelength in the fluid in the eye regardless of how many material media it has passed through, since the frequency remains the same at each boundary.

Example 22.3

Wavelength Change from Glass to Water

The index of refraction of glass is 1.50 and that of water is 1.33. If light of wavelength 285 nm *in glass* passes into water, what is the wavelength in the water?

Strategy The key is to remember that the frequency is the same as the wave passes from one medium to another.

Solution Frequency, wavelength, and speed are related by

$$v = \lambda f$$

Solving for frequency, $f = v/\lambda$. Since the frequencies are equal,

$$\frac{v_w}{\lambda_w} = \frac{v_g}{\lambda_g}$$

The speed of light in a material is $v = c/n$. Solving for λ_w and substituting $v = c/n$ gives

$$\lambda_w = v_w \frac{\lambda_g}{v_g} = \frac{c}{n_w} \times \frac{n_g \lambda_g}{c} = \frac{1.50 \times 285 \text{ nm}}{1.33} = 321 \text{ nm}$$

Discussion Water has a smaller index of refraction, so the speed of light in water is greater than in glass. Since wavelength is the distance traveled in one period, the wavelength in water is longer (321 nm > 285 nm).

Practice Problem 22.3 Wavelength Change from Air to Water

The speed of visible light in water is 2.25×10^8 m/s. When light of wavelength 592 nm in air passes into water, what is its wavelength in water?

Dispersion

Although EM waves of every frequency travel through vacuum at the same speed c, the speed of EM waves in a material medium *does* depend on frequency. Therefore, the index of refraction is not a constant for a given material; it is a function of frequency. Variation of the speed of a wave with frequency is called **dispersion**. Dispersion causes white light to separate into colors when it passes through a glass prism (Fig. 22.15). The dispersion of the light into different colors arises because each color travels at a slightly different speed in the same medium.

A **nondispersive** medium is one for which the variation in the index of refraction is negligibly small for the range of frequencies of interest. No medium (apart from vacuum) is truly nondispersive, but many can be treated as nondispersive for a restricted range of frequencies. For most optically transparent materials, the index of refraction increases with increasing frequency; blue light travels more slowly through glass than does red light. In other parts of the EM spectrum, or even for visible light in unusual materials, n can decrease with increasing frequency instead.

Figure 22.15 A prism separates a beam of white light (coming in from the left) into the colors of the spectrum.

22.6 CHARACTERISTICS OF ELECTROMAGNETIC WAVES IN VACUUM

The various characteristics of EM waves in vacuum can be derived from the basic laws of electromagnetism (Maxwell's equations, Section 22.2). Such a derivation requires higher level mathematics, so we state the characteristics without proof.

- EM waves in vacuum travel at speed $c = 3.00 \times 10^8$ m/s, independent of frequency. The speed is also independent of amplitude.
- The electric and magnetic fields oscillate at the *same frequency*. Thus, a single frequency f and a single wavelength $\lambda = c/f$ pertain to both the electric and magnetic fields of the wave.
- The electric and magnetic fields oscillate *in phase* with each other. That is, at a given instant, the electric and magnetic fields are at their maximum magnitudes at a

common set of points. Similarly, the fields are both zero at a common set of points at any instant.

- The amplitudes of the electric and magnetic fields are proportional to each other. The ratio is c:

$$E_m = cB_m \qquad (22\text{-}6)$$

- Since the fields are in phase and the amplitudes are proportional, the instantaneous magnitudes of the fields are proportional at any point:

$$E(x, y, z, t) = cB(x, y, z, t) \qquad (22\text{-}7)$$

- The EM wave is *transverse*; that is, the electric and magnetic fields are each perpendicular to the direction of propagation of the wave.
- The fields are also perpendicular to *each other*. Therefore, $\vec{E}$, $\vec{B}$, and the velocity of propagation are three mutually perpendicular vectors.
- At any point, $\vec{E} \times \vec{B}$ is always in the direction of propagation.
- The electric energy density is equal to the magnetic energy density at any point. The wave carries exactly half its energy in the electric field and half in the magnetic field.

Example 22.4

Traveling EM Wave

The x-, y-, and z-components of the electric field of an EM wave in vacuum are

$$E_y(x, y, z, t) = -60.0\,\frac{V}{m} \times \cos\,[(4.0\text{ m}^{-1})x + \omega t],\ E_x = E_z = 0$$

(a) In what direction does the wave travel? (b) Find the value of ω. (c) Write an expression for the components of the magnetic field of the wave.

Strategy   Parts (a) and (b) require some general knowledge about waves, but nothing specific to EM waves. Turning back to Chapter 11 may help refresh your memory. Part (c) involves the relationship between the electric and magnetic fields, which *is* particular to EM waves. The instantaneous magnitude of the magnetic field is given by $B(x, y, z, t) = E(x, y, z, t)/c$. We must also determine the direction of the magnetic field: $\vec{E}$, $\vec{B}$, and the velocity of propagation are three mutually perpendicular vectors and $\vec{E} \times \vec{B}$ must be in the direction of propagation.

Solution   (a) Since the electric field depends on the value of x but not on the values of y or z, the wave moves parallel to the x-axis. Imagine riding along a crest of the wave—a point where

$$\cos\,[(4.0\text{ m}^{-1})x + \omega t] = 1$$

Then

$$(4.0\text{ m}^{-1})x + \omega t = 2\pi n$$

where n is some integer. A short time later, t is a little bigger, so x must be a little smaller so that $(4.0\text{ m}^{-1})x + \omega t$ is still equal to $2\pi n$. Since the x-coordinate of a crest gets smaller as time passes, the wave is moving in the $-x$-direction.

(b) The constant multiplying x, 4.0 m^{-1}, is the *wavenumber*, a quantity related to the wavelength. Since the wave repeats in a distance λ and the cosine function repeats every 2π radians, $k(x + \lambda)$ must be 2π radians greater than kx:

$$k(x + \lambda) = kx + 2\pi$$

or

$$k = \frac{2\pi}{\lambda}$$

Therefore, the wavenumber is $k = 4.0$ m^{-1}. The speed of the wave is c. Since any periodic wave travels a distance λ in a time T,

$$T = \frac{\lambda}{c}$$

$$\omega = \frac{2\pi}{T} = \frac{2\pi c}{\lambda} = kc = 4.0\text{ m}^{-1} \times 3.00 \times 10^8\text{ m/s}$$

$$= 1.2 \times 10^9\text{ rad/s}$$

(c) Since the wave moves in the $-x$-direction and the electric field is in the $\pm y$-direction, the magnetic field must be in the $\pm z$-direction to make three perpendicular directions. Since the magnetic field is in phase with the electric field, with the same wavelength and frequency, it must take the form

$$B_z(x, y, z, t) = \pm B_m \cos\,[(4.0\text{ m}^{-1})x + (1.2 \times 10^9\text{ s}^{-1})t],$$

$$B_x = B_y = 0$$

The amplitudes are proportional:

$$B_m = \frac{E_m}{c} = \frac{60.0\text{ V/m}}{3.00 \times 10^8\text{ m/s}} = 2.00 \times 10^{-7}\text{ T}$$

Continued on next page

Example 22.4 Continued

The last step is to decide which sign is correct. At $x = t = 0$, the electric field is in the $-y$-direction. $\vec{E} \times \vec{B}$ must be in the $-x$-direction (the direction of propagation). Then

$$(-y\text{-direction}) \times (\text{direction of } \vec{B}) = (-x\text{-direction})$$

Trying both possibilities with the right-hand rule (Fig. 22.16), we find that $\vec{B}$ is in the $+z$-direction at $x = t = 0$. Then the magnetic field is written

$$B_z(x, y, z, t) = (2.00 \times 10^{-7} \text{ T}) \cos [(4.0 \text{ m}^{-1})x + (1.2 \times 10^9 \text{ s}^{-1})t],$$

$$B_x = B_y = 0$$

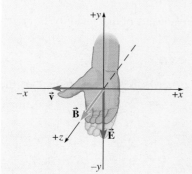

Figure 22.16

Using the right-hand rule to find the direction of $\vec{B}$.

Discussion   When $\cos [(4.0 \text{ m}^{-1})x + (1.2 \times 10^9 \text{ s}^{-1})t]$ is negative, then $\vec{E}$ is in the $+y$-direction and $\vec{B}$ is in the $-z$-direction. Since both fields reverse direction, it is still true that $\vec{E} \times \vec{B}$ is in the direction of propagation.

Practice Problem 22.4   Another Traveling Wave

The x-, y-, and z-components of the electric field of an EM wave in vacuum are

$$E_x(x, y, z, t) = 32 \frac{\text{V}}{\text{m}} \times \cos [ky - (6.0 \times 10^{11} \text{ s}^{-1})t],$$

$$E_y = E_z = 0$$

where k is positive. (a) In what direction does the wave travel? (b) Find the value of k. (c) Write an expression for the components of the magnetic field of the wave.

22.7   ENERGY TRANSPORT BY EM WAVES

Electromagnetic waves carry energy, as do all waves. Life on Earth exists only because the energy of EM radiation from the Sun can be harnessed by green plants, which through photosynthesis convert some of the energy in light to chemical energy. Photosynthesis sustains not only the plants themselves, but also animals that eat plants and fungi that derive their energy from decaying plants and animals—the entire food chain can be traced back to the Sun as energy source. Only a few exceptions exist, such as the bacteria that live in geothermal vents on the ocean floor. The heat flow from the interior of the Earth does not originate with the Sun; it comes from radioactive decay.

Most industrial sources of energy are derived from electromagnetic energy from the Sun. Fossil fuels—petroleum, coal, and natural gas—come from the remains of plants and animals. Solar cells convert the incident sunlight's energy directly into electricity (Fig. 22.17); the Sun is also used to heat water and homes directly. Hydroelectric power plants rely on the Sun to evaporate water, in a sense pumping it back uphill so that it can once again flow down rivers and turn turbines. Wind can be harnessed to generate electricity, but the winds are driven by uneven heating of Earth's surface by the Sun. The only energy sources we have that do not come from the Sun's EM radiation are nuclear fission and geothermal energy.

Figure 22.17 A solar panel farm in the Sierra Nevada Mountains.

Energy Density

The energy in light is stored in the oscillating electric and magnetic fields in the wave. For an EM wave in vacuum, the energy densities (SI unit: J/m^3) are

$$u_E = \frac{1}{2}\epsilon_0 E^2 \tag{17-19}$$

and

$$u_B = \frac{1}{2\mu_0}B^2 \tag{20-18}$$

It can be proved (Problem 36) that the two energy densities are equal for an EM wave in vacuum, using the relationship between the magnitudes of the fields [Eq. (22-7)]. Thus, for the total energy density, we can write

$$u = \epsilon_0 E^2 = \frac{1}{\mu_0} B^2 \qquad (22\text{-}8)$$

Since the fields vary from point to point and also change with time, so do the energy densities. Since the fields oscillate rapidly, in most cases we are concerned with the *average* energy densities—the average of the squares of the fields. Recall that an rms (root mean square) value is defined as the square root of the average of the square (Section 21.1):

$$E_{\text{rms}} = \sqrt{\langle E^2 \rangle} \quad \text{and} \quad B_{\text{rms}} = \sqrt{\langle B^2 \rangle} \qquad (22\text{-}9)$$

The angle brackets around a quantity denote the average value of that quantity. Squaring both sides, we have

$$E_{\text{rms}}^2 = \langle E^2 \rangle \quad \text{and} \quad B_{\text{rms}}^2 = \langle B^2 \rangle$$

Then the average energy density can be written in terms of the rms values of the fields:

$$\langle u \rangle = \epsilon_0 \langle E^2 \rangle = \epsilon_0 E_{\text{rms}}^2 \qquad (22\text{-}10)$$

$$\langle u \rangle = \frac{1}{\mu_0} \langle B^2 \rangle = \frac{1}{\mu_0} B_{\text{rms}}^2 \qquad (22\text{-}11)$$

Intensity

The energy density tells us how much energy is stored in the wave per unit volume; this energy is being carried with the wave at speed c. Suppose light falls at normal incidence on a surface (such as a photographic film or a leaf) and we want to know how much energy hits the surface. For one thing, the energy arriving at the surface depends on how long it is exposed—the reason exposure time is a critical parameter in photography. Also important is the surface area; a large leaf receives more energy than a small one, everything else being equal. Thus, the most useful quantity to know is how much energy arrives at a surface per unit time per unit area—or the average power per unit area. If light hits a surface of area A at normal incidence, the **intensity** (I) is

$$I = \frac{\langle P \rangle}{A} \qquad (22\text{-}12)$$

The SI units of I are

$$\frac{\text{energy}}{\text{time} \cdot \text{area}} = \frac{\text{J}}{\text{s} \cdot \text{m}^2} = \frac{\text{W}}{\text{m}^2}$$

The intensity depends on how much energy is in the wave (measured by u) and the speed at which the energy moves (which is c). If a surface of area A is illuminated by light at normal incidence, how much energy falls on it in a time Δt? The wave moves a distance $c\,\Delta t$ in that time, so all the energy in a volume $Ac\,\Delta t$ hits the surface during that time (Fig. 22.18). (We are not concerned with what happens to the energy—whether it is absorbed, reflected, or transmitted.) The intensity is then

$$I = \frac{\langle u \rangle V}{A\,\Delta t} = \frac{\langle u \rangle A c \Delta t}{A\,\Delta t} = \langle u \rangle c \qquad (22\text{-}13)$$

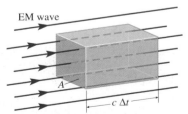

Figure 22.18 Geometry for finding the relationship between energy density and intensity.

EM wave

A

$c\,\Delta t$

From Eq. (22-13), the intensity I is proportional to average energy density $\langle u \rangle$, which is proportional to the squares of the rms electric and magnetic fields [Eqs. (22-10) and (22-11)]. If the fields are sinusoidal functions of time, the rms values are $1/\sqrt{2}$ times the amplitudes [Eq. (21-3)]. Therefore, *the intensity is proportional to the squares of the electric and magnetic field amplitudes.*

 Intensity is proportional to amplitude *squared*.

Example 22.5

EM Fields of a Lightbulb

At a distance of 4.00 m from a 100.0-W lightbulb, what are the intensity and the rms values of the electric and magnetic fields? Assume that all of the electric power goes into EM radiation (mostly in the infrared) and that the radiation is isotropic (equal in all directions).

Strategy   Since the radiation is isotropic, the intensity depends only on the distance from the lightbulb. Imagine a sphere surrounding the lightbulb at a distance of 4.00 m. Radiant energy must pass through the surface of the sphere at a rate of 100.0 W. We can figure out the intensity (average power per unit area) and from it the rms values of the fields.

Solution   All of the energy radiated by the lightbulb crosses the surface of a sphere of radius 4.00 m. Therefore, the intensity at that distance is the power radiated divided by the surface area of the sphere:

$$I = \frac{\langle P \rangle}{A} = \frac{\langle P \rangle}{4\pi r^2} = \frac{100.0 \text{ W}}{4\pi \times 16.0 \text{ m}^2} = 0.497 \text{ W/m}^2$$

To solve for E_{rms}, we relate the intensity to the average energy density and then the energy density to the field:

$$\langle u \rangle = \frac{I}{c} = \epsilon_0 E_{\text{rms}}^2$$

$$E_{\text{rms}} = \sqrt{\frac{I}{\epsilon_0 c}} = \sqrt{\frac{0.497 \text{ W/m}^2}{8.85 \times 10^{-12} \frac{\text{C}^2}{\text{N} \cdot \text{m}^2} \times 3.00 \times 10^8 \text{ m/s}}}$$

$$= 13.7 \text{ V/m}$$

Similarly, for B_{rms},

$$B_{\text{rms}} = \sqrt{\frac{\mu_0 I}{c}} = \sqrt{\frac{4\pi \times 10^{-7} \frac{\text{T} \cdot \text{m}}{\text{A}} \times 0.497 \text{ W/m}^2}{3.00 \times 10^8 \text{ m/s}}}$$

$$= 4.56 \times 10^{-8} \text{ T}$$

Discussion   A good check would be to calculate the ratio of the two rms fields:

$$\frac{E_{\text{rms}}}{B_{\text{rms}}} = \frac{13.7 \text{ V/m}}{4.56 \times 10^{-8} \text{ T}} = 3.00 \times 10^8 \text{ m/s} = c$$

as expected.

Practice Problem 22.5   Field of Lightbulb at Greater Distance

What are the rms fields 8.00 m away from the lightbulb? [*Hint:* Look for a shortcut rather than redoing the whole calculation.]

If a surface is illuminated by light of intensity I, but the surface is not perpendicular to the incident light, the rate at which energy hits the surface is less than IA. As Fig. 22.19 shows, a perpendicular surface of area $A \cos \theta$ casts a shadow over the surface of area A and thus intercepts all the energy. The angle θ is measured between the direction of the incident light and the normal (a direction *perpendicular* to the surface). Thus, a surface that is not perpendicular to the incident wave receives energy at a rate

$$\langle P \rangle = IA \cos \theta \qquad (22\text{-}14)$$

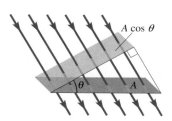

Figure 22.19 The surface of area $A \cos \theta$, which is perpendicular to the incoming wave, intercepts the same light energy as would a surface of area A for which the incoming wave is incident at an angle θ from the normal.

If Eq. (22-14) reminds you of flux, then congratulations on your alertness! The intensity is often called the *flux density*. Electric and magnetic fields are sometimes called *electric flux density* and *magnetic flux density*. However, the flux involved with intensity is not the same as the electric or magnetic fluxes that we defined in Eqs. (16-7) and (20-5). The intensity is the *power* flux density.

Example 22.6

Power per Unit Area from the Sun in Summer and Winter

The intensity of sunlight reaching Earth's surface on a clear day is about 1.0 kW/m^2. At a latitude of 40.0° north, find the average power per unit area reaching Earth at noon on the summer solstice (Fig. 22.20a). The difference is due to the 23.5° inclination of Earth's rotation axis. In summer, the axis is inclined toward the Sun, while in winter it is inclined away from the Sun.

Strategy   Because Earth's surface is not perpendicular to the Sun's rays, the power per unit area falling on Earth is less than 1.0 kW/m^2. We must find the angle that the Sun's rays make with the *normal* to the surface.

Solution   A radius going from Earth's center to the surface is normal to the surface at that point, assuming the Earth to be a sphere. We need to find the angle between the normal and an incoming ray. At a latitude of 40.0°, the angle between the radius and Earth's axis of rotation is 90.0° − 40.0° = 50.0° (Fig. 22.20a). From the figure, θ + 50.0° + 23.5° = 90.0° and therefore θ = 16.5°. The average power per unit area is then

$$\frac{\langle P \rangle}{A} = I \cos \theta = 1.0 \times 10^3 \text{ W/m}^2 \times \cos 16.5° = 960 \text{ W/m}^2$$

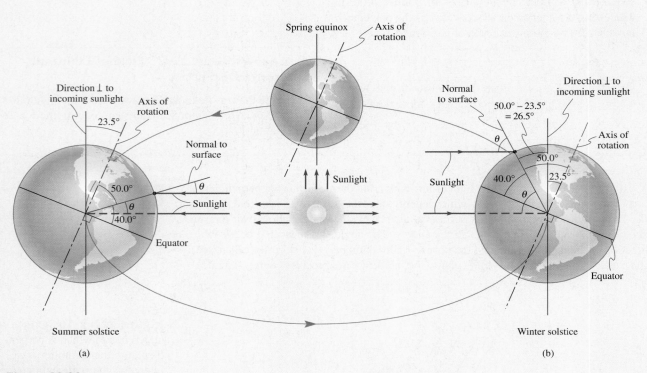

Figure 22.20

(a) At noon on the summer solstice in the northern hemisphere, the rotation axis is inclined 23.5° toward the Sun. At a latitude of 40.0° north, the incoming sunlight is nearly normal to the surface of the Earth. (b) At noon on the winter solstice in the northern hemisphere, the rotation axis is inclined 23.5° *away from* the Sun. At a latitude of 40.0° north, the incoming sunlight makes a large angle with the normal to the surface.

Continued on next page

Example 22.6 Continued

Discussion In Practice Problem 22.6, you will find that the power per unit area at the winter solstice is less than half that at the summer solstice. The intensity of sunlight hasn't changed; what changes is how the energy is spread out on the surface. Fewer of the Sun's rays hit a given surface area when the surface is tilted more.

The Earth is actually a bit *closer* to the Sun in the northern hemisphere's winter than in summer. The angle at which the Sun's radiation hits the surface and the num-

ber of hours of daylight are much more important in determining the incident power than is the small difference in distance from the Sun.

Practice Problem 22.6   Average Power on the Winter Solstice

What is the average power per unit area at a latitude of 40.0° north at noon on the winter solstice (Fig. 22.20b)?

22.8   POLARIZATION

Linear Polarization

Imagine a transverse wave traveling along the *z*-axis. Since this discussion applies to any transverse wave, let us use a transverse wave on a string as an example. In what directions can the string be displaced to produce transverse waves on this string? The displacement could be in the ±*x*-direction, as in Fig. 22.21a. Or it could be in the ±*y*-direction, as in Fig. 22.21b. Or it could be in any direction in the *xy*-plane. In Fig. 22.21c, the displacement of any point on the string from its equilibrium position is parallel to a line that makes an angle θ with the *x*-axis. These three waves are said to be **linearly polarized**. For the wave in Fig. 22.21a, we would say that the wave is polarized in the ±*x*-direction (or, for short, in the *x*-direction).

Linearly polarized waves are also called **plane polarized**; the two terms are synonymous, despite what you might guess. Each wave in Fig. 22.21 is characterized by a single plane, called the **plane of vibration**, in which the entire string vibrates. For example, the plane of vibration for Fig. 22.21a is the *xz*-plane. Both the direction of propagation of the wave and the direction of motion of every point of the string lie in the plane of vibration.

Any transverse wave can be linearly polarized in any direction perpendicular to the direction of propagation. EM waves are no exception. But there are two fields in an EM wave, which are perpendicular to each other. Knowing the direction of one of the fields is sufficient, since $\vec{E} \times \vec{B}$ must point in the direction of propagation. By convention, the direction of polarization of EM waves is taken to be the *electric* field direction.

Polarization of an EM wave:
direction of its electric field

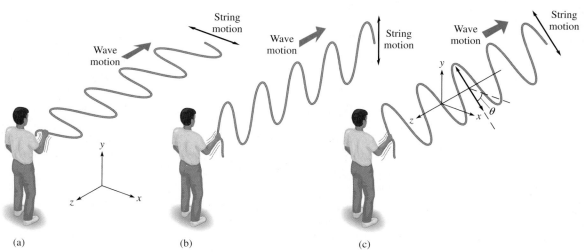

Figure 22.21 Transverse waves on a string with three different linear (plane) polarizations.

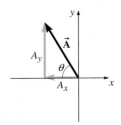

Figure 22.22 Any linearly polarized wave can be thought of as a superposition of two perpendicular polarizations, since displacements—as well as electric and magnetic fields—are vectors.

Both electric and magnetic dipole antennas emit radio waves that are linearly polarized. If an FM radio broadcast is transmitted using a horizontal electric dipole antenna, the radio waves at any receiver are linearly polarized. The direction of polarization varies from place to place. If you are due west of the transmitter, the waves that reach you are polarized along the north-south direction, since they must be in the horizontal plane and perpendicular to the direction of propagation (which is west in this case). For best reception, an electric dipole antenna should be aligned with the direction of polarization of the radio waves, since it is the electric field that drives current in the antenna.

In Section 22.3, we said that if an electric dipole antenna is not lined up with the electric field of the wave, then the emf is reduced by a factor of $\cos \theta$, where θ is the angle between $\vec{E}$ and the antenna. Think about this in terms of polarization. Any linearly polarized wave can be thought of as the superposition of two perpendicular linearly polarized waves along any axes we choose. Displacements are vectors and vectors can always be written as the sum of perpendicular components; therefore, the transverse wave on the string in Fig. 22.21c can be thought of as the superposition of two waves, one polarized in the x-direction and the other in the y-direction. If the amplitude of the wave is A, the amplitude of the "x-component wave" is $A \cos \theta$ and the amplitude of the "y-component wave" is $A \sin \theta$ (see Fig. 22.22).

The same is true for EM waves, since the electric and magnetic fields are vectors. Any linearly polarized EM wave can be regarded as the sum of two waves polarized along perpendicular axes. If an electric dipole antenna makes an angle θ with the electric field of a wave, only the component of $\vec{E}$ along the antenna makes electrons move back and forth along the antenna. If we think of the wave as two perpendicular polarizations, the antenna responds to the polarization parallel to it while the perpendicular polarization has no effect.

Random Polarization

The light coming from an incandescent lightbulb is **unpolarized** or **randomly polarized**. The direction of the electric field changes rapidly and in a random way. Antennas emit linearly polarized waves because the motion of the electrons up and down the antenna is orderly and always along the same line. Thermal radiation (which is mostly IR, but also includes visible light) from a lightbulb is caused by the thermal vibrations of huge numbers of atoms. The atoms are essentially independent of each other; nothing makes them vibrate in step or in the same direction. The wave is therefore made up of the superposition of a huge number of waves whose electric fields are in random, uncorrelated directions. Thermal radiation is always unpolarized, whether it comes from a lightbulb, from a wood stove (mostly IR), or from the Sun.

Polarizers

Devices called *polarizers* transmit linearly polarized waves in a fixed direction regardless of the polarization state of the incident waves. A polarizer for transverse waves on a string is shown in Fig. 22.23. The vertical slot enables the string to slide vertically without friction, but prevents any horizontal motion. When a vertically polarized wave is sent down the string toward the slot, it passes through (Fig. 22.23a). A horizontally polarized wave does not pass through (Fig. 22.23b); it is reflected since the slot acts like a fixed end for horizontal motion. The direction of the slot is called the *transmission axis* since the polarizer transmits waves polarized in that direction.

What if a linearly polarized wave is sent toward the polarizer, as in Fig. 22.23c, where the incident wave is polarized at an angle θ to the transmission axis? The incident wave can be decomposed into components parallel and perpendicular to the transmission axis; the parallel wave passes through. If the incident wave has amplitude A, then the transmitted wave has amplitude $A \cos \theta$ (Fig. 22.23d).

A polarizer for microwaves consists of many parallel strips of metal (Fig. 22.24). The spacing of the strips must be significantly less than the wavelength of the

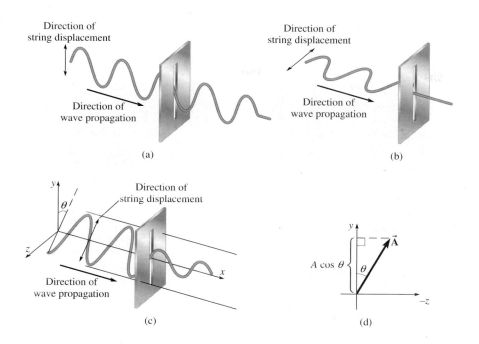

Figure 22.23 A vertical slot allows vertically polarized waves to pass through (a), but not horizontally polarized waves (b). If the incident wave is polarized at an angle θ to the vertical (c), a vertically polarized wave of amplitude $A \cos \theta$ is transmitted (d).

microwaves. The strips act as little antennas. The parallel component of the electric field of the incident wave makes currents flow up and down the metal strips. These currents dissipate energy, so some of the wave is absorbed. The antennas also produce a wave of their own; it is out of phase with the incident wave, so it cancels the parallel-component of $\vec{E}$ in the forward-going wave and sends a reflected wave back. Between absorption and reflection, none of the electric field parallel to the metal strips gets through the polarizer. The microwaves that are transmitted are linearly polarized *perpendicular to the strips.* Although the microwave polarizer *looks* similar to the polarizer for waves on a string, the electric field does not pass through the "slots" between the metal strips! The transmission axis of the polarizer is *perpendicular* to the strips.

Sheet polarizers for visible light operate on a principle similar to that of the wire grid polarizer. A sheet polarizer contains many long hydrocarbon chains with iodine atoms attached. In production, the sheet is stretched so that these long molecules are all aligned in the same direction. The iodine atoms allow electrons to move easily along the chain, so the aligned polymers behave as parallel conducting wires, and their spacing is close enough that it does to visible light what a wire grid polarizer does to microwaves. The sheet polarizer has a transmission axis perpendicular to the aligned polymers.

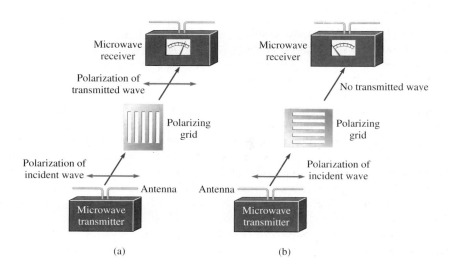

Figure 22.24 A polarizing grid for microwaves. (a) A horizontally polarized microwave beam passes through the polarizer if its strips are oriented vertically, but (b) is blocked by a polarizer with horizontal strips.

Figure 22.25 (a) Unpolarized light is incident on three polarizers oriented in different directions. The transmitted intensity is the same for all three. (b) Linearly polarized light is incident on the same three polarizers. Note that the transmitted intensity for $\theta = 0$ is slightly less than the incident intensity—these are not *ideal* polarizers.

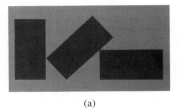

(a)

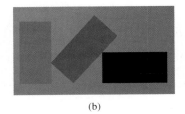

(b)

If randomly polarized light is incident on an ideal polarizer, the transmitted intensity is half the incident intensity, regardless of the orientation of the transmission axis (Fig. 22.25a). The randomly polarized wave can be thought of as two perpendicular polarized waves that are *uncorrelated*—the relative phase of the two varies rapidly with time. Half of the energy of the wave is associated with each of the two perpendicular polarizations.

$$I = \tfrac{1}{2}I_0 \quad \text{(incident wave unpolarized, ideal polarizer)} \qquad (22\text{-}15)$$

If, instead, the incident wave is linearly polarized, then the component of $\vec{E}$ parallel to the transmission axis gets through (Fig. 22.25b). If θ is the angle between the incident polarization and the transmission axis, then

> When applying Malus's law, be sure to use the correct angle. In Eqs. (22-16), θ is the angle between the *polarization direction of the incident light* and the transmission axis of the polarizer.

$$E = E_0 \cos \theta \quad \text{(incident wave polarized, ideal polarizer)} \qquad (22\text{-}16a)$$

Since intensity is proportional to the square of the amplitude, the transmitted intensity is

$$I = I_0 \cos^2 \theta \quad \text{(incident wave polarized, ideal polarizer)} \qquad (22\text{-}16b)$$

Equation (22-16b) is called **Malus's law** after its discoverer Étienne-Louis Malus (1775–1812), an engineer and one of Napoleon's captains.

Example 22.7

Unpolarized Light Incident on Two Polarizers

Randomly polarized light of intensity I_0 is incident on two sheet polarizers (Fig. 22.26). The transmission axis of the first polarizer is vertical; that of the second makes a 30.0° angle with the vertical. What is the intensity and polarization state of the light after passing through the two?

Strategy We treat each polarizer separately. First we find the intensity of light transmitted by the first polarizer. The light transmitted by a polarizer is always linearly polarized parallel to the transmission axis of the polarizer, since only the component of $\vec{E}$ parallel to the transmission axis gets through. Then we know the intensity and polarization state of the light that is incident on the second polarizer.

Solution When randomly polarized light passes through a polarizer, the transmitted intensity is half the incident intensity [Eq. (22-15)] since the wave has equal amounts of energy associated with its two perpendicular (but uncorrelated) components.

$$I_1 = \tfrac{1}{2}I_0$$

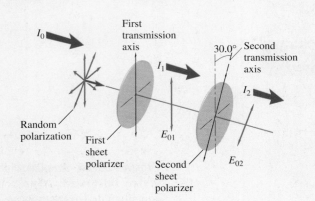

Figure 22.26
The circular disks are polarizing sheets with their transmission axes marked.

Continued on next page

Example 22.7 Continued

The light is now linearly polarized parallel to the transmission axis of the first polarizer, which is vertical.

The component of the electric field parallel to the transmission axis of the second polarizer passes through. The amplitude is thus reduced by a factor cos 30.0° and, since intensity is proportional to amplitude squared, the intensity is reduced by a factor $\cos^2$ 30.0° (Malus's law). The intensity transmitted through the second polarizer is

$$I_2 = I_1 \cos^2 30.0° = \tfrac{1}{2}I_0 \cos^2 30.0° = 0.375\, I_0$$

The light is now linearly polarized 30.0° from the vertical.

Discussion   For problems involving two or more polarizers in series, treat each polarizer in turn. Use the intensity and polarization state of the light that emerges from one polarizer as the incident intensity and polarization for the next polarizer.

Practice Problem 22.7   Minimum and Maximum Intensities

If randomly polarized light of intensity I_0 is incident on two polarizers, what are the maximum and minimum possible intensities of the transmitted light as the angle between the two transmission axes is varied?

Liquid Crystal Displays

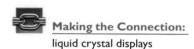

Making the Connection:

liquid crystal displays

Liquid crystal displays (LCDs) are commonly found in flat-panel computer screens, calculators, digital watches, and digital meters. In each segment of the display, a liquid crystal layer is sandwiched between two finely grooved surfaces with their grooves perpendicular (Fig. 22.27a). As a result the molecules twist 90° between the two surfaces. When a voltage is applied across the liquid crystal layer, the molecules line up in the direction of the electric field (Fig. 22.27b).

Unpolarized light from a small fluorescent bulb is polarized by one polarizing sheet. The light then passes through the liquid crystal and then through a second polarizing sheet with its transmission axis perpendicular to the first. When no voltage is applied, the liquid crystal rotates the polarization of the light by 90° and the light can pass through the second polarizer (Fig. 22.27a). When a voltage is applied, the liquid crystal transmits light without changing its polarization; the second polarizer blocks transmission of the light (Fig. 22.27b). When you look at an LCD display, you see the light transmitted by the second sheet. If a segment has a voltage applied to it, no light is

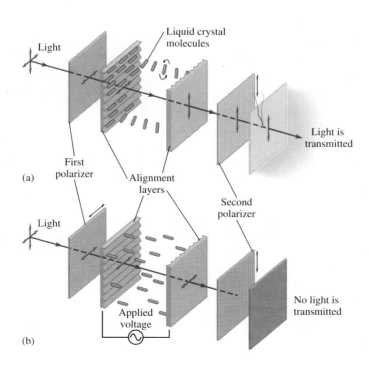

Figure 22.27 (a) When no voltage is applied to the liquid crystal, it rotates the polarization of the light so it can pass through the second polarizing sheet. (b) When a voltage is applied to the liquid crystal, no light is transmitted through the second polarizing sheet.

(a)

(b)

Figure 22.28 Photo of a lake in Yosemite National Park taken without (a) and with (b) a polarizing filter in front of the camera's lens. The filter reduces the amount of reflected glare from the surface of the lake.

Making the Connection:
colors of the sky during the day and at sunset

Figure 22.29 An astronaut walks away from the lunar module *Intrepid* while a brilliant Sun shines above the Apollo 12 base. Notice that the sky is dark even though the Sun is above the horizon; the Moon lacks an atmosphere to scatter sunlight and form a blue sky.

transmitted; we see a black segment. If a segment of liquid crystal does not have an applied voltage, it transmits light and we see the same gray color as the background.

Polarization by Scattering

While the radiation emitted by the Sun is unpolarized, much of the sunlight that we see is **partially polarized**. Partially polarized light is a mixture of unpolarized and linearly polarized light. A sheet polarizer can be used to distinguish linearly polarized, partially polarized, and unpolarized light. The polarizer is rotated and the transmitted intensity at different angles is noted. If the incident light is unpolarized, the intensity stays constant as the polarizer is rotated. If the incident light is linearly polarized, the intensity is zero in one orientation and maximum at a perpendicular orientation. If partially polarized light is analyzed in this way, the transmitted intensity varies as the polarizer is rotated, but it is not zero for *any* orientation; it is maximum in one orientation and minimum (but nonzero) in a perpendicular orientation. A polarizer used to analyze the polarization state of light is often called an *analyzer*.

Natural, unpolarized light becomes partially polarized when it is scattered or reflected. So, unless you look straight at the Sun (which can cause severe eye damage—do not try it!), the sunlight that reaches you has been scattered and/or reflected and thus is partially polarized. Common Polaroid sunglasses consist of a sheet polarizer, oriented to absorb the preferential direction of polarization of light reflected from horizontal surfaces, such as a road or the water on a lake, and to reduce the glare of scattered light in the air. Polaroid sunglasses are often used in boating and aviation because they preferentially cut down on glare rather than indiscriminately reducing the intensity for all polarization states (Fig. 22.28).

How do scattering and reflection make the light partially polarized? Let's look at scattering; polarization by reflection is discussed in Section 23.5. The blue sky we see on sunny days is sunlight that is scattered by molecules in the air. On the Moon, there is no blue sky because there is no atmosphere. Even during the day, the sky is as black as at night, although the Sun and the Earth may be brightly shining above (Fig. 22.29). Earth's atmosphere scatters blue light, with its shorter wavelengths, more than light with longer wavelengths. At sunrise and sunset, we see the light left over after much of the blue is scattered out—primarily red and orange.

PHYSICS AT HOME

Take a pair of inexpensive Polaroid sunglasses outside on a sunny day and analyze the polarization of the sky in various directions (but do not look directly at the Sun, even through sunglasses!). Get a second pair of sunglasses so you can put two polarizers in series. Rotate the one closest to you while holding the other in the same orientation. When is the transmitted intensity maximum? When is it minimum?

The same scattering process that makes the sky blue and the sunset red also polarizes the scattered light. Figure 22.30 shows unpolarized sunlight being scattered by a molecule in the atmosphere. In this case, the incident light is horizontal, as would occur shortly before sunset. In response to the electric field of the wave, charges in the molecule oscillate—the molecule becomes an oscillating dipole. Since the incoming wave is unpolarized, the dipole does not oscillate along a single axis, but does so in random directions perpendicular to the incident wave. As an oscillating dipole, the molecule radiates EM waves. An oscillating dipole radiates most strongly in directions perpendicular to its axis; *it does not radiate at all in directions parallel to its axis.*

North-south oscillation of the molecular dipole radiates in the three directions A, B, and C equally, since those directions are all perpendicular to the north-south axis of the dipole. Vertical oscillation of the molecular dipole radiates most strongly in a horizontal plane (including A). Vertical oscillation radiates more weakly in direction B and not at all in direction C. Therefore, in direction C, the light is linearly polarized in the

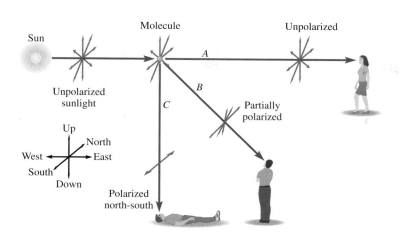

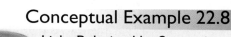

Figure 22.30 Unpolarized sunlight is scattered by the atmosphere. (In this illustration, it is early evening, so the incident light from the Sun comes in horizontally from west to east.) A person looking straight up at the sky sees light that is scattered through 90°. This light (*C*) is polarized north-south, which is perpendicular both to the direction of propagation of the incident light (east) and to the direction of propagation of the scattered light (down).

north-south direction. Generalizing this observation, light scattered through 90° is polarized in a direction that is perpendicular both to the direction of the incident light and to the direction of the scattered light.

Conceptual Example 22.8

Light Polarized by Scattering

At noon, if you look at the sky just above the horizon toward the east, in what direction is the light polarized?

Strategy At noon, sunlight travels straight down (approximately). Some of the light is scattered by the atmosphere through roughly 90° and then travels westward toward the observer. We consider the unpolarized light from the Sun to be a random mixture of two perpendicular polarizations. Looking at each polarization by itself, we determine how effectively a molecule can scatter the light downward. A sketch of the situation is crucial.

Solution and Discussion Figure 22.31 shows light traveling downward from the Sun as a mixture of north-south and east-west polarizations. Now we treat the two polarizations one at a time.

The north-south electric fields cause charges in the molecule to oscillate along a north-south axis. An oscillating dipole radiates most strongly in all directions perpendicular to the dipole axis, including in the westward direction of the scattered light we want to analyze.

The east-west electric fields produce an oscillating dipole with an east-west axis. An oscillating dipole radi-

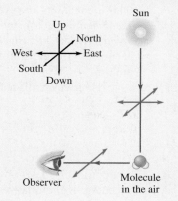

Figure 22.31
Light traveling downward from the Sun is an uncorrelated mixture of both east-west and north-south polarizations. The two polarizations are represented by double-headed arrows. The light scattered westward is polarized along the north-south direction.

ates only weakly in directions nearly parallel to its axis. Therefore, the light scattered westward is polarized in the north-south direction.

Conceptual Practice Problem 22.8
Looking North

Just before sunset, if you look north at the sky just over the horizon, in what direction is the light partially polarized?

How Bees Navigate on Cloudy Days

A bee has a compound eye consisting of thousands of transparent fibers called the ommatidia. Each ommatidium has one end on the hemispherical surface of the compound eye (Fig. 22.32) and is sensitive to light coming from the direction along which the fiber is aligned.

Making the Connection:
navigation of bees

Each ommatidium is made up of nine cells. One of these cells is sensitive to the polarization of the incident light. The bee can therefore detect the polarization state of light coming from various directions. When the Sun is not visible, the bee can infer the position of the Sun from the polarization of scattered light, as was established by a series of ingenious experiments by Karl von Frisch and others in the 1960s. Using polarizing sheets, von Frisch et al. could change the apparent polarization state of the scattered sunlight and watch the effects on the flight of the bees.

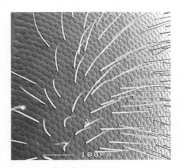

Figure 22.32 Electron micrograph of the compound eye of a bee. The "bumps" are the outside surfaces of the ommatidia.

22.9   THE DOPPLER EFFECT FOR EM WAVES

In Section 12.8 we saw that the observed frequency of sound waves is affected by the motion of the source and/or the observer with respect to the wave medium. This frequency shift is called the *Doppler effect*. When the source and observer are approaching (getting closer together), the observed frequency is *higher* than the frequency of the source. Each successive wavefront generated by the source takes less and less time to reach the observer, since the distance the wave must travel is getting shorter and shorter. The time between the arrival of successive wavefronts at the observer (T_o) is less than the time interval between the origination of the wavefronts at the source (T_s); therefore, the observed frequency ($f_o = 1/T_o$) is greater than the source frequency ($f_s = 1/T_s$). If the source and observer are receding (getting farther apart), the observed frequency is less than the source frequency.

The Doppler effect exists for all kinds of waves, including EM waves. However, the Doppler formula [Eq. (12-14)] derived for sound cannot be correct for EM waves. Those equations involve the velocity of the source and the observer *relative to the medium through which the sound travels*. For sound waves in air, v_s and v_o are measured *relative to the air*. Since EM waves are not vibrations in a mechanical medium, the Doppler shift for light can only involve the *relative* velocity of the observer and the source.

Using Einstein's relativity, the Doppler shift formula for light can be derived:

$$f_o = f_s \sqrt{\frac{1 + v_{rel}/c}{1 - v_{rel}/c}} \qquad\qquad (22\text{-}17)$$

In Eq. (22-17), v_{rel} is positive if the source and observer are approaching and negative if receding. If the relative speed of source and observer is much less than c, a simpler expression can be found using the binomial approximations found in Appendix A.5:

$$\left(1 + \frac{v_{rel}}{c}\right)^{1/2} \approx 1 + \frac{v_{rel}}{2c}$$

and

$$\left(1 - \frac{v_{rel}}{c}\right)^{-1/2} \approx 1 + \frac{v_{rel}}{2c}$$

Substituting these approximations into Eq. (22-17),

$$f_o \approx f_s \left(1 + \frac{v_{rel}}{2c}\right)^2$$

$$f_o \approx f_s \left(1 + \frac{v_{rel}}{c}\right) \qquad\qquad (22\text{-}18)$$

where in the last step we used the binomial approximation once more.

Example 22.9

A Speeder Caught by Radar

A police car is moving at 38.0 m/s (85.0 mi/h) to catch up with a speeder directly ahead. The speed limit is 29.1 m/s (65.0 mi/h). A police car radar "clocks" the speed of the other car by emitting microwaves with frequency 3.0×10^{10} Hz and observing the frequency of the reflected wave. The reflected wave, when combined with the outgoing wave, produces beats at a rate of 1400 s^{-1}. How fast is the speeder going? [*Hint:* First find the frequency "observed" by the speeder. The electrons in the metal car body oscillate and emit the reflected wave with this same frequency. For the reflected wave, the speeder is the source and the police car is the observer.]

Strategy There are *two* Doppler shifts, since the EM wave is reflected off the car. We can first think of the car as the observer, receiving a Doppler-shifted radar wave from the police car (Fig. 22.33a). Then the car "rebroadcasts" this wave back to the police car (Fig. 22.33b). This time the speeder's car is the source and the police car is the observer. The relative speed of the two cars is *much* less than the speed of light, so we use the approximate formula [Eq. (22-18)].

There are three different frequencies in the problem. Let's call the frequency emitted by the police car $f_1 = 3.0 \times 10^{10}$ Hz, the frequency received by the speeder f_2, and the frequency of the reflected wave as observed by the police car f_3. The police car is catching up to the speeder, so the source and observer are approaching; therefore, v_{rel} is positive and the Doppler shift is toward higher frequencies.

Solution The beat frequency is

$$f_{beat} = f_3 - f_1 \qquad (12\text{-}11)$$

The frequency observed by the speeder is

$$f_2 = f_1\left(1 + \frac{v_{rel}}{c}\right)$$

Now the speeder's car emits a microwave of frequency f_2. The frequency observed by the police car is

$$f_3 = f_2\left(1 + \frac{v_{rel}}{c}\right) = f_1\left(1 + \frac{v_{rel}}{c}\right)^2$$

We need to solve for v_{rel}. We can avoid solving a quadratic equation by using the binomial approximation:

$$f_3 = f_1\left(1 + \frac{v_{rel}}{c}\right)^2 \approx f_1\left(1 + 2\frac{v_{rel}}{c}\right)$$

Solving for v_{rel},

$$v_{rel} = \frac{1}{2}c\left(\frac{f_3}{f_1} - 1\right) = \frac{1}{2}c\left(\frac{f_3 - f_1}{f_1}\right) = \frac{1}{2}c\left(\frac{f_{beat}}{f_1}\right)$$

$$= \frac{1}{2} \times 3.00 \times 10^8 \text{ m/s} \times \frac{1400 \text{ Hz}}{3.0 \times 10^{10} \text{ Hz}} = 7.0 \text{ m/s}$$

Since the two are approaching, the speeder is moving at less than 38.0 m/s. Relative to the road, the speeder is moving at

$$38.0 \text{ m/s} - 7.0 \text{ m/s} = 31.0 \text{ m/s} (= 69.3 \text{ mi/h})$$

Perhaps the police officer will be kind enough to give only a warning this time.

Discussion Using the approximate form for the Doppler shift greatly simplifies the algebra. Using the exact form would be much more difficult and in the end would give the same answer. The speeds involved are so much less than c that the error is truly negligible.

Practice Problem 22.9   Reflection from Stationary Objects

Suppose the police car is moving at 23 m/s. What beat frequency results when the radar is reflected from stationary objects?

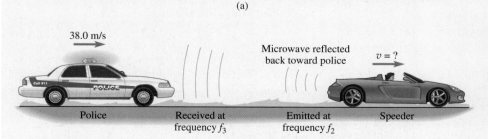

38.0 m/s

Emitted microwave travels toward speeder

$v = ?$

Police   Emitted at frequency f_1 Received at frequency f_2 Speeder

(a)

38.0 m/s

Microwave reflected back toward police

$v = ?$

Police   Received at frequency f_3 Emitted at frequency f_2 Speeder

(b)

Figure 22.33

(a) The police car emits microwaves at frequency f_1. The speeder receives them at a Doppler-shifted frequency f_2. (b) The wave is reflected at frequency f_2; the police car receives the reflected wave at frequency f_3.

Making the Connection:

doppler shift for distant stars and galaxies

Radar used by meteorologists can provide information about the position of storm systems. Now they use *Doppler radar*, which also provides information about the velocity of storm systems. Another important application of the Doppler shift of visible light is the evidence it gives for the expansion of the universe. Light reaching Earth from distant stars is *red-shifted*. That is, the spectrum of visible light is shifted downward in frequency toward the red. According to *Hubble's law*, the speed at which a galaxy moves away from ours is proportional to how far from us the galaxy is. Thus, the Doppler shift can be used to determine a star or galaxy's distance from Earth.

Looking out at the universe, the red shift tells us that other galaxies are moving away from ours in all directions; the farther away the galaxy, the faster it is receding from us and the greater the Doppler shift of the light that reaches Earth. This doesn't mean that Earth is at the center of the universe; in a uniformly expanding universe, observers on a planet *anywhere* in the universe would see distant galaxies moving away from it in all directions. Ever since the Big Bang, the universe has been expanding. Whether it continues to expand forever, or whether the expansion will stop and the universe collapse into another big bang, is a central question studied by cosmologists and astrophysicists.

MASTER THE CONCEPTS

- EM waves consist of oscillating electric and magnetic fields that propagate away from their source. EM waves always have both electric and magnetic fields.

- The Ampère-Maxwell law is Ampère's law modified by Maxwell so that a changing electric field generates a magnetic field:

$$\sum B_\parallel \Delta l = \mu_0 \left(I + \epsilon_0 \frac{\Delta \Phi_E}{\Delta t} \right) \qquad (22\text{-}1)$$

- The Ampère-Maxwell law, along with Gauss's law, Gauss's law for magnetism, and Faraday's law, are called Maxwell's equations. They describe completely the electric and magnetic fields. Maxwell's equations say that $\vec{E}$- and $\vec{B}$-field lines do not have to be tied to matter. Instead, they can break free and electromagnetic waves can travel far from their sources.

- Radiation from a dipole antenna is weakest along the antenna's axis and strongest in directions perpendicular to the axis. Electric dipole antennas and magnetic dipole antennas can be used either as sources of EM waves or as receivers of EM waves.

- The electromagnetic spectrum—the range of frequencies and wavelengths of EM waves—is traditionally divided into named regions. From lowest to highest frequency, they are: radio waves, microwaves, infrared, visible, ultraviolet, x-rays, and gamma rays.

- EM waves of any frequency travel through vacuum at a speed

$$c = \frac{1}{\sqrt{\epsilon_0 \mu_0}} = 3.00 \times 10^8 \text{ m/s} \qquad (22\text{-}3)$$

- EM waves can travel through matter, but they do so at speeds less than c. The index of refraction for a material is defined as

$$n = \frac{c}{v} \qquad (22\text{-}4)$$

where v is the speed of EM waves through the material.

- The speed of EM waves (and therefore also the index of refraction) in *matter* depends on the frequency of the wave.

- When an EM wave passes from one medium to another, the wavelength changes; the frequency remains the same. The wave in the second medium is created by the oscillating charges at the boundary, so the fields in the second medium must oscillate at the same frequency as the fields in the first.

- Properties of EM waves in vacuum:

  The electric and magnetic fields oscillate at the *same frequency* and are *in phase*.

$$E(x, y, z, t) = cB(x, y, z, t) \qquad (22\text{-}7)$$

  $\vec{E}$, $\vec{B}$, and the direction of propagation are three mutually perpendicular directions.

  $\vec{E} \times \vec{B}$ is always in the direction of propagation.

  The electric energy density is equal to the magnetic energy density.

- Energy density (SI unit: J/m^3) of an EM wave in vacuum:

$$\langle u \rangle = \epsilon_0 \langle E^2 \rangle = \epsilon_0 E_{\text{rms}}^2 = \frac{1}{\mu_0} \langle B^2 \rangle = \frac{1}{\mu_0} B_{\text{rms}}^2 \qquad (22\text{-}10, 11)$$

- The intensity (SI unit: W/m^2) is

$$I = \langle u \rangle c \qquad (22\text{-}13)$$

  Intensity is proportional to the squares of the electric and magnetic field amplitudes.

- The average power incident on a surface of area A is

$$\langle P \rangle = IA \cos \theta \qquad (22\text{-}14)$$

where θ is 0° for normal incidence and 90° for grazing incidence.

MASTER THE CONCEPTS *continued*

- The polarization of an EM wave is the direction of its electric field.
- If unpolarized waves pass through a polarizer, the transmitted intensity is half the incident intensity:

$$I = \tfrac{1}{2} I_0 \qquad (22\text{-}15)$$

- If a linearly polarized wave is incident on a polarizer, the component of $\vec{\mathbf{E}}$ parallel to the transmission axis gets through. If θ is the angle between the incident polarization and the transmission axis, then

$$E = E_0 \cos \theta \qquad (22\text{-}16a)$$

Since intensity is proportional to the square of the amplitude, the transmitted intensity is

$$I = I_0 \cos^2 \theta \qquad (22\text{-}16b)$$

- The Doppler effect for EM waves:

$$f_o = f_s \sqrt{\frac{1 + v_{rel}/c}{1 - v_{rel}/c}} \qquad (22\text{-}17)$$

where v_{rel} is positive if the source and observer are approaching, and negative if receding. If the relative speed of source and observer is much less than c,

$$f_o \approx f_s \left(1 + \frac{v_{rel}}{c} \right) \qquad (22\text{-}18)$$

Conceptual Questions

1. In Section 22.3, we stated that an electric dipole antenna should be aligned with the electric field of an EM wave for best reception. If a magnetic dipole antenna is used instead, should its axis be aligned with the magnetic field of the wave? Explain.

2. A magnetic dipole antenna has its axis aligned with the vertical. The antenna sends out radio waves. If you are due south of the antenna, what is the polarization state of the radio waves that reach you?

3. Linearly polarized light of intensity I_0 shines through two polarizing sheets. The second of the sheets has its transmission axis perpendicular to the polarization of the light before it passes through the first sheet. Must the intensity transmitted through the second sheet be zero, or is it possible that some light gets through? Explain.

4. Using Faraday's law, explain why it is impossible to have a magnetic wave without any electric component.

5. According to Maxwell, why is it impossible to have an electric wave without any magnetic component?

6. Zach insists that the seasons are caused by the elliptical shape of Earth's orbit. He says that it is summer when Earth is closest to the Sun and winter when it is farthest away from the Sun. What evidence can you think of to show that the seasons are *not* due to the change in distance between Earth and the Sun?

7. Why are days longer in summer than in winter?

8. Describe the polarization of radio waves transmitted from a horizontal electric dipole antenna that travel parallel to the Earth's surface.

9. The figure shows a magnetic dipole antenna transmitting an electromagnetic wave. At a point P far from the antenna, what are the directions of the electric and magnetic fields of the wave?

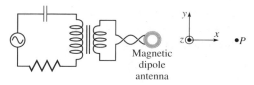

Conceptual Question 9 and Problem 28

10. In everyday experience, visible light seems to travel in straight lines while radio waves do not. Explain.

11. A light wave passes through a hazy region in the sky. If the electric field vector of the emerging wave is $\tfrac{1}{4}$ that of the incident wave, what is the ratio of the transmitted intensity to the incident intensity?

12. Can sound waves be polarized? Explain.

13. Until the Supreme Court ruled it to be unconstitutional, drug enforcement officers examined buildings at night with a camera sensitive to infrared. How did this help them identify marijuana growers?

14. The amplitudes of an EM wave are related by $E_m = cB_m$. Since $c = 3.00 \times 10^8$ m/s, a classmate says that the electric field in an EM wave is much larger than the magnetic field. How would you reply?

15. Why is it warmer in summer than in winter?

16. Why is the antenna on a cell phone shorter than the radio antenna on a car?

Multiple-Choice Questions

1. The radio station that broadcasts your favorite music is located exactly north of your home; it uses a horizontal electric dipole antenna directed north-south. In order to receive this broadcast, you need to
    (a) orient the receiving antenna horizontally, north-south.
    (b) orient the receiving antenna horizontally, east-west.
    (c) use a vertical receiving antenna.
    (d) move to a town farther to the east or to the west.
    (e) use a magnetic dipole antenna instead of an electric dipole antenna.

2. Which of these statements correctly describes the orientation of the electric field ($\vec{E}$), the magnetic field ($\vec{B}$), and the velocity of propagation ($\vec{v}$) of an electromagnetic wave?
    (a) $\vec{E}$ is perpendicular to $\vec{B}$; $\vec{v}$ may have any orientation relative to $\vec{E}$.
    (b) $\vec{E}$ is perpendicular to $\vec{B}$; $\vec{v}$ may have any orientation perpendicular to $\vec{E}$.
    (c) $\vec{E}$ is perpendicular to $\vec{B}$; $\vec{B}$ is parallel to $\vec{v}$.
    (d) $\vec{E}$ is perpendicular to $\vec{B}$; $\vec{E}$ is parallel to $\vec{v}$.
    (e) $\vec{E}$ is parallel to $\vec{B}$; $\vec{v}$ is perpendicular to both $\vec{E}$ and $\vec{B}$.
    (f) Each of the three vectors is perpendicular to the other two.

3. An electromagnetic wave is created by
    (a) all electric charges.
    (b) an accelerating electric charge.
    (c) an electric charge moving at constant velocity.
    (d) a stationary electric charge.
    (e) a stationary bar magnet.
    (f) a moving electric charge, whether accelerating or not.

4. The speed of an electromagnetic wave in vacuum depends on
    (a) the amplitude of the electric field but not on the amplitude of the magnetic field.
    (b) the amplitude of the magnetic field but not on the amplitude of the electric field.
    (c) the amplitude of both fields.
    (d) the angle between the electric and magnetic fields.
    (e) the frequency and wavelength.
    (f) none of the above.

5. If the wavelength of an electromagnetic wave is about the diameter of an apple, what type of radiation is it?
    (a) X-ray   (b) UV   (c) Infrared
    (d) Microwave   (e) Visible light   (f) Radio wave

6. The Sun is directly overhead and you are facing toward the north. Light coming to your eyes from the sky just above the horizon is
    (a) partially polarized north-south.
    (b) partially polarized east-west.
    (c) partially polarized up-down.
    (d) randomly polarized.
    (e) linearly polarized up-down.

7. A dipole radio transmitter has its rod-shaped antenna oriented vertically. At a point due south of the transmitter, the radio waves have their magnetic field
    (a) oriented north-south.
    (b) oriented east-west.
    (c) oriented vertically.
    (d) oriented in any horizontal direction.

8. A vertical electric dipole antenna
    (a) radiates uniformly in all directions.
    (b) radiates uniformly in all horizontal directions, but more strongly in the vertical direction.
    (c) radiates most strongly and uniformly in the horizontal directions.
    (d) does not radiate in the horizontal directions.

9. A beam of light is linearly polarized. You wish to rotate its direction of polarization by 90° using one or more *ideal* polarizing sheets. To get maximum transmitted intensity, you should use how many sheets?
    (a) 1   (b) 2   (c) 3
    (d) As many as possible
    (e) There is no way to rotate the direction of polarization 90° using polarizing sheets.

10. Light passes from one medium (in which the speed of light is v_1) into another (in which the speed of light is v_2). If $v_1 < v_2$, as the light crosses the boundary,
    (a) both f and λ decrease.
    (b) neither f nor λ change.
    (c) f increases, λ decreases.
    (d) f does not change, λ increases.
    (e) both f and λ increase.
    (f) f does not change, λ decreases.
    (g) f decreases, λ increases.

Problems

Ⓒ   Combination conceptual/quantitative problem
⬛   Biological or medical application
No ✦ Easy to moderate difficulty level
✦   More challenging
✦✦   Most challenging
Blue # Detailed solution in the Student Solutions Manual
☐1 2☐ Problems paired by concept

22.2 Maxwell's Equations

Problems 1–4. Apply the Ampère-Maxwell law to one of the circular paths in Fig. 22.3 to find the magnitude of the magnetic field at the locations specified.

✦ 1. Find B outside the wire at a distance $r \geq R$ from the central axis. [*Hint:* The electric field inside the wire is constant, so there is no changing electric flux.]

✦✦ 2. Find B outside the gap in the wire at a distance $r \geq R$ from the central axis. [*Hint:* What is the rate of change of electric flux through the circle in terms of the current I?]

3. Find B inside the gap in the wire at a distance $r \leq R$ from the central axis. [*Hint:* Only the rate of change of electric flux $\Delta\Phi_E/\Delta t$ *through the interior of the circular path* goes into the Ampère-Maxwell law.]

4. Find B inside the wire at a distance $r \leq R$ from the central axis. [*Hint:* Only the current through the interior of the circular path goes into the Ampère-Maxwell law.]

22.3 Antennas

5. A dipole radio transmitter has its rod-shaped antenna oriented vertically. At a point due south of the transmitter, what is the orientation of the magnetic field of the radio waves?

6. A vertical antenna in Syracuse, New York, emits radio waves. This radiation is received in Cortland, New York, with an antenna in the form of a circular coil of wire. If Cortland is directly south of Syracuse, how should the coil be oriented for best reception?

7. Using Faraday's law, show that if a magnetic dipole antenna's axis makes an angle θ with the magnetic field of an EM wave, the induced emf in the antenna is reduced from its maximum possible value by a factor of cos θ. [*Hint:* Assume that, at any instant, the magnetic field everywhere inside the loop is uniform.]

8. A magnetic dipole antenna is used to detect an electromagnetic wave. The antenna is a coil of 50 turns with radius 5.0 cm. The EM wave has frequency 870 kHz, electric field amplitude 0.50 V/m, and magnetic field amplitude 1.7×10^{-9} T. (a) For best results, should the axis of the coil be aligned with the electric field of the wave, or with the magnetic field, or with the direction of propagation of the wave? (b) Assuming it is aligned correctly, what is the amplitude of the induced emf in the coil? (Since the wavelength of this wave is *much* larger than 5.0 cm, it can be assumed that at any instant the fields are uniform within the coil.) (c) What is the amplitude of the emf induced in an electric dipole antenna of length 5.0 cm aligned with the electric field of the wave?

22.4 The Electromagnetic Spectrum; 22.5 Speed of EM Waves in Vacuum and in Matter

9. What is the wavelength of the radio waves broadcast by an FM radio station with a frequency of 90.9 MHz?

10. What is the frequency of the microwaves in a microwave oven? The wavelength is 12 cm.

11. The currents in household wiring and power lines alternate at a frequency of 60.0 Hz. (a) What is the wavelength of the EM waves emitted by the wiring? (b) Compare this wavelength to the Earth's radius. (c) In what part of the EM spectrum are these waves?

12. In order to study the structure of a crystalline solid, you want to illuminate it with EM radiation whose wavelength is the same as the spacing of the atoms in the crystal (0.20 nm). (a) What is the frequency of the EM radiation? (b) In what part of the EM spectrum (radio, visible, etc.) does it lie?

13. In musical acoustics, a frequency ratio of 2:1 is called an octave. Humans with extremely good hearing can hear sounds ranging from 20 Hz to 20 kHz, which is approximately 10 octaves (since $2^{10} = 1024 \approx 1000$). (a) Approximately how many octaves of visible light are humans able to perceive? (b) Approximately how many octaves wide is the microwave region?

14. You and a friend are sitting in the outfield bleachers of a major league baseball park, 140 m from home plate on a day when the temperature is 20°C. Your friend is listening to the radio commentary with headphones while watching. The broadcast network has a microphone located 17 m from home plate to pick up the sound as the bat hits the ball. This sound is transferred as an EM wave a distance of 75,000 km by satellite from the ball park to the radio. (a) When the batter hits a hard line drive, who will hear the "crack" of the bat first, you or your friend, and what is the shortest time interval between the bat hitting the ball and one of you hearing the sound? (b) How much later does the other person hear the sound?

15. In the United States, the ac household current oscillates at a frequency of 60 Hz. In the time it takes for the current to make one oscillation, how far has the electromagnetic wave traveled from the current-carrying wire? This distance is the wavelength of a 60-Hz EM wave. Compare this length to the distance from Boston to Los Angeles (4200 km).

16. What is the speed of light in a diamond that has an index of refraction of 2.4168?

17. The speed of light in topaz is 1.85×10^8 m/s. What is the index of refraction of topaz?

18. How long does it take sunlight to travel from the Sun to the Earth?

19. How long does it take light to travel from this text to your eyes? Assume a distance of 50.0 cm.

20. The index of refraction of water is 1.33. (a) What is the speed of light in water? (b) What is the wavelength in water of a light wave with a vacuum wavelength of 515 nm?

21. Light of wavelength 692 nm in air passes into window glass with an index of refraction of 1.52. (a) What is the wavelength of the light inside the glass? (b) What is the frequency of the light inside the glass?

22. How far does a beam of light travel in 1 ns?

23. By expressing ϵ_0 and μ_0 in base SI units (kg, m, s, A), prove that the *only* combination of the two with dimensions of speed is $(\epsilon_0\mu_0)^{-1/2}$.

22.6 Characteristics of Electromagnetic Waves in Vacuum

24. The electric field in a microwave traveling through air has amplitude 0.60 mV/m and frequency 30 GHz. Find the amplitude and frequency of the magnetic field.

25. The magnetic field in a radio wave traveling through air has amplitude 2.5×10^{-11} T and frequency 3.0 MHz. (a) Find the amplitude and frequency of the electric field. (b) The wave is traveling in the $-y$-direction. At $y = 0$ and $t = 0$, the magnetic field is 1.5×10^{-11} T in the $+z$-direction. What are the magnitude and direction of the electric field at $y = 0$ and $t = 0$?

26. ✦ The magnetic field of an EM wave is given by $B_y = B_m \sin{(kz + \omega t)}$, $B_x = 0$, and $B_z = 0$. (a) In what direction is this wave traveling? (b) Write expressions for the components of the electric field of this wave.

27. ✦ The electric field of an EM wave is given by $E_z = E_m \sin{(ky - \omega t + \pi/6)}$, $E_x = 0$, and $E_z = 0$. (a) In what direction is this wave traveling? (b) Write expressions for the components of the magnetic field of this wave.

28. ✦ An EM wave is generated by a magnetic dipole antenna as shown in the figure with Conceptual Question 9. The current in the antenna is produced by an LC resonant circuit. The wave is detected at a distant point P. Using the coordinate system in the figure, write equations for the x-, y-, and z-components of the EM fields at a distant point P. (If there is more than one possibility, just give one consistent set of answers.) Define all quantities in your equations in terms of L, C, E_m (the electric field amplitude at point P), and universal constants.

22.7 Energy Transport by EM Waves

29. The intensity of the sunlight that reaches Earth's upper atmosphere is approximately 1400 W/m². (a) What is the average energy density? (b) Find the rms values of the electric and magnetic fields.

30. The cylindrical beam of a 10.0-mW laser is 0.85 cm in diameter. What is the rms value of the electric field?

31. In astronomy it is common to expose a photographic plate to a particular portion of the night sky for quite some time in order to gather plenty of light. Before leaving a plate exposed to the night sky, Matt decides to test his technique by exposing two photographic plates in his lab to light coming through several pinholes. The source of light is 1.8 m from one photographic plate and the exposure time is 1.0 h. For how long should Matt expose a second plate located 4.7 m from the source if the second plate is to have equal exposure (that is, the same energy collected)?

32. A 1.0-m² solar panel on a satellite that keeps the panel oriented perpendicular to radiation arriving from the Sun absorbs 1.4 kJ of energy every second. The satellite is located at 1.00 AU from the Sun. (The Earth-Sun distance is defined to be 1.00 AU.) How long would it take

an identical panel that is also oriented perpendicular to the incoming radiation to absorb the same amount of energy, if it were on an interplanetary exploration vehicle 1.55 AU from the Sun?

33. Fernando detects the electric field from an isotropic source that is 22 km away by tuning in an electric field with an rms amplitude of 55 mV/m. What is the average power of the source?

34. A certain star is 14 million light-years from Earth. The intensity of the light that reaches Earth from the star is 4×10^{-21} W/m². At what rate does the star radiate EM energy?

35. The intensity of the sunlight that reaches Earth's upper atmosphere is approximately 1400 W/m². (a) What is the total average power output of the Sun, assuming it to be an isotropic source? (b) What is the intensity of sunlight incident on Mercury, which is 5.8×10^{10} m from the Sun?

36. Prove that, in an EM wave traveling in vacuum, the electric and magnetic energy densities are equal; that is, prove that

$$\frac{1}{2}\epsilon_0 E^2 = \frac{1}{2\mu_0}B^2$$

at any point and at any instant of time.

37. Verify that the equation $I = \langle u \rangle c$ is dimensionally consistent (that is, check the units).

38. ⒢ The solar panels on the roof of a house measure 4.0 m by 6.0 m. Assume they convert 12% of the incident EM wave's energy to electrical energy. (a) What average power do the panels supply when the incident intensity is 1.0 kW/m² and the panels are perpendicular to the incident light? (b) What average power do the panels supply when the incident intensity is 0.80 kW/m² and the light is incident at an angle of 60.0° from the normal? (c) Take the average daytime power requirement of a house to be about 2 kW. How do your answers to (a) and (b) compare? What are the implications for the use of solar panels?

39. The radio telescope in Arecibo, Puerto Rico, has a diameter of 305 m. It can detect radio waves from space with intensities as small as 10^{-26} W/m². (a) What is the average power incident on the telescope due to a wave at normal incidence with intensity 1.0×10^{-26} W/m²? (b) What is the average power incident on the Earth's surface? (c) What are the rms electric and magnetic fields?

22.8 Polarization

40. Unpolarized light passes through two polarizers in turn with polarization axes at 45° to each other. What is the fraction of the incident light intensity that is transmitted?

41. Light polarized in the x-direction shines through two polarizing sheets. The first sheet's transmission axis makes an angle θ with the x-axis and the transmission axis of the second is parallel to the y-axis. (a) If the

incident light has intensity I_0, what is the intensity of the light transmitted through the second sheet? (b) At what angle θ is the transmitted intensity maximum?

42. Unpolarized light is incident on a system of three polarizers. The second polarizer is oriented at an angle of 30.0° with respect to the first and the third is oriented at an angle of 45.0° with respect to the first. If the light that emerges from the system has an intensity of 23.0 W/m^2, what is the intensity of the incident light?

43. Unpolarized light is incident on four polarizing sheets with their transmission axes oriented as shown in the figure. What percentage of the initial light intensity is transmitted through this set of polarizers?

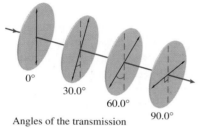

Angles of the transmission axes from the vertical

 44. A polarized beam of light has intensity I_0. We want to rotate the direction of polarization by 90.0° using polarizing sheets. (a) Explain why we must use at least two sheets. (b) What is the transmitted intensity if we use two sheets, each of which rotates the direction of polarization by 45.0°? (c) What is the transmitted intensity if we use four sheets, each of which rotates the direction of polarization by 22.5°?

45. Vertically polarized microwaves traveling into the page are directed at each of three metal plates (a, b, c) that have parallel slots cut in them. (a) Which plate transmits microwaves best? (b) Which plate reflects microwaves best? (c) If the intensity *transmitted through* the *best* transmitter is I_1, what is the intensity transmitted through the second-best transmitter?

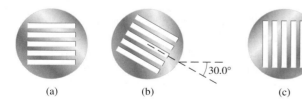

(a)   (b)   (c)

46. Two sheets of polarizing material are placed with their transmission axes at right angles to each other. A third polarizing sheet is placed between them with its transmission axis at 45° to the axes of the other two. (a) If unpolarized light of intensity I_0 is incident on the system, what is the intensity of the transmitted light? (b) What is the intensity of the transmitted light when the middle sheet is removed?

22.9 The Doppler Effect for EM Waves

47. If the speeder in Example 22.9 were going *faster* than the police car, how fast would it have to go so that the reflected microwaves produce the same number of beats per second?

48. Light of wavelength 659.6 nm is emitted by a star. The wavelength of this light as measured on Earth is 661.1 nm. How fast is the star moving with respect to Earth? Is it moving toward Earth or away from it?

49. What must be the relative speed between source and receiver if the wavelength of an EM wave as measured by the receiver is twice the wavelength as measured by the source? Are source and observer moving closer together or farther apart?

50. How fast would you have to drive in order to see a red light as green? Take $\lambda = 630$ nm for red and $\lambda = 530$ nm for green.

Comprehensive Problems

51. Calculate the frequency of an EM wave with a wavelength the size of (a) the thickness of a piece of paper (60 μm), (b) a 91-m-long soccer field, (c) the diameter of Earth, (d) the distance from Earth to the Sun.

52. The intensity of solar radiation that falls on a detector on Earth is 1.00 kW/m^2. The detector is a square that measures 5.00 m on a side and the normal to its surface makes an angle of 30.0° with respect to the Sun's radiation. How long will it take for the detector to measure 420 kJ of energy?

53. Astronauts on the Moon communicated with mission control in Houston via EM waves. There was a noticeable time delay in the conversation due to the round-trip transit time for the EM waves between the Moon and the Earth. How long was the time delay?

54. The antenna on a cordless phone radiates microwaves at a frequency of 2.0 GHz. What is the maximum length of the antenna if it is not to exceed half of a wavelength?

55. Two identical television signals are sent between two cities that are 400.0 km apart. One signal is sent through the air, and the other signal is sent through a fiber optic network. The signals are sent at the same time but the one traveling through air arrives 7.7×10^{-4} s before the one traveling through the glass fiber. What is the index of refraction of the glass fiber?

56. An AM radio station broadcasts at 570 kHz. (a) What is the wavelength of the radio wave in air? (b) If a radio is tuned to this station and the inductance in the tuning circuit is 0.20 mH, what is the capacitance in the tuning circuit? (c) In the vicinity of the radio, the amplitude of the electric field is 0.80 V/m. The radio uses a coil antenna of radius 1.6 cm with 50 turns. What is the maximum emf induced in the antenna, assuming it is

oriented for best reception? Assume that the fields are sinusoidal functions of time.

57. A 60.0-mW pulsed laser produces a pulse of EM radiation with wavelength 1060 nm (in air) that lasts for 20.0 ps (picoseconds). (a) In what part of the EM spectrum is this pulse? (b) How long (in cm) is a single pulse in air? (c) How long is it in water ($n = 1.33$)? (d) How many wavelengths fit in one pulse? (e) What is the total electromagnetic energy in one pulse?

58. The range of wavelengths allotted to the radio broadcast band is from about 190 m to 550 m. If each station needs exclusive use of a frequency band 10 kHz wide, how many stations can operate in the broadcast band?

59. Polarized light of intensity I_0 is incident on a pair of polarizing sheets. Let θ_1 and θ_2 be the angles between the direction of polarization of the incident light and the transmission axes of the first and second sheets, respectively. Show that the intensity of the transmitted light is $I = I_0 \cos^2 \theta_1 \cos^2 (\theta_1 - \theta_2)$.

60. An unpolarized beam of light (intensity I_0) is moving in the x-direction. The light passes through three ideal polarizers whose transmission axes are (in order) at angles 0.0°, 45.0°, and 30.0° counterclockwise from the y-axis in the yz-plane. (a) What is the intensity and polarization of the light that is transmitted by the last polarizer? (b) If the polarizer in the middle is removed, what is the intensity and polarization of the light transmitted by the last polarizer?

61. What are the three lowest angular speeds for which the wheel in Fizeau's apparatus (Fig. 22.13) allows the reflected light to pass through to the observer? Assume the distance between the notched wheel and the mirror is 8.6 km and that there are 5 notches in the wheel.

62. A microwave oven can heat 350 g of water from 25.0°C to 100.0°C in 2.00 min. (a) At what rate is energy absorbed by the water? (b) Microwaves pass through a waveguide of cross-sectional area 88.0 cm². What is the average intensity of the microwaves in the waveguide? (c) What are the rms electric and magnetic fields inside the waveguide?

63. A sinusoidal EM wave has an electric field amplitude $E_m = 32.0$ mV/m. What are the intensity and average energy density? [Hint: Recall the relationship between amplitude and rms value for a quantity that varies sinusoidally.]

64. Energy carried by an EM wave coming through the air can be used to light a bulb that is not connected to a battery or plugged into an electrical outlet. Suppose a receiving antenna is attached to a bulb and the bulb is found to dissipate a maximum power of 1.05 W when the antenna is aligned with the electric field coming from a distant source. The wavelength of the source is large compared to the antenna length. When the antenna is rotated so it makes an angle of 20.0° with the incoming electric field, what is the power dissipated by the bulb?

65. A 10-W laser emits a beam of light 4.0 mm in diameter. The laser is aimed at the Moon. By the time it reaches the Moon, the beam has spread out to a diameter of 85 km. Ignoring absorption by the atmosphere, what is the intensity of the light (a) just outside the laser and (b) where it hits the surface of the Moon?

66. To measure the speed of light, Galileo and a colleague stood on different mountains with covered lanterns. Galileo uncovered his lantern and his friend, seeing the light, uncovered his own lantern in turn. Galileo measured the elapsed time from uncovering his lantern to seeing the light signal response. The elapsed time should be the time for the light to make the round trip plus the reaction time for his colleague to respond. To determine reaction time, Galileo repeated the experiment while he and his friend were close to one another. He found the same time whether his colleague was nearby or far away and concluded that light traveled almost instantaneously. Suppose the reaction time of Galileo's colleague was 0.25 s and for Galileo to observe a difference, the complete round trip would have to take 0.35 s. How far apart would the two mountains have to be for Galileo to observe a finite speed of light? Is this feasible?

67. Suppose some astronauts have landed on Mars. (a) When Mars and Earth are on the same side of the Sun and as close as they can be to one another, how long does it take for radio transmissions to travel one way between the two planets? (b) Suppose the astronauts ask a question of mission control personnel on Earth. What is the shortest possible time they have to wait for a response? The average distance from Mars to the Sun is 2.28×10^{11} m.

Answers to Practice Problems

22.1 (a) EM waves from the transmitting antenna travel outward in all directions. Since the wave travels from the transmitter to the receiver in the +z-direction (the direction of propagation), the direction from the receiver to the transmitter is the −z-direction. (b) $E_y(t) = E_m \cos (kz - \omega t)$, where $k = 2\pi/\lambda$ is the wavenumber; $E_x = E_z = 0$.

22.2 1 ly = 9.5×10^{15} m

22.3 444 nm

22.4 (a) +y-direction; (b) 2.0×10^3 m^{-1}; (c) $B_z(x, y, z, t) = (-1.1 \times 10^{-7}$ T$) \cos [(2.0 \times 10^3$ m$^{-1})y - (6.0 \times 10^{11}$ s$^{-1})t]$, $B_x = B_y = 0$

22.5 The rms fields are proportional to $\sqrt{I}$ and I is proportional to $1/r^2$, so the rms fields are proportional to $1/r$. $E_{rms} = 6.84$ V/m; $B_{rms} = 2.28 \times 10^{-8}$ T

22.6 450 W/m²

22.7 minimum zero (when transmission axes are perpendicular); maximum is $\frac{1}{2}I_0$ (when transmission axes are parallel)

22.8 vertically

22.9 4.6 kHz

Reflection and Refraction of Light

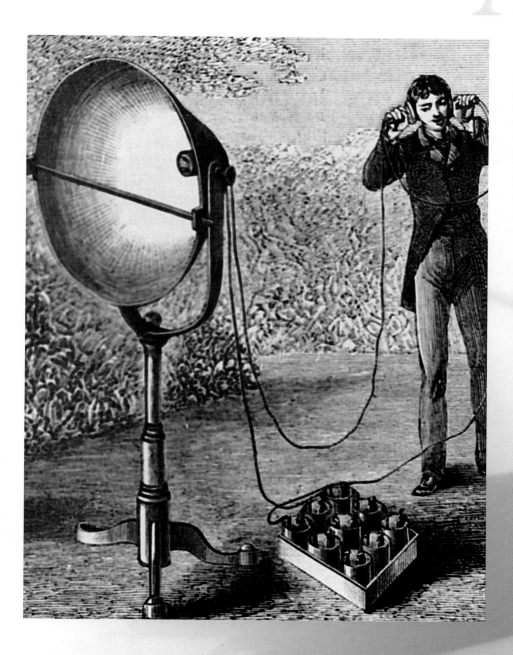

Alexander Graham Bell is famous today for the invention of the telephone in the 1870s. However, Bell believed his most important invention was the *Photophone*. Instead of sending electrical signals over metal wires, the Photophone sent light signals through the air, relying on focused beams of sunlight and reflections from mirrors. What prevented Bell's Photophone from becoming as commonplace as the telephone many years ago? (See p. 852 for the answer.)

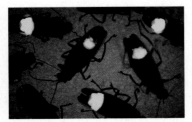

Figure 23.1 The light flash of a firefly is caused by a chemical reaction between oxygen and the substance luciferin. The reaction is catalyzed by the enzyme luciferase.

Making the Connection:

colors from reflection and absorption of light

23.1   WAVEFRONTS, RAYS, AND HUYGENS'S PRINCIPLE

Sources of Light

When we speak of *light*, we mean electromagnetic radiation that we can see with the unaided eye. Light is produced in many different ways. The filament of an incandescent lightbulb emits light due to its high surface temperature; at $T \approx 3000$ K, a significant fraction of the thermal radiation occurs in the visible range. The light emitted by a firefly is the result of a chemical reaction, not of a high surface temperature (Fig. 23.1). A fluorescent substance—such as the one painted on the inside of a fluorescent lightbulb—emits visible light after absorbing ultraviolet radiation.

Most objects we see are not sources of light; we see them by the light they reflect or transmit. Some fraction of the light incident on an object is absorbed, some fraction is transmitted through the object, and the rest is reflected. The nature of the material and its surface determine the relative amounts of absorption, transmission, and reflection at a given wavelength. Grass appears green because it reflects wavelengths that the brain interprets as green. Terra-cotta roof tiles reflect wavelengths that the brain interprets as red/orange (see Fig. 23.2).

Wavefronts and Rays

Since EM waves share many properties in common with all waves, we can use other waves (such as water waves) to aid visualization. A pebble dropped into a pond starts a disturbance that propagates radially outward in all directions on the surface of the water

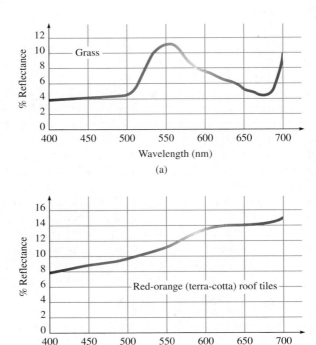

Figure 23.2 Reflectance—percentage of incident light that is reflected—as a function of wavelength for (a) grass and (b) some terra-cotta roof tiles. Source: Reproduced from the ASTER Spectral Library through the courtesy of the Jet Propulsion Laboratory, California Institute of Technology, Pasadena, California. Copyright © 1999, California Institute of Technology. ALL RIGHTS RESERVED.

Figure 23.3 Concentric circular ripples travel on the surface of a pond outward from the point where a fish broke the water surface to catch a bug.

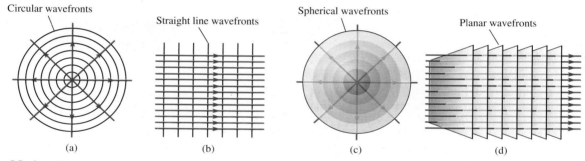

Circular wavefronts

Straight line wavefronts

Spherical wavefronts

Planar wavefronts

(a)   (b)   (c)   (d)

Figure 23.4 Wavefronts and rays for waves with (a) circular wavefronts, (b) straight line wavefronts, (c) spherical wavefronts, and (d) planar wavefronts.

(Fig. 23.3). A **wavefront** is a set of points of equal phase. Each of the circular wave crests in Fig. 23.3 can be considered a wavefront. A water wave with straight line wavefronts can be created by repeatedly dipping a long bar into water.

A **ray** points in the direction of propagation of a wave and is perpendicular to the wavefronts. For a circular wave, the rays are radii pointing outward from the point of origin of the wave (Fig. 23.4a); for a linear wave, the rays are a set of lines parallel to each other, perpendicular to the wavefronts (Fig. 23.4b).

While a surface water wave can have wavefronts that are circles or lines, a wave traveling in three dimensions, such as light, has wavefronts that are spheres, planes, or other *surfaces*. If a small source emits light equally in all directions, the wavefronts are spherical and the rays point radially outward (Fig. 23.4c). Far away from such a point source, the rays are nearly parallel to each other and the wavefronts nearly planar, so the wave can be represented as a plane wave (Fig. 23.4d). The Sun can be considered a point source when viewed from across the galaxy; even on Earth we can treat the sunlight falling upon a small lens as a collection of nearly parallel rays.

Huygens's Principle

Long before the development of electromagnetic theory, the Dutch scientist Christiaan Huygens (1629–1695) developed a geometric method for explaining the behavior of light when it travels through a medium, when it passes from one medium to another, or when it runs into a barrier from which it is reflected.

Huygens's Principle

At some time t, consider every point on a wavefront as a source of a new spherical wave. These *wavelets* move outward at the same speed as the original wave. At a later time $t + \Delta t$, each wavelet has a radius $v\Delta t$, where v is the speed of propagation of the wave. The wavefront at $t + \Delta t$ is a surface tangent to the wavelets. (In situations where no reflection occurs, we ignore the backward-moving wavefront.)

Geometric Optics

Geometric optics is an *approximation* to the behavior of light that applies only when interference and diffraction are negligible. In order for diffraction to be negligible, the sizes of objects and apertures must be *large* compared to the wavelength of the light. In the realm of geometric optics, the propagation of light can be analyzed using rays alone. In a homogeneous material, the rays are straight lines. At a boundary between two different materials, both reflection and transmission may occur. Huygens's principle enables us to derive the laws that determine the directions of the reflected and transmitted rays.

Conceptual Example 23.1

Wavefronts from a Plane Wave

Apply Huygens's principle to a plane wave. In other words, draw the wavelets from points on a planar wavefront and use them to sketch the wavefront at a later time.

Strategy   Since we are limited to a two-dimensional sketch, we draw a wavefront of a plane wave as a straight line. We choose a few points on the wavefront as sources of wavelets. Since there is no backward-moving wave, the wavelets are hemispheres; we draw them as semicircles. Then we draw a line tangent to the wavelets to represent the surface tangent to the wavefronts; this surface is the new wavefront.

Solution and Discussion   In Fig. 23.5a, we first draw a wavefront and four points. We imagine each point as a source of wavelets, so we draw four semicircles of equal radius, one centered on each of the four points. Finally, we draw a line tangent to the four semicircles; this line represents the wavefront at a later time.

Why draw a straight line instead of a wavy line that follows the semicircles along their edges as in Fig. 23.5b? Remember that Huygens's principle says that *every* point on the wavefront is a source of wavelets. We only draw wavelets from a few points, but we must remember that wavelets come from every point on the wavefront. Imagine drawing in more and more wavelets; the surface tangent to them would get less and less wavy, ultimately becoming a plane.

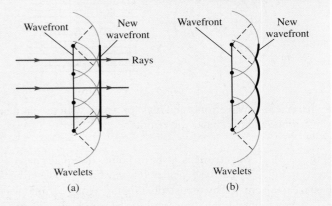

Figure 23.5

(a) Application of Huygens's principle to a plane wave. (b) This construction is not complete because it does not show wavelets coming from *every point* on the wavefront.

At the edges, the new wavefront is curved. This distortion of the wavefront at the edges is an example of diffraction. If a plane wavefront is large, then the wavefront at a later time is a plane with only a bit of curvature at the edges; for many purposes, the diffraction at the edges is negligible.

Conceptual Practice Problem 23.1
A Spherical Wave

Repeat Example 23.1 for the spherical light wave due to a point source.

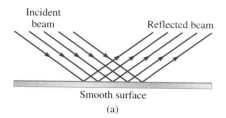

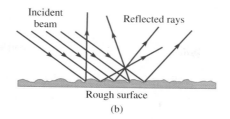

23.2   THE REFLECTION OF LIGHT

Specular and Diffuse Reflection

Reflection from a smooth surface is called *specular reflection*; rays incident at a given angle all reflect at the same angle (Fig. 23.6a). Reflection from a rough, irregular surface is called *diffuse reflection* (Fig. 23.6b). Diffuse reflection is more common in everyday life and enables us to see our surroundings. Specular reflection is more important in optical instruments.

The roughness of a surface is a matter of degree; what appears smooth to the unaided eye can be quite rough on the atomic scale. Thus, there is not a sharp distinction between diffuse and specular reflection. If the sizes of the pits and holes in the rough surface of Fig. 23.6b were small compared to the wavelengths of visible light, the reflection would be specular. When the sizes of the pits are much larger than the wavelengths of visible light, the reflection is diffuse. A polished glass surface looks smooth to visible light, because the wavelengths of visible light are thousands of times larger than the spacing between atoms in the glass. The same surface looks rough to x-rays with wavelengths smaller than the atomic spacing. The metal mesh in the door of a microwave oven reflects microwaves well because the size of the holes is small compared to the 12-cm wavelength of the microwaves.

The Laws of Reflection

Huygens's principle illustrates how specular reflection occurs. In Fig. 23.7, plane wavefronts travel toward a polished metal surface. Every point on an incident wavefront serves as a source of secondary wavelets. Points on an incident wavefront just make the wavefront advance toward the surface. When a point on an incident wavefront contacts the metal, the wavelet propagates *away* from the surface—forming the reflected wavefront—since light cannot penetrate the metal. Wavelets emitted from these points all travel at the same speed, but they are emitted at different times. At any given instant, a wavelet's radius is proportional to the time interval since it was emitted.

Although Huygens's principle is a geometric construction, the construction is validated by modern wave theory. We now know that the reflected wave is generated by

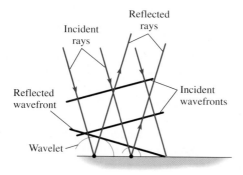

Figure 23.7 A plane wave strikes a metal surface. The wavelets emitted by each point on an incident wavefront when it reaches the surface form the reflected wave.

Figure 23.8 The angles of incidence and of reflection are measured between the ray and the *normal* to the surface (not between the ray and the surface). The incident ray, the reflected ray, and the normal all lie in the same plane.

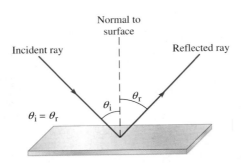

charges at the surface that oscillate in response to the incoming electromagnetic wave; the oscillating charges emit EM waves, which add up to form the reflected wave.

The laws of reflection summarize the relationship between the directions of the incident and reflected rays. The laws are formulated in terms of the angles between a ray and a *normal*—a line *perpendicular* to the surface where the ray touches the surface. The **angle of incidence** (θ_i) is the angle between an incident ray and the normal (Fig. 23.8); the **angle of reflection** (θ_r) is the angle between the reflected ray and the normal. In Problem 9 you can go on to prove that

$$\theta_i = \theta_r \tag{23-1}$$

The other law of reflection says that the incident ray, the reflected ray, and the normal all lie in the same plane (the **plane of incidence**).

Laws of Reflection

1. The angle of incidence equals the angle of reflection.
2. The reflected ray lies in the same plane as the incident ray and the normal to the surface at the point of incidence. The two rays are on opposite sides of the normal.

For diffuse reflection from rough surfaces, the angles of reflection for the incoming rays are still equal to their respective angles of incidence. However, the normals to the rough surface are at random angles with respect to each other, so the reflected rays travel in many directions (Fig. 23.6b).

Reflection and Transmission

So far we have considered only specular reflection from a totally reflecting surface such as polished metal. When light reaches a boundary between two *transparent* media, such as from air to glass, some of the light is reflected and some is transmitted into the new medium. The reflected light still follows the same laws of reflection (as long as the surface is smooth so that the reflection is specular). Generally, much more of the light is transmitted than is reflected. For normal incidence on an air-glass surface, only 4% of the incident intensity is reflected; 96% is transmitted.

23.3   THE REFRACTION OF LIGHT: SNELL'S LAW

In Section 22.5, we showed that when light passes from one transparent medium to another, the wavelength changes (unless the speeds of light in the two media are the same) while the frequency stays the same. In addition, Huygens's principle helps us understand why *light rays change direction* as they cross the boundary between the two media—a phenomenon known as **refraction**.

Refraction: the changing of direction of a light ray as it passes from one medium into another.

We can use Huygens's principle to understand how refraction occurs. Figure 23.9a shows a plane wave incident on a planar boundary between air and glass. In the air, a series of planar wavefronts moves toward the glass. The distance between the wavefronts is equal to one wavelength. Once the wavefront reaches the glass boundary and enters the

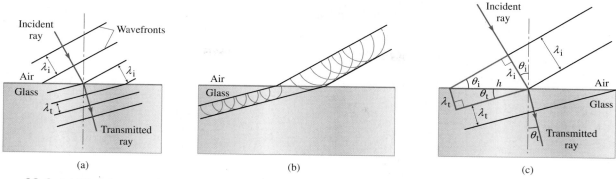

Figure 23.9 (a) Wavefronts and rays at a glass-air boundary. The reflected wavefronts are omitted. Note that the wavefronts are closer together in glass because the wavelength is smaller. (b) Huygens's construction for a wavefront partly in air and partly in glass. (c) Geometry for finding the angle of the transmitted ray.

new material, the wave slows down—light moves more slowly through glass than through air. Since the wavefront approaches the boundary at an angle to the normal, the portion of the wavefront that is still in air continues at the same merry pace while the part that has entered the glass moves more slowly. Figure 23.9b shows a Huygens's construction for a wavefront that is partly in glass. The wavelets have smaller radii in glass since the speed of light is smaller in glass than in air.

Figure 23.9c shows two right triangles that are used to relate the angle of incidence θ_i to the angle of the transmitted ray (or angle of refraction) θ_t. The two triangles share the same hypotenuse (h). Using some trigonometry, we find that

$$\sin \theta_i = \frac{\lambda_i}{h} \quad \text{and} \quad \sin \theta_t = \frac{\lambda_t}{h}$$

Eliminating h yields

$$\frac{\sin \theta_i}{\sin \theta_t} = \frac{\lambda_i}{\lambda_t} \tag{23-2}$$

It is more convenient to rewrite this relationship in terms of the indices of refraction. Recall that when light passes from one transparent medium to another, the *frequency f does not change* (see Section 22.5). Since $v = f\lambda$, λ is directly proportional to v. By definition [$n = c/v$, Eq. (22-4)], the index of refraction n is *inversely* proportional to v. Therefore, λ is inversely proportional to n:

$$\frac{\lambda_i}{\lambda_t} = \frac{v_i/f}{v_t/f} = \frac{v_i}{v_t} = \frac{c/n_i}{c/n_t} = \frac{n_t}{n_i} \tag{23-3}$$

By replacing λ_i/λ_t with n_t/n_i in Eq. (23-2) and cross multiplying, we obtain

Snell's Law

$$n_i \sin \theta_i = n_t \sin \theta_t \tag{23-4}$$

This law of refraction was discovered experimentally by Dutch professor Willebrord Snell (1580–1626). To determine the direction of the transmitted ray *uniquely*, two additional statements are needed:

Laws of Refraction

1. $n_i \sin \theta_i = n_t \sin \theta_t$, where the angles are measured from the normal.
2. The incident ray, the transmitted ray, and the normal all lie in the same plane—the plane of incidence.
3. The incident and transmitted rays are on *opposite sides* of the normal (see Fig. 23.10).

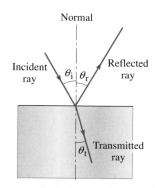

Figure 23.10 The incident ray, the reflected ray, the transmitted ray, and the normal all lie in the same plane. All angles are measured with respect to the normal. Notice that the reflected and transmitted rays are always on the opposite side of the normal from the incident ray.

Table 23.1

Indices of Refraction for $\lambda = 589.3$ nm in Vacuum (at 20°C unless otherwise noted)

Material	Index	Material	Index
Solids		**Liquids**	
Ice (at 0°C)	1.309	Water	1.333
Fluorite	1.434	Acetone	1.36
Fused quartz	1.458	Ethyl alcohol	1.361
Polystyrene	1.49	Carbon tetrachloride	1.461
Lucite	1.5	Glycerine	1.473
Plexiglas	1.51	Sugar solution (80%)	1.49
Crown glass	1.517	Benzene	1.501
Plate glass	1.523	Carbon disulfide	1.628
Sodium chloride	1.544	Methylene iodide	1.74
Light flint glass	1.58		
Dense flint glass	1.655	**Gases at 0°C, 1 atm**	
Sapphire	1.77		
Zircon	1.923	Helium	1.000 036
Diamond	2.419	Ethyl ether	1.000 152
Titanium dioxide	2.9	Water vapor	1.000 250
Gallium phosphide	3.5	Dry air	1.000 293
		Carbon dioxide	1.000 449

Mathematically, Snell's law treats the two media as interchangeable, so the path of a light ray transmitted from one medium to another is correct if the direction of the ray is reversed.

The index of refraction of a material depends on the temperature of the material and on the frequency of the light. Table 23.1 lists indices of refraction for several materials for yellow light with a *wavelength in vacuum* of 589.3 nm. (It is customary to specify the vacuum wavelength instead of the frequency.) In many circumstances the slight variation of n over the visible range of wavelengths can be ignored.

PHYSICS AT HOME

Fill a clear drinking glass with water and then put a pencil in the glass. Look at the pencil from many different angles. Why does the pencil look as if it is bent?

Example 23.2

Ray Traveling Through a Window Pane

A beam of light strikes one face of a window pane with an angle of incidence of 30.0°. The index of refraction of the glass is 1.52. The beam travels through the glass and emerges from a parallel face on the opposite side. Ignore reflections. (a) Find the angle of refraction for the ray inside the glass. (b) Show that the rays in air on either side of the glass (the incident and emerging rays) are parallel to each other.

Strategy First we draw a ray diagram. We are only concerned with the rays transmitted at each boundary, so we omit reflected rays from the diagram. At each boundary we draw a normal, label the angles of incidence and refraction, and apply Snell's law. When the ray passes from air ($n = 1.00$) to glass ($n = 1.52$), it bends *closer to*

Continued on next page

Example 23.2 Continued

the normal: since $n_1 \sin \theta_1 = n_2 \sin \theta_2$, a larger n means a smaller θ. Likewise, when the ray passes from glass to air, it bends *away from* the normal.

Solution   (a) Figure 23.11 is a ray diagram. At the first air-glass boundary, Snell's law yields

$$n_1 \sin \theta_1 = n_2 \sin \theta_2$$

$$\sin \theta_2 = \frac{n_1}{n_2} \sin \theta_1 = \frac{1.00}{1.52} \sin 30.0° = 0.3289$$

The angle of refraction is

$$\theta_2 = \sin^{-1} 0.3289 = 19.2°$$

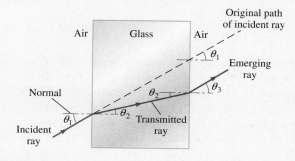

Figure 23.11

A ray of light travels through a window pane.

(b) At the second boundary, from glass to air, we apply Snell's law again. Since the surfaces are parallel, the two normals are parallel. The angle of refraction at the first boundary and the angle of incidence at the second are alternate interior angles, so the angle of incidence at the second boundary must be θ_2.

$$n_2 \sin \theta_2 = n_3 \sin \theta_3$$

We do not need to solve for θ_3 numerically. From the first boundary we know that $n_1 \sin \theta_1 = n_2 \sin \theta_2$; therefore, $n_1 \sin \theta_1 = n_3 \sin \theta_3$. Since $n_1 = n_3$, $\theta_3 = \theta_1$. The two rays—emerging and incident—are parallel to each other.

Discussion   Note that the emerging ray is parallel to the incident ray, but it is *displaced* (see the dashed line in Fig. 23.11). If the two glass surfaces were not parallel, then the two normals would not be parallel. Then the angle of incidence at the second boundary would not be equal to the angle of refraction at the first; the emerging ray would *not* be parallel to the incident ray.

Practice Problem 23.2   Fish Eye View

A fish is at rest beneath the still surface of a pond. If the Sun is 33° above the horizon, at what angle above the horizontal does the fish see the Sun? [*Hint:* Draw a diagram that includes the normal to the surface; be careful to correctly identify the angles of incidence and refraction.]

PHYSICS AT HOME

Place a coin at the far edge of the bottom of an empty mug. Sit in a position so that you are just unable to see the coin. Then, without moving your head, utter the magic word *REFRACTION* as you pour water carefully into the mug on the near side; pour slowly so that the coin does not move. The coin becomes visible when the mug is filled with water (Fig. 23.12).

(a)

(b)

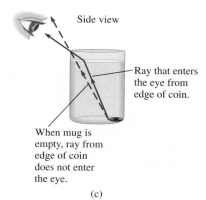

(c)

Figure 23.12 (a) The coin at the bottom of the mug is not visible. (b) After the mug is filled with water, the coin is visible. (c) Refraction at the water-air boundary bends light rays from the coin so they enter the eye.

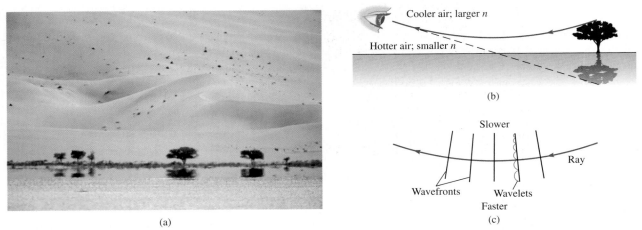

(a)

Figure 23.13 (a) Mirage seen in the desert in Namibia. Note that the images are upside down. (b) A ray from the Sun bends upward into the eye of the observer. (c) The bottom of the wavefront moves faster than the top.

Making the Connection:

mirages

Mirages

Refraction of light in the air causes the *mirages* seen in the desert or on a hot road in summer (Fig. 23.13a). The hot ground warms the air near it, so light rays from the sky travel through warmer and warmer air as they approach the ground. Since the speed of light in air increases with increasing temperature, light travels faster in the hot air near the ground than in the cooler air above. The temperature change is gradual, so there is no *abrupt* change in the index of refraction; instead of being bent abruptly, rays gradually curve upward (Fig. 23.13b).

The wavelets from points on a wavefront travel at different speeds; the radius of a wavelet closer to the ground is larger than that of a wavelet higher up (Fig. 23.13c). The brain interprets the rays coming upward into the eye as coming from the ground even though they really come from the sky. What may look like a body of water on the ground is actually an image of the blue sky overhead.

A *superior mirage* occurs when the layer of air near Earth's surface is *colder* than the air above, due to a snowy field or to the ocean. A ship located just *beyond* the horizon can sometimes be seen because light rays from the ship are gradually bent downward (Fig. 23.14). Ships and lighthouses seem to float in the sky or appear much taller than they are. Refraction also allows the Sun to be seen before it actually rises above the horizon and after it is already below the horizon at sunrise and sunset.

Figure 23.14 (a) Superior mirage of a house seen in Finland's southwestern archipelago; (b) a sketch of the light rays that form a superior mirage of a house.

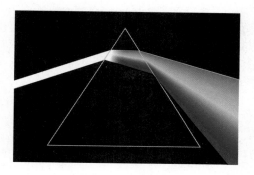

Figure 23.15 Dispersion of white light by a prism. (See also the photo in Fig. 22.15.)

Dispersion in a Prism

When natural white light enters a triangular prism, the light emerging from the far side of the prism is separated into a continuous spectrum of colors from red to violet (Fig. 23.15). The separation occurs because the prism is dispersive—that is, the speed of light in the prism depends on the frequency of the light (see Section 22.5).

Natural white light is a mixture of light at all the frequencies in the visible range. At the front surface of the prism, each light ray of a particular frequency refracts at an angle determined by the index of refraction of the prism at that frequency. The index of refraction increases with increasing frequency, so it is smallest for red and increases gradually until it is largest for violet. As a result, violet bends the most and red the least. Refraction occurs again as light leaves the prism. The geometry of the prism is such that the different colors are spread apart farther at the back surface.

Rainbows

Rainbows are formed by the dispersion of light in water. A ray of sunlight that enters a raindrop is separated into the colors of the spectrum. At each air-water boundary there may be both reflection and refraction. The rays that contribute to a *primary rainbow*—the brightest and often the only one seen—pass into the raindrop, reflect off the back of the raindrop, and then are transmitted back into the air (Fig. 23.16a). Refraction occurs both where the ray enters the drop (air-water) and again when it leaves (water-air), just as for a prism. Since the index of refraction varies with frequency, sunlight is separated into the spectral colors. For relatively large water droplets, as occur in a gentle summer shower, the rays emerge with an angular separation between red and violet of about 2° (Fig. 23.16b).

A person looking into the sky away from the Sun sees red light coming from raindrops higher in the sky and violet light coming from lower droplets (Fig. 23.16c). The rainbow is a circular arc that subtends an angle of 42° for red and 40° for violet, with the other colors falling in between.

In good conditions, a double rainbow can be seen. The secondary rainbow has a larger radius, is less intense, and has its colors reversed (Fig. 23.16d). It arises from rays that undergo *two reflections* inside the raindrop before emerging. The angles subtended by a secondary rainbow are 50.5° for red and 54° for violet.

Making the Connection:
rainbows

23.4   TOTAL INTERNAL REFLECTION $\left(\text{Critical Angle}\right)$

According to Snell's law, if a ray is transmitted from a slower medium into a faster medium (from a higher index of refraction to a lower one), the refracted ray bends *away* from the normal (Fig. 23.17, ray *b*). That is, the angle of refraction is greater than the angle of incidence. As the angle of incidence is increased, the angle of refraction eventually reaches 90° (Fig. 23.17, ray *c*). At 90°, the refracted ray is parallel to the surface. It isn't transmitted into the faster medium; it just moves along the surface. The angle of

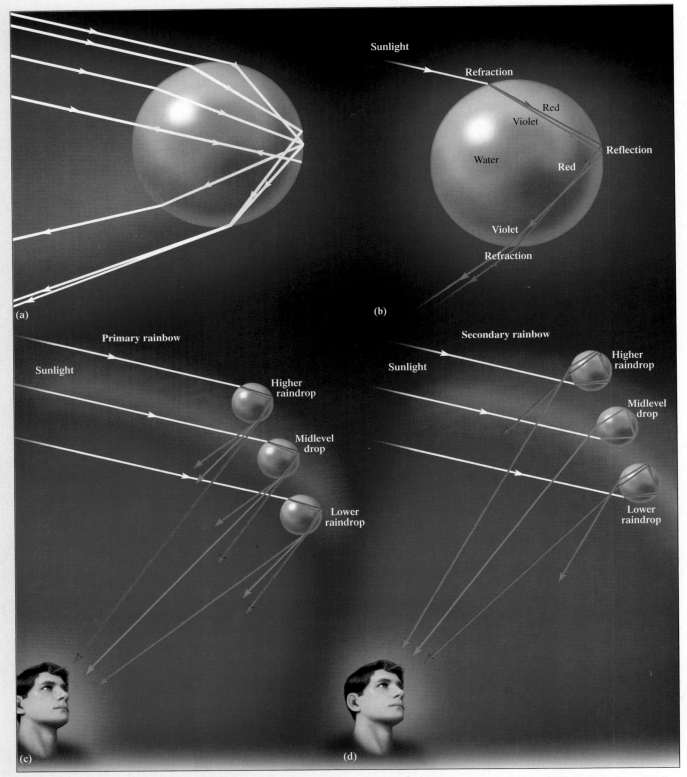

Labels in figure:
(a)

Sunlight
Refraction
Red
Violet
Water
Reflection
Red
Violet
Refraction
(b)

Primary rainbow
Sunlight
Higher raindrop
Midlevel drop
Lower raindrop
(c)

Secondary rainbow
Sunlight
Higher raindrop
Midlevel drop
Lower raindrop
(d)

Figure 23.16 (a) Rays of sunlight that are incident on the upper half of a raindrop and reflect once inside the raindrop. While the incident rays are parallel, the emerging rays are not. The pair of rays along the bottom edge shows where the emerging light has the highest intensity. Only the rays of maximum intensity are shown in parts (b) and (c). (b) Because the index of refraction of water depends on frequency, the angle at which the light leaves the drop depends on frequency. At each boundary, both reflection and transmission occur. Reflected or transmitted rays that do not contribute to the primary rainbow are omitted. (c) Light from many different raindrops contributes to the appearance of a rainbow. Angles are exaggerated for clarity. (d) Light rays that reflect twice inside the raindrop form the secondary rainbow. Note that the order of the colors is reversed: now violet is highest and red is lowest.

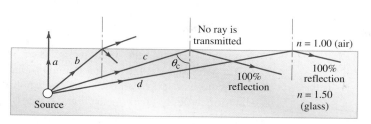

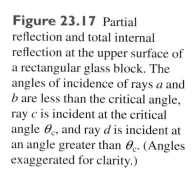

Figure 23.17 Partial reflection and total internal reflection at the upper surface of a rectangular glass block. The angles of incidence of rays *a* and *b* are less than the critical angle, ray *c* is incident at the critical angle θ_c, and ray *d* is incident at an angle greater than θ_c. (Angles exaggerated for clarity.)

incidence for which the angle of refraction is 90° is called the **critical angle** θ_c for the boundary between the two media. From Snell's law,

$$n_i \sin \theta_c = n_t \sin 90°$$

Critical angle:

$$\theta_c = \sin^{-1} \frac{n_t}{n_i} \qquad (23-5a)$$

where the subscripts "i" and "t" refer to the media in which the incident and transmitted rays travel. Since we are discussing an incident ray in a slower medium, $n_i > n_t$.

For an angle of incidence greater than θ_c, the refracted ray can't bend away from the normal *more* than 90°; to do so would be reflection rather than refraction, and a different law governs the angle of reflection. Mathematically, there is no angle whose sine is greater than 1 (= sin 90°), so it is impossible to satisfy Snell's law if $n_i \sin \theta_i > n_t$ (which is equivalent to saying $\theta_i > \theta_c$). If the angle of incidence is greater than θ_c, there cannot be a transmitted ray; if there is no ray transmitted into the faster medium, all the light must be reflected from the boundary (Fig. 23.17, ray *d*). This is called **total internal reflection**.

● The **critical angle** is the minimum angle of incidence for which no light is transmitted past the boundary.

$$\text{no transmitted ray for } \theta_i \geq \theta_c \qquad (23-5b)$$

Total reflection cannot occur when a ray in a faster medium hits a boundary with a slower medium. In that case the refracted ray bends *toward* the normal, so the angle of refraction is always less than the angle of incidence. Even at the largest possible angle of incidence, 90°, the angle of refraction is less than 90°. Total internal reflection can only occur when the incident ray is in the slower medium.

Example 23.3

Total Internal Reflection in a Triangular Glass Prism

A beam of light is incident on the triangular glass prism in air. What is the largest angle of incidence θ_i below the normal (as shown in Fig. 23.18) so that the beam undergoes total reflection from the back of the prism (the hypotenuse)? The prism has an index of refraction $n = 1.50$.

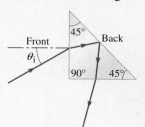

Figure 23.18

Strategy In this problem it is easiest to work backward. Total internal reflection occurs if the angle of incidence at the back of the prism is greater than or equal to the critical angle. We start by finding the critical angle and then work backward using geometry and Snell's law to find the corresponding angle of incidence at the front of the prism.

Solution To find the critical angle from Snell's law, we set the angle of refraction equal to 90°.

$$n_i \sin \theta_c = n_a \sin 90°$$

Continued on next page

Example 23.3 Continued

The incident ray is in the internal medium (glass). Therefore, $n_i = 1.50$ and $n_a = 1.00$.

$$\sin \theta_c = \frac{n_a}{n_i} \sin 90° = \frac{1.00}{1.50} \times 1.00 = 0.667$$

$$\theta_c = \sin^{-1} 0.667 = 41.8°$$

In Fig. 23.19, we draw an enlarged ray diagram and label the angle of incidence at the back of the prism as θ_c. The

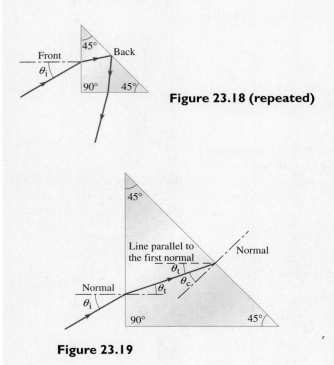

Figure 23.18 (repeated)

Figure 23.19

angles of incidence and refraction at the front are labeled θ_i and θ_t; they are related through Snell's law:

$$1.00 \sin \theta_i = 1.50 \sin \theta_t$$

What remains is to find the relationship between θ_t and θ_c. By drawing a line at the second boundary that is parallel to the normal at the first boundary, we can use alternate interior angles to label θ_t (see Fig. 23.19). The angle between the two normals is 45.0°, so

$$\theta_t = 45.0° - \theta_c = 45.0° - 41.8° = 3.2°$$

Then

$$\sin \theta_i = 1.50 \sin \theta_t = 1.50 \times 0.05582 = 0.0837$$

$$\theta_i = \sin^{-1} 0.0837 = 4.8°$$

Discussion   For a beam incident below the normal at angles from 0 to 4.8°, total internal reflection occurs at the back. If a beam is incident at an angle greater than 4.8°, then the angle of incidence at the back is less than the critical angle, so transmission into the air occurs there. Conceptual Practice Problem 23.3 considers what happens to a beam incident above the normal.

If we had mixed up the two indices of refraction, we would have wound up trying to take the inverse sine of 1.5. That would be a clue that we made a mistake.

Conceptual Practice Problem 23.3
Ray Incident from Above the Normal

Draw a ray diagram for a beam of light incident on the prism of Fig. 23.18 from *above* the normal. Show that at *any* angle of incidence, the beam undergoes total internal reflection at the back of the prism.

Total Internal Reflection in Prisms

Making the Connection:

periscope

Optical instruments such as periscopes, single-lens reflex (SLR) cameras, binoculars, and telescopes often use prisms to reflect a beam of light. Fig. 23.20a shows a simple periscope. Light is reflected through a 90° angle by each of two prisms; the net result is a displacement of the beam. A similar scheme is used in binoculars (Fig. 23.20b). In an SLR camera, one of the prisms is replaced by a movable mirror. When the mirror is in place, the light through the camera lens is diverted up to the viewfinder, so you can see

Figure 23.20 (a) A periscope uses two reflecting prisms to shift the beam of light. (b) In binoculars, the light undergoes total internal reflection twice in each prism.

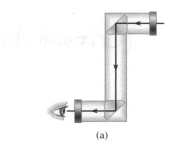

(a)

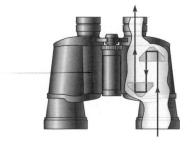

(b)

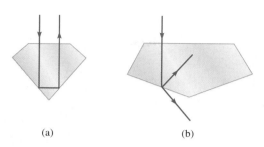

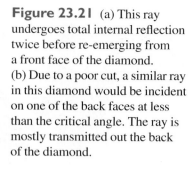

(a)   (b)

Figure 23.21 (a) This ray undergoes total internal reflection twice before re-emerging from a front face of the diamond. (b) Due to a poor cut, a similar ray in this diamond would be incident on one of the back faces at less than the critical angle. The ray is mostly transmitted out the back of the diamond.

exactly what will appear on film. Depressing the shutter moves the mirror out of the way so the light falls onto the film instead. In binoculars and telescopes, *erecting prisms* are often used to turn an upside-down image right-side-up.

An advantage of using prisms instead of mirrors in these applications is that 100% of the light is reflected. A typical mirror reflects only about 90%—remember that the oscillating electrons that produce the reflected wave are moving in a metal with some electrical resistance, so energy dissipation occurs.

The brilliant sparkle of a diamond is due to total internal reflection. The cuts are made so that most of the light incident on the front faces is totally reflected several times inside the diamond and then re-emerges toward the viewer. A poorly cut diamond allows too much light to emerge away from the viewer (see Fig. 23.21).

Fiber Optics

Making the Connection:
fiber optics

Total internal reflection is the principle behind fiber optics, a technology that has revolutionized both communications and medicine. At the center of an optical fiber is a transparent cylindrical core made of glass or plastic with a relatively high index of refraction (Fig. 23.22). The core may be as thin as a few μm in diameter—quite a bit thinner than a human hair. Surrounding the core is a coating called the cladding, which is also transparent but has a lower index of refraction than the core. The "mismatch" in the indices of refraction is maximized so that the critical angle at the core-cladding boundary is as small as possible.

Light signals travel nearly parallel to the axis of the core. It is impossible to have light rays enter the fiber *perfectly* parallel to the axis of the fiber, so the rays eventually hit the cladding *at a large angle of incidence.* As long as the angle of incidence is greater than the critical angle, the ray is totally reflected back into the core; no light leaks out into the cladding. A ray may typically reflect from the cladding thousands of times per meter of fiber, but since the ray is totally reflected each time, the signal can travel long distances—kilometers in some cases—before any appreciable signal loss occurs.

The fibers are flexible so they can be bent as necessary. The smaller the critical angle, the more tightly a fiber can be bent. If the fiber is kinked (bent too tightly), rays

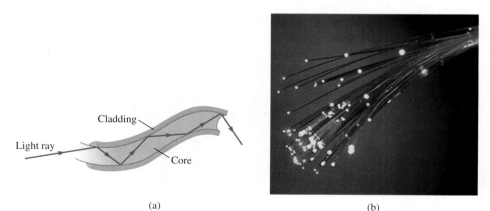

(a)   (b)

Figure 23.22 (a) An optical fiber. (b) A bundle of optical fibers.

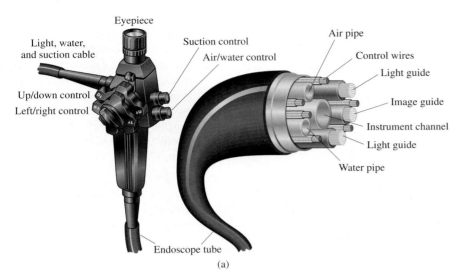

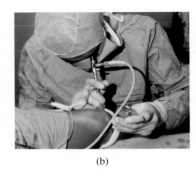

Figure 23.23 (a) An endoscope. (b) Arthroscopic knee surgery. An arthroscope is similar to an endoscope, but is used in the diagnosis and treatment of injuries to the joints.

strike the boundary at less than the critical angle, resulting in dramatic signal loss as light passes into the cladding.

Optical fiber is far superior to copper wire in its capacity to carry information. A single optical fiber can carry tens of thousands of phone conversations, while a pair of copper wires can only carry about 20 at the most. Electrical signals in copper wires also lose strength much more rapidly (due in part to the electrical resistance of the wires) and are susceptible to electrical interference. Over 80% of the long-distance phone calls in the world are carried by fiber optics; computer networks and video increasingly use fiber optics as well.

In medicine, bundles of optical fibers are at the heart of the endoscope (Fig. 23.23), which is fed through the nose, mouth, or rectum, or through a small incision, into the body. One bundle of fibers carries light into a body cavity or an organ and illuminates it; another bundle transmits an image back to the doctor for viewing.

The endoscope is not limited to diagnosis; it can be fitted with instruments enabling a physician to take tissue samples, perform surgery, cauterize blood vessels, or suction out debris. Surgery performed using an endoscope uses much smaller incisions than traditional surgery; as a result, recovery is much faster. A gallbladder operation that used to require an extended hospital stay can now be done on an outpatient basis in many cases.

Making the Connection:
endoscope

Bell's Photophone

Almost a century before the invention of fiber optics, Bell's Photophone used light to carry a telephone signal. The Photophone projected the voice toward a mirror, which vibrated in response. A focused beam of sunlight reflecting from the mirror captured the vibrations. Other mirrors were used to reflect the signal as necessary until it was transformed back into sound at the receiving end. The light traveled in straight line paths through air between the mirrors.

Bell's Photophone worked only intermittently. Many things could interfere with a transmission, including cloudy weather. With nothing to keep the beam from spreading out, it worked only over short distances. Not until the invention of fiber optics in the 1970s could light signals travel reliably over long distances without significant loss or interference.

23.5   POLARIZATION BY REFLECTION

Brewster's angle: the angle of incidence for which the reflected light is totally polarized.

In Section 22.8 we mentioned that unpolarized light is partially or totally polarized by reflection (Fig. 23.24a). Using Snell's law, we can find the angle of incidence—called **Brewster's angle** θ_B—for which the reflected light is totally polarized. The reflected

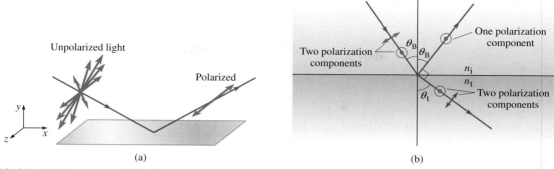

Figure 23.24 (a) Unpolarized light is partially or totally polarized by reflection. (b) When light is incident at Brewster's angle, the reflected and transmitted rays are perpendicular and the reflected light is totally polarized perpendicular to the plane of the page. (The three polarization directions are shown in different colors in (b) merely to help distinguish them; these colors have nothing to do with the color of the light.)

light is totally polarized *when the reflected and transmitted rays are perpendicular to each other* (Fig. 23.24b). These rays are perpendicular if $\theta_B + \theta_t = 90°$. Since the two angles are complementary, $\sin \theta_t = \cos \theta_B$. Then

$$n_i \sin \theta_B = n_t \sin \theta_t = n_t \cos \theta_B$$

$$\frac{\sin \theta_B}{\cos \theta_B} = \frac{n_t}{n_i} = \tan \theta_B$$

Brewster's angle:

$$\theta_B = \tan^{-1} \frac{n_t}{n_i} \qquad (23\text{-}6)$$

The value of Brewster's angle depends on the indices of refraction of the two media. Unlike the critical angle for total internal reflection, Brewster's angle exists regardless of which index of refraction is larger.

Why is the reflected light totally polarized when the reflected and transmitted rays are perpendicular? In Fig. 23.24, the unpolarized incident light is represented as a mixture of two perpendicular polarization components: one perpendicular to the plane of incidence and one in the plane of incidence. Note that the polarization components in the plane of incidence, represented by red and blue arrows, are not in the same direction; polarization components must be perpendicular to the ray since light is a transverse wave.

The same oscillating charges at the surface of the second medium radiate both the reflected light and the transmitted light. The oscillations are along the blue and green directions. The blue direction of oscillation contributes nothing to the reflected ray because an oscillating charge does not radiate along its axis of oscillation. Thus, when the light is incident at Brewster's angle, *the reflected light is totally polarized perpendicular to the plane of incidence.* At other angles of incidence, the reflected light is *partially* polarized perpendicular to the plane of incidence. If light is incident at Brewster's angle and is polarized in the plane of incidence (that is, it has no polarization component perpendicular to the plane of incidence), no light is reflected.

23.6 THE FORMATION OF IMAGES THROUGH REFLECTION OR REFRACTION

When you look into a mirror, you see an image of yourself. What do we mean by an *image*? It *appears* as if your identical twin were standing behind the mirror. If you were looking at an actual twin, each point on your twin would reflect light in many different directions. Some of that light enters your eye. In essence, what your eye does is take the

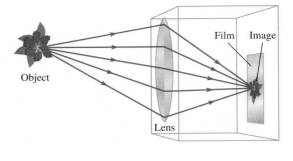

Figure 23.25 Formation of a real image by a camera lens. If the film and the back of the camera were not there, the rays would continue on, diverging from the image point.

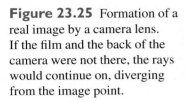 An image is *real* if light rays from a point on the object converge to the corresponding point on the image. An image is *virtual* if light rays from a point on the object are directed as if they diverged from a point on the image, even though the rays do not actually pass through the image point.

rays diverging from a given point and trace them backward to figure out where they come from. Your brain interprets light reflected from the mirror in the same way: all the light rays from any point on you (the object whose image is being formed) must reflect from the mirror *as if they came from a single point behind the mirror.*

Ideally, in the formation of an image, there is a one-to-one correspondence of points on the object and points on the image. If rays from one point on the object seem to come from many different points, the overlap of light from different points would look blurred. (A real lens or mirror may deviate somewhat from ideal behavior, causing some degree of blurring in the image.)

There are two kinds of images. For the plane mirror, the light rays *seem* to come from a point behind the mirror, but we know there aren't actually any light rays back there. In a **virtual image**, we trace light rays from a point on the object back to a point from which they *appear* to diverge, even though the rays do not actually come from that point. In a **real image**, the rays actually *do* pass through the image point. A camera lens forms a real image of the object being photographed on the film. The light rays have to actually be there to expose the film! The rays from a point on the object must all reach the same point on the film or else the picture will come out blurry. If the film and the back of the camera were not there to interrupt the light rays, they would diverge from the image point (Fig. 23.25). An image must be real if it is projected onto a surface such as film, a viewing screen, or a detector.

Projecting a real image onto a screen is only one way to view it. Real images can also be viewed directly (as virtual images are viewed) by looking into the lens or mirror. However, to view a real image, the viewer must be located *beyond the image* so that the rays from a point on the object all diverge from a point on the image. In Fig. 23.25, if the film is removed, the image can be viewed by looking into the lens from points beyond the image (that is, to the right of where the film is placed).

Finding an Image Using a Ray Diagram

- Draw two (or more) rays coming from a single off-axis point on the object toward whatever forms the image (usually a lens or mirror). (Only two rays are necessary since they *all* map to the same image point.)
- Trace the rays, applying the laws of reflection and refraction as needed, until they reach the observer.
- Extrapolate the rays backward along straight line paths until they intersect at the image point.
- If light rays actually go through the image point, the image is real. If they do not, the image is virtual.
- To find the image of an extended object, find the images of two or more points on the object.

Example 23.4

A Kingfisher Looking for Prey

A small fish is at a depth d below the surface of a still pond. What is the *apparent* depth of the fish as viewed by a belted kingfisher—a bird that dives underwater to catch fish? Assume the kingfisher is directly above the fish. Use $n = \frac{4}{3}$ for water.

Strategy   The apparent depth is the depth of the *image* of the fish. Light rays coming from the fish toward the surface are refracted as they pass into the air. We choose a point on the fish and trace the rays from that point into the air; then we trace the refracted rays backward along straight lines until they meet at the image point. The kingfisher directly above sees not only a ray coming straight up ($\theta_i = 0$); it also sees rays at small but nonzero angles of incidence. We may be able to use small-angle approximations for these angles. However, for clarity in the ray diagram, we exaggerate the angles of incidence.

Solution   In Fig. 23.26a we sketch a fish under water at a depth d. From a point on the fish, rays diverge toward the surface. At the surface they are bent away from the

normal (since air has a lower index of refraction). The image point is found by tracing the refracted rays straight backward (dashed lines) to where they meet. We label the image depth d'. From the ray diagram, we see that $d' < d$; the apparent depth is less than the actual depth.

Only two rays need be used to locate the image. To simplify the math, one of them can be the ray normal to the surface. The other ray is incident on the water surface at angle θ_i. This ray leaves the water surface at angle θ_t, where

$$n_w \sin \theta_i = n_a \sin \theta_t \tag{1}$$

To find d', we use two right triangles (Fig. 23.26b) that share the same side s—the distance between the points at which the two chosen rays intersect the water surface. The angles θ_i and θ_t are known since they are alternate interior angles with the angles at the surface. From these triangles,

$$\tan \theta_i = \frac{s}{d} \quad \text{and} \quad \tan \theta_t = \frac{s}{d'}$$

Continued on next page

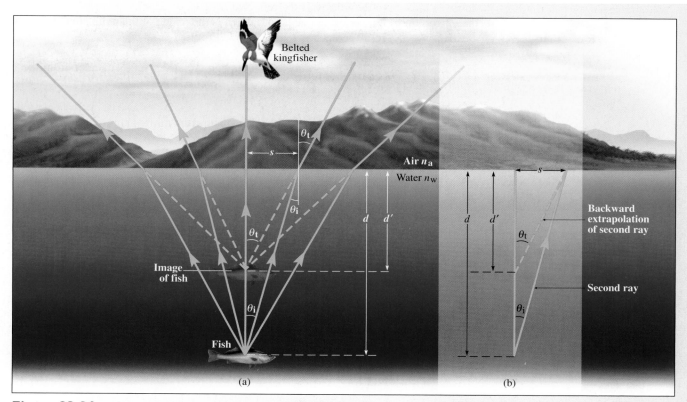

Figure 23.26   (a) Formation of the image of the fish. (b) Two right triangles that share side s enable us to solve for the image depth d' in terms of d.

Example 23.4 Continued

For small angles, we can set $\tan \theta \approx \sin \theta$. Then Eq. (1) becomes

$$n_w \frac{s}{d} = n_a \frac{s}{d'}$$

After eliminating s, we solve for the ratio d'/d:

$$\frac{\text{apparent depth}}{\text{actual depth}} = \frac{d'}{d} = \frac{n_a}{n_w} = \frac{3}{4}$$

The apparent depth of the fish is $\frac{3}{4}$ of the actual depth.

Discussion   The result is valid only for small angles of incidence—that is, for a viewer directly above the fish.

The apparent depth depends on the angle at which the fish is viewed.

The image of the fish is virtual. The light rays seen by the kingfisher *seem* to come from the location of the image, but they do not.

Practice Problem 23.4   Evading the Predator

Suppose the fish looks upward and sees the kingfisher. If the kingfisher is a height h above the surface of the pond, what is its apparent height h' as viewed by the fish?

23.7   PLANE MIRRORS

A shiny metal surface is a good reflector of light. An ordinary mirror is *back-silvered*; that is, a thin layer of shiny metal is applied to the *back* of a flat piece of glass. A back-silvered mirror actually produces two reflections: a faint one, seldom even noticed, from the front surface of the glass and a strong one from the metal. *Front-silvered* mirrors are used in precision work, since they produce only one reflection; they are not practical for everyday use because the metal coating is easily scratched. If we ignore the faint reflection from the glass, then back-silvered mirrors are treated the same as front-silvered mirrors.

Light reflected from a mirror follows the laws of reflection discussed in Section 23.2. Figure 23.27a shows a point source of light located in front of a plane mirror; an observer looks into the mirror. If the reflected rays are extrapolated backward through the mirror, they all intersect at one point, which is the image of the point source. Using any two rays and some geometry, you can show (Problem 45) that

> For a plane mirror, a point source and its image are at the same distance from the mirror (on opposite sides); both lie on the same normal line.

The rays only *appear* to originate at the image behind the mirror; no rays travel through the mirror.

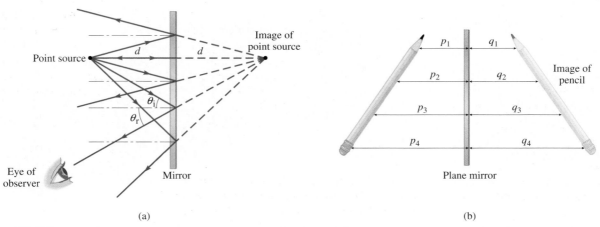

Figure 23.27 (a) A plane mirror forms an image of a point source. The source and image are equidistant from the mirror and lie on the same normal line. (b) Sketching the image of a pencil in front of a plane mirror.

We treat an extended object in front of a plane mirror as a set of point sources (the points on the surface of the object). In Fig. 23.27b, a pencil is in front of a mirror. To sketch the image, we first construct normals to the mirror from several points on the pencil. Then each image point is placed a distance behind the mirror equal to the distance from the mirror to the corresponding point on the object.

Conceptual Example 23.5

Mirror Length for a Full-Length Image

Grant is carrying his niece Dana on his shoulders (Fig. 23.28). What is the minimum vertical length of a plane mirror in which Grant can see a full image (from his toes to the top of Dana's head)? How should this minimum-length mirror be placed on the wall?

Strategy   Ray diagrams are *essential* in geometric optics. A ray diagram is most helpful if we carefully decide which rays are most important to the solution. Here, we want to make sure Grant can see the images of two particular points: his toes and the top of Dana's head. If he can see those two points, he can see everything between them. In order for Grant to see the image of a point, a ray of light from that point must reflect from the mirror and enter Grant's eye.

Solution and Discussion   After drawing Grant, Dana, and the mirror (Fig. 23.28), we want to draw a ray from Grant's toes that strikes the mirror and is reflected to his eye. The line *DH* is a normal to the mirror surface. Since the angle of incidence is equal to the angle of reflection, the

triangles *CHD* and *EHD* are congruent and $CD = DE = GH$. Therefore,

$$GH = \tfrac{1}{2}CE$$

Similarly, we draw a ray from the top of Dana's head to the mirror that is reflected into Grant's eye and find that

$$FG = \tfrac{1}{2}AC$$

The length of the mirror is

$$FH = FG + GH = \tfrac{1}{2}(AC + CE) = \tfrac{1}{2}AE$$

Therefore, the length of the mirror must be *one-half* the distance from Grant's toes to Dana's head.

The minimum-length mirror only allows a full-length view if it is hung properly. The top of the mirror (*F*) must be a distance *AB* below the top of Dana's head. A full-length mirror is *not* necessary to get a full-length view. Extending the mirror all the way to the floor is of no use; the bottom of the mirror only needs to be halfway between the floor and the eyes of the shortest person who uses the mirror. Note that the distance *s* between Grant and the mirror has no effect on the result. That is, you need the same height mirror whether you're up close to it or farther back.

Practice Problem 23.5   Two Sisters with One Mirror

Sarah's eyes are 1.72 m above the floor when she is wearing her dress shoes, and the top of her head is 1.84 m above the floor. Sarah has a mirror that is 0.92 m in length, hung on the wall so she can just see a full-length image of herself. Suppose Sarah's sister Michaela is 1.62 m tall and her eyes are 1.52 m above the floor. If Michaela uses Sarah's mirror without moving it, can she see a full-length image of herself? Draw a ray diagram to illustrate.

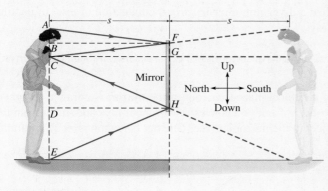

Figure 23.28
Conceptual Example 23.5.

PHYSICS AT HOME

You can easily demonstrate *multiple* images using two plane mirrors. Set up two plane mirrors at a 90° angle on a table and place an object with lettering on it between them. You should see three images. The image straight back is due to rays that reflect twice—once from each mirror. Draw a ray diagram to illustrate the formation of each image. In which of the images is the lettering reversed? (See Conceptual Question 4 for some insight into the apparent left-right reversal.)

Figure 23.29 Two plane mirrors at an angle of 72° form four images.

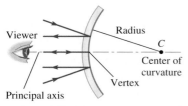

Figure 23.30 A convex mirror's center of curvature is behind the mirror.

🌑 The notation $\overline{AF}$ means the length of the line segment from A to F.

image behind mirror → upright = virtual

PHYSICS AT HOME (continued)

One way to think about multiple images is that each mirror forms an image of the other mirror; then the image-mirrors produce images of images. To explore further, gradually reduce the angle between the mirrors (see Fig. 23.29).

23.8   SPHERICAL MIRRORS

Convex Spherical Mirror

In a spherical mirror, the reflecting surface is a section of a sphere. A **convex mirror** curves *away from* the viewer; its *center of curvature* is *behind* the mirror (Fig. 23.30). An extended radius drawn from the center of curvature through the **vertex**—the center of the surface of the mirror—is the **principal axis** of the mirror.

In Fig. 23.31a, a ray parallel to the principal axis is incident on the surface of a convex mirror at point A, which is close to the vertex V. (In the diagram, the distance between points A and V is exaggerated for clarity.) A radial line from the center of curvature through point A is normal to the mirror. The angle of incidence is equal to the angle of reflection: $\theta_i = \theta_r = \theta$.

By alternate interior angles, we know that

$$\angle ACF = \theta$$

Triangle *AFC* is isosceles since it has two equal angles; therefore,

$$\overline{AF} = \overline{FC}$$

Since the incident ray is close to the principal axis, θ is small. As a result,

$$\overline{AF} + \overline{FC} \approx R \quad \text{and} \quad \overline{VF} \approx \overline{AF} \approx \tfrac{1}{2}R$$

where $\overline{AC} = \overline{VC} = R$ is the radius of curvature of the mirror. Note that this derivation is true for *any* angle θ *as long as it is sufficiently small*. Thus, all rays parallel to the axis *that are incident near the vertex* are reflected by the convex mirror so that they *appear* to originate from point F, which is called the **focal point** of the mirror (Fig. 23.31b). A convex mirror is also called a **diverging mirror** since the reflection of a set of parallel rays is a set of diverging rays.

The focal point of a convex mirror is on the principal axis a distance $\tfrac{1}{2}R$ behind the mirror.

To find the image of an object placed in front of the mirror, we draw a few rays. Figure 23.32 shows an object in front of a convex mirror. Four rays are drawn from the point at the top of the object to the mirror surface. One ray (shown in green) is parallel

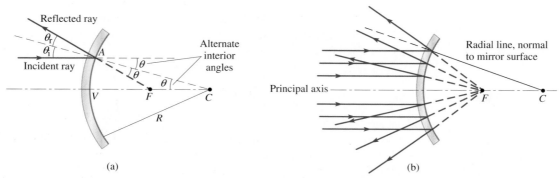

Figure 23.31 (a) Location of the focal point (F) of a convex mirror. (b) Parallel rays reflected from a convex mirror *appear to be* coming from the focal point.

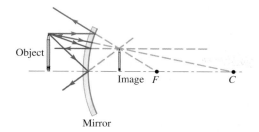

<table>
<tr><td>

Principal rays for convex mirrors

1. A ray parallel to the principal axis is reflected as if it came from a focal point.
2. A ray along a radius is reflected back upon itself.
3. A ray directed toward the focal point is reflected parallel to the principal axis.
4. A ray incident on the vertex of the mirror reflects at an equal angle to the axis.

</td></tr>
</table>

Figure 23.32 Using the principal rays to locate the image formed by a convex mirror. The rays are shown in different colors merely to help distinguish them; the actual color of the light along each ray is the same—whatever the color of the top of the object is.

to the principal axis; it is reflected as if it were coming from the focal point. Another ray (red) is headed along a radius toward the center of curvature C; it reflects back upon itself since the angle of incidence is zero. A third ray (blue) heads directly toward the focal point F. Since a ray parallel to the axis is reflected as if it came from F, a ray going toward F is reflected parallel to the axis. Why? Because the law of reflection is reversible; we can reverse the direction of a ray and the law of reflection still holds. A fourth ray (brown), incident on the mirror at its vertex, reflects making an equal angle with the axis (since the axis is normal to the mirror).

These four reflected rays—as well as other reflected rays from the top of the object—meet at one point when extended behind the mirror. That is the location of the top of the image. The bottom of the image lies on the principal axis because the bottom of the object is on the principal axis; rays along the principal axis are radial rays, so they reflect back upon themselves at the surface of the mirror. From the ray diagram, we can conclude that the image is upright, virtual, smaller than the object, and closer to the mirror than the object. Note that the image is *not* at the focal point; the rays coming from a point on the object are *not* all parallel to the principal axis. If the object were far from the mirror, then the rays from any point would be nearly parallel to each other. Rays from a point on the principal axis would meet at the focal point; rays from a point not on the axis would meet at a point in the **focal plane**—the plane perpendicular to the axis passing through the focal point.

The four rays we chose to draw are called the **principal rays** only because they are easier to draw than other rays. Principal rays are easier to draw, but they are not more important than other rays in forming an image. Any two of them can be drawn to locate an image, but it is wise to draw a third as a check.

A convex mirror enables one to see a larger area than the same size plane mirror (Fig. 23.33). The outward curvature of the convex mirror enables the viewer to see light rays coming from larger angles. Convex mirrors are sometimes used in stores to enable clerks to watch for shoplifting. The passenger's side mirror in most cars is convex to enable the driver to see farther out to the side.

Figure 23.33 A convex mirror shows an image of the skyline of Winnipeg, Manitoba (Canada). The field of view shown by the convex mirror is larger than would be shown by a plane mirror of equal size.

Concave Spherical Mirror

A **concave mirror** curves *toward* the viewer; its center of curvature is *in front* of the mirror. A concave mirror is also called a **converging mirror** since it makes parallel rays converge to a point (Fig. 23.34). In Problem 55 you can show that rays parallel to the mirror's principal axis pass through the focal point F at a distance $R/2$ from the vertex, assuming the angles of incidence are small.

The location of the image of an object placed in front of a concave mirror can be found by drawing two or more rays. As for the convex mirror, there are four principal rays—rays that are easiest to draw. The principal rays are similar to those for a convex mirror, the difference being that the focal point is in *front* of a concave mirror.

Figure 23.35 illustrates the use of principal rays to find an image. In this case, the object is between the focal point and the center of curvature. The image is real because it is in front of the mirror; the principal rays actually do pass through the image point. Depending on the location of the object, a concave mirror can form either real or virtual images. The images can be larger or smaller than the object.

Mirrors designed for shaving or for applying cosmetics are often concave in order to form a magnified image (Fig. 23.36a). Dentists use concave mirrors for the same reason. Whenever an object is within the focal point of a concave mirror, the image is virtual, upright, and larger than the object (Fig. 23.36b).

In automobile headlights, the lightbulb filament is placed at the focal point of a concave mirror. Light rays coming from the filament are reflected out in a beam of parallel rays. (Sometimes the shape of the mirror is parabolic rather than spherical; a parabolic mirror reflects *all* the rays from the focal point into a parallel beam, not just those close to the principal axis.)

Making the Connection:

shaving or cosmetic mirrors

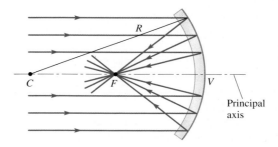

Figure 23.34 Reflection of rays parallel to the principal axis of a concave mirror. Point C is the mirror's center of curvature and F is the focal point. Both points are in *front* of the mirror, in contrast to the convex mirror.

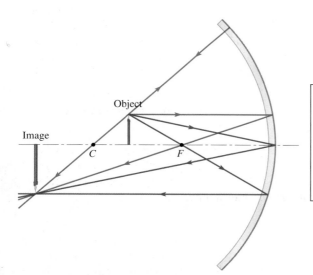

Principal rays for concave mirrors

1. A ray parallel to the principal axis is reflected through the focal point.
2. A ray along a radius is reflected back upon itself.
3. A ray along the direction from the focal point to the mirror is reflected parallel to the principal axis.
4. A ray incident on the vertex of the mirror reflects at an equal angle to the axis.

Figure 23.35 An object between the focal point and the center of curvature of a concave mirror forms a real image that is inverted and larger than the object. (The angles and the curvature of the mirror are exaggerated for clarity.)

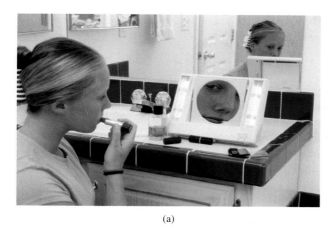

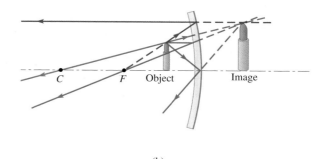

(a)   (b)

Figure 23.36 (a) Putting on makeup is made easier because the image is enlarged. (b) Formation of an image when the object is between the focal point and the concave mirror's surface.

Example 23.6

Scale Diagram for a Concave Mirror

Make a scale diagram showing a 1.5-cm-tall object located 10.0 cm in front of a concave mirror with a radius of curvature of 8.0 cm. Locate the image graphically and estimate its position and height.

Strategy For a scale diagram, we should use a piece of graph paper and choose a scale that fits on the paper—although sometimes it is helpful to make a rough sketch first to get some idea of where the image is. Drawing two principal rays enables us to find the image. Using the third principal ray is a good check. Since the mirror is concave, the center of curvature and the focal point are both in front of the mirror.

Solution To start, we draw the mirror and the principal axis; then we mark the focal point and center of curvature at the correct distances from the vertex (Fig. 23.37). The green ray goes from the top of the object to the mirror parallel to the principal axis. It is reflected by the mirror so that it passes through the focal point. The blue ray travels from the tip of the object through the focal point F. This ray is reflected from the mirror along a line parallel to the principal axis. The intersection of the two rays determines the location of the tip of the image. By measuring the image on the graph paper, we find that the image is 6.7 cm from the mirror and is 1.0 cm high.

Discussion As a check, the red ray travels through the center of curvature along a radius. Assuming the mirror

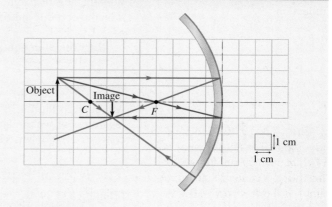

Figure 23.37
Example 23.6.

extends far enough to reflect this ray, it strikes the mirror perpendicular to the surface since it is on a radial line. The reflected ray travels back along the same radial line and intersects the other two rays at the tip of the image, verifying our result.

Practice Problem 23.6   Another Graphical Solution

Draw a scale diagram to locate the image of an object 1.5 cm tall and 6.0 cm in front of the same mirror. Estimate the position and height of the image. Is it real or virtual? [*Hint:* Draw a rough sketch first.]

Transverse Magnification

The image formed by a mirror or a lens is, in general, not the same size as the object. It may also be inverted (upside down). The **transverse magnification** m (also called the *lateral* or *linear* magnification) is a ratio that gives both the relative size of the image—

in any direction perpendicular to the principal axis—and its orientation. The magnitude of m is the ratio of the image size to the object size:

$$|m| = \frac{\text{image size}}{\text{object size}} \tag{23-7}$$

If $|m| < 1$, the image is smaller than the object. The sign of m is determined by the orientation of the image. For an inverted (upside-down) image, $m < 0$; for an upright (right-side-up) image, $m > 0$.

Let h be the height of the object (really the *displacement* of the top of the object from the axis) and h' be the height of the image. If the image is inverted, h' and h have opposite signs. Then the definition of the transverse magnification is

$$m = \frac{h'}{h} \tag{23-8}$$

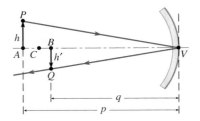

P

h

B

A C   h'   V

Q

q

p

Figure 23.38 Right triangles $\triangle PAV$ and $\triangle QBV$ are similar because the angle of incidence for the ray equals the angle of reflection.

Using Fig. 23.38, we can find a relationship between the magnification and p and q, the **object distance** and the **image distance**. Note that p and q are measured along the principal axis to the vertex of the mirror. The two right triangles $\triangle PAV$ and $\triangle QBV$ are similar, so

$$\frac{h}{p} = \frac{-h'}{q}$$

Why the negative sign? In this case, if h is positive, then h' is negative, since the image is on the opposite side of the axis from the object. The magnification is then

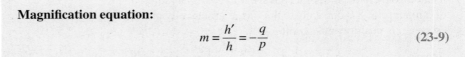

Magnification equation:

$$m = \frac{h'}{h} = -\frac{q}{p} \tag{23-9}$$

Although in Fig 23.38 the object is beyond the center of curvature, Eq. (23-9) is true regardless of where the object is placed. It applies to any spherical mirror, concave or convex (see Problem 53), as well as to plane mirrors.

The Mirror Equation

From Fig. 23.39, we can derive an equation relating the object distance p, the image distance q, and the **focal length** $f = \frac{1}{2}R$ (the distance from the focal point to the mirror). Note that p, q, and f are all measured along the principal axis to the vertex V of the mirror. Triangles $\triangle PAC$ and $\triangle QBC$ are similar. Note that $\overline{AC} = p - R$ and $\overline{BC} = R - q$, where R is the radius of curvature. Then

$$\frac{\overline{PA}}{\overline{AC}} = \frac{\overline{QB}}{\overline{BC}} \quad \text{or} \quad \frac{h}{p - R} = \frac{-h'}{R - q}$$

Rearranging yields

$$\frac{h'}{h} = -\frac{R - q}{p - R}$$

Since h'/h is the magnification,

$$\frac{h'}{h} = -\frac{q}{p} = -\frac{R - q}{p - R} \tag{23-9}$$

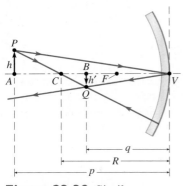

P

h

B

A   C   h' F   V

Q

q

R

p

Figure 23.39 Similar triangles $\triangle PAC$ and $\triangle QBC$ used to derive the lens equation.

Substituting $f = R/2$, cross multiplying, and dividing by p, q, and f (Problem 56), we obtain the **mirror equation**.

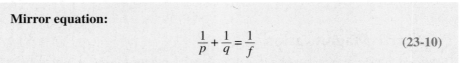

Mirror equation:

$$\frac{1}{p} + \frac{1}{q} = \frac{1}{f} \tag{23-10}$$

We derived the magnification and mirror equations for a concave mirror forming a real image, but the equations apply as well to convex mirrors and to virtual images if we

Table 23.2

Sign Conventions for Mirrors

Quantity	When Positive (+)	When Negative (–)
Object distance p	Always*	Never*
Image distance q	Real image	Virtual image
Focal length f	Converging mirror (concave): $f = \frac{1}{2}R$	Diverging mirror (convex): $f = -\frac{1}{2}R$
Magnification m	Upright image	Inverted image

*In Chapter 23, we consider only real objects. Chapter 24 discusses multiple-lens systems, in which *virtual* objects are possible.

use the sign conventions for q and f listed in Table 23.2. Note that q is negative when the image is behind the mirror and f is negative when the focal point is behind the mirror.

The magnification equation and the sign convention for q imply that *real images of real objects are always inverted* (if both p and q are positive, m is negative); *virtual images of real objects are always upright* (if p is positive and q is negative, m is positive). The same rule can be established by drawing ray diagrams. A real image is always in front of the mirror (where the light rays are); a virtual image is behind the mirror.

If an object is far from the mirror ($p = \infty$), the mirror equation gives $q = f$. Rays coming from a faraway object are nearly parallel to each other. After reflecting from the mirror, the rays converge at the focal point for a concave mirror or appear to diverge from the focal point for a convex mirror. If the faraway object is not on the principal axis, the image is formed above or below the focal point (Fig. 23.40).

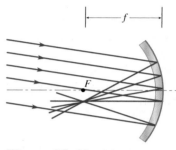

Figure 23.40 A faraway object above the principal axis forms an image at $q = f$.

Example 23.7

Passenger's Side Mirror

An object is located 30.0 cm from a passenger's side mirror. The image formed is upright and $\frac{1}{3}$ the size of the object. (a) Is the image real or virtual? (b) What is the focal length of the mirror? (c) Is the mirror concave or convex?

Strategy The magnitude of the magnification is the ratio of the image size to the object size, so $|m| = \frac{1}{3}$. The sign of the magnification is positive for an upright image and negative for an inverted image. Therefore, we know that $m = +\frac{1}{3}$. The object distance is $p = 30.0$ cm. The magnification is also related to the object and image distances, so we can find q. The sign of q indicates whether the image is real or virtual. Then the mirror equation can be used to find the focal length of the mirror. The sign of the focal length tells us whether the mirror is concave or convex.

Solution (a) The magnification is related to the image and object distances:

$$m = -\frac{q}{p} \qquad (23\text{-}9)$$

Solving for the image distance,

$$q = -mp = -\frac{1}{3} \times 30.0 \text{ cm} = -10.0 \text{ cm}$$

Since q is negative, the image is virtual.

(b) Now we can use the mirror equation to find the focal length:

$$\frac{1}{f} = \frac{1}{p} + \frac{1}{q} = \frac{q+p}{pq}$$

$$f = \frac{pq}{q+p}$$

$$= \frac{30.0 \text{ cm} \times (-10.0 \text{ cm})}{-10.0 \text{ cm} + 30.0 \text{ cm}}$$

$$= -15.0 \text{ cm}$$

(c) Since the focal length is negative, the mirror is convex.

Discussion As expected, the passenger's side mirror is convex. With all the distances known, we can sketch a ray diagram (Fig. 23.41) to check the result.

Continued on next page

Example 23.7 Continued

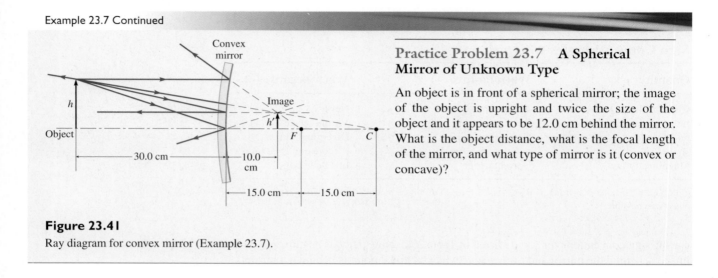

Figure 23.41

Ray diagram for convex mirror (Example 23.7).

Practice Problem 23.7   A Spherical Mirror of Unknown Type

An object is in front of a spherical mirror; the image of the object is upright and twice the size of the object and it appears to be 12.0 cm behind the mirror. What is the object distance, what is the focal length of the mirror, and what type of mirror is it (convex or concave)?

PHYSICS AT HOME

Look at each side of a *shiny* metal spoon. (Stainless steel gets dull with use; the newer the spoon the better. A polished silver spoon would be ideal.) One side acts as a convex mirror; the other acts as a concave mirror. For each, notice whether your image is upright or inverted and enlarged or diminished in size. Next, decide whether each image is real or virtual. Which side gives you a larger field of view (in other words, enables you to see a bigger part of the room)? Try holding the spoon at different distances to see what changes. (Keep in mind that the focal length of the spoon is small. If you hold the spoon less than a focal length from your eye, you won't be able to see clearly—your eye cannot focus at such a small distance. Thus, it is not possible to get close enough to the concave side to see a virtual image.)

23.9   THIN LENSES

Whereas mirrors form images through reflection, lenses form images through refraction. In a spherical lens, each of the two surfaces is a section of a sphere. The **principal axis** of a lens passes through the centers of curvature of the lens surfaces. The **optical center** of a lens is a point on the principal axis through which rays pass without changing direction.

We can understand the behavior of a lens by regarding it as an assembly of prisms (Fig. 23.42). The angle of deviation of the ray—the angle that the ray emerging from the prism makes with the incident ray—is proportional to the angle between the two faces of the prism (see Fig. 23.43 and Problem 19). The two faces of a lens are parallel where they intersect the principal axis. A ray striking the lens at the center emerges in the same direction as the incident ray since the refraction of an entering ray is undone as the ray emerges. However, the ray is *displaced*; it is not along the same line as the incident ray. As long as we consider only *thin lenses*—lenses whose thickness is small

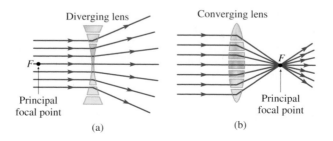

Figure 23.42 (a) and (b) Lenses made by combining prism sections.

compared to the focal length—the displacement is negligible; the ray passes straight through the lens.

The curved surfaces of a lens mean that the angle β between the two faces gradually increases as we move away from the center. Thus, the angle of deviation of a ray increases as the point where it strikes the lens moves away from the center. We restrict our consideration to **paraxial rays**: rays that strike the lens close to the principal axis (so that β is small) and do so at a small angle of incidence. For paraxial rays and thin lenses, a ray incident on the lens at a distance d from the center has an angle of deviation δ that is proportional to d (see Fig. 23.44 and Problem 91).

Lenses are classified as **diverging** or **converging**, depending on what happens to the rays as they pass through the lens. A diverging lens bends light rays outward, away from the principal axis. A converging lens bends light rays inward, toward the principal axis (Fig. 23.45a). If the incident rays are already diverging, a converging lens may not be able to make them converge; it may only make them diverge less (Fig. 23.45b). Lenses take many possible shapes (Fig. 23.46); the two surfaces may have different radii of curvature. Note that converging lenses are thickest at the center and diverging lenses are thinnest at the center, assuming the index of refraction of the lens is greater than that of the surrounding medium.

Focal Points and Principal Rays

Any lens has two focal points. The distance between each focal point and the optical center is the magnitude of the **focal length** of the lens. The focal length of a lens with spherical surfaces depends on four quantities: the radii of curvature of the two surfaces and the indices of refraction of the lens and of the surrounding medium (usually, but not necessarily, air). For a diverging lens, incident rays parallel to the principal axis are refracted by the lens so that they appear to diverge from the **principal focal point**, which is *before* the lens (Fig. 23.42a). For a converging lens, incident rays parallel to the axis are refracted by the lens so they converge to the principal focal point *past* the lens (Fig. 23.42b).

Two rays suffice to locate the image formed by a thin lens, but a third ray is useful as a check. The three rays that are generally the easiest to draw are called the **principal rays** (Table 23.3). The third principal ray makes use of the **secondary focal point**, which is on the opposite side of the lens from the principal focal point. The behavior of ray 3 can be understood by reversing the direction of all the rays, which also interchanges the two focal points. Figure 23.47 illustrates how to draw the principal rays.

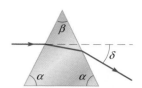

Figure 23.43 The angle of deviation δ increases as the angle β between the two faces increases. For small β, δ is proportional to β.

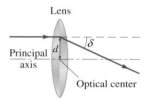

Figure 23.44 The angle of deviation of a paraxial ray striking the lens a distance d from the principal axis is proportional to d. To simplify ray diagrams, we draw rays as if they bend at a vertical line through the optical center rather than bending at each of the two lens surfaces.

Figure 23.45 (a) When diverging rays strike a converging lens, the lens bends them inward. (b) If they are diverging too rapidly, the lens may not be able to bend them enough to make them converge. In that case, the rays diverge less rapidly after they leave the lens.

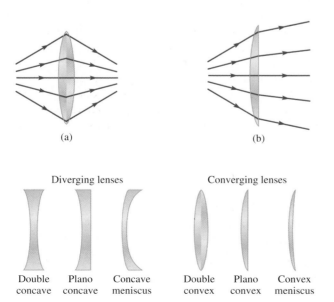

(a)   (b)

Diverging lenses   Converging lenses

Double concave   Plano concave   Concave meniscus   Double convex   Plano convex   Convex meniscus

Figure 23.46 Shapes of some diverging and converging lenses.

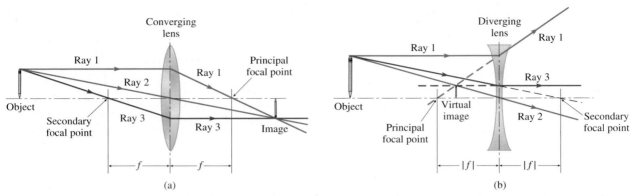

Figure 23.47 (a) The three principal rays for a converging lens forming a real image. (b) The three principal rays for a diverging lens forming a virtual image.

Table 23.3

Principal Rays and Principal Focal Points for Thin Lenses

	Converging Lens	Diverging Lens
Ray 1. An incident ray parallel to the principal axis	Passes through the principal focal point	Appears to come from the principal focal point
Ray 2. A ray incident at the optical center	Passes straight through the lens	Passes straight through the lens
Ray 3. A ray that *emerges* parallel to the principal axis	Appears to come from the secondary focal point	Appears to have been heading for the secondary focal point
Location of the principal focal point	Past the lens	Before the lens

Conceptual Example 23.8

Orientation of Virtual Images

A lens forms an image of an object placed before the lens. Using a ray diagram, show that if the image is virtual, then it must also be upright, regardless of whether the lens is converging or diverging.

Strategy   The principal rays are usually the easiest to draw. Principal rays 1 and 3 behave differently for converging and diverging lenses. They also deal with focal points, whereas the problem implies that the location of the object with respect to the focal points is irrelevant (except that we know a virtual image is formed). Ray 2 passes undeviated through the center of the lens. It behaves the same way for both types of lens and does not depend on the location of the focal points.

Solution and Discussion   Figure 23.48 shows an object in front of a lens (which could be either converging or diverging). Principal ray 2 from the top of the object passes straight through the center of the lens. We extrapolate the refracted ray backward and sketch a few possibili-

ties for the location of the image—with only one ray we do not know the actual location. We do know that a point on a virtual image is located not where the rays emerging from the lens meet, but rather where the *backward extrapolation of those rays* meet. In other words, the position of

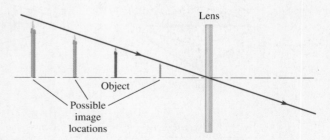

Figure 23.48

The principal ray passing undeviated through the center of a lens shows that virtual images of real objects are upright.

Continued on next page

Conceptual Example 23.8 Continued

a virtual image is always before the lens (on the same side as the *incident* rays). Therefore, the image is on the same side of the lens as the object. From Fig. 23.48, we see that, just as for mirrors, the virtual image is upright—the image of the point at the top of the object is always above the principal axis.

Conceptual Practice Problem 23.8
Orientation of Real Images

A converging lens forms a real image of an object placed before the lens. Using a ray diagram, show that the image is inverted.

The Magnification and Thin Lens Equations

We can derive the thin lens equation and the magnification equation from the geometry of Fig. 23.49. From the similar right triangles $\triangle EGC$ and $\triangle DBC$, we write

$$\tan \alpha = \frac{h}{p} = \frac{-h'}{q}$$

As in the derivation of the mirror equation, h' is a signed quantity. For an inverted image, h' is negative; $-h'$ is the (positive) length of side BD. The magnification is given by

Magnification equation:

$$m = \frac{h'}{h} = -\frac{q}{p} \qquad (23\text{-}9)$$

From two other similar right triangles $\triangle ACF$ and $\triangle DBF$,

$$\tan \beta = \frac{h}{f} = \frac{-h'}{q-f}$$

or

$$\frac{q-f}{f} = \frac{-h'}{h} = \frac{q}{p}$$

After dividing through by q and rearranging, we obtain the **thin lens equation**.

Thin lens equation:

$$\frac{1}{p} + \frac{1}{q} = \frac{1}{f} \qquad (23\text{-}10)$$

The magnification and thin lens equations have exactly the same form as the corresponding equations derived for mirrors. The derivations used a converging lens and a real image, but they apply to all cases—either kind of lens and either kind of image—as long as we use the same sign conventions for q and f as for spherical mirrors (Table 23.4).

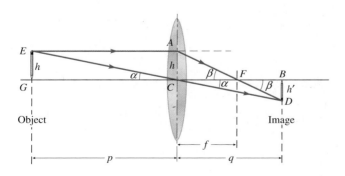

Figure 23.49 Ray diagram showing two of the three principal rays for derivation of thin lens equation and magnification.

Table 23.4

Sign Conventions for Mirrors and Lenses

Quantity	When Positive (+)	When Negative (−)
Object distance p	Always (for now)	Never (for now)
Image distance q	Real image	Virtual image
Focal length f	Converging lens or mirror	Diverging lens or mirror
Magnification m	Upright image	Inverted image

Example 23.9
Zoom Lens

A wild daisy 1.2 cm in diameter is 90.0 cm from a camera's zoom lens. The focal length of the lens has magnitude 150.0 mm. (a) Find the distance between the lens and the film. (b) How large is the image of the daisy?

Strategy   The problem can be solved using the lens and magnification equations. The lens must be *converging* to form a real image on the film, so $f = +150.0$ mm. The image must be formed on the film, so the distance from the lens to the film is q. After finishing the algebraic solution, we sketch a ray diagram as a check.

Given: $h = 1.2$ cm; $p = 90.0$ cm; $f = +15.00$ cm
Find: q, h'

Solution   (a) Since p and f are known, we find q from the thin lens equation

$$\frac{1}{p} + \frac{1}{q} = \frac{1}{f}$$

Let us solve for q.

$$q = \left(\frac{1}{f} - \frac{1}{p}\right)^{-1}$$

Substituting numerical values,

$$q = \left(\frac{1}{15.00 \text{ cm}} - \frac{1}{90.0 \text{ cm}}\right)^{-1} = +18.0 \text{ cm}$$

The film is 18.0 cm from the lens.

(b) From the magnification equation,

$$m = \frac{h'}{h} = -\frac{q}{p} = -\frac{18.0 \text{ cm}}{90.0 \text{ cm}} = -0.200$$

$$h' = mh = -0.200 \times 1.2 \text{ cm}$$
$$= -0.24 \text{ cm}$$

The image of the daisy is 0.24 cm in diameter.

Discussion   Figure 23.50 shows a ray diagram using the three principal rays that confirms the algebraic solution.

Practice Problem 23.9   Finding the Focal Length of a Lens

A 3.00-cm-tall object is placed 60.0 cm in front of a lens. The virtual image formed is 0.50 cm tall. What is the focal length of the lens? Is it converging or diverging?

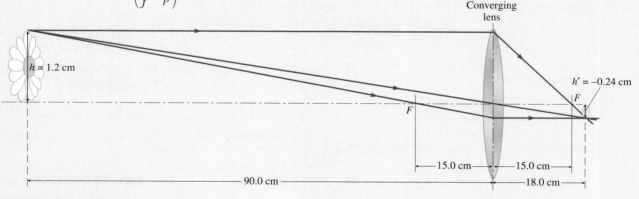

Figure 23.50
Ray diagram for Example 23.9.

PHYSICS AT HOME

If you or a friend are farsighted and have eyeglasses, put the glasses on a table so that you can look through the lenses. Increase your distance from the lenses until you see a clear image of distant objects. Why is the image inverted? Is the image real or virtual? The eyeglasses certainly form an upright image when they are worn as intended. Are the lenses converging or diverging?

Objects and Images at Infinity

Suppose an object is a large distance from a lens ("at infinity"). Substituting $p = \infty$ in the lens equation yields $q = f$. The rays from a faraway object are nearly parallel to each other when they strike the lens, so the image is formed in the principal **focal plane** (the plane perpendicular to the axis passing through the principal focal point). Similarly, if an object is placed in the principal focal plane of a converging lens, then $p = f$ and $q = \infty$. The image is at infinity—that is, the rays emerging from the lens are parallel, so they appear to be coming from an object at infinity.

MASTER THE CONCEPTS

- A wavefront is a set of points of equal phase. A ray points in the direction of propagation of a wave and is perpendicular to the wavefronts. Huygens's principle is a geometric construction used to analyze the propagation of a wave. Every point on a wavefront is considered a source of spherical wavelets. A surface tangent to the wavelets at a later time is the wavefront at that time.

- Geometric optics deals with the propagation of light when interference and diffraction are negligible. The chief tool used in geometric optics is the ray diagram. At a boundary between two different media, light can be reflected as well as transmitted. The laws of reflection and refraction give the directions of the reflected and transmitted rays. In the laws of reflection and refraction, angles are measured between rays and a normal to the boundary.

- Laws of reflection:
  1. The angle of incidence equals the angle of reflection.
  2. The reflected ray lies in the same plane as the incident ray and the normal to the surface at the point of incidence.

- Laws of refraction:
  1. $n_i \sin \theta_i = n_t \sin \theta_t$ (Snell's law).
  2. The incident ray, the transmitted ray, and the normal all lie in the same plane—the plane of incidence.
  3. The incident and transmitted rays are on *opposite sides* of the normal.

- When a ray is incident on a boundary from a material with a higher index of refraction to one with a lower index of refraction, total internal reflection occurs (there is no transmitted ray) if the angle of incidence exceeds the critical angle

$$\theta_c = \sin^{-1} \frac{n_t}{n_i} \qquad (23\text{-}5a)$$

- When a ray is incident on a boundary, the reflected ray is totally polarized perpendicular to the plane of incidence if the angle of incidence is equal to Brewster's angle

$$\theta_B = \tan^{-1} \frac{n_t}{n_i} \qquad (23\text{-}6)$$

- In the formation of an image, there is a one-to-one correspondence of points on the object and points on the image. In a virtual image, light rays *appear* to diverge from the image point, but they really don't. In a real image, the rays actually *do* pass through the image point.

- Finding an image using a ray diagram:
  1. Draw two (or more) rays coming from a single point on the object toward the lens or mirror.
  2. Trace the rays, applying the laws of reflection and refraction as needed, until they reach the observer.
  3. Extrapolate the rays backward along straight line paths until they intersect at the image point.

- The easiest rays to trace for a mirror or lens are called the principal rays.

- A plane mirror forms an unmagnified, upright, virtual image of an object that is located at the same distance behind the mirror as the object is in front of the mirror. The object and image are both located on a normal from the object to the mirror surface.

MASTER THE CONCEPTS *continued*

- The magnitude of the transverse magnification m is the ratio of the image size to the object size; the sign of m is determined by the orientation of the image. For an inverted (upside-down) image, $m < 0$; for an upright (right-side-up) image, $m > 0$. For either lenses or mirrors,

$$m = \frac{h'}{h} = -\frac{q}{p} \qquad (23\text{-}9)$$

- The mirror/thin lens equation relates the object and image distances to the focal length:

$$\frac{1}{p} + \frac{1}{q} = \frac{1}{f} \qquad (23\text{-}10)$$

- These sign conventions enable the magnification and mirror/thin lens equations to apply to all kinds of mirrors and lenses and both kinds of image:

Quantity	When Positive (+)	When Negative (−)
Object distance p	Always (for now)	Never (for now)
Image distance q	Real image	Virtual image
Focal length f	Converging lens or mirror	Diverging lens or mirror
Magnification m	Upright image	Inverted image

Conceptual Questions

1. Describe the difference between specular and diffuse reflection. Give some examples of each.

2. What is the difference between a virtual and a real image? State a method for demonstrating the presence of a real image.

3. Water droplets in air create rainbows. Describe the physical situation that causes a rainbow. Should you look toward or away from the Sun to see a rainbow? Why is the secondary rainbow fainter than the primary rainbow?

4. Why does a mirror hanging in a vertical plane seem to interchange left and right but not up and down? [*Hint:* Refer to Fig. 23.28. Instead of calling Grant's hands left and right, call them east and west. In Grant's image, are the east and west hands reversed? Note that Grant faces south while his image faces north.]

5. A framed poster is covered with glass that has a rougher surface than regular glass. How does a rough surface reduce glare?

6. Explain how a plane mirror can be thought of as a special case of a spherical mirror. What is the focal length of a plane mirror? Does the spherical mirror equation work for plane mirrors with this choice of focal length? What is the transverse magnification for any image produced by a plane mirror?

7. A ray of light passes from air into water, striking the surface of the water with an angle of incidence of 45°. Which of these quantities change as the light enters the water: wavelength, frequency, speed of propagation, direction of propagation?

8. If the angle of incidence is greater than the angle of refraction for a light beam passing an interface, what can be said about the relative values of the indices of refraction and the speed of light in the first and second media?

9. A concave mirror has focal length f. (a) If you look into the mirror from a distance less than f, is the image you see upright or inverted? (b) If you stand at a distance greater than $2f$, is the image upright or inverted? (c) If you stand at a distance between f and $2f$, an image is formed but you cannot see it. Why not? Sketch a ray diagram and compare the locations of the object and image.

10. The focal length of a concave mirror is 4.00 m and an object is placed 3.00 m in front of the mirror. Describe the image in terms of real, virtual, upright, and inverted.

11. Why is the passenger's side mirror in many cars convex rather than plane or concave?

12. When a virtual image is formed by a mirror, is it in front of the mirror or behind it? What about a real image?

13. Light rays travel from left to right through a lens. If a virtual image is formed, on which side of the lens is it? On which side would a real image be found?

14. Why is the brilliance of an artificial diamond made of cubic zirconium ($n = 1.9$) distinctly inferior to the real thing ($n = 2.4$) even if the two are cut exactly the same way? How would an artificial diamond made of glass compare?

15. The surface of the water in a swimming pool is completely still. Describe what you would see looking straight up toward the surface from under water. [*Hint:* Sketch some rays. Consider both reflected and transmitted rays at the water surface.]

16. A ray reflects from a spherical mirror at point P. Explain why a radial line from the center of curvature through point P always bisects the angle between the incident and reflected rays.

17. Why must projectors and cameras form real images? Does the lens in the eye form real or virtual images on the retina?

18. Is it possible for a plane mirror to produce a real image of an object in front of the mirror? Explain. If it is possible, sketch a ray diagram to demonstrate. If it is not possible, sketch a ray diagram to show which way a curved mirror must curve (concave or convex) to produce a real image.

19. A slide projector forms a real image of the slide on a screen using a converging lens. If the bottom half of the lens is blocked by covering it with opaque tape, does the bottom half of the image disappear, or does the top half disappear, or is the entire image still visible on the screen? If the entire image is visible, is anything different about it? [*Hint:* It may help to sketch a ray diagram.]

20. A lens is placed at the end of a bundle of optical fibers in an endoscope. The purpose of the lens is to make the light rays parallel before they enter the fibers (in other words, to put the image at infinity). What is the advantage of using a lens with the same index of refraction as the core of the fibers?

21. A converging lens made from dense flint glass is placed into a container of transparent glycerine. Describe what happens to the focal length.

22. Polaroid sunglasses are useful for cutting out reflected glare due to reflection from horizontal surfaces. In which direction should the transmission axis of Polaroid sunglasses be oriented: vertically or horizontally? Explain.

23. Suppose you are facing due north at sunrise. Sunlight is reflected by a store's display window as shown. Is the reflected light partially polarized? If so, in what direction?

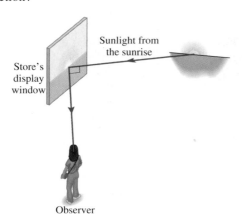

Store's display window

Sunlight from the sunrise

Observer

Multiple-Choice Questions

1. The image of an object in a plane mirror
   (a) is always smaller than the object.
   (b) is always the same size as the object.
   (c) is always larger than the object.
   (d) can be larger, smaller, or the same size as the object, depending on the distance between the object and the mirror.

2. Which statements are true? The rays in a plane wave are
   1. parallel to the wavefronts.
   2. perpendicular to the wavefronts.
   3. directed radially outward from a central point.
   4. parallel to each other.
   (a) 1, 2, 3, 4   (b) 1, 4   (c) 2, 3   (d) 2, 4

3. The image of a slide formed by a slide projector is correctly described by which of the listed terms?
   (a) real, upright, enlarged
   (b) real, inverted, diminished
   (c) virtual, inverted, enlarged
   (d) virtual, upright, diminished
   (e) real, upright, diminished
   (f) real, inverted, enlarged
   (g) virtual, inverted, diminished

4. During a laboratory experiment with an object placed in front of a concave mirror, the image distance q is determined for several different values of object distance p. How might the focal length f of the mirror be determined from a graph of the data?
   (a) Plot q versus p; slope $= f$
   (b) Plot q versus p; slope $= 1/f$
   (c) Plot $1/p$ versus $1/q$; y-intercept $= 1/f$
   (d) Plot q versus p; y-intercept $= 1/f$
   (e) Plot q versus p; y-intercept $= f$
   (f) Plot $1/p$ versus $1/q$; slope $= 1/f$

5. A man runs toward a plane mirror at 5 m/s and the mirror, on rollers, simultaneously approaches him at 2 m/s. The speed at which his image moves (relative to the ground) is
   (a) 14 m/s   (b) 7 m/s   (c) 3 m/s
   (d) 9 m/s   (e) 12 m/s

6. Two converging lenses, of exactly the same size and shape, are held in sunlight, the same distance above a sheet of paper. The figure shows the paths of some rays through the two lenses. Which lens is made of material with a higher index of refraction? How do you know?

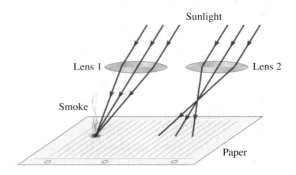

Sunlight

Lens 1   Lens 2

Smoke

Paper

   (a) Lens 1, because its focal length is smaller
   (b) Lens 1, because its focal length is greater
   (c) Lens 2, because its focal length is smaller
   (d) Lens 2, because its focal length is greater
   (e) Impossible to answer with the information given

7. Which of these statements correctly describe the images formed by an object placed before a single thin lens?

    1. Real images are always enlarged.
    2. Real images are always inverted.
    3. Virtual images are always upright.
    4. Convex lenses never produce virtual images.

    (a) 1 and 3   (b) 2 and 3
    (c) 2 and 4   (d) 2, 3, and 4
    (e) 1, 2, and 3   (f) 4 only

8. Light reflecting from the surfaces of lakes, roads, and automobile hoods is

    (a) partially polarized in the horizontal direction.
    (b) partially polarized in the vertical direction.
    (c) polarized only if the Sun is directly overhead.
    (d) polarized only if it is a clear day.
    (e) randomly polarized.

9. A point source of light is placed at the focal point of a converging lens; the rays of light coming out of the lens are parallel to the principal axis. Now suppose the source is moved closer to the lens but still on the axis. Which statement is true about the light rays coming out of the lens?

    (a) They diverge from each other.
    (b) They converge toward each other.
    (c) They still emerge parallel to the principal axis.
    (d) They emerge parallel to each other but not parallel to the axis.
    (e) No rays emerge because a virtual image is formed.

10. A light ray inside a glass prism is incident at Brewster's angle on a surface of the prism with air outside. Which of these is true?

    (a) There is no transmitted ray; the reflected ray is plane polarized.
    (b) The transmitted ray is plane polarized; the reflected ray is partially polarized.
    (c) There is no transmitted ray; the reflected ray is partially polarized.
    (d) The transmitted ray is partially polarized; the reflected ray is plane polarized.
    (e) The transmitted ray is plane polarized; there is no reflected ray.

Problems

 Combination conceptual/quantitative problem
 Biological or medical application
No ✦   Easy to moderate difficulty level
✦   More challenging
✦✦   Most challenging
Blue #   Detailed solution in the Student Solutions Manual
[1 2]   Problems paired by concept

23.1 Wavefronts, Rays, and Huygens's Principle

1. Sketch the wavefronts and rays for the light emitted by an isotropic point source (*isotropic* = same in all directions). Use Huygens's principle to illustrate the propagation of one of the wavefronts.

© 2. Apply Huygens's principle to a 5-cm-long planar wavefront approaching a reflecting wall at normal incidence. The wavelength is 1 cm and the wall has a wide opening (width = 4 cm). The center of the incoming wavefront approaches the center of the opening. Repeat the procedure until you have wavefronts on both sides of the wall. Without worrying about the details of edge effects, what are the general shapes of the wavefronts on each side of the reflecting wall?

© 3. Repeat Problem 2 for an opening of width 0.5 cm.

23.2 The Reflection of Light

4. A plane wave reflects from the surface of a sphere. Draw a ray diagram and sketch some wavefronts for the reflected wave.

5. A spherical wave (from a point source) reflects from a planar surface. Draw a ray diagram and sketch some wavefronts for the reflected wave.

6. Light rays from the Sun, which is at an angle of 35° above the western horizon, strike the still surface of a pond. (a) What is the angle of incidence of the Sun's rays on the pond? (b) What is the angle of reflection of the rays that leave the pond surface? (c) In what direction and at what angle from the pond surface are the reflected rays traveling?

7. A light ray reflects from a plane mirror as shown in the figure. What is the angle of deviation δ?

8. Two plane mirrors form a 70.0° angle as shown. For what angle θ is the final ray horizontal?

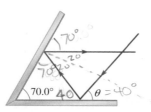

9. Choose two rays in Fig. 23.7 and use them to prove that the angle of incidence is equal to the angle of reflection. [*Hint:* Choose a wavefront at two different times, one before reflection and one after. The time for light to travel from one wavefront to the other is the same for the two rays.]

23.3 The Refraction of Light: Snell's Law

10. Sunlight strikes the surface of a lake at an angle of incidence of 30.0°. At what angle with respect to the normal would a fish see the Sun?

11. Sunlight strikes the surface of a lake. A diver sees the Sun at an angle of 42.0° with respect to the vertical. What angle do the Sun's rays in air make with the vertical?

12. A beam of light in air is incident upon a stack of four flat transparent materials with indices of refraction 1.20, 1.40, 1.32, and 1.28. If the angle of incidence for the beam on the first of the four materials is 60.0°, what angle does the beam make with the normal when it emerges into the air after passing through the entire stack?

13. At a marine animal park, Alison is looking through a glass window and watching dolphins swim underwater. If the dolphin is swimming directly toward her at 15 m/s, how fast does the dolphin appear to be moving?

14. A light ray in the core ($n = 1.40$) of a cylindrical optical fiber travels at an angle $\theta_1 = 49.0°$ with respect to the *axis of the fiber*. A ray is transmitted through the cladding ($n = 1.20$) and into the air. What angle θ_2 does the exiting ray make with the outside surface of the cladding?

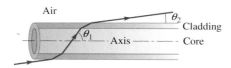

Problems 14 and 15

15. A light ray in the core ($n = 1.40$) of a cylindrical optical fiber is incident on the cladding. See the figure with Problem 14. A ray is transmitted through the cladding ($n = 1.20$) and into the air. The emerging ray makes an angle $\theta_2 = 5.00°$ with the outside surface of the cladding. What angle θ_1 did the ray in the core make with the axis?

16. A glass lens has a scratch-resistant plastic coating on it. The speed of light in the glass is $0.67c$ and the speed of light in the coating is $0.80c$. A ray of light in the coating is incident on the plastic-glass boundary at an angle of 12.0° with respect to the normal. At what angle with respect to the normal is the ray transmitted into the glass?

17. In Figure 23.12, a coin is right up against the far edge of the mug. In picture (a) the coin is just hidden from view and in picture (b) we can almost see the whole coin. If the mug is 6.5 cm in diameter and 8.9 cm tall, what is the diameter of the coin?

✦ 18. A horizontal light ray is incident on a crown glass prism as shown in the figure where $\beta = 30.0°$. Find the angle of deviation δ of the ray—the angle that the ray emerging from the prism makes with the incident ray.

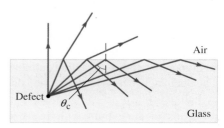

✦ 19. A horizontal light ray is incident on a prism as shown in the   Problems 18 and 19

figure with Problem 18 where β is a *small angle* (exaggerated in the figure). Find the angle of deviation δ of the ray—the angle that the ray emerging from the prism makes with the incident ray—as a function of β and n, the index of refraction of the prism and show that δ is proportional to β.

Ⓒ 20. A diamond in air is illuminated with white light. On one particular facet, the angle of incidence is 26.00°. Inside the diamond, red light ($\lambda = 660.0$ nm in vacuum) is refracted at 10.48° with respect to the normal; blue light ($\lambda = 470.0$ nm in vacuum) is refracted at 10.33°. (a) What are the indices of refraction for red and blue light in diamond? (b) What is the ratio of the speed of red light to the speed of blue light in diamond? (c) How would a diamond look if there were no dispersion?

✦ 21. The prism in the figure is made of crown glass. Its index of refraction ranges from 1.517 for the longest visible wavelengths to 1.538 for the shortest. Find the range of refraction angles for the light transmitted into air through the right side of the prism.

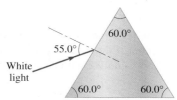

23.4 Total Internal Reflection

22. Calculate the critical angle for a sapphire surrounded by air.

23. (a) Calculate the critical angle for a diamond surrounded by air. (b) Calculate the critical angle for a diamond under water. (c) Explain why a diamond sparkles less under water than in air.

24. Is there a critical angle for a light ray coming from a medium with an index of refraction 1.2 and incident on a medium that has an index of refraction 1.4? If so, what is the critical angle that allows total internal reflection in the first medium?

Ⓒ 25. The figure shows some light rays reflected from a small defect in the glass toward the surface of the glass. (a) If $\theta_c = 40.00°$, what is the index of refraction of the glass? (b) Is there any point above the glass at which a viewer would not be able to see the defect? Explain.

Ⓒ 26. A 45° prism has an index of refraction of 1.6. Light is normally incident on the left side of the prism. Does light exit the back of the prism (for example, at point P)?

If so, what is the angle of refraction with respect to the normal at point P? If not, what happens to the light?

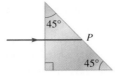

Problems
26, 27, and 96

27. Light incident on a 45.0° prism as shown in the figure undergoes total internal reflection at point P. What can you conclude about the index of refraction of the prism? (Determine either a minimum or maximum possible value.)

28. The angle of incidence θ of a ray of light in air is adjusted gradually as it enters a shallow tank made of Plexiglas and filled with carbon disulfide. Is there an angle of incidence for which light is transmitted into the carbon disulfide but not into the Plexiglas at the bottom of the tank? If so, find the angle. If not, explain why not.

29. Repeat Problem 28 for a Plexiglas tank filled with carbon tetrachloride instead of carbon disulfide.

30. What is the index of refraction of the core of an optical fiber if the cladding has $n = 1.20$ and the critical angle at the core-cladding boundary is 45.0°?

23.5 Polarization by Reflection

31. Some glasses used for viewing 3D movies are polarized, one lens having a vertical transmission axis and the other horizontal. While standing in line on a winter afternoon for a 3D movie and looking through his glasses at the road surface, Maurice notices that the left lens cuts down reflected glare significantly, but the right lens does not. The glare is minimized when the angle between the reflected light and the horizontal direction is 37°. (a) Which lens has the transmission axis in the vertical direction? (b) What is Brewster's angle for this case? (c) What is the index of refraction of the material reflecting the light?

32. (a) Sunlight reflected from the still surface of a lake is totally polarized when the incident light is at what angle with respect to the horizontal? (b) In what direction is the reflected light polarized? (c) Is any light incident at this angle transmitted into the water? If so, at what angle below the horizontal does the transmitted light travel?

33. (a) Sunlight reflected from the smooth ice surface of a frozen lake is totally polarized when the incident light is at what angle with respect to the horizontal? (b) In what direction is the reflected light polarized? (c) Is any light incident at this angle transmitted into the ice? If so, at what angle below the horizontal does the transmitted light travel?

34. Light travels in a medium with index n_1 toward a boundary with another material of index $n_2 < n_1$. (a) Which is larger, the critical angle or Brewster's angle? Does the answer depend on the values of n_1 and n_2 (other than assuming $n_2 < n_1$)? (b) What can you say

about the critical angle and Brewster's angle for light coming the other way (from the medium with index n_2 toward the medium with n_1)?

23.6 The Formation of Images Through Reflection or Refraction

35. A defect in a diamond appears to be 2.0 mm below the surface when viewed from directly above that surface. How far beneath the surface is the defect?

36. An insect is trapped inside a piece of amber ($n = 1.546$). Looking at the insect from directly above, it appears to be 7.00 mm below a smooth surface of the amber. How far below the surface is the insect?

37. A penny is at the bottom of a bowl full of water. When you look at the water surface from the side, with your eyes at the water level, the penny appears to be just barely under the surface and a horizontal distance of 3.0 cm from the edge of the bowl. If the penny is actually 8.0 cm below the water surface, what is the horizontal distance between the penny and the edge of the bowl? [*Hint:* The rays you see pass from water to air with refraction angles close to 90°.]

23.7 Plane Mirrors

38. Norah wants to buy a mirror so that she can check on her appearance from top to toe before she goes off to work. If Norah is 1.64 m tall, how tall a mirror does she need?

39. Daniel's eyes are 1.82 m from the floor when he is wearing his dress shoes, and the top of his head is 1.96 m from the floor. Daniel has a mirror that is 0.98 m in length. How high from the floor should the bottom edge of the mirror be located if Daniel is to see a full-length image of himself? Draw a ray diagram to illustrate your answer.

40. A rose in a vase is placed 0.250 m in front of a plane mirror. Nagar looks into the mirror from 2.00 m in front of it. How far away from Nagar is the image of the rose?

41. Entering a darkened room, Gustav strikes a match in an attempt to see his surroundings. At once he sees what looks like another match about 4 m away from him. As it turns out, a mirror hangs on one wall of the room. How far is Gustav from the wall with the mirror?

42. In an amusement park maze with all the walls covered with mirrors, Pilar sees Hernando's reflection from a series of three mirrors. If the reflected angle from mirror 3 is 55° for the mirror arrangement shown in the figure, what is the angle of incidence on mirror 1?

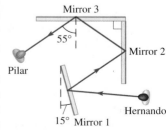

43. Maurizio is standing in a rectangular room with two adjacent walls and the ceiling all covered by plane mirrors. How many images of himself can Maurizio see?

44. Hannah is standing in the middle of a room with two opposite walls that are separated by 10.0 m and covered by plane mirrors. There is a candle in the room 1.50 m from one mirrored wall. Hannah is facing the opposite mirrored wall and sees many images of the candle. How far from Hannah are the closest four images of the candle that she can see?

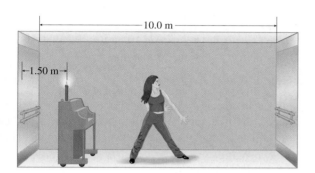

45. A point source of light is in front of a plane mirror. (a) Prove that all the reflected rays, when extended back behind the mirror, intersect in a single point. [*Hint:* See Fig. 23.27a and use similar triangles.] (b) Show that the image point lies on a line through the object and perpendicular to the mirror, and that the object and image distances are equal. [*Hint:* Use any pair of rays in Fig. 23.27a.]

23.8 Spherical Mirrors

46. An object 2.00 cm high is placed 12.0 cm in front of a convex mirror with radius of curvature of 8.00 cm. Where is the image formed? Draw a ray diagram to illustrate.

47. A 1.80-cm-high object is placed 20.0 cm in front of a concave mirror with a 5.00-cm focal length. What is the position of the image? Draw a ray diagram to illustrate.

48. In her job as a dental hygienist, Kathryn uses a convex mirror to see the back of her patient's teeth. When the mirror is 1.20 cm from a tooth, the image is upright and 3.00 times as large as the tooth. What are the focal length and radius of curvature of the mirror?

49. An object is placed in front of a concave mirror with a 25.0-cm radius of curvature. A real image twice the size of the object is formed. At what distance is the object from the mirror? Draw a ray diagram to illustrate.

50. An object is placed in front of a convex mirror with a 25.0-cm radius of curvature. A virtual image half the size of the object is formed. At what distance is the object from the mirror? Draw a ray diagram to illustrate.

51. The right-side rearview mirror of Mike's car says that objects in the mirror are closer than they appear. Mike

decides to do an experiment to determine the focal length of this mirror. He holds a plane mirror next to the rearview mirror and views an object that is 163 cm away from each mirror. The object appears 3.20 cm wide in the plane mirror, but only 1.80 cm wide in the rearview mirror. What is the focal length of the rearview mirror?

52. A concave mirror has a radius of curvature of 5.0 m. An object, initially 2.0 m in front of the mirror, is moved back until it is 6.0 m from the mirror. Describe how the image location changes.

53. Derive the magnification equation, $m = h'/h = -q/p$, for a *convex* mirror. Draw a ray diagram as part of the solution. [*Hint:* Draw a ray that is not one of the three principal rays, as was done in the derivation for a concave mirror.]

54. In a subway station, a convex mirror allows the attendant to view activity on the platform. A woman 1.64 m tall is standing 4.5 m from the mirror. The image formed of the woman is 0.500 m tall. (a) What is the radius of curvature of the mirror? (b) The mirror is 0.500 m in diameter. If the woman's shoes appear at the bottom of the mirror, does her head appear at the top—in other words, does the image of the woman fill the mirror from top to bottom? Explain.

55. Show that when rays parallel to the principal axis reflect from a concave mirror, the reflected rays all pass through the focal point at a distance $R/2$ from the vertex. Assume that the angles of incidence are small. [*Hint:* Follow the similar derivation for a *convex* mirror in the text.]

56. Starting with Fig. 23.39, perform all the algebraic steps to obtain the mirror equation in the form of Eq. (23-10).

23.9 Thin Lenses

57. (a) For a converging lens with a focal length of 3.50 cm, find the object distance that will result in an inverted image with an image distance of 5.00 cm. Use a ray diagram to verify your calculations. (b) Is the image real or virtual? (c) What is the magnification?

58. Sketch a ray diagram to show that when an object is placed more than twice the focal length away from a converging lens, the image formed is inverted, real, and diminished in size.

59. Sketch a ray diagram to show that when an object is placed at twice the focal length from a converging lens, the image formed is inverted, real, and the same size as the object.

60. Sketch a ray diagram to show that when an object is placed between twice the focal length and the focal length from a converging lens, the image formed is inverted, real, and enlarged in size.

61. Sketch a ray diagram to show that when an object is a distance equal to the focal length from a converging lens, the emerging rays from the lens are parallel to each other, so the image is at infinity.

62. When an object is placed 6.0 cm in front of a converging lens, a virtual image is formed 9.0 cm from the lens. What is the focal length of the lens?

63. An object of height 3.00 cm is placed 12.0 cm from a diverging lens of focal length –12.0 cm. Draw a ray diagram to find the height and position of the image.

64. A diverging lens has a focal length of –8.00 cm. (a) What are the image distances for objects placed at these distances from the lens: 5.00 cm, 8.00 cm, 14.0 cm, 16.0 cm, 20.0 cm? In each case, describe the image as real or virtual, upright or inverted, and enlarged or diminished in size. (b) If the object is 4.00 cm high, what is the height of the image for the object distances of 5.00 cm and 20.0 cm?

65. A converging lens has a focal length of 8.00 cm. (a) What are the image distances for objects placed at these distances from the thin lens: 5.00 cm, 14.0 cm, 16.0 cm, 20.0 cm? In each case, describe the image as real or virtual, upright or inverted, and enlarged or diminished in size. (b) If the object is 4.00 cm high, what is the height of the image for the object distances of 5.00 cm and 20.0 cm?

66. Sketch a ray diagram to show that if an object is placed less than the focal length from a converging lens, the image is virtual and upright.

67. For each of the lenses in the figure, list whether the lens is converging or diverging.

(a) (b) (c) (d)

68. In order to read his book, Stephen uses a pair of reading glasses. When he holds the book at a distance of 25 cm from his eyes, the glasses form an upright image a distance of 52 cm from his eyes. (a) Is this a converging or diverging lens? (b) What is the magnification of the lens? (c) What is the focal length of the lens?

69. A standard "35-mm" slide measures 24.0 mm by 36.0 mm. Suppose a slide projector produces a 60.0-cm by 90.0-cm image of the slide on a screen. The focal length of the lens is 12.0 cm. (a) What is the distance between the slide and the screen? (b) If the screen is moved farther from the projector, should the lens be moved closer to the slide or farther away?

70. An object that is 6.00 cm tall is placed 40.0 cm in front of a diverging lens. The magnitude of the focal length of the lens is 20.0 cm. Find the image position and size. Is the image real or virtual? Upright or inverted?

Comprehensive Problems

71. Samantha puts her face 32.0 cm from a makeup mirror and notices that her image is magnified by 1.80 times. (a) What kind of mirror is this? (b) Where is her face

relative to the radius of curvature or focal length? (c) What is the radius of curvature of the mirror?

72. A converging lens made of glass ($n = 1.5$) is placed under water ($n = 1.33$). Describe how the focal length of the lens under water compares to the focal length in air? Draw a diagram to illustrate your answer.

73. An object 8.0 cm high forms a virtual image 3.5 cm high located 4.0 cm behind a mirror. (a) Find the object distance. (b) Describe the mirror: is it plane, convex, or concave? (c) What are its focal length and radius of curvature?

74. A point source of light is placed 10 cm in front of a concave mirror; the reflected rays are parallel. What is the radius of curvature of the mirror?

75. A radar station is located at a height of 24.0 m above the shoreline. When the radar is aimed at a spot 150.0 m out to sea, it detects a whale at the bottom of the ocean. If it takes 2.10 μs for the radar to send out a beam and receive it again, how deep is the ocean where the whale is swimming?

76. A ray of light in air is incident at an angle of 60.0° with the surface of some benzene contained in a shallow tank made of crown glass. What is the angle of refraction of the light ray when it enters the glass at the bottom of the tank?

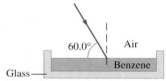

77. A ray of light passes from air through dense flint glass and then back into air. The angle of incidence on the first glass surface is 60.0°. The thickness of the glass is 5.00 mm; its front and back surfaces are parallel. How far is the ray displaced as a result of traveling through the glass?

78. A glass prism bends a ray of blue light more than a ray of red light since its index of refraction is slightly higher for blue than for red. Does a diverging glass lens have the same focal point for blue light and for red light? If not, for which color is the focal point closer to the lens?

79. A laser beam is traveling through an unknown substance. When it encounters a boundary with air, the angle of reflection is 25.0° and the angle of refraction is 37.0°. (a) What is the index of refraction of the substance? (b) What is the speed of light in the substance? (c) At what minimum angle of incidence would the light be totally internally reflected?

80. In many cars the passenger's side mirror says: "Objects in the mirror are closer than they appear." (a) Does this mirror form real or virtual images? (b) Since the image is diminished in size, is the mirror concave or convex? Why? (c) Show that the image must actually be *closer* to the mirror than is the object. (d) How then can the image seem to be farther away?

81. A scuba diver in a lake aims her underwater spotlight at the lake surface. (a) If the beam makes a 75° angle of incidence with respect to a normal to the water surface, is it reflected, transmitted, or both? Find the angles of the reflected and transmitted beams (if they exist). (b) Repeat for a 25° angle of incidence.

82. Laura is walking directly toward a plane mirror at a speed of 0.8 m/s relative to the mirror. At what speed is her image approaching the mirror?

83. Xi Yang is practicing for his driver's license test. He notices in the rearview mirror that a tree, located directly behind the automobile, is approaching his car as he is backing up. If the car is moving at 8.0 km/h in reverse, how fast *relative to the car* does the image of the tree appear to be approaching?

84. A plane mirror reflects a beam of light. Show that the rotation of the mirror by an angle α causes the beam to rotate through an angle 2α.

85. A 3.00-cm-high pin, when placed at a certain distance in front of a concave mirror, produces an upright image 9.00 cm high, 30.0 cm from the mirror. Find the position of the pin relative to the mirror and the image. Draw a ray diagram to illustrate.

86. A dentist holds a small mirror 1.9 cm from a surface of a patient's tooth. The image formed is upright and 5.0 times as large as the object. (a) Is the image real or virtual? (b) What is the focal length of the mirror? Is it concave or convex? (c) If the mirror is moved closer to the tooth, does the image get larger or smaller? (d) For what range of object distances does the mirror produce an upright image?

87. An object of height 5.00 cm is placed 20.0 cm from a converging lens of focal length 15.0 cm. Draw a ray diagram to find the height and position of the image.

88. A letter on a page of the compact edition of the *Oxford English Dictionary* is 0.60 mm tall. A magnifying glass (a single thin lens) held 4.5 cm above the page forms an image of the letter that is 2.4 cm tall. (a) Is the image real or virtual? (b) Where is the image? (c) What is the focal length of the lens? Is it converging or diverging?

89. An object is placed 10.0 cm in front of a lens. An upright, virtual image is formed 30.0 cm away from the lens. What is the focal length of the lens? Is the lens converging or diverging?

Ⓒ 90. A manufacturer is designing a shaving mirror, which is intended to be held close to the face. If the manufacturer wants the image formed to be upright and as large as possible, what characteristics should he choose? (type of mirror? long or short focal length relative to the object distance of face to mirror?)

✦ 91. Show that the deviation angle δ for a ray striking a thin converging lens at a distance d from the principal axis is given by $\delta = d/f$. Therefore, a ray is bent through an

angle δ that is proportional to d and does *not* depend on the angle of the incident ray (as long as it is paraxial). [*Hint:* Look at the figure and use the small-angle approximation $\sin \theta \approx \tan \theta \approx \theta$ (in radians)].

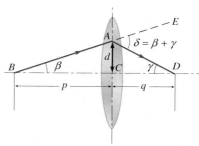

(Angles are greatly exaggerated for ease in labeling.)

92. The focal length of a thin lens is −20.0 cm. A screen is placed 160 cm from the lens. What is the y-coordinate of the point where the light ray shown hits the screen? The incident ray is parallel to the central axis and is 1.0 cm from that axis.

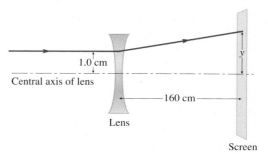

✦✦ 93. The angle of deviation through a triangular prism is defined as the angle between the incident ray and the emerging ray (angle δ). It can be shown that when the angle of incidence i is equal to the angle of refraction r' for the emerging ray, the angle of deviation is at a minimum. Show that the minimum deviation angle ($\delta_{min} = D$) is related to the prism angle A and the index of refraction n, by

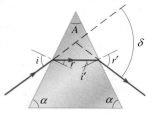

$$n = \frac{\sin \frac{1}{2}(A + D)}{\sin \frac{1}{2} A}$$

[*Hint:* For an isosceles triangular prism, the minimum angle of deviation occurs when the ray inside the prism is parallel to the base, as shown in the figure.]

94. A ray of light is reflected from two mirrored surfaces as shown in the figure. If the initial angle of incidence is 34°, what are the values of angles α and β? (The figure is not to scale.)

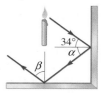

95. A beam of light consisting of a mixture of red, yellow, and blue light originates from a source submerged in some carbon disulfide. The light beam strikes an interface between the carbon disulfide and air at an angle of incidence of 37.5° as shown in the figure. The carbon disulfide has the following indices of refraction for the wavelengths present: red (656.3 nm), $n = 1.6182$; yellow (589.3 nm), 1.6276; blue (486.1 nm), 1.6523. Which color(s) is/are recorded by the detector located above the surface of the carbon disulfide?

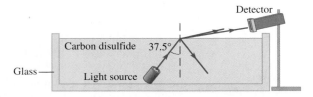

96. A ray of light is incident normally from air onto a glass ($n = 1.50$) prism as shown in the figure with Problem 26. (a) Draw all of the rays that emerge from the prism and give angles to represent their directions. (b) Repeat part (a) with the prism immersed in water ($n = 1.33$). (c) Repeat part (a) with the prism immersed in a sugar solution ($n = 1.50$).

97. A concave mirror has a radius of curvature of 14 cm. If a pointlike object is placed 9.0 cm away from the mirror on its principal axis, where is the image?

98. A glass block ($n = 1.7$) is submerged in an unknown liquid. A ray of light inside the block undergoes total internal reflection. What can you conclude concerning the index of refraction of the liquid?

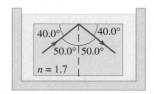

99. Ray diagrams often show objects that conveniently have one end on the principal axis. Draw a ray diagram and locate the image for the object shown in the figure that extends beyond the principal axis.

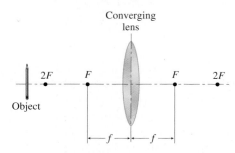

100. A 5.0-cm-tall object is placed 50.0 cm from a lens with focal length −20.0 cm. (a) How tall is the image? (b) Is the image upright or inverted?

◆ 101. The vertical displacement d of light rays parallel to the axis of a lens is measured as a function of the vertical displacement h of the incident ray from the principal axis as shown in part (a) of the figure. The data are graphed in part (b) of the figure. The distance D from the lens to the screen is 1.0 m. What is the focal length of the lens for paraxial rays?

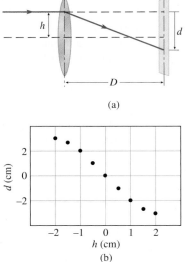

Answers to Practice Problems

23.1

23.2 51°

23.3 If $\theta_i = 0$, then $\theta_t = 0$ and the angle of incidence at the back of the prism is 45°, which is larger than the critical angle (41.8°). If $\theta_i > 0$, then $\theta_t > 0$ and the angle of incidence at the back is greater than 45°.

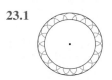

23.4 $\frac{4}{3}h$

23.5 No, she can't see her feet; the bottom of the mirror is 10 cm too high.

23.6 12 cm in front of the mirror, 3.0 cm tall, real

23.7 $p = 6.00$ cm, $f = +12$ cm, concave

23.8

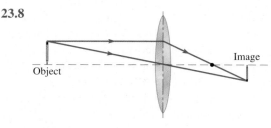

23.9 −12 cm (diverging)

Chapter 24

Optical Instruments

The Hubble Space Telescope, orbiting the Earth at an altitude of about 600 km, was launched in 1990 by the crew of the space shuttle *Discovery*. What is the advantage of having a telescope in space when there are telescopes on Earth with larger light-gathering capabilities? What justifies the cost of two billion dollars to place this 12.5-ton instrument into orbit? (See p. 898 for the answer.)

24.1   LENSES IN COMBINATION

Optical instruments generally involve two or more lenses in combination. Let's start this chapter by considering what happens when light rays emerging from a lens pass through another lens. We will find that the image formed by the first lens serves as the object for the second lens.

- In a series of lenses, the image formed by one lens serves as the object for the next lens.

Suppose that light rays diverge from a point on the image formed by the first lens. These rays are refracted by the second lens the same way as if they were coming from a point on an object. Therefore, the location and size of the image formed by the second lens can be found by applying the lens equation, where the object distance p is the distance from the image formed by the first lens to the second lens. For lenses in combination, we apply the lens equation to each lens in turn, where the object for a given lens is the image formed by the previous lens. Remember that for any application of the lens equation, the object and image distances p and q are measured from the center of the same lens. This same procedure holds true for combinations of lenses and mirrors.

In Chapter 23, all objects were real; p was always positive. With more than one lens, it is possible to have a **virtual object** for which p is *negative*. If one lens produces a real image that would have formed *past* the second lens—so that the rays are converging to a point past the second lens—that image becomes a virtual object for the second lens (Fig. 24.1). Before the real image could form from the first lens, the presence of the second lens intervenes; the rays striking the second lens are converging to a point rather than diverging from a point. This seemingly complicated situation is treated simply by using a negative object distance for a virtual object.

- Rays from a real object are diverging as they enter a lens; rays from a virtual object are *converging* as they enter a lens.

When a lens forms a real image, *its position with respect to the second lens* determines whether it is a real or a virtual object for the second lens. If the first lens would have formed a real image past the second lens, the image becomes a virtual object for the second lens. If the first lens forms a real or virtual image before the second lens, the image is a real object for the second lens.

For a system of two thin lenses separated by a distance s, we can apply the thin lens equation separately to each lens:

$$\frac{1}{p_1} + \frac{1}{q_1} = \frac{1}{f_1}$$

$$\frac{1}{p_2} + \frac{1}{q_2} = \frac{1}{f_2}$$

Figure 24.1 (a) Lens 1, a converging lens, forms a real image of an object. (b) Now lens 2 is placed a distance $s < q_1$ past lens 1. Lens 2 interrupts the light rays before they come together to form the real image, but we can think of the image that *would have* formed as the *virtual object* for lens 2. For a virtual object, p is negative.

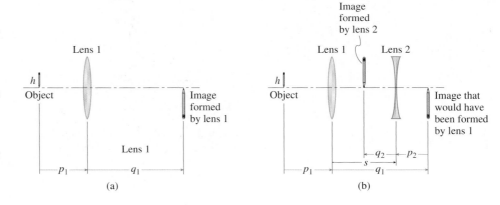

The object distance p_2 for the second lens is

$$p_2 = s - q_1 \qquad (24\text{-}1)$$

Equation (24-1) gives the correct sign for p_2 in every case. If $q_1 < s$, then the image formed by the first lens is on the incident side of the second lens and, thus, is a real object for the second lens ($p_2 > 0$). If $q_1 > s$, then the second lens interrupts the light rays before they form an image. The image that would have been formed by the first lens is beyond the second lens, so the image becomes a virtual object for the second lens ($p_2 < 0$).

Ray Diagrams for Two Lenses

In a ray diagram for a two-lens system, *only one of the principal rays for the first lens is a principal ray for the second lens.* Figure 24.2 shows a system where lens 1 is converging and lens 2 is diverging. Ray 1 comes from the object through focal point F_1' and emerges from lens 1 parallel to the principal axis. Ray 1 is a principal ray for lens 2, emerging as if it came directly from F_2. In the absence of lens 2, ray 1 would have continued parallel to the axis. To locate the image formed by lens 1, we choose another principal ray (ray 2) and trace it, ignoring lens 2. These two rays locate the image formed by lens 1. Since it lies beyond lens 2, it becomes a virtual object. We do not yet know what happens to ray 2 when it strikes lens 2.

To find the final image, we need another principal ray for lens 2. Ray 3 passes undeflected through the center of lens 2; we extrapolate it back through lens 1 to the object. The intersection of rays 1 and 3 locates the final image, which is virtual. Now we can finish ray 2; it must emerge from lens 2 as if coming from the image point.

Magnification

Suppose N lenses are used in combination. Let h be the size of the object, h_1 the size of the image formed by the first lens, and so forth. Since

$$\frac{h_N}{h} = \frac{h_1}{h} \times \frac{h_2}{h_1} \times \frac{h_3}{h_2} \times \cdots \times \frac{h_N}{h_{N-1}}$$

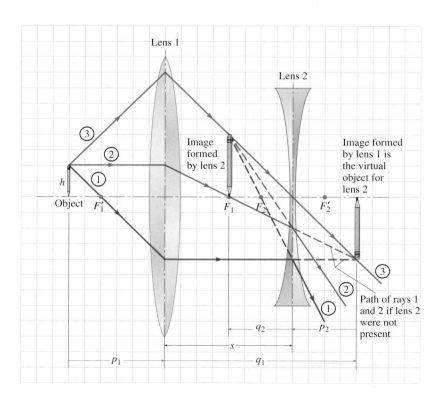

Figure 24.2 Ray diagram for a two-lens combination.

the total transverse magnification due to the *N* lenses is the *product* (*not* the sum) of the magnifications due to the individual lenses:

Total transverse magnification:

$$m_{\text{total}} = m_1 \times m_2 \times \cdots \times m_N \qquad (24\text{-}2)$$

Conceptual Example 24.1

Virtual Image as Object

Two lenses are used in combination. Suppose the first lens forms a virtual image. Does that image serve as a virtual object for the second lens?

Strategy   The distinction between a real and virtual object depends on whether the rays incident on the second lens are converging or diverging.

Solution and Discussion   If the first lens forms a virtual image, then the rays from any point on the object *diverge* as they emerge from the first lens. To find the image point, we trace those rays backward to find the point from which they seem to originate. Since the rays incident on the second lens are diverging, the image must become a *real* object for the second lens.

Another approach: the image formed by the first lens is located *before* the second lens (that is, on the same side as the incident light rays). Thus, the rays behave as if they diverge from an actual object at the same location—as a real object.

Conceptual Practice Problem 24.1
Real Image as Object

Two lenses are used in combination. Suppose the first lens forms a *real* image. Does that image serve as a real object or as a virtual object for the second lens? If either is possible, what determines whether the object is real or virtual?

Example 24.2

Two Converging Lenses

Two converging lenses, separated by a distance of 40.0 cm, are used in combination. The focal lengths are $f_1 = +10.0$ cm and $f_2 = +12.0$ cm. An object, 4.00 cm high, is placed 15.0 cm in front of the first lens. Find the intermediate and final image distances, the total transverse magnification, and the height of the final image.

Strategy   We draw a diagram to help visualize what is happening and then apply the lens equation to each lens in turn. The total magnification is the product of the separate magnifications due to the two lenses.

Given: $p_1 = +15.0$ cm; $f_1 = +10.0$ cm; $f_2 = +12.0$ cm; separation $s = 40.0$ cm; $h = 4.00$ cm

To find: q_1; q_2; m; h'

Solution   Figure 24.3 is a ray diagram that uses two principal rays for each lens to find the intermediate and final images. From the ray diagram, we expect that the intermediate image is real and to the left of lens 2; the final image is virtual, inverted, to the left of lens 1, and greatly enlarged.

The thin lens equation, applied to lens 1, enables us to solve for q_1.

$$\frac{1}{p_1} + \frac{1}{q_1} = \frac{1}{f_1} \qquad (23\text{-}10)$$

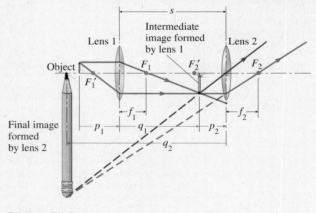

Figure 24.3
Ray diagram for Example 24.2. The intermediate real image formed by lens 1 is found using two of the principal rays, shown in red and green. The green ray is also a principal ray for lens 2. The principal ray that passes straight through the center of lens 2, shown in blue, is not actually present—lens 1 is not large enough to send a ray toward lens 2 in that direction. Nevertheless, we can still use it to locate the final image.

Continued on next page

Example 24.2 Continued

Rearranging the equation and substituting values, we have

$$\frac{1}{q_1} = \frac{1}{f_1} - \frac{1}{p_1} = \frac{1}{10.0 \text{ cm}} - \frac{1}{15.0 \text{ cm}} = \frac{1}{30 \text{ cm}}$$

Therefore, $q_1 = +30$ cm.

From Fig. 24.3, the object distance for lens 2 (p_2) is the separation of the two lenses (s) minus the image distance for the image formed by lens 1 (q_1).

$$p_2 = s - q_1 = 40.0 \text{ cm} - 30 \text{ cm} = 10 \text{ cm}$$

The object distance is positive because the object is real: it is on the left of lens 2 and the rays from the object are diverging as they enter lens 2. We apply the thin lens equation to the second lens to find q_2.

$$\frac{1}{q_2} = \frac{1}{f_2} - \frac{1}{p_2} = \frac{1}{12.0 \text{ cm}} - \frac{1}{10 \text{ cm}} = -\frac{1}{60 \text{ cm}}$$

$$q_2 = -60 \text{ cm}$$

The image is 60 cm to the left of lens 2 or, equivalently, 20 cm to the left of lens 1. The image distance is negative, so the image is virtual.

For a single lens the magnification is

$$m = -\frac{q}{p} \qquad (23\text{-}9)$$

For a combination of two lenses the total magnification is

$$m = m_1 \times m_2 = -\frac{q_1}{p_1} \times \left(-\frac{q_2}{p_2}\right)$$

$$= \left(-\frac{30 \text{ cm}}{15.0 \text{ cm}}\right) \times \left(-\frac{-60 \text{ cm}}{10 \text{ cm}}\right) = -12$$

The final image is inverted, as indicated by the negative value of m, and its height is

$$4.00 \text{ cm} \times 12 = 48 \text{ cm}$$

Discussion Now we compare the numerical results with the ray diagram. As expected, the intermediate image is real and to the left of lens 2 ($q_1 = 30$ cm $< s = 40.0$ cm). The final image is virtual ($q_2 < 0$), inverted ($m < 0$), and enlarged ($|m| > 1$).

Practice Problem 24.2 Object Located at More Than Twice the Focal Length

Repeat Example 24.2 if the same object is placed 25.0 cm before the first lens and the second lens is moved so it is only 10.0 cm from the first lens. Are you able to predict anything about the final image by sketching a ray diagram?

24.2 CAMERAS

One of the simplest optical instruments is the camera, which often has only one lens to produce an image, or even—in a pinhole camera—no lens. Figure 24.4 shows a simple 35-mm camera. The camera uses a converging lens to form a real image on the film. The image must be real in order to *expose* the film (that is, cause a chemical reaction). Light rays from a point on an object being photographed must converge to a corresponding point on the film.

In good-quality cameras, the distance between the lens and the film can be adjusted in accordance with the lens equation so that a sharp image forms on the film. For distant objects, the lens must be one focal length from the film. For closer objects, the lens must be a little farther than that, since the image forms past the focal point. Simple fixed focus cameras have a lens that cannot be moved. Such cameras may give good results for faraway objects, but for closer objects it is more important that the lens position be adjustable.

Making the Connection:
cameras

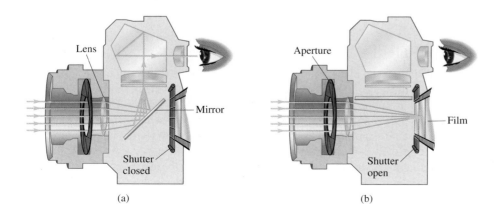

(a)   (b)

Figure 24.4 This 35-mm camera uses a single converging lens to form real images on the film. 35 mm is not the focal length of the lens; it is the width of the film. The camera is focused on objects at different distances by moving the lens closer to or farther away from the film. (a) The shutter is closed, preventing exposure of the film. (b) The mirror swings out of the way and the shutter opens for a short time to expose the film.

A digital camera does away with film, replacing it with a CCD (charge-coupled device) array that receives the image in much the same way that film does. The digital image is stored by the CCD array until it is transferred to magnetic or some other type of storage. After the transfer, the registers of the CCD array are cleared in preparation for receiving a new image. Eventually the stored images are processed by a computer for viewing on the computer screen or for printing.

● Cameras, slide projectors, and movie projectors form real images.

A slide or movie projector is the inverse of a camera. A light source is placed at the focal point of a converging lens so that nearly parallel light rays exit the lens and illuminate the slide. Another converging lens then forms an inverted, real image on a distant screen.

Example 24.3

Fixed Focus Camera

A camera lens has a focal length of 50.0 mm. Photographs are taken of objects located at various positions, from an infinite distance away to as close as 6.00 m from the lens. (a) For an object at infinity, at what distance from the lens is the image formed? (b) For an object at a distance of 6.00 m, at what distance from the lens is the image formed?

Strategy   We apply the thin lens equation for the two object distances and find the two image distances.

Solution   (a) The thin lens equation is

$$\frac{1}{p} + \frac{1}{q} = \frac{1}{f}$$

For an object at infinity, $1/p = 1/\infty = 0$. Then

$$0 + \frac{1}{q} = \frac{1}{f}$$

Therefore, $q = f$. The image distance is equal to the focal length; the image is 50.0 mm from the lens.

(b) This time $p = 6.00$ m from the camera:

$$\frac{1}{6.00 \text{ m}} + \frac{1}{q} = \frac{1}{50.0 \times 10^{-3} \text{ m}}$$

Solving for q yields

$$\frac{1}{q} = \frac{1}{50.0 \times 10^{-3} \text{ m}} - \frac{1}{6.00 \text{ m}}$$

or

$$q = 50.4 \text{ mm}$$

Discussion   The images are formed within 0.4 mm of each other, so the camera can form reasonably well focused images for objects from 6 m to infinity with a fixed distance between lens and film.

Practice Problem 24.3   Close-Up Photograph

Suppose the same lens is used with an adjustable camera to take a photograph of an object at a distance of 1.50 m. To what distance from the film should the lens be moved?

Regulating Exposure of the Film

A diaphragm made of overlapping metal blades acts like the iris of the eye; it regulates the size of the *aperture*—the opening through which light is allowed into the camera (see Fig. 24.4). The *shutter* is the mechanism that regulates the *exposure time*—the time interval during which light is allowed through the aperture. The aperture size and exposure time are selected so that the correct amount of light energy reaches the film. If they are chosen incorrectly, the film is over- or underexposed.

Depth of Field

Once a lens is focused by adjusting its distance q from the film, only objects in a plane at a particular distance p from the lens form sharp images on the film. Rays from a point on an object not in this plane expose a *circle* on the film (the *circle of least confusion*) instead of a single point (Fig. 24.5a). For some range of distances from the plane, the circle of least confusion is small enough to form an acceptably clear image on the film. This range of distances is called the *depth of field*.

A diaphragm can be placed before the lens to reduce the aperture size, reducing the size of the circle of least confusion (Fig. 24.5b). Thus, reducing the aperture size causes

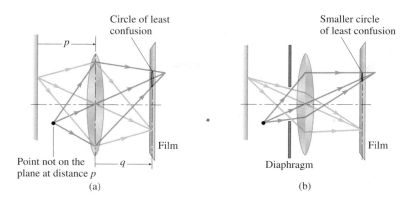

Figure 24.5 (a) The circle of least confusion for a point not on the plane in focus. (b) Reduction of the aperture size reduces the circle of least confusion and thereby increases the depth of field.

an increase in the depth of field. The trade-off is that, with a smaller aperture, a longer exposure time is necessary to correctly expose the film, which can be problematic if the subject is in motion or if the camera is not held steady by a tripod. Some compromise must be made between using a small aperture—so that more of the surroundings are focused—and using a short exposure time so that motion of the subject and/or camera does not blur the image.

Pinhole Camera

Even simpler than a camera with one lens is a **pinhole camera**, or *camera obscura* ("dark room"). To make a pinhole camera, a tiny pinhole is made in one side of a box (Fig. 24.6a). An inverted, real "image" is formed on the opposite side of the box. A photographic plate (a glass plate coated with a photosensitive emulsion) or film placed on the back wall can record the image.

Artists made use of the camera obscura by working in a chamber with a small opening that admitted light rays from a scene outside the chamber. The image could be projected onto a canvas and the artist could trace the outline of the scene on the canvas. Jan van Eyck, Titian, Caravaggio, Vermeer, and Canaletto are just a few of the artists known or believed to have used a camera obscura to achieve realistic naturalism (Fig. 24.6b). In the eighteenth and nineteenth centuries, the camera obscura was commonly used to copy paintings and prints.

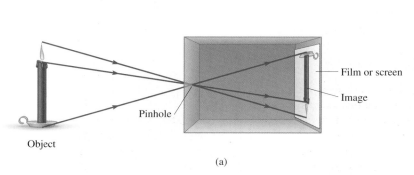

Figure 24.6 (a) A small pinhole camera. (b) *The Concert* was painted by Jan Vermeer around 1666. A camera obscura probably contributed to the accuracy of the perspective and the near-photographic detail in Vermeer's paintings.

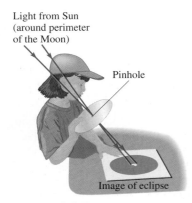

Light from Sun
(around perimeter
of the Moon)

Pinhole

Image of eclipse

Figure 24.7 A pinhole camera arrangement for viewing an eclipse of the Sun.

Making the Connection:

human eye

● Simplified model of the human eye: a single converging lens of variable focal length at a fixed distance from the retina

PHYSICS AT HOME

A safe way to view the Sun is through a pinhole camera arrangement (Fig. 24.7). (This is a good way to view a solar eclipse.) Poke a pinhole in a piece of cardboard, a paper plate, or an aluminum pie pan. Then hold a white sheet of cardboard below the pinhole and view the image of the Sun on it. (Remember not to look directly at the Sun, even during an eclipse; severe damage to your eyes can occur.)

The pinhole camera does not form a *true* image—rays from a point on an object do not converge to a single point on the wall. The pinhole admits a narrow cone of rays diverging from each point on the object; the cone of rays makes a small circular spot on the wall. If this spot is small enough, the image appears clear to the eye. A smaller pinhole results in a dimmer, *sharper* "image" unless the hole is so small that diffraction spreads the spots out significantly.

24.3   THE EYE

The human eye is similar to a digital camera. The camera forms a real image on a CCD array; the eye forms a real image on the *retina*, a membrane with approximately 125 million photoreceptor cells (the *rods* and *cones*). The focusing mechanism is different, though. In the camera, the lens moves toward or away from the film to keep the image on the film as the object distance changes. In the eye, the lens is at a fixed distance from the retina, but it has a variable focal length; the focal length is adjusted to keep the image distance constant as the object distance varies.

Figure 24.8 shows the anatomy of the eye. It is approximately spherical, with an average diameter of 2.5 cm. A bulge in front is filled with the *aqueous fluid* (or aqueous "humor") and covered on the outside by a transparent membrane called the *cornea*. The aqueous fluid is kept at an overpressure to maintain the slight outward bulge. The curved surface of the cornea does most of the refraction of light rays entering the eye. The adjustable *lens* does the fine tuning. For most purposes, we can consider the cornea and the lens to act like a single lens, about 2.0 cm from the retina, with adjustable focal length. In order to see objects at distances of 25 cm or greater from the eye, which is considered normal vision, the focal length of the eye must vary between 1.85 cm and 2.00 cm if the retina is 2.00 cm from the eye (see Problem 22).

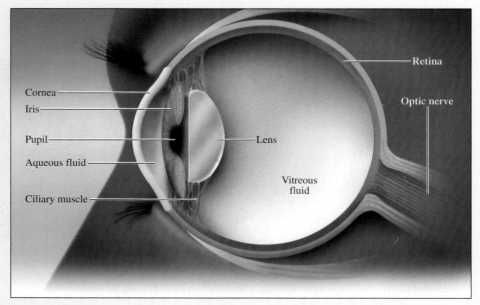

Figure 24.8 Anatomy of the eye.

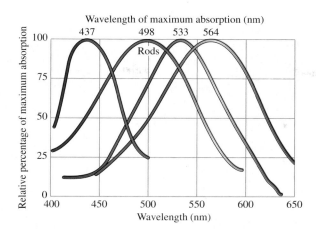

Figure 24.9 How the sensitivities of the rods and the three types of cones depend on the vacuum wavelength of the incident light. (Rods are *much* more sensitive than cones, so if the vertical scale were absolute instead of relative, the graph for the rods would be much taller than the others.)

The spherical volume of the eye behind the lens is filled with a jelly-like material called the *vitreous fluid*. The indices of refraction of the aqueous fluid and the vitreous fluid are approximately the same as that of water (1.333). The index of the lens, made of a fibrous, jelly-like material, is a bit higher (1.437). The cornea has an index of refraction of 1.351.

The eye has an adjustable aperture (the *pupil*) that functions like the diaphragm in a camera to control the amount of light that enters. The size of the pupil is adjusted by the *iris*, a ring of muscular tissue (the colored portion of the eye). In bright light, the iris expands to reduce the size of the pupil and limit the amount of light entering the eye. In dim light, the iris contracts to allow more light to enter through the dilated pupil. The expansion and contraction of the iris is a *reflex* action in response to changing light conditions. In ordinary light the diameter of the pupil is about 2 mm; in dim light it is about 8 mm.

On the retina, the photoreceptor cells are densely concentrated in a small region called the *macula lutea*. The cones come in three different types that respond to different wavelengths of light (Fig. 24.9). Thus, the cones are responsible for color vision. Centered within the macula lutea is the *fovea centralis*, of diameter 0.25 mm, where the cones are tightly packed together and where the most acute vision occurs in bright light. The muscles that control eye movement ensure that the image of an object being examined is centered on the fovea centralis.

PHYSICS AT HOME

Each retina has a *blind spot* with no rods or cones, located where the optic nerve leaves the retina. The blind spot is not usually noticed because the brain fills in the missing information. To observe the blind spot, draw a cross and a dot, about 10 cm apart, on a sheet of white paper. Cover your left eye and hold the paper far from your eyes with the dot on the right. Keep your eye focused on the cross as you slowly move the paper toward your face. The dot disappears when the image falls on the blind spot. Continue to move the paper even closer to your eye; you will see the spot again when its image moves off the blind spot.

The rods are more sensitive to dim light than the cones but do not have different types sensitive to different wavelengths, so we cannot distinguish colors in very dim light. Outside the macula the photoreceptor cells are much less densely packed and they are all rods. However, the rods outside the macula are more densely packed than the rods inside the macula. If you are trying to see a dim star in the sky, it helps to look a little to the side of the star so the image of the star falls outside the macula where there are more rods.

Accommodation

Variation in the focal length of the flexible lens is called **accommodation**; it is the result of an actual change in the shape of the lens of the eye through the action of the *ciliary*

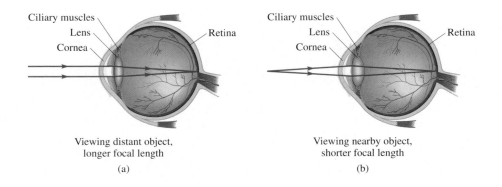

Viewing distant object,
longer focal length
(a)

Viewing nearby object,
shorter focal length
(b)

Figure 24.10 The lens of the eye has (a) a longer focal length when viewing distant objects and (b) a shorter focal length when viewing nearby objects.

muscles. The adjustable shape of the lens allows for accommodation for various object distances, while still forming an image at the fixed image distance determined by the separation of lens and retina. When the object being viewed is far away, the ciliary muscles relax; the lens is relatively flat and thin, giving it a longer focal length (Fig. 24.10a). For closer objects, the ciliary muscles squeeze the lens into a thicker, more rounded shape (Fig. 24.10b), giving the lens a shorter focal length.

Accommodation enables an eye to form a sharp image on the retina of objects at a range of distances from the **near point** to the **far point**. A young adult with good vision has a near point at 25 cm or less and a far point at infinity. A child can have a near point as small as 10 cm. Corrective lenses (eyeglasses or contact lenses) or surgery can compensate for an eye with a near point greater than 25 cm and/or a far point less than infinity.

Optometrists write prescriptions in terms of the **refractive power** (P) of a lens rather than the focal length. (Refractive power is different from "magnifying power," which is a synonym for the angular magnification of an optical instrument.) The refractive power is simply the reciprocal of the focal length:

$$P = \frac{1}{f} \qquad (24\text{-}3)$$

Refractive power is usually measured in **diopters** (symbol D), which is an inverse meter ($1\ \mathrm{D} = 1\ \mathrm{m}^{-1}$). The shorter the focal length, the more "powerful" the lens because the rays are bent more. Converging lenses have positive refractive powers and diverging lenses have negative refractive powers.

Why use refractive power instead of focal length? When two or more thin lenses with refractive powers $P_1, P_2, \ldots$ are sufficiently close together, they act as a single thin lens with refractive power

$$P = P_1 + P_2 + \cdots \qquad (24\text{-}4)$$

as can be shown in Problem 8 by substituting P for $1/f$.

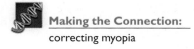

Making the Connection:

correcting myopia

Myopia

A myopic eye can see nearby objects clearly but not distant objects. Myopia (nearsightedness) occurs when the shape of the eyeball is elongated or when the curvature of the cornea is excessive. A myopic eye forms the image of a distant object *in front of* the retina (Fig. 24.11a). The refractive power of the lens is too large; the eye makes the rays converge too soon. A diverging corrective lens (with negative refractive power) can compensate for nearsightedness by bending the rays outward (Fig. 24.11b).

For objects at any distance from the eye, the diverging corrective lens forms a virtual image closer to the eye than is the object. For an object at infinity, the corrective lens forms an image *at the far point* of the eye (Fig. 24.11c). For less distant objects, the virtual image is closer than the far point. The eye is able to focus rays from this image onto the retina since it is never past the far point.

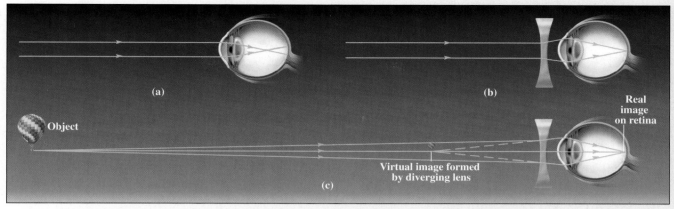

Figure 24.11 (a) In a nearsighted eye, parallel rays from a point on a distant object converge before they reach the retina. (b) A diverging lens corrects for the nearsighted eye by bending the rays outward just enough that the eye brings them back together at the retina. (c) The diverging lens forms a virtual image closer to the eye than the object; the eye can make the rays from this image converge into a real image on the retina. (Not to scale.)

Example 24.4

Correction for a Nearsighted Eye

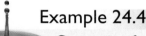 Without her contact lenses, Dana cannot see clearly an object more than 40.0 cm away. What refractive power should her contact lenses have to give her normal vision?

Strategy The far point for Dana's eyes is 40.0 cm. For an object at infinity, the corrective lens must form a virtual image 40.0 cm from the eye. We use the lens equation with $p = \infty$ and $q = -40.0$ cm to find the focal length or refractive power of the corrective lens. The image distance is negative because the image is virtual—it is formed on the same side of the lens as the object.

Solution The thin lens equation is

$$\frac{1}{p} + \frac{1}{q} = \frac{1}{f} = P$$

Since $p = \infty$, $1/p = 0$. Then

$$0 + \frac{1}{-40.0 \text{ cm}} = \frac{1}{f}$$

Solving for the focal length,

$$f = -40.0 \text{ cm}$$

The refractive power of the lens in diopters is the inverse of the focal length in meters.

$$P = \frac{1}{f} = \frac{1}{-40.0 \times 10^{-2} \text{ m}} = -2.50 \text{ D}$$

Discussion The focal length and refractive power are negative, as expected for a diverging lens. We might have anticipated that $f = -40.0$ cm without using the thin lens equation. Rays coming from a distant source are nearly parallel. Parallel rays incident on a diverging lens emerge such that they appear to come from the focal point before the lens. Thus, the image is at the focal point on the incident side of the lens.

Practice Problem 24.4   What Happens to the Near Point?

Suppose Dana's *near* point (without her contact lenses) is 10.0 cm. What is the closest object she can see clearly with her contact lenses on? [*Hint:* For what object distance do the contact lenses form a virtual image 10.0 cm before the lenses?]

Hyperopia

A hyperopic (farsighted) eye can see distant objects clearly but not nearby objects; the near point is too large. The refractive power of the eye is too small; the cornea and lens do not refract the rays enough to make them converge on the retina (Fig. 24.12a). A converging lens can correct for hyperopia by bending the rays inward so they converge sooner (Fig. 24.12b). In order to have normal vision, the near point should be 25 cm (or less). Thus, for an object at 25 cm from the eye, the corrective lens forms a virtual image at the eye's near point.

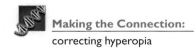

Making the Connection:
correcting hyperopia

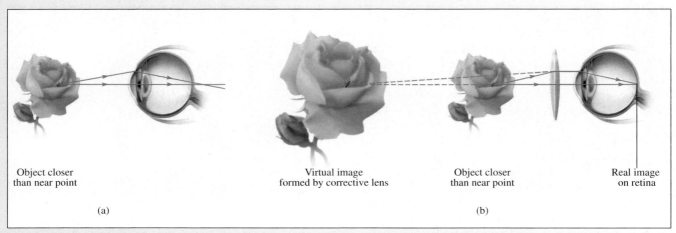

Object closer   Virtual image   Object closer   Real image
than near point   formed by corrective lens   than near point   on retina

(a)   (b)

Figure 24.12 (a) A farsighted eye forms an image of a nearby object past the retina. (Not to scale.) (b) A converging corrective lens forms a virtual image farther away from the eye than the object. Rays from this virtual image can be brought together by the eye to form a real image on the retina.

Example 24.5

Correction for Farsighted Eye

Winifred is unable to focus on objects closer than 2.50 m from her eyes. What refractive power should her corrective lenses have?

Strategy For an object 25 cm from Winifred's eye, the corrective lens must form a virtual image at the near point of Winifred's eye (2.50 m from the eye). We use the thin lens equation with $p = 25$ cm and $q = -2.50$ m to find the focal length. As in the last example, the image distance is negative because it is a virtual image formed on the same side of the lens as the object.

Solution From the thin lens equation,

$$\frac{1}{p} + \frac{1}{q} = \frac{1}{f}$$

Substituting $p = 0.25$ m and $q = -2.50$ m,

$$\frac{1}{0.25\text{ m}} + \frac{1}{-2.50\text{ m}} = \frac{1}{f}$$

Solving for the focal length,

$$f = 0.28\text{ m}$$

The refractive power is

$$P = \frac{1}{f} = +3.6\text{ D}$$

Discussion This solution assumes that the corrective lens is very close to the eye, as for a contact lens. If Winifred wears eyeglasses that are 2.0 cm away from her eyes, then the object and image distances we should use—since they are measured from the *lens*—are $p = 23$ cm and $q = -2.48$ m. The thin lens equation then gives $P = +3.9$ D.

Practice Problem 24.5   Using Eyeglasses

A man can clearly see an object that is 2.00 m away (or more) without using his eyeglasses. If the eyeglasses have a refractive power of +1.50 D, how close can an object be to the eyeglasses and still be clearly seen by the man? Assume the eyeglasses are 2.0 cm from the eye.

Presbyopia

As a person ages, the lens of the eye becomes less flexible and the eye's ability to accommodate decreases, a phenomenon known as presbyopia. Older people have difficulty focusing on objects held close to the eyes; from the age of about 40 years many people need eyeglasses for reading. At age 60, a near point of 50 cm is typical; in some people it may be 1 m or even more. Reading glasses for a person suffering from presbyopia are similar to those used by a farsighted person.

24.4   THE SIMPLE MAGNIFIER

We use magnifiers and microscopes to enlarge objects too small to see with the naked eye. But what do we mean by *enlarged* in this context? The apparent size of an object depends on the size of the image *formed on the retina* of the eye. For the unaided eye, the retinal image size is proportional to the angle subtended by the object. Figure 24.13 shows two identical objects being viewed from different distances. Imagine rays from the top and bottom of each object that are incident on the center of the lens of the eye. The angle θ is called the **angular size** of the object. The image on the retina subtends the same angle θ; the angular size of the image is the same as that of the object. Rays from the object at a greater distance subtend a smaller angle; the angular size depends on distance from the eye.

A magnifying glass, microscope, or telescope serves to make the image on the retina larger *than it would be if viewed with the unaided eye.* Since the size of the image on the retina is proportional to the angular size, we measure the usefulness of an optical instrument by its **angular magnification**—the ratio of the angular size using the instrument to the angular size with the unaided eye.

Definition of angular magnification:

$$M = \frac{\theta_{\text{aided}}}{\theta_{\text{unaided}}} \tag{24-5}$$

The *transverse* magnification (the ratio of the image size to the object size) isn't as useful here. The transverse magnification of a telescope-eye combination is minute: the Moon is *much* larger than the image of the Moon on the retina, even using a telescope. The telescope makes the image of the Moon larger than it would be in unaided viewing.

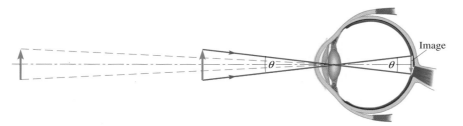

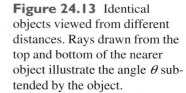

Figure 24.13 Identical objects viewed from different distances. Rays drawn from the top and bottom of the nearer object illustrate the angle θ subtended by the object.

PHYSICS AT HOME

On a clear night with the Moon visible, go outside, shut one eye, and hold a pencil at arm's length between your open eye and the Moon so it blocks your view of the Moon. Compare the angular size of the Moon to the angular width of the pencil. Estimate the distance from your eye to the pencil and the pencil's width. Use this information and the Earth-Moon distance (4×10^5 km) to estimate the diameter of the Moon. Compare your estimate to the actual diameter of the Moon (3.5×10^3 km).

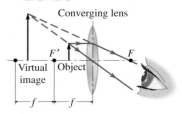

When you want to see something in greater detail, you naturally move your eye closer to the object to increase the angular size of the object. But the eye's ability to accommodate for nearby objects is limited; anything closer than the near point cannot be seen clearly. Thus, the maximum angle subtended at the unaided eye by an object occurs when the object is located at the near point.

A **simple magnifier** is a converging lens placed so that the object distance is less than the focal length. The virtual image formed is enlarged, upright, and farther away from the lens than the object (Fig. 24.14). Typically, the image is put well beyond the near point so that it is viewed by a more relaxed eye at the expense of a small reduction in angular magnification. The angle subtended by the enlarged virtual image seen by the eye is much larger than the angle subtended by the object when placed at the near point.

Figure 24.14 A converging lens used as a magnifying glass forms an enlarged virtual image. The object distance is less than the focal length.

If a small object of height h is viewed with the unaided eye (Fig. 24.15a), the angular size when it is placed at the near point (a distance N from the eye) is

$$\theta \approx \frac{h}{N} \quad \text{(in radians)}$$

where we assume $h \ll N$ and, thus, θ is small enough that $\tan \theta \approx \theta$. If the object is now placed at the focal point of a converging lens, the image is formed at infinity and can be viewed with a relaxed eye (Fig. 24.15b). The angular size of the image is

$$\theta_\infty \approx \frac{h}{f} \quad \text{(in radians)}$$

Then the angular magnification M is

$$M = \frac{\theta_\infty}{\theta} = \frac{h/f}{h/N} = \frac{N}{f} \tag{24-6}$$

When calculating the angular magnification of an optical instrument, it is customary to assume a typical near point of $N = 25$ cm.

Equation (24-6) gives the angular magnification when the object is placed at the focal point of the magnifier. If the object is placed closer to the magnifier, the angular magnification is somewhat larger. In many cases, the small increase in angular magnification is not worth the added eyestrain of viewing an image closer to the eye (see Problem 35).

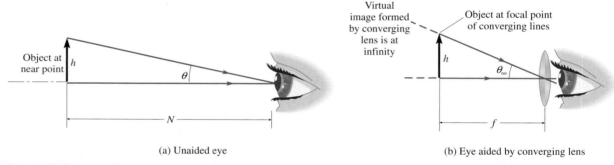

(a) Unaided eye   (b) Eye aided by converging lens

Figure 24.15 (a) The angle θ subtended at the eye by an object placed at the near point. (b) The magnifier forms a virtual image of the object at infinity. The angle θ_∞ subtended by the virtual image is larger than θ.

Example 24.6
A Magnifying Glass

A converging lens with a focal length of 4.00 cm is used as a simple magnifier. The lens forms a virtual image at your near point, 25.0 cm from your eye. Where should the object be placed and what is the angular magnification? Assume that the magnifier is held close to your eye.

Strategy   We can use 25.0 cm as the image distance from the *lens*; if the magnifier is near the eye, distances from the lens are approximately the same as distances from the eye. We apply the thin lens equation to find the object distance with the focal length and image distance known.

Solution   By rearranging the thin lens equation to solve for the object distance, we obtain

$$p = \frac{fq}{q - f}$$

We now substitute $q = -25.0$ cm (negative for a virtual image) and $f = +4.00$ cm.

$$p = \frac{4.00 \text{ cm} \times (-25.0 \text{ cm})}{-25.0 \text{ cm} - 4.00 \text{ cm}}$$

$$= 3.45 \text{ cm}$$

Continued on next page

Example 24.6 Continued

The object is placed 3.45 cm from the lens. The angular size (in radians) of the image formed is

$$\theta = \frac{h}{p}$$

where h is the size of the object. The object is *not* at the focal point of the lens, so the angular size is not h/f as it is in Fig. 24.15b. If the object were to be viewed without the magnifier, while placed at the near point of $N = 25.0$ cm, the angular size would be

$$\theta_0 = \frac{h}{N}$$

The angular magnification is

$$M = \frac{h/p}{h/N} = \frac{N}{p} = \frac{25.0\ \text{cm}}{3.45\ \text{cm}} = 7.25$$

Discussion   If the object had been placed at the principal focal point, 4.00 cm from the lens, to form a final image at infinity, the angular magnification would have been

$$M = \frac{N}{f} = \frac{25.0\ \text{cm}}{4.00\ \text{cm}} = 6.25$$

Practice Problem 24.6   Where to Place an Object with a Magnifier

The focal length of a simple magnifier is 12.0 cm. Assume the viewer's eye is held close to the lens. (a) What is the angular magnification of an object if the magnifier forms a final image at the viewer's near point (25.0 cm)? (b) What is the angular magnification if the final image is at infinity?

24.5   COMPOUND MICROSCOPES

The simple magnifier is limited to angular magnifications of 15–20 at most. By contrast, the **compound microscope**, which uses two converging lenses, enables angular magnifications of 2000 or more. The compound microscope was probably invented in Holland around 1600.

A small object to be viewed under the microscope is placed *just beyond* the focal point of a converging lens called the **objective**. The function of the objective is to form an enlarged real image. A second converging lens, called the **ocular** or **eyepiece**, is used to view the real image formed by the objective lens (Fig. 24.16). The eyepiece acts as a simple magnifier; it forms an enlarged virtual image. The position of the final image can be anywhere between the near point of the observer and infinity. Usually it is placed at infinity, since that enables viewing with a relaxed eye and doesn't decrease the angular magnification very much. To form a final image at infinity, the image formed by the objective is located at the focal point of the eyepiece. Inside the barrel of the microscope, the positions of the two lenses are adjusted so that the image formed by the objective falls at or within the focal point of the eyepiece.

If we used just the eyepiece as a simple magnifier to view the object, the angular magnification would be

$$M_e = \frac{N}{f_e}\quad\text{(due to eyepiece)}$$

where f_e is the focal length of the eyepiece and the virtual image is at infinity for ease of viewing. Customarily we assume $N = 25$ cm. The objective forms an image that is larger than the object; as shown in Problem 44, the transverse magnification due to the objective is

$$m_o = -\frac{L}{f_o}\quad\text{(due to objective)}$$

where L (the **tube length**) is the distance between the focal points of the two lenses. Since the image of the objective is placed at the focal point of the eyepiece, as in Fig. 24.16, the tube length is

$$L = q_o - f_o \tag{24-7}$$

Many microscopes are designed with a tube length of 16 cm.

Making the Connection:
microscopes

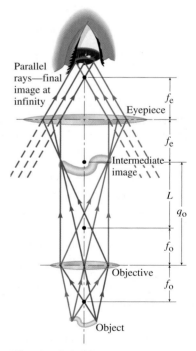

Figure 24.16 A compound microscope. To form a final image at infinity, the intermediate image must be located at the focal point of the eyepiece.

When we view the image with the eyepiece, the eyepiece provides the same angular magnification as before (M_e), but it magnifies an image already m_o times as large as the object. The total angular magnification is the product of m_o and M_e:

Angular magnification due to a microscope:

$$M_{total} = m_o M_e = -\frac{L}{f_o} \times \frac{N}{f_e} \qquad (24\text{-}8)$$

The negative sign in Eq. (24-8) means that the final image is inverted. Sometimes with microscopes and telescopes the sign is ignored and the angular magnification (also called the *magnifying power*) is reported as a positive number.

Equation (24-8) shows that, for large magnification, both focal lengths should be small. Microscopes are often made so that any one of several different objective lenses can be swung into position, depending on the magnification desired. The manufacturer usually provides the values of the magnification ($|m_o|$ and M_e) instead of the focal lengths of the lenses. For example, if an eyepiece is labeled "5×," then $M_e = 5$.

> Remember that the tube length L in Eq. (24-8) is *the distance between the focal points* of the two lenses in a compound microscope.

Example 24.7

Magnification by a Microscope

A compound microscope has an objective lens of focal length 1.40 cm and an eyepiece with a focal length of 2.20 cm. The objective and the eyepiece are separated by 19.6 cm. The final image is at infinity. (a) What is the angular magnification? (b) How far from the objective should the object be placed?

Strategy Since the final image is at infinity, Eq. (24-8) can be used to find the angular magnification M. We first find the tube length L of the microscope. From Fig. 24.16, the distance between the lenses is the sum of the two focal lengths plus the tube length. We assume the typical near point of $N = 25$ cm. To find where the object should be placed, we apply the thin lens equation to the objective. The image formed by the objective is at the focal point of the eyepiece since the final image is at infinity.

Given: $f_o = 1.40$ cm, $f_e = 2.20$ cm, lens separation = 19.6 cm

To find: (a) total angular magnification M; (b) object distance p_o

Solution   (a) The tube length is

$$L = \text{distance between lenses} - f_o - f_e$$

$$= 19.6 \text{ cm} - 1.40 \text{ cm} - 2.20 \text{ cm} = 16.0 \text{ cm}$$

Then the angular magnification is

$$M = -\frac{L}{f_o} \times \frac{N}{f_e}$$

$$= -\frac{16.0 \text{ cm}}{1.40 \text{ cm}} \times \frac{25 \text{ cm}}{2.20 \text{ cm}} = -130$$

The negative magnification indicates that the final image is inverted.

(b) To have the final image at infinity, the image formed by the objective lens must be located at the focal point of the eyepiece. From Fig. 24.16, the intermediate image distance is

$$q_o = L + f_o = 16.0 \text{ cm} + 1.40 \text{ cm} = 17.4 \text{ cm}$$

Then the object distance is found using the thin lens equation

$$\frac{1}{p_o} + \frac{1}{q_o} = \frac{1}{f_o}$$

Solving for the object distance, p

$$p_o = \frac{f_o q_o}{q_o - f_o}$$

$$= \frac{1.40 \text{ cm} \times 17.4 \text{ cm}}{17.4 \text{ cm} - 1.40 \text{ cm}}$$

$$= 1.52 \text{ cm}$$

Discussion   We can check the result for part (b) to see if the object is just past the focal point of the objective. The object is 1.52 cm from the objective while the focal point is 1.40 cm, so the object is just 1.2 mm past the focal point.

Practice Problem 24.7   Object Distance for Good Focus

An observer with a near point of 25 cm looks through a microscope with an objective lens of focal length $f_o = 1.20$ cm. When an object is placed 1.28 cm from the objective, the angular magnification is −198 and the final image is formed at infinity. (a) What is the tube length L for this microscope? (b) What is the focal length of the eyepiece?

The Transmission Electron Microscope

Many other kinds of microscope, both optical and nonoptical, are in use. The one most similar to the optical compound microscope is the *transmission electron microscope* (TEM). In the 1920s, Ernst Ruska (1906–1988) found that a magnetic field due to a coil could act as a lens for electrons. An optical lens functions by changing the directions of the light rays; the magnetic coil changes the directions of the electrons' trajectories. Ruska was able to use the lens to form an image of an object irradiated with electrons. Eventually he coupled two such lenses together to form a microscope. By 1933 he had produced the first electron microscope, using an electron beam to form images of tiny objects with far greater clarity than the conventional optical microscope. Ruska's microscope is called a *transmission* microscope because the electron beam passes right through the thin slice of a sample being studied.

Resolution

A large magnification is of little use if the image is blurry. *Resolution* is the ability to form clear and distinct images of points very close to each other on an object. High resolution is a desirable quality in a microscope. The ultimate limit on the resolution of an optical instrument is limited by diffraction—the spreading out of light rays. Diffraction limits the size of an object, or the separation of two objects, that can be distinguished to approximately the wavelength of the light used. Thus, we cannot expect to see anything smaller than about 400 nm using a compound optical microscope. An atom, roughly 0.2–0.5 nm in diameter, is much smaller than the wavelength of light, so a microscope cannot resolve details on the atomic scale. Ultraviolet microscopes can do a little better (about 100 nm) due to the shorter wavelength. Transmission electron microscopes can resolve details down to about 0.5 nm.

24.6   TELESCOPES

Refracting Telescopes

Making the Connection:
telescopes

The most common type of telescope for nonscientific work is the **refracting telescope**, which has two converging lenses that function just as those in a compound microscope. The refracting telescope has an objective lens that forms a real image of the object; the eyepiece (ocular) is used to view this real image. The microscope is used to view *tiny* objects placed close to the objective lens; the purpose of the objective is to form an *enlarged* image. The telescope is used to view objects whose *angular* sizes are small because they are far away; the objective forms an image that is tiny compared to the object, but the image is available for closeup viewing through the eyepiece.

In an *astronomical* refracting telescope, the object is so far away that the rays from a point on the object can be assumed to be parallel; the object distance is taken as infinity (Fig. 24.17). The objective forms a real, diminished image at its principal focus. By placing this image at the secondary focal point of the eyepiece, the final image is at infinity for ease of viewing. Thus, the principal focal point of the objective must coincide with the secondary focal point of the eyepiece, in contrast to the microscope in which the two are separated by a distance L (the tube length). When an astronomical telescope is connected to a camera to record the image, the camera lens replaces the eyepiece and the image formed by the objective is *not* placed at the focal point of the camera lens because the camera lens must form a real image *on the film*.

The objective is located at one end of the telescope barrel and the eyepiece is at the other end. Then the *barrel length* of the telescope is the sum of the focal lengths of the objective and the eyepiece.

$$\text{barrel length} = f_o + f_e \qquad\qquad (24\text{-}9)$$

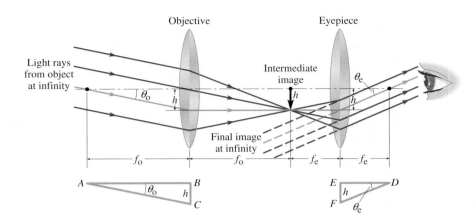

Figure 24.17 An astronomical refracting telescope.

In Fig. 24.17, a highlighted ray passing through the secondary focal point of the objective leaves the lens parallel to the principal axis, then continues to the eyepiece and is refracted so that it goes through the principal focal point of the eyepiece. Two small right triangles from the diagram are redrawn below the diagram for clarity. The hypotenuse (*AC, FD*) of each triangle is along the highlighted ray. The leg (*BC, EF*) of each triangle from the principal axis to the hypotenuse is of length *h* because the line connecting *C* to *F* is parallel to the principal axis and passes through the tip of the image.

The angle that would be subtended if viewed by the unaided eye is the same as the angle subtended at the objective (θ_o). The angle subtended at the observer's eye looking through the eyepiece at the final image formed at infinity is θ_e. From the two small right triangles and the small angle approximation, the angular size of the object for the unaided eye is

$$\theta_o \approx \tan \theta_o = \frac{h}{AB} = \frac{h}{f_o}$$

The angular size of the final image is

$$\theta_e \approx \tan \theta_e = -\frac{h}{DE} = -\frac{h}{f_e}$$

The final image is inverted, so its angular size is negative. With a telescope, the magnification that is of interest is again the *angular* magnification: the ratio of the angle subtended at the eye by the final magnified image to the angle subtended for the unaided eye. Then the angular magnification is

Angular magnification due to an astronomical telescope:

$$M = \frac{\theta_e}{\theta_o} = -\frac{f_o}{f_e} \qquad (24\text{-}10)$$

where the negative sign indicates an inverted image. As for microscopes, the angular magnification is usually reported as a positive number. For the greatest magnification, the objective lens has as long a focal length as possible, while the eyepiece has as short a focal length as possible.

Example 24.8

Yerkes Refracting Telescope

The Yerkes telescope in southern Wisconsin (Fig. 24.18) is the largest refracting telescope in the world. Its objective lens is 1.016 m (40 in.) in diameter and has a focal length of 19.8 m (65 ft). If the magnifying power is 508, what is the focal length of the eyepiece?

Strategy The magnifying power is the magnitude of the angular magnification. For an astronomical refracting telescope, the angular magnification is negative.

Continued on next page

Example 24.8 Continued

Figure 24.18
The Yerkes refracting telescope, first operated in 1897, is still the largest *refracting* telescope in the world. It is part of the Department of Astronomy and Astrophysics at the University of Chicago.

Solution From Eq. (24-10), the angular magnification is

$$M = \frac{\theta_e}{\theta_o} = -\frac{f_o}{f_e}$$

Solving for f_e yields

$$f_e = -\frac{f_o}{M}$$

Now we substitute $M = -508$ and $f_o = 19.8$ m:

$$f_e = -\frac{19.8 \text{ m}}{-508} = 3.90 \text{ cm}$$

Discussion The focal length of the eyepiece is positive, which is correct. The eyepiece serves as a simple magnifier used to view the image formed by the objective. The simple magnifier is a converging lens—that is, a lens with positive focal length.

Practice Problem 24.8   Replacing the Eyepiece

If the eyepiece used with the Yerkes telescope in Example 24.8 is changed to one with focal length 2.54 cm that produces a final image at infinity, what is the new angular magnification?

An inverted image is no problem when the telescope is used as an astronomical telescope. When a telescope is used to view terrestrial objects, such as a bird perched high on a tree limb or a rock singer on stage at an outdoor concert, the final image must be upright. Binoculars are essentially a pair of telescopes with reflecting prisms that invert the image so the final image is upright.

Another way to make a terrestrial telescope is to add a third lens between the objective and the eyepiece to invert the image again so that the final image is upright. The Galilean telescope, invented by Galileo in 1609, produces an upright image without using a third lens. The upright image is obtained by using a *diverging* lens as the eyepiece (see Problem 50). The eyepiece is located so that the image formed by the objective becomes a *virtual* object for the eyepiece, which then forms an upright virtual image. The barrel length for a Galilean telescope is shorter than for telescopes with only converging lenses.

Reflecting Telescopes

Reflecting telescopes use one or more mirrors in place of lenses. There are several advantages to mirrors over lenses; these advantages become overwhelming in the large telescopes that must be used to gather enough light rays to be able to see distant, faint stars. (Large telescopes also minimize the loss of resolution due to diffraction.) Since the index of refraction varies with wavelength, a lens has slightly different focal lengths for different wavelengths; thus, dispersion distorts the image. A mirror works by reflection rather than refraction, so it has the same focal length for all wavelengths. Large mirrors are much easier to build than large lenses. When making a large glass lens, the glass becomes so heavy that it deforms due to its own weight. It also suffers from stresses and strains as it cools from a molten state; such stresses reduce the optical quality of the lens. A large mirror need not be so heavy, since only the *surface* is important; it can be supported everywhere under its surface, while a lens can only be supported at the edge. Another advantage of the reflecting telescope is that the heaviest part—the large concave mirror—is located at the base of the telescope, making the instrument stable. The largest lens used with a refracting telescope—a little over 1 m (3.3 ft) in diameter—is in the

Making the Connection:
reflecting telescopes

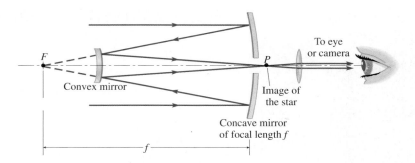

Figure 24.19 Cassegrain focus arrangement of a reflecting telescope directing rays from a distant star to an eye or a camera.

Yerkes telescope. By comparison, the primary mirror in each of the twin Keck reflecting telescopes in Hawaii has a diameter ten times as large—10 m (33 ft).

Figure 24.19 shows one kind of reflecting telescope, known as the Cassegrain arrangement. Parallel light rays from a distant star are reflected from a concave mirror toward its focal point F. Before the rays can reach the focal point, they are intercepted in their path by a smaller convex mirror. The convex mirror directs the rays through a hole in the center of the large concave mirror so that they come to a focus at a point P. A camera or an electronic recording instrument can be placed at point P, or a lens can be used to direct the rays to a viewer's eye.

Making the Connection:
Hubble Space Telescope

Hubble Space Telescope

A famous telescope using the Cassegrain arrangement is the Hubble Space Telescope (HST). The HST orbits Earth at an altitude of over 600 km; its primary mirror is 2.4 m in diameter. Why put a telescope in orbit? The atmosphere limits the amount of detail that is seen by any telescope on Earth. The density of the air in the atmosphere at any location is continually fluctuating; as a result, light rays from distant stars are bent by different amounts, making it impossible to bring the rays to a sharp focus. There are systems that correct for atmospheric fluctuations, but since the HST is above the atmosphere, it avoids the whole problem.

Accomplishments of the HST (Fig. 24.20) include clear images of quasars, the most energetic objects of the universe; the first surface map of Pluto; the discovery of

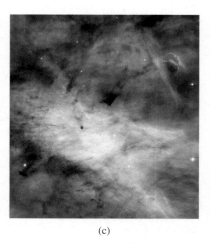

(a)   (b)   (c)

Figure 24.20 Three stunning images captured by the Advanced Camera for Surveys aboard the Hubble Space Telescope. (a) The Cone Nebula, a pillar of cold gas and dust. Hydrogen atoms absorb ultraviolet radiation and emit light, causing the red "halo" around the pillar. (b) Collision of two spiral galaxies known as the "Mice." A similar fate may await our galaxy a few billion years from now. (c) The center of the Omega Nebula, a region of flowing gas and newly formed stars surrounded by a cloud of hydrogen. Light emitted by excited atoms of nitrogen and sulfur produces the rose-colored region right of center. Other colors are produced by excited atoms of hydrogen and oxygen.

Figure 24.21 The radio telescope at Arecibo, Puerto Rico, occupies nearly twenty acres of a remote hilltop region.

intergalactic helium left over from the big bang (the birth of the universe); and clear evidence for the existence of black holes (objects so dense that nothing, not even light, can escape their gravitational pull). The HST has provided evidence of gravitational lensing, in which the gravity from massive galaxies bends light rays inward like a lens to form images of even more distant objects behind them.

The HST has provided a deeper look back in time than any other optical telescope, providing views of galaxies at an early stage of the universe and evidence for the age of the universe. In 2011, NASA plans to replace the HST with the James Webb Space Telescope, with a mirror several times larger than the HST's. It will be placed a million miles from Earth on the side away from the Sun.

Radio Telescopes

The EM radiation traveling to Earth from celestial bodies is not limited to the visible part of the spectrum. Radio telescopes detect radio waves from space. The radio telescope at Arecibo, Puerto Rico (Fig. 24.21), is the most sensitive radio telescope in the world. The bowl of the telescope, 305 m (0.19 mi) in diameter and 51 m (167 ft) deep, is made from metallic mesh panels instead of solid metal; it reflects just as well as a solid metal surface because the holes are much smaller than the wavelengths of the radio waves. A detector is suspended in midair at the focal point, 137 m above the bowl. Arecibo takes only a few minutes to gather information from a radio source that would require several hours of observation with a smaller radio telescope.

A home satellite dish is a small version of a radio telescope. It is directed toward a satellite and forms a real image of the microwaves beamed down to Earth from the satellite. When the dish is properly aimed to receive the signal sent by the satellite from a TV station, the microwaves of that station are focused on the antenna of the receiver.

Making the Connection:
radio telescopes

24.7   ABERRATIONS OF LENSES AND MIRRORS

Real lenses and mirrors deviate from the behavior of an ideal lens or mirror. There are many kinds of **aberrations**; in this section we consider only two of them. In Chapter 25, we consider in more detail the limits on the resolution of optical instruments due to diffraction.

Spherical Aberration

The derivations of the lens and mirror equations assume that light rays are paraxial—that they are nearly parallel to the principal axis and not too far away from the axis. That assumption enabled us to use small-angle approximations. Rays for which the angle of incidence on the lens or mirror is *not* small do not all converge to the same focal point (or appear to diverge from the same focal point). Then rays from a point on the object do not correspond to a single image point; the image is blurred due to **spherical aberration**. Spherical aberration can be minimized by placing a diaphragm before the lens or mirror so that only rays traveling rather close to the principal axis can reach the lens and pass through it. The image formed is in better focus (sharper) but is less bright.

For mirrors, spherical aberration can be avoided by using a *parabolic* mirror instead of a spherical mirror. A parabolic mirror focuses parallel rays to a point even if they are not paraxial. Large astronomical reflecting telescopes use parabolic mirrors. Since light rays are reversible, if a point light source is placed at the focal point of a parabolic mirror, the reflected rays form a parallel beam. Searchlights and automobile headlights use parabolic reflectors to send out fairly parallel rays in a well-defined beam of light.

Chromatic Aberration

Another aberration of lenses (but not of mirrors) is due to dispersion. When light composed of several wavelengths passes through a lens, the various wavelengths are bent by differing amounts due to dispersion; this lens defect is called **chromatic aberration**. One way to correct for chromatic aberration is to use a combination of lenses consisting of different materials so that the aberrations from one lens cancel those from another.

PHYSICS AT HOME

Look at a TV or computer monitor with your unaided eye (or through your usual eyeglasses). Then make a fist with one hand, leaving an opening like a small tunnel to peer through with one eye. Look at the same screen through your hand; you will see a much sharper image. Slowly expand the opening made by your fist and watch the image become fuzzy. People with poor or changing eyesight sometimes squint in order to see more clearly.

MASTER THE CONCEPTS

- In a series of lenses, the image formed by one lens becomes the object for the next lens.
- If one lens produces a real image that would have formed *past* a second lens—so that the rays are converging to a point past the second lens—that image becomes a *virtual object* for the second lens. In the thin lens equation, p is *negative* for a virtual object.
- When the image formed by one lens serves as the object for a second lens a distance s away, the object distance p_2 for the second lens is

$$p_2 = s - q_1 \qquad (24\text{-}1)$$

- The total transverse magnification of an image formed by two or more lenses is the product of the magnifications due to the individual lenses.

$$m_{\text{total}} = m_1 \times m_2 \times \cdots \times m_N \qquad (24\text{-}2)$$

- A typical camera has a single converging lens. To focus on an object, the distance between the lens and the film is adjusted so that a real image is formed on the film.
- The aperture size and the exposure time must be chosen to allow just enough light to expose the film. The *depth of field* is the range of distances from the plane of sharp focus for which the lens forms an acceptably clear image on the film. Greater depth of field is possible with a smaller aperture.
- In the human eye, the cornea and the lens refract light rays to form a real image on the photoreceptor cells in the retina. For most purposes, we can consider the cornea and the lens to act like a single lens with an adjustable focal length. The adjustable shape of the lens allows for accommodation for various object distances, while still forming an image at the fixed image distance determined by the separation of lens and retina. The nearest and farthest object distances that the eye can accommodate are called the near point and far point. A young adult with good

MASTER THE CONCEPTS *continued*

vision has a near point at 25 cm or less and a far point at infinity.

- The refractive power of a lens is the reciprocal of the focal length:

$$P = \frac{1}{f} \qquad (24\text{-}3)$$

Refractive power is measured in diopters (1 D = 1 m^{-1}).

- A myopic (nearsighted) eye has a far point less than infinity; for objects past the far point, it forms an image before the retina. A diverging corrective lens (with negative refractive power) can compensate for nearsightedness by bending light rays outward.

- A hyperopic (farsighted) eye has too large a near point; the refractive power of the eye is too small. For objects closer than the near point, the eye forms an image past the retina. A converging lens can correct for hyperopia by bending the rays inward so they converge sooner.

- As a person ages, the lens of the eye becomes less flexible and the eye's ability to accommodate decreases, a phenomenon known as presbyopia.

- *Angular* magnification is the ratio of the angular size using the instrument to the angular size as viewed by the unaided eye.

$$M = \frac{\theta_{\text{aided}}}{\theta_{\text{unaided}}} \qquad (24\text{-}5)$$

- The simple magnifier is a converging lens placed so that the object distance is less than the focal length. The virtual image formed is enlarged and upright. If the image is formed at infinity for ease of viewing, the angular magnification M is

$$M = \frac{N}{f} \qquad (24\text{-}6)$$

where N, the near point, is usually taken to be 25 cm.

- The compound microscope consists of two converging lenses. A small object to be viewed is placed *just beyond* the focal point of the objective, which forms an enlarged real image. The eyepiece (ocular) acts as a simple magnifier to view the image formed by the objective. If the final image is at infinity, the angular magnification due to the microscope is

$$M_{\text{total}} = m_{\text{o}} M_{\text{e}} = -\frac{L}{f_{\text{o}}} \times \frac{N}{f_{\text{e}}} \qquad (24\text{-}8)$$

where N is the near point (usually 25 cm) and L (the tube length) is the distance between the focal points of the two lenses.

- An astronomical refracting telescope uses two converging lenses. As in the microscope, the objective forms a real image and the eyepiece functions as a magnifier for viewing the real image. The angular magnification is

$$M = -\frac{f_{\text{o}}}{f_{\text{e}}} \qquad (24\text{-}10)$$

- In a reflecting telescope, a concave mirror takes the place of the objective lens.

- Spherical aberration occurs because rays that are not paraxial are brought to a focus at a different spot than are paraxial rays.

- Chromatic aberration is caused by dispersion in the lens.

Conceptual Questions

1. Why must a camera or a slide projector use a converging lens? Why must the objective of a microscope or telescope be a converging lens (or a converging mirror)? Why can the eyepiece of a telescope be either converging or diverging?

2. A magnifying glass can be held over a piece of white paper and its position adjusted until the image of an overhead light is formed on the paper. Explain.

3. If a piece of white cardboard is placed at the location of a virtual object, what (if anything) would be seen on the cardboard?

4. Why is a refracting telescope with a large angular magnification longer than one with a smaller magnification?

5. Why are astronomical observatories often located on mountaintops?

6. Why do some telescopes produce an inverted image?

7. Why is the receiving antenna of a satellite dish placed at a set distance from the dish?

8. Two magnifying glasses are labeled with their angular magnifications. Glass A has a magnification of "2×" ($M = 2$) and glass B has a magnification of 4×. Which has the longer focal length? Explain.

9. What causes chromatic aberration? What can be done to compensate for chromatic aberration?

10. For human eyes, about 70% of the refraction occurs at the cornea; less than 25% occurs at the two surfaces of the lens. Why? [*Hint:* Consider the indices of refraction.] Is the same thing true for fish eyes?

11. If rays from points on an object are converging as they enter a lens, is the object real or virtual?

12. What are some of the advantages of using mirrors rather than lenses for astronomical telescopes?

13. When snorkeling, you wear goggles in order to see clearly. Why is your vision blurry without the goggles? A nearsighted person notices that he is able to see nearby objects *more* clearly when he is underwater (without goggles or corrective lenses) than in air (without corrective lenses). Why might this be true?

14. When the muscles of the eye remain tensed for a significant period of time, eyestrain results. How much is this a concern for a person using (a) a microscope, (b) a telescope, and (c) a simple magnifier?

15. Both a microscope and a telescope can be constructed from two converging lenses. What are the differences? Why can't a telescope be used as a microscope? Why can't a microscope be used as a telescope?

16. In her bag, a photographer is carrying three exchangeable camera lenses with focal lengths of 400.0 mm, 50.0 mm, and 28.0 mm. Which lens should she use for (a) wide angle shots (a cathedral, taken from the square in front), (b) everyday use (children at play), and (c) telephoto work (lions in Africa taken from across a river)?

17. The figure shows a schematic diagram of a defective eye. What is this defect called?

18. Draw a simple eye diagram labeling the cornea, the lens, the iris, the retina, and the aqueous and vitreous fluids.

19. On a camping trip, you discover that no one has brought matches. A friend suggests using his eyeglasses to focus sunlight onto some dry grass and shredded bark to get a fire started. Could this scheme work if your friend is nearsighted? What about if he is farsighted? Explain.

Multiple-Choice Questions

1. The compound microscope is made from two lenses. Which statement is true concerning the operation of the compound microscope?
   (a) Both lenses form real images.
   (b) Both lenses form virtual images.
   (c) The lens closest to the object forms a virtual image; the other lens forms a real image.
   (d) The lens closest to the object forms a real image; the other lens forms a virtual image.

2. Which of these statements best explains why a telescope enables us to see details of a distant object such as the Moon or a planet more clearly?

(a) The image formed by the telescope is larger than the object.
(b) The image formed by the telescope subtends a larger angle at the eye than the object does.
(c) The telescope can also collect radio waves that sharpen the visual image.

3. Siu-Ling has a far point of 25 cm. Which statement here is true?
   (a) She may have normal vision.
   (b) She is myopic and requires diverging lenses to correct her vision.
   (c) She is myopic and requires converging lenses to correct her vision.
   (d) She is hyperopic and requires diverging lenses to correct her vision.
   (e) She is hyperopic and requires converging lenses to correct her vision.

4. The figure shows a schematic diagram of a defective eye and some lenses. Which of the lenses shown can correct for this defect?

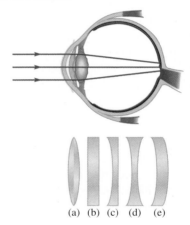

(a) (b) (c) (d) (e)

5. A nearsighted person wears corrective lenses. One of the focal points of the corrective lenses should be
   (a) at the cornea.   (b) at the retina.
   (c) at infinity.   (d) past the retina.
   (e) at the near point.   (f) at the far point.

6. An astronomical telescope has an angular magnification of 10. The length of the barrel is 33 cm. What are the focal lengths of the objective and the eyepiece, in that order respectively, from the choices listed?
   (a) 3 cm, 30 cm   (b) 30 cm, 3 cm
   (c) 20 cm, 13 cm   (d) 0.3 m, 3 m

7. A compound microscope has three possible objective lenses (focal lengths f_o) and two eyepiece lenses (focal lengths f_e). For maximum angular magnification, the objective and eyepiece should be chosen such that
   (a) f_o and f_e are both the largest available.
   (b) f_o and f_e are both the smallest available.
   (c) f_o is the largest available; f_e is the smallest available.
   (d) f_e is the largest available; f_o is the smallest available.
   (e) f_e and f_o are nearly the same.

8. What causes chromatic aberration?
   (a) Light is an electromagnetic wave and has intrinsic diffraction properties.
   (b) Different wavelengths of light give different angles of refraction at the lens-air interface.
   (c) The coefficient of reflection is different for light of different wavelengths.
   (d) The outer edges of the lens produce a focus at a different point from that formed by the central portion of the lens.
   (e) The absorption of light in the glass varies with wavelength.

9. What causes spherical aberration?
   (a) Light is an electromagnetic wave and has intrinsic diffraction properties.
   (b) Different wavelengths of light give different angles of refraction at the lens-air interface.
   (c) The lens surface is not perfectly smooth.
   (d) The outer edges of the lens produce a focus at a different point from that formed by the central portion of the lens.

10. Reducing the aperture on a camera
    (a) reduces the depth of field and requires a longer exposure time.
    (b) reduces the depth of field and requires a shorter exposure time.
    (c) increases the depth of field and requires a longer exposure time.
    (d) increases the depth of field and requires a shorter exposure time.
    (e) does not change the depth of field and requires a longer exposure time.
    (f) does not change the depth of field and requires a shorter exposure time.

Problems

C	Combination conceptual/quantitative problem
🐟	Biological or medical application
No ✦	Easy to moderate difficulty level
✦	More challenging
✦✦	Most challenging
Blue #	Detailed solution in the Student Solutions Manual
1 2	Problems paired by concept

24.1 Lenses in Combination

1. An object is placed 12.0 cm in front of a lens of focal length 5.0 cm. Another lens of focal length 4.0 cm is placed 2.0 cm past the first lens. (a) Where is the final image? Is it real or virtual? (b) What is the overall magnification?

2. A converging lens and a diverging lens, separated by a distance of 30.0 cm, are used in combination. The con-

verging lens has a focal length of 15.0 cm. The diverging lens is of unknown focal length. An object is placed 20.0 cm in front of the converging lens; the final image is virtual and is formed 12.0 cm *before* the diverging lens. What is the focal length of the diverging lens?

3. Two converging lenses are placed 88.0 cm apart. An object is placed 1.100 m to the left of the first lens, which has a focal length of 25.0 cm. The final image is located 15.0 cm to the right of the second lens. (a) What is the focal length of the second lens? (b) What is the total magnification?

4. A converging lens with a focal length of 15.0 cm and a diverging lens are placed 25.0 cm apart, with the converging lens on the left. A 2.00-cm-high object is placed 22.0 cm to the left of the converging lens. The final image is 34.0 cm to the left of the converging lens. (a) What is the focal length of the diverging lens? (b) What is the height of the final image? (c) Is the final image upright or inverted?

5. An object is located 16.0 cm in front of a converging lens with focal length 12.0 cm. To the right of the converging lens, separated by a distance of 20.0 cm, is a diverging lens of focal length –10.0 cm. Find the location of the final image by ray tracing and verify using the lens equations.

6. An object is located 10.0 cm in front of a converging lens with focal length 12.0 cm. To the right of the converging lens is a second converging lens, 30.0 cm from the first lens, of focal length 10.0 cm. Find the location of the final image by ray tracing and verify by using the lens equations.

7. Verify the locations and sizes of the images formed by the two lenses in Fig. 24.1b using the lens equation and the following data: $f_1 = +4.00$ cm, $f_2 = -2.00$ cm, $s = 8.00$ cm (where s is the distance between the lenses), $p_1 = +6.00$ cm, and $h = 2.00$ mm. (Note that the vertical scale is different from the horizontal scale.)

✦ 8. Show that if two thin lenses are close together (s, the distance between the lenses, is negligibly small), the two lenses can be replaced by a single equivalent lens with focal length f_{eq}. Find the value of f_{eq} in terms of f_1 and f_2.

24.2 Cameras

9. You would like to project an upright image at a position 32.0 cm to the right of an object. You have a converging lens with focal length 3.70 cm located 6.00 cm to the right of the object. By placing a second lens at 24.65 cm to the right of the object, you obtain an image in the proper location. (a) What is the focal length of the second lens? (b) Is this lens converging or diverging? (c) What is the total magnification? (d) If the object is 12.0 cm high, what is the image height?

10. You plan to project an inverted image 30.0 cm to the right of an object. You have a diverging lens with focal

length −4.00 cm located 6.00 cm to the right of the object. Once you put a second lens at 18.0 cm to the right of the object, you obtain an image in the proper location. (a) What is the focal length of the second lens? (b) Is this lens converging or diverging? (c) What is the total magnification? (d) If the object is 12.0 cm high, what is the image height?

11. A converging lens with focal length 3.00 cm is placed 4.00 cm to the right of an object. A diverging lens, with focal length −5.00 cm is placed 17.0 cm to the right of the converging lens. (a) At what location(s), if any, can you place a screen in order to display an image? (b) Repeat part (a) for the case where the lenses are separated by 10.0 cm.

✦✦ 12. A converging lens with a focal length of 3.00 cm is placed 24.00 cm to the right of a concave mirror with a focal length of 4.00 cm. An object is placed between the mirror and the lens, 6.00 cm to the right of the mirror and 18.00 cm to the left of the lens. Name three places where you could find an image of this object. For each image tell whether it is inverted or upright and give the total magnification.

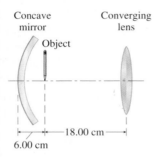

13. A camera uses a 200.0-mm focal length telephoto lens to take pictures from a distance of infinity to as close as 2.0 m. What are the minimum and maximum distances from the lens to the film?

14. Kim says that she was less than 10 ft away from the president when she took a picture of him with her 50-mm focal length camera lens. The picture shows the upper half of the president's body (or 3.0 ft of his total height). On the negative of the film, this part of his body is 18 mm high. How close was Kim to the president when she took the picture?

15. A statue is 6.6 m from the opening of a pinhole camera, and the screen is 2.8 m from the pinhole. (a) Is the image erect or inverted? (b) What is the magnification of the image? (c) To get a brighter image, we enlarge the pinhole to let more light through, but then the image looks blurry. Why? (d) To admit more light and still have a sharp image, we replace the pinhole with a lens. Should it be a converging or diverging lens? Why? (e) What should the focal length of the lens be?

16. Esperanza uses a 35-mm camera with a standard lens of focal length 50.0 mm to take a photo of her son Carlos, who is 1.2 m tall and standing 3.0 m away. (a) What must be the distance between the lens and the film to get a properly focused picture? (b) What is the magnification of the image? (c) What is the height of the image of Carlos on the film?

17. A person on a safari wants to take a photograph of a hippopotamus from a distance of 75.0 m. The animal is 4.00 m long and its image is to be 1.20 cm long on the film. (a) What focal length lens should be used? (b) What would be the size of the image if a lens of 50.0-mm focal length were used? (c) How close to the hippo would the person have to be to capture a 1.20-cm-long image using a 50.0-mm lens?

18. Jim plans to take a picture of McGraw Tower with a 35-mm camera that has a 50.0-mm focal length lens. A roll of 35-mm film is 35 mm wide; each frame is 24 mm by 36 mm. The tower has a height of 52 m and Jim wants a detailed close-up picture. How close to the tower should Jim be to capture the largest possible image of the entire tower on his film?

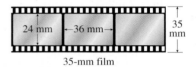

A strip of 35-mm film
(Problems 18, 20, 21, 56, and 68)

19. A photographer wishes to take a photograph of the Eiffel Tower (300 m tall) from across the Seine River, a distance of 300 m from the tower. What focal length lens should she use to get an image that is 20 mm high on the film?

20. If a slide of width 36 mm (see the figure with Problem 18) is to be projected onto a screen of 1.50 m width located 12.0 m from the projector, what focal length lens is required to fill the width of the screen?

21. A slide projector has a lens of focal length 12 cm. Each slide is 24 mm by 36 mm (see the figure with Problem 18). The projector is used in a room where the screen is 5.0 m from the projector. How large must the screen be?

24.3 The Eye

Unless the problem states otherwise, assume that the distance from the cornea-lens system to the retina is 2.0 cm and the normal near point is 25 cm.

22. If the distance from the lens system (cornea + lens) to the retina is 2.00 cm, show that the focal length of the lens system must vary between 1.85 cm and 2.00 cm to see objects from 25.0 cm to infinity.

23. Suppose that the lens system (cornea + lens) in a particular eye has a focal length that can vary between 1.85 and 2.00 cm, but the distance from the lens system to the retina is only 1.90 cm. (a) Is this eye nearsighted or farsighted? Explain. (b) What range of distances can the eye see clearly without corrective lenses?

24. If Michaela needs to wear reading glasses with refractive power of +3.0 D, what is her uncorrected near point? Neglect the distance between the glasses and the eye.

 25. The uncorrected far point of Colin's eye is 2.0 m. What refractive power contact lens enables him to clearly distinguish objects at large distances?

26. The distance from the lens system (cornea + lens) of a particular eye to the retina is 1.75 cm. What is the focal length of the lens system when the eye produces a clear image of an object 25.0 cm away?

 27. A nearsighted man cannot clearly see objects more than 2.0 m away. The distance from the lens of the eye to the retina is 2.0 cm, and the eye's power of accommodation is 4.0 D (the focal length of the cornea-lens system increases by a maximum of 4.0 D over its relaxed focal length when accommodating for nearby objects). (a) As an amateur optometrist, what corrective eyeglass lenses would you prescribe to enable him to clearly see distant objects? Assume the corrective lenses are 2.0 cm from the eyes. (b) Find the nearest object he can see clearly with and without his glasses.

28. Anne is farsighted; the nearest object she can see clearly without corrective lenses is 2.0 m away. It is 1.8 cm from the lens of her eye to the retina. (a) Sketch a ray diagram to show (qualitatively) what happens when she tries to look at something closer than 2.0 m without corrective lenses. (b) What should the focal length of her contact lenses be so that she can see clearly objects as close as 20.0 cm from her eye?

24.4 The Simple Magnifier

29. Thomas wants to use his 5.5-D reading glasses as a simple magnifier. What is the angular magnification of this lens when Thomas's eye is relaxed?

30. (a) What is the focal length of a magnifying glass that gives an angular magnification of 8.0 when the image is at infinity? (b) How far must the object be from the lens? Assume the lens is held close to the eye.

31. Keesha is looking at a beetle with a magnifying glass. She wants to see an upright, enlarged image at a distance of 25 cm. The focal length of the magnifying glass is +5.0 cm. Assume that Keesha's eye is close to the magnifying glass. (a) What should be the distance between the magnifying glass and the beetle? (b) What is the angular magnification?

32. Callum is examining a stamp that is 3.00 cm square in size with a magnifying glass of refractive power +40.0 D. The magnifier forms an image of the stamp at a distance of 25.0 cm. Assume that Callum's eye is close to the magnifying glass. (a) What is the distance between the stamp and the magnifier? (b) What is the angular magnification? (c) How large is the image formed by the magnifier?

33. A simple magnifying glass can focus sunlight enough to heat up paper or dry grass and start a fire. A magnifying glass with a diameter of 4.0 cm has a focal length of 6.0 cm. (a) Using the information found on the inside back cover of the book, estimate the size of the image of the Sun when the magnifying glass focuses the image to its smallest size. (b) If the intensity of the Sun falling on the magnifying glass is 0.85 kW/m², what is the intensity of the image of the Sun?

34. An insect that is 5.00 mm long is placed 10.0 cm from a converging lens with a focal length of 12.0 cm. (a) What is the position of the image? (b) What is the size of the image? (c) Is the image upright or inverted? (d) Is the image real or virtual? (e) What is the angular magnification if the lens is close to the eye?

35. A simple magnifier gives the *maximum* angular magnification when it forms a virtual image at the near point of the eye instead of at infinity. For simplicity, assume that the magnifier is right up against the eye, so that distances from the magnifier are approximately the same as distances from the eye. (a) For a magnifier with focal length f, find the object distance p such that the image is formed at the near point, a distance N from the lens. (b) Show that the angular size of this image as seen by the eye is

$$\theta = \frac{h(N+f)}{Nf}$$

where h is the height of the object. [*Hint:* Refer to Fig. 24.15.] (c) Now find the angular magnification and compare it to the angular magnification when the virtual image is at infinity.

24.5 Compound Microscopes

36. The figure shows a schematic diagram of a microscope. For the object and image locations shown, which of the points (A, B, C, or D) represents a focal point of the eyepiece? Draw a ray diagram.

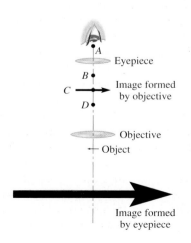

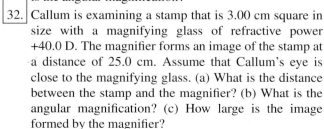

37. The eyepiece of a microscope has a focal length of 1.25 cm and the objective lens focal length is 1.44 cm. (a) If the tube length is 18.0 cm, what is the angular magnification of the microscope? (b) What objective focal length would be required to double this magnification?

38. Jordan is building a compound microscope using an eyepiece with a focal length of 7.50 cm and an objective with a focal length of 1.500 cm. He will place the specimen a distance of 1.600 cm from the objective. (a) How far apart should Jordan place the lenses? (b) What will be the angular magnification of this microscope?

39. The wing of an insect is 1.0 mm long. When viewed through a microscope, the image is 1.0 m long and is located 5.0 m away. Determine the angular magnification.

40. A microscope has an eyepiece that gives an angular magnification of 5.00 for a final image at infinity and an objective lens of focal length 15.0 mm. The tube length of the microscope is 16.0 cm. (a) What is the transverse magnification due to the objective lens alone? (b) What is the angular magnification due to the microscope? (c) How far from the objective should the object be placed?

41. Repeat Problem 40(c) using a different eyepiece that gives an angular magnification of 5.00 for a final image at the viewer's near point (25.0 cm) instead of at infinity.

42. A microscope has an objective lens of focal length 5.00 mm. The objective forms an image 16.5 cm from the lens. The focal length of the eyepiece is 2.80 cm. (a) What is the distance between the lenses? (b) What is the angular magnification? The near point is 25.0 cm. (c) How far from the objective should the object be placed?

43. Repeat Problem 42 if the eyepiece location is adjusted slightly so that the final image is at the viewer's near point (25.0 cm) instead of at infinity.

44. Use the thin lens equation to show that the transverse magnification due to the objective of a microscope is $m_o = -L/f_o$. [Hints: The object is near the focal point of the objective; do not assume it is at the focal point. Eliminate p_o to find the magnification in terms of q_o and f_o. How is L related to q_o and f_o?]

24.6 Telescopes

45. (a) If you were stranded on an island with only a pair of 3.5-D reading glasses, could you make a telescope? If so, what would be the length of the telescope and what would be the best possible angular magnification? (b) Answer the same questions if you also had a pair of 1.3-D reading glasses.

46. A telescope mirror has a radius of curvature of 10.0 m. It is used to take a picture of the Moon (radius 1740 km, distance from Earth 385,000 km). What is the diameter of the image of the Moon produced by this mirror?

47. An old refracting telescope in a museum is 45.0 cm long and the caption states that the telescope magnifies images by a factor of 30.0. Assuming these numbers are for viewing an object an infinite distance away with minimum eyestrain, what is the focal length of each of the two lenses?

48. The objective lens of an astronomical telescope forms an image of a distant object at the focal point of the eyepiece, which has a focal length of 5.0 cm. If the two lenses are 45.0 cm apart, what is the angular magnification?

49. A refracting telescope is used to view the Moon (diameter 3474 km, distance from Earth 384,500 km). The focal lengths of the objective and eyepiece are +2.40 m and +16.0 cm, respectively. (a) What should be the distance between the lenses? (b) What is the diameter of the image produced by the objective? (c) What is the angular magnification?

50. The eyepiece of a Galilean telescope is a diverging lens. The focal points F_o and F'_e coincide. In one such telescope, the lenses are a distance $d = 32$ cm apart and the focal length of the objective is 36 cm. A rhinoceros is viewed from a large distance. (a) What is the focal length of the eyepiece? (b) At what distance from the eyepiece is the final image? (c) Is the final image formed by the eyepiece real or virtual? Upright or inverted? (d) What is the angular magnification? [Hint: The angular magnification is β/α.]

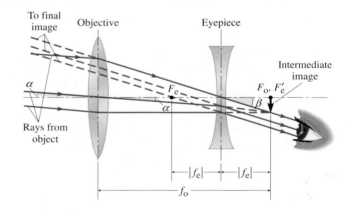

Comprehensive Problems

51. Good lenses used in cameras and other optical devices are actually compound lenses, made of five or more lenses put together to minimize distortions, including chromatic aberration. Suppose a converging lens with a focal length of 4.00 cm is placed right next to a diverging lens with focal length of −20.0 cm. An object is placed 2.50 m to the left of this combination. (a) Where will the image be located? (b) Is the image real or virtual?

52. Two converging lenses, separated by a distance of 50.0 cm, are used in combination. The first lens, located to the left, has a focal length of 15.0 cm. The second lens, located to the right, has a focal length of 12.0 cm. An object, 3.00 cm high, is placed at a distance of 20.0 cm in front of the first lens. (a) Find the intermediate and final image distances relative to the corresponding lenses. (b) What is the total magnification? (c) What is the height of the final image?

53. An object is located at $x = 0$. At $x = 2.50$ cm is a converging lens with a focal length of 2.00 cm, at $x = 16.5$ cm is an unknown lens, and at $x = 19.8$ cm is another converging lens with focal length 4.00 cm. An upright image is formed at $x = 39.8$ cm. For each lens, the object distance exceeds the focal length. The magnification of the system is 6.84. (a) Is the unknown lens diverging or converging? (b) What is the focal length of the unknown lens? (c) Draw a ray diagram to confirm your answer.

54. A camera has a telephoto lens of 240-mm focal length. The lens can be moved in and out a distance of 16 mm from the film plane by rotating the lens barrel. If the lens can focus objects at infinity, what is the closest object distance that can be focused?

55. You have two lenses of focal length 25.0 cm (lens 1) and 5.0 cm (lens 2). (a) To build an astronomical telescope that gives an angular magnification of 5.0, how should you use the lenses (which for objective and which for eyepiece)? Explain. (b) How far apart should they be?

56. The Ortiz family is viewing slides from their summer vacation trip to the Grand Canyon. Their slide projector has a projection lens of 10.0-cm focal length and the screen is located 2.5 m from the projector. (a) What is the distance between the slide and the projection lens? (b) What is the magnification of the image? (c) How wide is the image of a slide of width 36 mm on the screen? (See the figure with Problem 18.)

57. A slide projector, using slides of width 5.08 cm, produces an image that is 2.00 m wide on a screen 3.50 m away. What is the focal length of the projector lens?

58. Veronique is nearsighted; she cannot see clearly anything more than 6.00 m away without her contacts. One day she doesn't wear her contacts; rather, she wears an old pair of glasses prescribed when she could see clearly up to 8.00 m away. Assume the glasses are 2.0 cm from her eyes. What is the greatest distance an object can be placed so that she can see it clearly with these glasses?

59. An object is placed 7.00 cm to the left of a converging lens of focal length 3.00 cm. A convex mirror with a radius of curvature of 4.00 cm is placed 12.00 cm to the right of the lens. (a) Where is the intermediate image formed by the lens? (b) Is the intermediate

image real or virtual and is it upright or inverted with respect to the object? (c) What is the magnification of this image? (d) Where is the image formed by the mirror? (e) Is the second image real or virtual and is it upright or inverted with respect to the original object? (f) What is the magnification due to the mirror? (g) What is the total magnification?

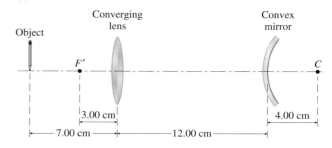

60. Refer to Problem 59. Draw ray diagrams for the two images. Mark the focal points with dots and draw three rays to determine each image. [*Hint:* The second image is very small, so start with a fairly large object.]

61. An object is placed 20.0 cm from a converging lens with focal length 15.0 cm (see the figure, not drawn to scale). A concave mirror with focal length 10.0 cm is located 75.0 cm to the right of the lens. (a) Describe the final image—is it real or virtual? Upright or inverted? (b) What is the location of the final image? (c) What is the total transverse magnification?

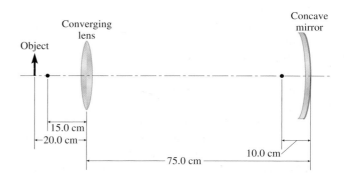

62. Two lenses, of focal lengths 3.0 cm and 30.0 cm, are used to build a small telescope. (a) Which lens should be the objective? (b) What is the angular magnification? (c) How far apart are the two lenses in the telescope?

63. (a) If Harry has a near point of 1.5 m, what focal length contact lenses does he require? (b) What is the power of these lenses in diopters?

64. An astronomical telescope provides an angular magnification of 12. The two converging lenses are 66 cm apart. Find the focal length of each of the lenses.

65. Two lenses, separated by a distance of 21.0 cm, are used in combination. The first lens has a focal length of

+30.0 cm; the second has a focal length of –15.0 cm. An object, 2.0 mm long, is placed 1.8 cm before the first lens. (a) What are the intermediate and final image distances relative to the corresponding lenses? (b) What is the total magnification? (c) What is the height of the final image?

C 66. A camera lens has a fixed focal length of magnitude 50.0 mm. The camera is focused on a 1.0-m-tall child who is standing 3.0 m from the lens. (a) Should the image formed be real or virtual? Why? (b) Is the lens converging or diverging? Why? (c) What is the distance from the lens to the film? (d) How tall is the image on the film? (e) To focus the camera, the lens is moved away from or closer to the film. What is the total distance the lens must be able to move if the camera can take clear pictures of objects at distances anywhere from 1.00 m to infinity?

67. A camera with a 50.0-mm lens can focus on objects located from 1.5 m to an infinite distance away by adjusting the distance between the lens and the film. When the focus is changed from that for a distant mountain range to that for a flower bed at 1.5 m, how far does the lens move with respect to the film?

68. The area occupied by one frame on 35-mm film is 24 mm by 36 mm—see the figure with Problem 18. The focal length of the camera lens is 50.0 mm. A picture is taken of a person 182 cm tall. What is the minimum distance from the camera for the person to stand so that the image fits on the film? Give two answers; one for each orientation of the camera.

69. A dissecting microscope is designed to have a large distance between the object and the objective lens. Suppose the focal length of the objective of a dissecting microscope is 5.0 cm, the focal length of the eyepiece is 4.0 cm, and the distance between the lenses is 32.0 cm. (a) What is the distance between the object and the objective lens? (b) What is the angular magnification?

70. A cub scout makes a simple microscope by placing two converging lenses of +18 D at opposite ends of a 28-cm-long tube. (a) What is the tube length of the microscope? (b) What is the angular magnification? (c) How far should an object be placed from the objective lens?

✦✦ 71. A microscope has an eyepiece of focal length 2.00 cm and an objective of focal length 3.00 cm. The eyepiece produces a virtual image at the viewer's near point (25.0 cm from the eye). (a) How far from the eyepiece is the image formed by the objective? (b) If the lenses

are 20.0 cm apart, what is the distance from the objective lens to the object being viewed? (c) What is the angular magnification?

72. A convex lens of power +12 D is used as a magnifier to examine a wildflower. What is the angular magnification if the final image is at (a) infinity or (b) the near point of 25 cm?

73. A refracting telescope has an objective lens with a focal length of 2.20 m and an eyepiece with a focal length of 1.5 cm. If you look through this telescope the wrong way, that is, with your eye placed at the objective lens, by what factor is the angular size of an observed object reduced?

74. Suppose the distance from the lens system of the eye (cornea + lens) to the retina is 18 mm. (a) What must the power of the lens be when looking at distant objects? (b) What must the power of the lens be when looking at an object 20.0 cm from the eye? (c) Suppose that the eye is farsighted; the person cannot see clearly objects that are closer than 1.0 m. Find the power of the contact lens you would prescribe so that objects as close as 20.0 cm can be seen clearly.

75. A man requires reading glasses with +2.0 D power to read a book held 40.0 cm away *with a relaxed eye.* Assume the glasses are 2.0 cm from his eyes. (a) What is his uncorrected far point? (b) What refractive power lenses should he use for distance vision? (c) His uncorrected near point is 1.0 m. What should the refractive powers of the two lenses in his bifocals be to give him clear vision from 25 cm to infinity?

Answers to Practice Problems

24.1 The object can be either real or virtual. If the real image forms before the second lens, it becomes a real object; if the second lens interrupts the light rays before they form the real image, it becomes a virtual object.

24.2 $q_1 = +16.7$ cm; $q_2 = 4.3$ cm; $m = -0.43$; $h' = 1.7$ cm

24.3 51.7 mm

24.4 13.3 cm

24.5 49.9 cm

24.6 (a) 3.08; (b) 2.08

24.7 (a) 18 cm; (b) 1.9 cm

24.8 –780

Interference and Diffraction

hen we look at plants and animals, most of the colors we see—brown eyes, green leaves, yellow sunflowers—are due to the selective absorption of light by pigments. In the leaves and stems of green plants, the chief pigment that absorbs some wavelengths and reflects the wavelengths we perceive as green is chlorophyll.

In some animals, color is produced in a different way. The shimmering, intense blue color of the wing of many species of the *Morpho* butterfly of Central and South America makes colors produced by pigments look flat. When the wing or the viewer moves, the color of the wing changes slightly, causing the shimmering quality we call *iridescence*. Iridescent colors are found in the wings or feathers of the Oregon swallowtail butterflies, ruby-throated hummingbirds, and many other species of butterflies and birds. Iridescent colors also appear in some beetles, in the scales of fish, and in the skins of snakes. How are these iridescent colors produced? (See p. 921 for the answer.)

**Concepts &
Skills to
Review**

- phase (Section 11.5)
- principle of superposition (Section 11.7)
- interference and diffraction (Section 11.9)
- wavefronts, rays, and Huygens's principle (Section 23.1)
- reflection and refraction (Sections 23.2 and 23.3)
- electromagnetic spectrum (Section 22.4)
- intensity (Section 22.7)

25.1   CONSTRUCTIVE AND DESTRUCTIVE INTERFERENCE

Chapters 23 and 24 dealt with topics in *geometric optics*: reflection, refraction, and image formation. For the most part, we were able to trace light rays propagating in straight-line paths; the rays changed direction only due to reflection or refraction at boundaries. Geometric optics is a useful approximation when objects and apertures are large compared to the wavelength of the light.

The present chapter is concerned with *physical optics*, in which the wave nature of light is made manifest. In physical optics we consider what happens when light propagates around obstacles or through apertures that are *not* large compared to the wavelength. In such situations we encounter interference and diffraction.

The distinction between interference and diffraction is not always clear-cut. Generally, **interference** refers to situations where waves from a small number of sources travel different paths and arrive at an observer with different phases. **Diffraction** is the spreading of waves after they travel around obstacles or through apertures. According to Huygens's construction, *every point* on a wavefront is a source of wavelets. The superposition of light from all these point sources must account for the phase differences due to the different paths traveled. Thus, instead of a small number of sources, in diffraction we have the superposition of waves from an *infinite* number of sources.

Any kind of wave can exhibit interference and diffraction because they are just manifestations of the principle of superposition, which says that the net wave disturbance at any point due to two or more waves is the sum of the disturbances due to each wave individually. Superposition is not a new principle for light. We used it earlier in our study of sound and other mechanical waves. We also used it to find the electric and magnetic fields due to more than one source; the electric and magnetic fields are the vector sums of the fields due to each source individually. Now we apply the principle of superposition to EM waves.

Coherent and Incoherent Sources

Why do we not commonly see interference effects with visible light? With light from a source such as the Sun, an incandescent bulb, or a fluorescent bulb, we do not see regions of constructive and destructive interference; rather, the *intensity* at any point is the sum of the intensities due to the individual waves. Light from any one of these sources is, at the atomic level, emitted by a vast number of *independent* sources. Waves from independent sources are **incoherent**; they do not maintain a fixed phase relationship with each other. We cannot accurately predict the phase (for instance, whether the wave is at a maximum or at a zero) at one point given the phase at another point. Incoherent waves have *rapidly fluctuating* phase relationships. The result is an averaging out of interference effects, so that the total intensity (or power per unit area) is just the sum of the intensities of the individual waves.

Only the superposition of **coherent** waves produces interference. Coherent waves must be locked in with a fixed phase relationship. *Coherent* and *incoherent* waves are idealized extremes; all real waves fall somewhere between the extremes. The light emitted by

- In the superposition of *incoherent* waves, the intensity is the sum of the intensities due to each wave individually.

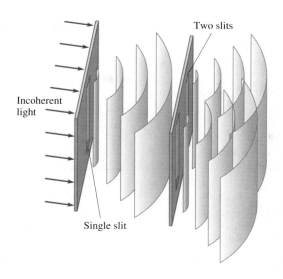

Figure 25.1 Young's technique for illuminating two slits with coherent light. The single slit on the left serves as a source of coherent light.

a laser can be highly coherent—two points in the beam can be coherent even if separated by as much as several kilometers. Light from a distant point source (such as a star other than the Sun) has some degree of coherence.

Thomas Young (1773–1829) performed the first visible-light interference experiments using a clever technique to obtain two coherent light sources from a single source (Fig. 25.1). When a single narrow slit is illuminated, the light wave that passes through the slit diffracts or spreads out. The single slit acts as a single coherent source to illuminate two other slits. These two other slits then act as sources of coherent light for interference.

Interference of Two Coherent Waves

If two waves are in step with each other, with the crest of one falling at the same point as the crest of the other, they are said to be *in phase*. The phase difference between the two waves that are in phase is an integral multiple of 2π rad: 0, $\pm 2\pi$ rad, $\pm 4\pi$ rad, and so forth, which we can express as $2m\pi$ rad, where m is any integer. The superposition of two waves that are in phase has an amplitude equal to the sum of the amplitudes of the two waves. For instance, in Fig. 25.2 two sinusoidal waves are in phase. The amplitudes of the two are $2A$ and $5A$. When the two waves are added together, the resulting wave has an amplitude of $2A + 5A = 7A$. The superposition of two waves that are *in phase* is called **constructive interference**.

For constructive interference, the intensity of the resulting wave (I) is *greater than* the sum of the intensities of the two waves individually ($I_1 + I_2$). Since intensity is proportional to amplitude squared (see Section 22.7), let $I = CA^2$, $I_1 = CA_1^2$, and $I_2 = CA_2^2$, where C is a constant. (For light and other EM waves, A_1, A_2, and A can represent either

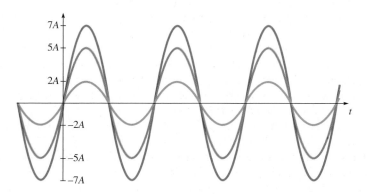

Figure 25.2 Two coherent waves (green and blue) with amplitudes $2A$ and $5A$. Since they are in phase, they interfere constructively. The superposition of the two (red) has an amplitude of $7A$. Note that shifting either of the waves a whole number of cycles to the right or left would not change the superposition of the two.

electric field amplitudes or magnetic field amplitudes since they are proportional to one another.) Since $A = A_1 + A_2$,

$$CA^2 = C(A_1 + A_2)^2 = CA_1^2 + CA_2^2 + 2CA_1A_2$$

Therefore,

$$I = I_1 + I_2 + 2\sqrt{I_1I_2}$$

Since intensity is power per unit area, where does the extra energy come from? Don't worry; energy is still conserved. If in some places $I > I_1 + I_2$, then in other places $I < I_1 + I_2$. Constructive interference does not manufacture energy; the energy is just redistributed. To summarize:

Constructive interference of two waves:

Phase difference	$\Delta\phi = 2m\pi$ rad $(m = 0, \pm1, \pm2, \dots)$	(25-1)
Amplitude	$A = A_1 + A_2$	(25-2)
Intensity	$I = I_1 + I_2 + 2\sqrt{I_1I_2}$	(25-3)

Two waves that are 180° out of phase are a half cycle apart; where one is at a crest the other is at a trough (Fig. 25.3). The superposition of two such waves is called **destructive interference**. The phase difference for destructive interference is π rad plus any integral multiple of 2π rad. Then $\Delta\phi = \pi + 2m\pi$ rad $= (m + \frac{1}{2})2\pi$ rad, where m is any integer. The destructive interference of two waves with amplitudes $2A$ and $5A$ gives a resulting amplitude of $3A$. If the two waves had the same amplitude, there would be complete cancellation—the superposition would have an amplitude of zero. Two waves can have any phase relationship between the two extremes of in phase or 180° out of phase. To summarize:

Destructive interference of two waves:

Phase difference	$\Delta\phi = (m + \frac{1}{2})2\pi$ rad $(m = 0, \pm1, \pm2, \dots)$	(25-4)
Amplitude	$A = \|A_1 - A_2\|$	(25-5)
Intensity	$I = I_1 + I_2 - 2\sqrt{I_1I_2}$	(25-6)

Phase Difference due to Different Paths

In interference, two or more coherent waves travel different paths to a point where we observe the superposition of the two. The paths may have different lengths, or pass through different media, or both. The difference in path lengths introduces a phase difference—it changes the phase relationship between the waves.

Suppose two waves start in phase but travel different paths in the same medium to a point where they interfere (Fig. 25.4). If the difference in path lengths Δl is an integral number of wavelengths,

$$\Delta l = m\lambda \quad (m = 0, \pm1, \pm2, \dots) \tag{25-7}$$

Figure 25.3 Destructive interference of two waves (green and blue) with amplitudes $2A$ and $5A$. The superposition of the two (red) has amplitude $3A$. Note that shifting either of the waves a whole number of cycles to the right or left would not change their superposition. Shifting one of the waves a *half* cycle right or left would change the superposition into *constructive* interference instead of destructive.

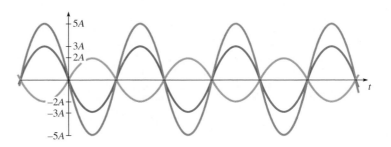

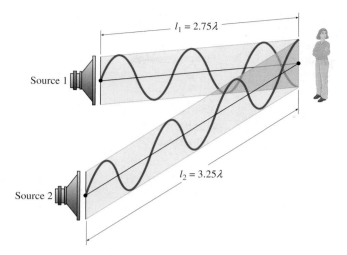

Figure 25.4 Two loudspeakers are fed the same electrical signal. The sound waves travel different distances to reach the observer. The phase difference between the two waves depends on the difference in the distances traveled. In this case, $l_2 - l_1 = 0.50\lambda$, so the waves arrive at the observer 180° out of phase. (The blue graphs represent pressure variations due to the two longitudinal sound waves.)

then one wave is simply going through a whole number of extra cycles, which leaves them in phase—they interfere constructively. Remember that one wavelength of path difference corresponds to a phase difference of 2π rad (see Section 11.9). Path lengths that are integral multiples of λ can be ignored since they do not change the relative phase between the two waves.

On the other hand, suppose two waves start in phase but the difference in path lengths is an odd number of *half* wavelengths:

 A path difference equal to an integral number of wavelengths does not change the superposition of two waves.

$$\Delta l = \pm\tfrac{1}{2}\lambda, \pm\tfrac{3}{2}\lambda, \pm\tfrac{5}{2}\lambda, \ldots = (m + \tfrac{1}{2})\lambda \quad (m = 0, \pm1, \pm2, \ldots) \qquad (25\text{-}8)$$

One wave travels a half cycle farther than the other (plus a whole number of cycles, which can be ignored). Now the waves are 180° out of phase; they interfere destructively.

In cases where the two paths are not completely in the same medium, we have to keep track of the number of cycles in each medium separately (since the wavelength changes as a wave passes from one medium into another).

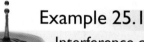

Example 25.1

Interference of Microwave Beams

A microwave transmitter (T) and receiver (R) are set up side by side (Fig. 25.5a). Two flat metal plates (M) that are good reflectors for microwaves face the transmitter and receiver, several meters away. The beam from the transmitter is broad enough to reflect from both metal plates. As the lower plate is slowly moved to the right, the microwave power measured at the receiver is observed to oscillate between minimum and maximum values (Fig. 25.5b). Approximately what is the wavelength of the microwaves?

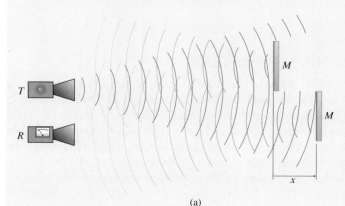

(a)

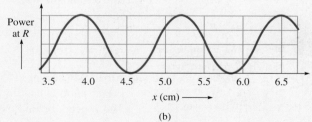

(b)

Figure 25.5

(a) Microwave transmitter and receiver and reflecting plates; (b) microwave power detected as a function of x.

Continued on next page

Example 25.1 Continued

Strategy Maximum power is detected when the waves reflected from the two plates interfere *constructively* at the receiver. Thus, the positions of the mirror that give maximum power must occur when the path difference is an integral number of wavelengths.

Solution When the lower plate is farther from the transmitter and receiver, the wave reflected from it travels some extra distance before reaching the receiver. If the metal plates are far enough from the transmitter and receiver, then the microwaves approach the plates and return almost along the same line. Then the extra distance traveled is approximately $2x$.

Constructive interference occurs when the path lengths differ by an integral number of wavelengths:

$$\Delta l = 2x = m\lambda \quad (m = 0, \pm 1, \pm 2, \ldots)$$

From one position of constructive interference to an adjacent one, the path length difference must change by one wavelength:

$$2\Delta x = \lambda$$

The maxima are at $x = 3.9$, 5.2, and 6.5 cm, so $\Delta x = 1.3$ cm. Then

$$\lambda = 2.6 \text{ cm}$$

 Discussion Note that the distance the lower plate is moved between maxima is *half* a wavelength, since the wave makes a round trip.

Practice Problem 25.1 Path Difference for Destructive Interference

Verify that at positions where minimum power is detected, the difference in path lengths is a half-integral number of wavelengths $[\Delta l = (m + \frac{1}{2})\lambda]$.

How a CD Is Read

In Example 25.1, EM waves from a single source are reflected from metal surfaces at two different distances from the source; the two reflected waves interfere at the detector. A similar system is used in reading an audio CD or a CD-ROM.

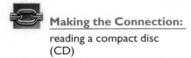

Making the Connection:

reading a compact disc (CD)

To manufacture a CD, a disk of polycarbonate plastic 1.2 mm thick is impressed with a series of *"pits"* arranged in a single spiral track (Fig. 25.6). The pits are 0.5 μm wide and at least 0.83 μm long. The disk is coated with a thin layer of aluminum and then with acrylic to protect the aluminum. To read the CD, a laser beam illuminates the aluminum layer from below; the reflected beam enters a detector. The laser beam is wide enough that when it reflects from a pit, part of it also reflects off the *land* (the flat part of the aluminum layer) on either side of the track. The height h of the pits is chosen so that light reflected from the land interferes destructively with light reflected from the pit (see Problem 62). Thus, a "pit" causes a minimum intensity to be detected. On the other hand, when the laser reflects from the land between pits, the intensity at the detector is a maximum. Changes between the two intensity levels represent the binary digits (the 0's and the 1's).

Making the Connection:

Michelson interferometer

25.2 THE MICHELSON INTERFEROMETER

Albert Michelson (1852–1931) invented the interferometer to determine whether the Earth's motion has any effect on the speed of light as measured by an observer on Earth. The concept behind the Michelson interferometer (Fig. 25.7) is not complicated, yet it is an extremely precise tool. A beam of coherent light is incident on a beam splitter S (a half-silvered mirror) that reflects only half of the incident light, while transmitting the rest. Thus, a single beam of coherent light from the source is separated into two beams, which travel different paths down the *arms* of the interferometer and are reflected back

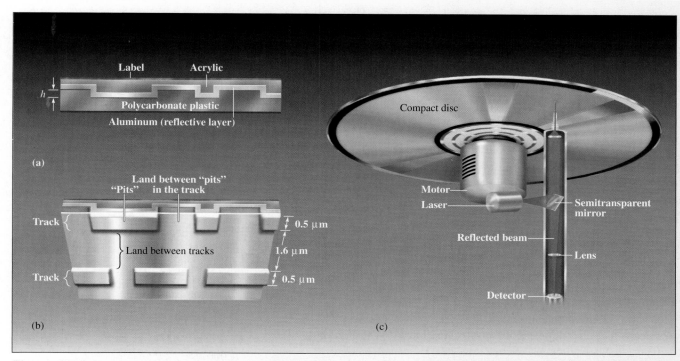

(a)

(b)

(c)

Figure 25.6 (a) Cross-sectional view of a CD. A laser beam passes through the polycarbonate plastic and reflects from the aluminum layer. (b) The "pits" are arranged in a spiral track. Surrounding the pits, the flat aluminum surface is called *land*. When the laser reflects from the bottom of a pit, it also reflects from the land on either side. (c) A motor spins the CD at between 200 and 500 rpm, keeping the track speed constant. Light from a laser is reflected by a semitransparent mirror toward the CD; light reflected by the CD is transmitted through this same mirror to the detector. The detector produces an electrical signal proportional to the variations in the intensity of reflected light.

by fully-silvered mirrors (M_1, M_2). At the half-silvered mirror, again half of each beam is reflected and half transmitted. Light sent back toward the source leaves the interferometer. The remainder combines into a single beam and is observed on a screen. A phase difference between the two beams may arise because the arms have different lengths or because the beams travel through different media in the two arms. If the two beams arrive at the screen in phase, they interfere constructively to produce maximum intensity (a *bright fringe*) at the screen; if they arrive 180° out of phase, they interfere destructively to produce a minimum intensity (a *dark fringe*).

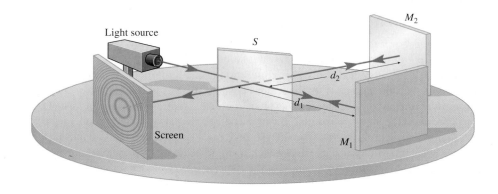

Figure 25.7 A Michelson interferometer.

Example 25.2

Measuring the Index of Refraction of Air

Suppose a transparent vessel 30.0 cm long is placed in one arm of a Michelson interferometer. The vessel initially contains air at 0°C and 1 atm. With light of vacuum wavelength 633 nm, the mirrors are arranged so that a bright spot appears at the center of the screen. As air is gradually pumped out of the vessel, the central region of the screen changes from bright to dark and back to bright 274 times—that is, 274 bright fringes are counted (not including the initial bright fringe). Calculate the index of refraction of air.

Strategy   As air is pumped out, the path lengths traveled in each of the two arms do not change, but the *number of wavelengths traveled* does change, since the index of refraction inside the vessel begins at some initial value n and decreases gradually to 1. Each new bright fringe means that the number of wavelengths traveled has changed by one more wavelength.

Solution   Let the index of refraction of air at 0°C and 1 atm be n. If the *vacuum* wavelength is $\lambda_0 = 633$ nm, then the wavelength in air is $\lambda = \lambda_0/n$. Initially, the number of wavelengths traveled during a round-trip through the air in the vessel is

$$\text{initial number of wavelengths} = \frac{\text{round-trip distance}}{\text{wavelength in air}}$$

$$= \frac{2d}{\lambda} = \frac{2d}{\lambda_0/n}$$

where $d = 30.0$ cm is the length of the vessel. As air is removed, the number of wavelengths decreases since, as n decreases, the wavelength gets longer. Assuming that

the vessel is completely evacuated in the end (or nearly so), the final number of wavelengths is

$$\text{final number of wavelengths} = \frac{\text{round-trip distance}}{\text{wavelength in vacuum}}$$

$$= \frac{2d}{\lambda_0}$$

The change in the number of wavelengths traveled, N, is equal to the number of bright fringes observed:

$$N = \frac{2d}{\lambda_0/n} - \frac{2d}{\lambda_0} = \frac{2d}{\lambda_0}(n-1)$$

Since $N = 274$, we can solve for n.

$$n = \frac{N\lambda_0}{2d} + 1$$

$$= \frac{274 \times 6.33 \times 10^{-7}\ \text{m}}{2 \times 0.300\ \text{m}} + 1$$

$$= 1.000\,289$$

Discussion   The measured value for the index of refraction of air is close to that given in Table 23.1 ($n = 1.000\,293$).

Conceptual Practice Problem 25.2   A Possible Alternative Method

Instead of counting the fringes, another way to measure the index of refraction of air might be to move one of the mirrors as the air is slowly pumped out of the vessel, maintaining a bright fringe at the screen. The distance the mirror moves could be measured and used to calculate n. If the mirror moved is the one in the arm that does *not* contain the vessel, should it be moved in or out? In other words, should that arm be made longer or shorter?

Making the Connection:

interference microscope

The Interference Microscope

An *interference microscope* enhances contrast in the image when viewing objects that are transparent or nearly so. A cell in a water solution is difficult to see with an ordinary microscope. The cell reflects only a small fraction of the light incident on it, so it transmits almost the same intensity as the water does and there is little contrast between the cell and the surrounding water. However, if the cell's index of refraction is different from that of water, light transmitted through the cell is phase-shifted compared to the light that passes water. The interference microscope exploits this phase difference. As with the Michelson interferometer, a single beam of light is split into two and then recombined. The light in *one* arm of the interferometer passes through the sample. When the beams are recombined, interference translates the phase differences that are invisible in an ordinary microscope into intensity differences that are easily seen.

25.3 THIN FILMS

The rainbow-like colors seen in soap bubbles and oil slicks are produced by interference. Suppose a wire frame is dipped into soapy water and then held vertically aloft with a thin film of soapy water clinging to the frame (Fig. 25.8). Due to gravity pulling downward, the film at the top of the wire frame is very thin—just a few molecules thick—while the film gets thicker and thicker toward the bottom. The film is illuminated with white light from behind the camera; the photo shows light *reflected* from the film. Unless otherwise stated, we will consider thin-film interference for *normal incidence* only. However, ray diagrams will show rays at *near*-normal incidence so they don't all lie on the same line in the diagram.

Figure 25.9 shows a light ray incident on a portion of a thin film. At each boundary, some light is reflected while most is transmitted. When looking at the light *reflected* from the film, we see the superposition of all the reflected rays (of which only the first three— labeled 1, 2, and 3— are shown). The interference of these rays determines what color we see. In most cases, we can consider the interference of the first two reflected rays and ignore the rest. Unless the indices of refraction on either side of a boundary are nearly the same, the amplitude of a reflected wave is a small fraction of the amplitude of the incident wave. Rays 1 and 2 each reflect only once; their amplitudes are nearly the same. Ray 3 reflects three times, so its amplitude is much smaller. Other reflected rays are even weaker.

Interference effects are much less pronounced in the transmitted light. Ray A is strong since it does not suffer a reflection. Ray B suffers two reflections, so it is much weaker than A. Ray C is even weaker since it goes through four reflections. Thus, the amplitude of the transmitted light for constructive interference is not much larger than the amplitude for destructive interference. Nevertheless, interference in the transmitted light must occur for energy to be conserved: if more of the energy of a particular wavelength is reflected, less is transmitted. In Problem 25 you can show that if a certain wavelength interferes constructively in reflected light, then it interferes destructively in transmitted light, and *vice versa*.

Phase Shifts due to Reflection

In Section 11.8, we saw that reflected waves are sometimes inverted, which is to say they are phase-shifted 180° with respect to the incident wave. Whenever a wave hits a boundary where the wave speed suddenly changes, reflection occurs. The reflected wave is inverted (Fig. 25.10a) if it reflects off a slower medium (a medium in which the wave

Figure 25.8 Viewing a film of soapy water by reflected light. (The background is dark so that only reflected light is shown in the photo; the camera and the light source are both on the same side of the film.) The thickness of the film gradually increases from the top of the frame toward the bottom.

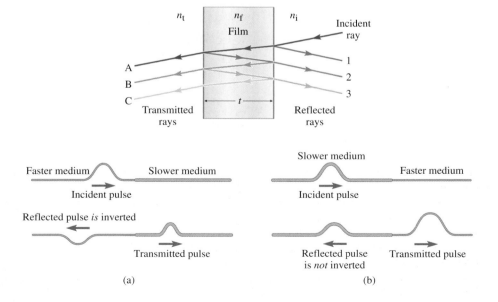

Figure 25.9 Rays reflected and transmitted by a thin film.

Figure 25.10 (a) A wave pulse on a string heads for a boundary with a slower medium (greater mass per unit length). The reflected pulse is inverted. (b) A pulse reflected from a *faster* medium is *not* inverted.

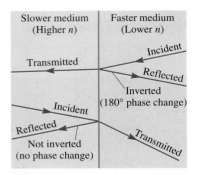

Figure 25.11 A 180° phase change due to reflection occurs when light reflects from a boundary with a slower medium.

travels more slowly); it is *not* inverted if it reflects off a faster medium (Fig. 25.10b). The transmitted wave is never inverted.

The same thing happens to EM waves:

> When light reflects at normal or near-normal incidence from a boundary with a slower medium (*higher* index of refraction), it is inverted (180° phase change); when light reflects from a faster medium (*lower* index of refraction), it is *not* inverted (no phase change). (See Fig. 25.11.)

To determine whether rays 1 and 2 in Fig. 25.9 interfere constructively or destructively, we must consider both the relative phase change due to reflection and the extra path length traveled by ray 2 in the film. Depending on the indices of refraction of the three media (the film and the media on either side), it may be that *neither* of the rays is inverted upon reflection, or that *both* are, or that one of the two is. If the index of refraction of the film n_f is *between* the other two indices (n_i and n_t), there is no *relative* phase difference due to reflection; either both are inverted or neither is. If the index of the film is the largest of the three or the smallest of the three, then one of the two rays is inverted; in either case there is a relative phase difference of 180°.

Problem-Solving Strategy for Thin Films

- Sketch a ray picture to show the first two reflected rays. Even if the problem concerns normal incidence, draw the incident ray with a *nonzero* angle of incidence to separate the various rays. Label the indices of refraction.
- Decide whether there is a relative phase difference of 180° between the rays due to reflection.
- If there is no relative phase difference due to reflection, then an extra path length of $m\lambda$ keeps the two rays in phase, resulting in constructive interference. An extra path length of $(m + \frac{1}{2})\lambda$ causes destructive interference. Remember that λ is the wavelength *in the film*, since that is the medium in which ray 2 travels the extra distance.
- If there is a 180° relative phase difference due to reflection, then an extra path length of $m\lambda$ preserves the 180° phase difference and leads to *destructive* interference. An extra path length of $(m + \frac{1}{2})\lambda$ causes *constructive* interference.
- Remember that ray 2 makes a round-trip in the film. For normal incidence, the extra path length is $2t$.

Example 25.3

Appearance of a Film of Soapy Water

A film of soapy water in air is held vertically and viewed in reflected light (as in Fig. 25.8). The film has index of refraction $n = 1.36$. (a) Explain why the film appears black at the top. (b) The light reflected perpendicular to the film at a certain point is missing the wavelengths 504 nm and 630.0 nm. No wavelengths between these two are missing. What is the thickness of the film at that point? (c) What other visible wavelengths are missing, if any?

Strategy First we sketch the first two reflected rays, labeling the indices of refraction and the thickness t of the film (Fig. 25.12). The sketch helps determine whether there is a relative phase difference of 180° due to reflection. Since

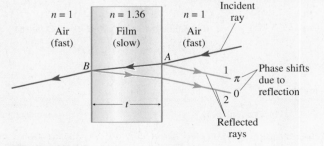

Figure 25.12

The first two rays reflected by the soap film. At A, reflected ray 1 is inverted. At B, reflected ray 2 is not inverted.

Continued on next page

Example 25.3 Continued

the top of the film appears black, there must be destructive interference for all visible wavelengths. Farther down the film, the wavelengths missing in reflected light are those that interfere destructively; we consider phase shifts both due to reflection and due to the extra path ray 2 travels in the film. We must remember to use the wavelength *in the film*, not the wavelength in vacuum, because ray 2 travels its extra distance within the film.

Solution   (a) The speed of light in the film is slower than in air. Therefore ray 1, which reflects from a slower medium (the film), is inverted; ray 2, which reflects from a faster medium (air), is not inverted. There is a relative phase difference of 180° between the two *regardless of wavelength*. Due to gravity, the film is thinnest at the top and thickest at the bottom. Ray 2 has a phase shift compared to ray 1 due to the extra distance traveled in the film. The only way to preserve destructive interference for *all* wavelengths is if the top of the film is thin compared to the wavelengths of visible light; then the phase change of ray 2 due to the extra path traveled is negligibly small.

(b) For light reflected perpendicular to the film (normal incidence), reflected ray 2 travels an extra distance $2t$ compared to ray 1, which introduces a phase difference between them. Since there is already a relative phase difference of 180° due to reflection, the path difference $2t$ must be an *integral* number of wavelengths to preserve destructive interference:

$$2t = m\lambda = m\frac{\lambda_0}{n}$$

Suppose $\lambda_{0,m} = 630.0$ nm is the vacuum wavelength for which the path difference is $m\lambda$ for a certain value of m. Since there are no missing wavelengths between the two, $\lambda_{0,(m+1)} = 504$ nm must be the vacuum wavelength for which the path difference is $m + 1$ times the wavelength in the film. Why not $m - 1$? 504 nm is smaller than 630.0 nm, so a *larger* number of wavelengths fits in the path difference $2t$.

$$2nt = m\lambda_{0,m} = (m + 1)\lambda_{0,(m+1)}$$

We can solve for m:

$$m \times 630.0 \text{ nm} = (m + 1) \times 504 \text{ nm} = m \times 504 \text{ nm} + 504 \text{ nm}$$
$$m \times 126 \text{ nm} = 504 \text{ nm}$$
$$m = 4.00$$

Then the thickness is

$$t = \frac{m\lambda_0}{2n} = \frac{4.00 \times 630.0 \text{ nm}}{2 \times 1.36} = 926.47 \text{ nm} = 926 \text{ nm}$$

(c) We already know the missing wavelengths for $m = 4$ and $m = 5$. Let's check other values of m.

$$2nt = 2 \times 1.36 \times 926.47 \text{ nm} = 2520 \text{ nm}$$

For $m = 3$,

$$\lambda_0 = \frac{2nt}{m} = \frac{2520 \text{ nm}}{3} = 840 \text{ nm}$$

which is IR rather than visible. There is no need to check $m = 1$ or 2 since they give wavelengths even larger than 840 nm—wavelengths even farther from the visible range. Therefore, we try $m = 6$:

$$\lambda_0 = \frac{2nt}{m} = \frac{2520 \text{ nm}}{6} = 420 \text{ nm}$$

This wavelength is generally considered to be visible. What about $m = 7$?

$$\lambda_0 = \frac{2nt}{m} = \frac{2520 \text{ nm}}{7} = 360 \text{ nm}$$

360 nm is UV. Thus, the only other missing visible wavelength is 420 nm.

Discussion   As a check, we can verify directly that the three missing wavelengths in vacuum travel an integral number of wavelengths in the film:

λ_0	$\lambda = \dfrac{\lambda_0}{1.36}$	$m\lambda$
420 nm	308.8 nm	6×308.8 nm = 1853 nm
504 nm	370.6 nm	5×370.6 nm = 1853 nm
630 nm	463.2 nm	4×463.2 nm = 1853 nm

Since the path difference is $2t = 2 \times 926.47$ nm = 1853 nm, the extra path is an integral number of wavelengths for all three.

Practice Problem 25.3   Constructive Interference in Reflected Light

What visible wavelengths interfere *constructively* in the reflected light where $t = 926$ nm?

Thin Films of Air

A thin air gap between two solids can produce interference effects. Figure 25.13a is a photograph of two glass slides separated by an air gap. The thickness of the air gap varies because the glass surfaces are not perfectly flat. The photo shows colored fringes. Each fringe of a given color traces out a curve along which the thickness of the air film is constant. In Fig. 25.13b, an instrument pushes gently down on the top slide. The resulting distortion in the surface of the top slide causes the fringes to move.

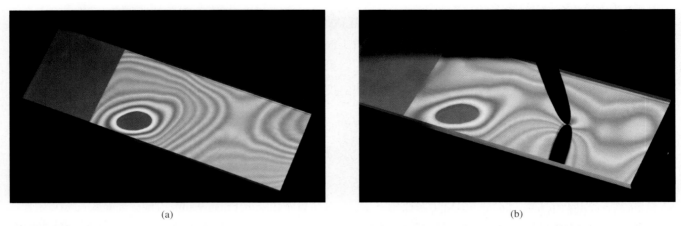

Figure 25.13 (a) Two glass slides with a narrow air gap between them. When illuminated with white light, interference fringes form in the reflected light. (b) Pressing on the glass changes the thickness of the air gap and distorts the interference fringes.

If a glass lens with a convex spherical surface is placed on a flat plate of glass, the air gap between the two increases in thickness as we move out from the contact point (Fig. 25.14). Assuming a perfect spherical shape, we expect to see alternating bright and dark circular fringes in reflected light. The fringes are called Newton's rings. Well past Newton's day, it was a puzzle that the center was a *dark* spot. Thomas Young figured out that the center is dark because of the phase shift on reflection. Young did an experiment producing Newton's rings with a lens made of crown glass ($n = 1.5$) on top of a flat plate made of flint glass ($n = 1.7$). When the gap between the two was filled with air, the center was dark in reflected light. Then he immersed the experiment in sassafras oil (which has an index of refraction between 1.5 and 1.7). Now the center spot was bright, since there was no longer a relative phase difference of 180° due to reflection.

Newton's rings can be used to check a lens to see if its surface is spherical. A perfectly spherical surface gives circular interference fringes that occur at predictable radii (see Problem 24).

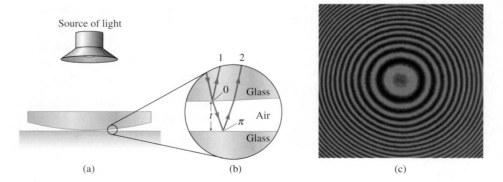

Figure 25.14 (a) The air gap between a convex, spherical glass surface and an optically flat glass plate. The curvature of the lens is exaggerated here. In reality, the air gap would be very thin and the glass surfaces *almost* parallel. (b) Light rays reflected from the top and bottom of the air gap. Ray 2 has a phase shift of π rad due to reflection, while ray 1 does not. Ray 2 also has a phase shift due to the extra path traveled in the air gap. For normal incidence, the extra path length is $2t$, where t is the thickness of the air gap. When viewed from above, we see the superposition of reflected rays 1 and 2. (c) A pattern of circular interference fringes, known as Newton's rings, is seen in reflected light.

Antireflective Coatings

A common application of thin film interference is the antireflective coatings on lenses (Fig. 25.15). The importance of these coatings increases as the number of lenses in an instrument increases—if even a small percentage of the incident light intensity is reflected at each surface, reflections at each surface of each lens can add up to a large fraction of the incident intensity being reflected.

The most common material used as an antireflective coating is magnesium fluoride (MgF_2). It has an index of refraction $n = 1.38$, between that of air ($n = 1$) and glass ($n \approx$ 1.5 or 1.6). The thickness of the film is chosen so destructive interference occurs for wavelengths in the middle of the visible spectrum.

Butterfly Wings

Interference from light reflected by step structures or partially overlapping scales produces the iridescent colors seen in many butterflies, moths, birds, and fish. A stunning example is the shimmering blue of the *Morpho* butterfly. Figure 25.16a shows the *Morpho* wing as viewed under an electron microscope. The tree-like structures that project up from the top surface of the wing are made of a transparent material. Light is thus reflected from a series of steps. Let us concentrate on two rays reflected from the tops of successive steps of thickness t_1 with spacing t_2 between the steps (Fig. 25.16b). Both are inverted on reflection, so there is no relative phase difference due to reflection. At normal incidence, the path difference is $2(t_1 + t_2)$. However, the ray passes through a thickness t_1 of the step where the index of refraction is $n = 1.5$. We cannot find the wavelength for constructive interference simply by setting the path difference equal to a whole number of wavelengths: which wavelength would we use?

Making the Connection:
antireflective coatings

Figure 25.15 The left side of this lens has an antireflective coating; the right side does not.

Making the Connection:
iridescent colors in
butterfly wings

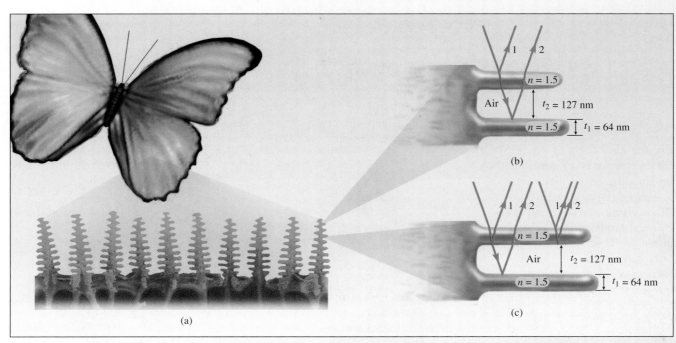

Figure 25.16 (a) *Morpho* wing as viewed under an electron microscope. (b) Light rays reflected from two successive steps interfere. Constructive interference produces the shimmering blue color of the wing. For clarity, the rays shown are not at normal incidence. (c) Two other pairs of rays that interfere.

To solve this sort of problem, we think of path differences in terms of numbers of wavelengths. The number of wavelengths traveled by ray 2 in a distance $2t_1$ (round-trip) through a thickness t_1 of the wing structure is

$$\frac{2t_1}{\lambda} = \frac{2t_1}{\lambda_0/n}$$

where λ_0 is the wavelength in vacuum and $\lambda = \lambda_0/n$ is the wavelength in the medium with index of refraction n. The number of wavelengths traveled in a distance $2t_2$ in air is

$$\frac{2t_2}{\lambda} = \frac{2t_2}{\lambda_0}$$

For constructive interference, the number of extra wavelengths traveled by ray 2, relative to ray 1, must be an integer:

$$\frac{2t_1}{\lambda_0/n} + \frac{2t_2}{\lambda_0} = m$$

We can solve this equation for λ_0 to find the wavelengths that interfere constructively:

$$\lambda_0 = \frac{2}{m}(nt_1 + t_2)$$

For $m = 1$,

$$\lambda_0 = 2(1.5 \times 64 \text{ nm} + 127 \text{ nm}) = 2 \times 223 \text{ nm} = 446 \text{ nm}$$

This is the dominant wavelength in the light we see when looking at the butterfly wing at normal incidence. We only considered reflections from two adjacent steps, but if those interfere constructively, so do all the other reflections from the tops of the steps. Constructive interference at higher values of m are outside the visible spectrum (in the UV).

Since the path length traveled by ray 2 depends on the angle of incidence, the wavelength of light that interferes constructively depends on the angle of view (see Conceptual Question 16). Thus, the color of the wing changes as the viewing angle changes, which gives the wing its shimmering iridescence.

So far we have ignored reflections from the bottoms of the steps. Rays reflected from the bottoms of two successive steps interfere constructively at the same wavelength of 446 nm, since the path difference is the same. The interference of two other pairs of rays (Fig. 25.16c) gives constructive interference only in UV since the path length difference is so small.

25.4   YOUNG'S DOUBLE-SLIT EXPERIMENT

In 1801, Thomas Young performed a double-slit interference experiment that not only demonstrated the wave nature of light, but also allowed the first measurement of the wavelength of light. Figure 25.17 shows the setup for Young's experiment. Coherent light of wavelength λ illuminates a mask in which two parallel slits have been cut. Each

Figure 25.17 Young's double-slit interference experiment. (a) The slit geometry. The center-to-center distance between the slits is d. From the point midway between the slits, a line perpendicular to the mask extends toward the center of the interference pattern on the screen and a line making an angle θ to the normal can be used to locate a particular point to either side of the center of the interference pattern. (b) Cylindrical wavefronts emerge from the slits and interfere to form a pattern of fringes on the screen.

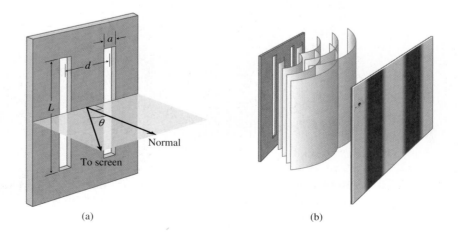

(a)   (b)

slit has width a, which is comparable to the wavelength λ, and length $L \gg a$; the centers of the slits are separated by a distance d. When light from the slits is observed on a screen at a great distance D from the slits, what pattern do we see—how does the intensity I of light falling on the screen depend on the angle θ, which measures the direction from the slits to a point on the screen?

Light from a *single* narrow slit spreads out primarily in directions perpendicular to the slit, since the wavefronts coming from it are cylindrical. Thus, the light from one narrow slit forms a band of light on the screen. The light does *not* spread out significantly in the direction *parallel* to the slit since the slit length L is *large* compared to the wavelength.

With *two* narrow slits, the two bands of light on the screen interfere with one another. The light from the slits starts out in phase, but travels different paths to reach the screen. We expect constructive interference at the center of the interference pattern ($\theta = 0$) since the waves travel the same distance and so are in phase when they reach the screen. Constructive interference also occurs wherever the path difference is an integral multiple of λ. Destructive interference occurs when the path difference is an odd number of half wavelengths. A gradual transition between constructive and destructive interference occurs since the path difference increases continuously as θ increases. This leads to the characteristic alternation of bright and dark bands (fringes) that are shown in Fig. 25.18a, a photograph of the screen from a double-slit experiment. Figure 25.18b

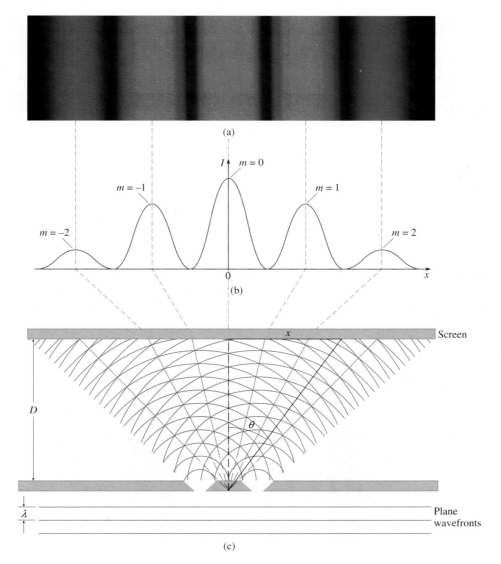

(a)

(b)

(c)

Figure 25.18 Double-slit interference pattern using red light. (a) Photo of the interference pattern on the screen. Constructive interference produces a high intensity of red light on the screen while destructive interference leaves the screen dark. (b) The intensity as a function of position x on the screen. The maxima (positions where the interference is constructive) are labeled with the associated value of m. (c) A Huygens construction for the double-slit experiment. The blue lines represent antinodes (points where the waves interfere constructively). Note the relationship between x, the position on the screen, and the angle θ: $\tan \theta = x/D$, where D is the distance from the slits to the screen.

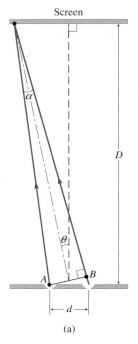

Screen

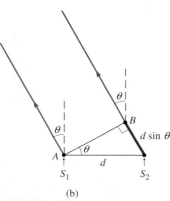

(a)

(b)

Figure 25.19 (a) Rays from two slits to a nearby screen. As the screen is moved farther away, α decreases—the rays become more nearly parallel. (b) In the limit of a distant screen, the two rays are parallel (but still meet at the same point on the screen). The difference in path lengths is $d \sin \theta$.

Figure 25.20 Water waves in a ripple tank exhibit two-source interference. Lines of antinodes correspond to the directions of maximum intensity in double-slit interference for light; lines of nodes correspond to the minima.

and c are a graph of the intensity on the screen and a Huygens construction for the same interference pattern, respectively.

To find where constructive or destructive interference occurs, we need to calculate the path difference. Figure 25.19a shows two rays going from the slits to a *nearby* screen. If the screen is moved farther from the slits, the angle α gets smaller. When the screen is far away, α is small and the rays are nearly parallel. In Fig. 25.19b, the rays are drawn as parallel for a distant screen. The distance that the rays travel from points A and B to the screen are equal; the path difference is the distance from the right slit to point B:

$$\Delta l = d \sin \theta \tag{25-9}$$

Maximum intensity at the screen is produced by constructive interference; for constructive interference, the path difference is an integral multiple of the wavelength:

Double-slit maxima:

$$d \sin \theta = m\lambda \quad (m = 0, \pm 1, \pm 2, \ldots) \tag{25-10}$$

The absolute value of m is often called the **order** of the maximum. Thus, the third-order maxima are those for which $d \sin \theta = \pm 3\lambda$. Minimum (zero) intensity at the screen is produced by destructive interference; for destructive interference, the path difference is an odd number of half wavelengths:

Double-slit minima:

$$d \sin \theta = (m + \tfrac{1}{2})\lambda \quad (m = 0, \pm 1, \pm 2, \ldots) \tag{25-11}$$

In Fig. 25.18, the bright and dark fringes appear to be equally spaced. In Problem 28, you can show that the interference fringes *are* equally spaced near the center of the interference pattern, where θ is a small angle.

Figure 25.20 shows the interference of *water waves* in a ripple tank. Surface waves are generated in the water by two point sources that vibrate up and down at the same frequency and in phase with each other, so they are coherent sources. The pattern of interference of the water waves far from the two sources is similar to the double-slit interference pattern for light. If d represents the distance between the sources, Eqs. (25-10) and (25-11) give the correct angles θ for constructive and destructive interference of *water* waves at a large distance. The advantage of the ripple tank is that it lets us see what the wavefronts look like. Notice the similarity between Fig. 25.20 and Fig. 25.18c.

Points where the interference is constructive are called **antinodes**. Just as for standing waves, here the superposition of two coherent waves causes some points—the antinodes—to have maximum amplitudes. There are also **nodes**—points of complete destructive interference. In a one-dimensional standing wave on a string, nodes and antinodes were single points. For the two-dimensional water waves in a ripple tank, the nodes and antinodes are *curves*. For three-dimensional light waves (or three-dimensional sound waves), the nodes and antinodes are *surfaces*.

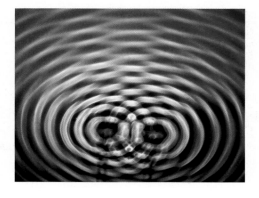

Example 25.4

Interference from Two Parallel Slits

A laser ($\lambda = 690.0$ nm) is used to illuminate two parallel slits. On a screen that is 3.30 m away from the slits, interference fringes are observed. The distance between adjacent bright fringes in the center of the pattern is 1.80 cm. What is the distance between the slits?

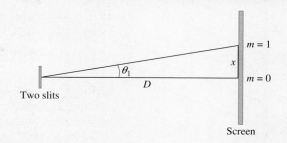

Figure 25.21

Sketch of the double-slit experiment for Example 25.4.

Strategy   Bright fringes occur at angles θ given by $d \sin \theta = m\lambda$. The distance between the $m = 0$ and $m = 1$ maxima is $x = 1.80$ cm. A sketch helps us see the relationship between the angle θ and the distances given in the problem.

Solution   The central bright fringe ($m = 0$) is at $\theta_0 = 0$. The next bright fringe ($m = 1$) is at an angle given by

$$d \sin \theta_1 = \lambda$$

Figure 25.21 is a sketch of the geometry of the situation. The angle between the lines going to the $m = 0$ and $m = 1$ maxima is θ_1. The distance between these two maxima on the screen is x and the distance from the slits to the screen is D. We can find θ_1 from x and D using trigonometry:

$$\tan \theta_1 = \frac{x}{D} = \frac{0.0180 \text{ m}}{3.30 \text{ m}} = 0.005455$$

$$\theta_1 = \tan^{-1} 0.005455 = 0.3125°$$

Now we substitute θ_1 into the condition for the $m = 1$ maximum.

$$d = \frac{\lambda}{\sin \theta_1} = \frac{690.0 \text{ nm}}{\sin 0.3125°} = \frac{690.0 \text{ nm}}{0.005454} = 0.127 \text{ mm}$$

Discussion   We might have noticed that since $x \ll D$, θ_1 is a small angle—that's why the sine and the tangent are the same to three significant figures. Using the small angle approximation ($\sin \theta \approx \tan \theta \approx \theta$ in radians) from the start gives

$$d\theta_1 = \lambda$$

and

$$\theta_1 = \frac{x}{D}$$

so

$$d = \frac{\lambda D}{x} = \frac{690.0 \text{ nm} \times 3.30 \text{ m}}{0.0180 \text{ m}} = 0.127 \text{ mm}$$

Practice Problem 25.4   Fringe Spacing When the Wavelength Is Changed

In a particular double-slit experiment, the distance between the slits is 50 times the wavelength of the light. (a) Find the angles in radians at which the $m = 0$, 1, and 2 maxima occur. (b) Find the angles at which the first two minima occur. (c) What is the distance between two maxima at the center of the pattern on a screen 2.0 m away?

Conceptual Example 25.5

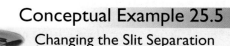

Changing the Slit Separation

A laser is used to illuminate two narrow parallel slits. The interference pattern is observed on a distant screen. What happens to the pattern observed if the distance between the slits is slowly decreased?

Solution and Discussion   When the slits are closer together, the path difference $d \sin \theta$ for a given angle gets smaller. Larger angles are required to produce a path difference that is a given multiple of the wavelength. The interference pattern therefore spreads out, with each maximum (other than $m = 0$) and minimum moving out to larger and larger angles.

Conceptual Practice Problem 25.5
Interference Pattern for $d < \lambda$

If the distance between two slits in a double-slit experiment is less than the wavelength of light, what would you see at a distant screen?

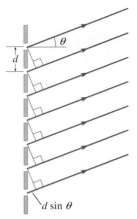

Figure 25.22 Light rays traveling from the slits of a grating to a point on a screen. Since the screen is far away, the rays are nearly parallel to each other; they all leave the grating at (nearly) the same angle θ. Since the distance between any two adjacent slits is d, the path difference between two adjacent rays is $d \sin \theta$.

● Maxima for a grating are at the same angles as maxima for two slits with the same d.

25.5   GRATINGS

Instead of having two parallel slits, a **grating** (sometimes called a "diffraction grating") consists of a large number of parallel, narrow, evenly spaced slits. Typical gratings have hundreds or thousands of slits. The slit separation of a grating is commonly characterized by the number of slits per cm (or the number per any other unit of distance), which is the reciprocal of the slit separation d:

$$\text{slits per cm} = \frac{1}{\text{cm per slit}} = \frac{1}{d}$$

Gratings are made with up to about 50,000 slits/cm, so slit separations are as small as 200 nm. The smaller the slit separation, the more widely different wavelengths of light are separated by the grating.

Figure 25.22 shows light rays traveling from the slits of a grating to a distant screen. Suppose light from the first two slits is in phase at the screen because the path difference $d \sin \theta$ is a whole number of wavelengths $m\lambda$. Then, since the slits are evenly spaced, the light from *all* the slits arrives at the screen in phase. The path difference between any pair of slits is an integral multiple of $d \sin \theta$ and therefore an integral multiple of λ. Therefore, the angles for constructive interference for a grating are the same as for two slits with the same separation:

Maxima for a grating:

$$d \sin \theta = m\lambda \quad (m = 0, \pm 1, \pm 2, \ldots) \tag{25-10}$$

As for two slits, $|m|$ is called the *order* of the maximum.

For two slits, there is a gradual change in intensity from maximum to minimum and back to maximum. By contrast, for a grating with a large number of slits, the maxima are narrow and the intensity everywhere else is negligibly small. How does the presence of many slits make the maxima so narrow?

Suppose we have a grating with $N = 100$ slits, numbered 0 to 99. The first-order maximum occurs at angle θ such that the path length difference between slits 0 and 1 is $d \sin \theta = \lambda$. Now suppose we look at a *slightly* greater angle $\theta + \Delta\theta$ such that $d \sin (\theta + \Delta\theta) = 1.01\lambda$. The rays from slits 0 and 1 are almost in phase; if there were only two slits, the intensity would be almost as large as the maximum. With 100 slits, each ray is 1.01λ longer than the previous ray. If the length of ray 0 is l_0, then the length of ray 1 is $l_0 + 1.01\lambda$, the length of ray 2 is $l_0 + 2.02\lambda$, and so forth. The length of ray 50 is $l_0 + 50.50\lambda$; thus, rays 0 and 50 interfere destructively since the path difference is an odd number of half wavelengths. Likewise, slits 1 and 51 interfere destructively ($51.51\lambda - 1.01\lambda = 50.50\lambda$); slits 2 and 52 interfere destructively; and so on. Since the light from every slit interferes destructively with the light from some other slit, the intensity at the screen is *zero*. The intensity goes from maximum at θ to zero at $\theta + \Delta\theta$.

The angle $\Delta\theta$ is called the *half width* of the maximum since it is the angle from the center of the maximum to one edge of the maximum (rather than from one edge to the other). By generalizing the argument, we find that the widths of the maxima are inversely proportional to the number of slits ($\Delta\theta \propto 1/N$). The larger the number of slits, the narrower the maxima. Increasing N also makes the maxima *brighter*. More slits let more light pass through and bunch the light energy into narrower maxima. Since light from N slits interferes constructively, the amplitudes of the maxima are proportional to N and the intensities are proportional to N^2. The maxima for a grating are narrow and occur at different angles for different wavelengths. Therefore:

A grating separates light with a mixture of wavelengths into its constituent wavelengths.

Example 25.6
Slit Spacing for a Grating

Bright white light shines on a grating. A cylindrical strip of color film is exposed by light emerging at all angles (–90° to +90°) from the grating (Fig. 25.23a). Figure 25.23b shows the resulting photograph. Estimate the number of slits per cm in the grating.

Strategy   The grating separates white light into the colors of the visible spectrum. Each color forms a maximum at angles given by $d \sin \theta = m\lambda$. From Fig. 25.23b, we see that more than just first-order maxima are present. If we can estimate the wavelength of the light that exposed the edge of the photo—light that left the grating at ±90°—and if we know what order maximum that is, we can find the slit separation.

Solution   The central ($m = 0$) maximum appears white due to constructive interference for *all* wavelengths. On either side of the central maximum lie the first-order maxima. The first-order violet (shortest wavelength) comes first (at the smallest angle), and red is last. Next comes a gap where there are no maxima. Then the second-order maxima begin with violet. The colors do not progress through the pure spectral colors as before because the third-order maxima start to appear before the second order is finished. The third-order spectrum is not complete;

the last color we see at either extreme ($\theta = \pm 90°$) is blue-green. Thus, the third-order maximum for blue-green light occurs at ±90°.

Wavelengths that appear blue-green are around 500 nm (Section 22.4). Using $\lambda = 500$ nm and $m = 3$ for the third-order maximum, we can solve for the slit separation.

$$d \sin \theta = m\lambda$$

$$d = \frac{m\lambda}{\sin \theta} = \frac{3 \times 500 \text{ nm}}{\sin 90°} = 1500 \text{ nm}$$

Then the number of slits per cm is

$$\frac{1}{d} = \frac{1}{1500 \times 10^{-9} \text{ m}} = 670{,}000 \text{ slits/m} = 6700 \text{ slits/cm}$$

Discussion   The final answer is reasonable for the number of slits per cm in a grating. We would suspect an error if it came out to be 67 million slits/cm, or 67 slits/cm.

For a maximum occurring at 90°, we *cannot* use the small angle approximation! We often look at maxima formed by gratings that occur at large angles for which the small angle approximation is not valid.

Practice Problem 25.6   Slit Spacing for a Full Third Order

How many slits per cm would a grating have if it just barely produced the full third-order spectrum? Would any of the fourth-order spectrum be produced by such a grating?

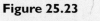

Figure 25.23
(a) White light incident on a grating. (b) The developed film.

CD Tracking

Data on a CD is encoded as bumps arranged in a spiral track 0.5 μm wide (Fig. 25.24). A 1.6-μm width of flat aluminum on either side separates two adjacent tracks. One of the hardest jobs of a CD player (or CD-ROM drive) is to keep the laser beam centered on the spiral track. One method to keep the laser on track uses a grating to split the laser beam into three beams. The central ($m = 0$) maximum is centered on the track. The first-order ($m = \pm 1$) maxima are tracking beams. They reflect from the flat aluminum surfaces (called *land*) on either side of the track onto detectors. Normally the reflected intensity is constant. If one of the tracking beams encounters the bumps in an adjacent track, the changes in reflected intensity signal that the position of the laser must be corrected.

Some fast CD-ROM drives use a grating to split a laser beam into seven beams—zeroth- through third-order maxima. Each beam is used to read a different track; thus, the drive reads seven tracks simultaneously.

Making the Connection:
CD player tracking

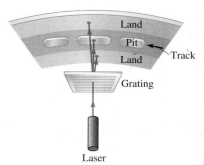

Figure 25.24   A three-beam tracking system.

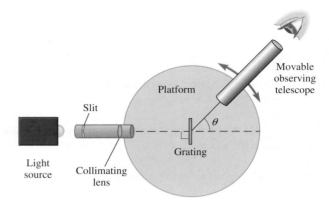

Figure 25.25 Overhead view of a grating spectroscope.

Making the Connection:

grating spectroscope

Spectroscopy

The **grating spectroscope** is a precision instrument to measure wavelengths of visible light (Fig. 25.25). *Spectroscope* means (roughly) *spectrum-viewing*. Light from the source first passes through a narrow, vertical slit, which is at the focal point of the collimating lens. Thus, the rays emerging from the lens are parallel to each other. The grating rests on a platform that is adjusted so that the incident rays strike the grating at normal incidence. The telescope can be moved in a circle around the grating to observe the maxima and to measure the angle θ at which each one occurs. The angles are then used along with the spacing of slits in the grating to determine the wavelength(s) present in the light source. The maxima are often called *spectral lines*—they appear as thin lines because they have the shape of the entry slit of the collimator.

Although thermal radiation (such as sunlight and incandescent light) contains a continuous spectrum of wavelengths, other sources of light contain a discrete spectrum composed of only a few narrow bands of wavelengths. A discrete spectrum is also called a line spectrum due to its appearance as a set of lines when viewed through a spectroscope. For example, fluorescent lights and gas discharge tubes produce discrete spectra. In a gas discharge tube, a glass tube is filled with a single gas at low pressure and an electrical current is passed through the gas. The light that is emitted is a discrete spectrum that is characteristic of the gas. Some older streetlights are sodium discharge tubes; they have a characteristic yellow color.

Figure 25.26 shows the spectrum of a sodium discharge tube, which includes two yellow lines at wavelengths of 589.0 nm and 589.6 nm (the *sodium doublet*). Imagine using a grating with fewer slits. The maxima would be wider; if they were too wide, the two yellow lines would overlap and appear as a single line. So a large number of slits is an advantage if we need to *resolve* (distinguish) wavelengths that are close together.

Reflection Gratings

In the **transmission gratings** we have been discussing, the light viewed is that transmitted by the transparent slits of the grating. Another common kind of grating is the **reflection grating**. Instead of slits, a reflection grating has a large number of parallel, thin reflecting surfaces separated by absorbing surfaces. Using Huygens's principle, the analysis of the reflection grating is exactly the same as for the transmission grating, except that the direction of travel of the wavelets is reversed. Reflection gratings are used in high resolution spectroscopy of astronomical x-ray sources. The spectra enable scientists to identify elements such as iron, oxygen, silicon, and magnesium in the corona of a star or in the remnants of a supernova.

Figure 25.26 Emission spectrum of sodium.

PHYSICS AT HOME

A compact disc can be used as a reflection grating, since it has a large number of equally spaced reflective tracks. Hold a CD at an angle so that the side without the label reflects light from the Sun or another light source. Tilt the CD back and forth slightly and look for the rainbow of colors that results from the interference of light reflecting from the narrowly spaced grooves of the CD. Next place the CD, label side down, on the floor directly below a ceiling light. Look down at the CD as you slowly walk away from it. The first-order maxima form a band of colors (violet to red). Once you are a meter or so away, gradually lower your head to the floor, watching the CD the whole time. You have now observed from $\theta = 0$ to $\theta = 90°$. Count how many orders of maxima you see for the different colors. Now estimate the spacing between tracks on the CD.

25.6   DIFFRACTION AND HUYGENS'S PRINCIPLE

Suppose a plane wave approaches an obstacle. Using geometric optics, we would expect the rays not blocked by the obstacle to continue straight ahead, forming a sharp, well-defined shadow on a screen beyond the obstacle. If the obstacle is large compared to the wavelength, then geometric optics gives a good *approximation* to what actually happens. If the obstacle is *not* large compared to the wavelength, we must return to Huygens's principle to show how a wave diffracts.

In Fig. 25.27a, a wavefront just reaches a barrier with an opening in it. Every point on that wavefront acts as a source of *spherical* wavelets. Points on the wavefront that are behind the barrier have their wavelets absorbed or reflected. Therefore, the propagation of the wave is determined by the wavelets generated by the unobstructed part of the wavefront. The Huygens constructions in Figs. 25.27b–d show that the wave diffracts around the edges of the barrier, something that would not be expected in geometric optics.

Figure 25.28 shows water waves in a ripple tank that pass through three openings of different widths. For the opening that is much wider than the wavelength (Fig. 25.28a), the spreading of the wavefronts is a small effect. Essentially, the part of the wavefront that is not obstructed just travels straight ahead, producing a sharp shadow. As the opening gets narrower (Fig. 25.28b), the spreading of the wavefronts becomes more pronounced. Diffraction is appreciable when the size of the opening approaches the size of the wavelength or is even smaller. In the case of Fig. 25.28c, where the opening is about the size of the wavelength, the opening acts almost like a point source of circular waves.

For the openings of intermediate size, a careful look at the waves shows that the amplitude is larger in some directions than in others (Fig. 25.28b). The source of this structure, due to the interference of wavelets from different points, is examined in Section 25.7.

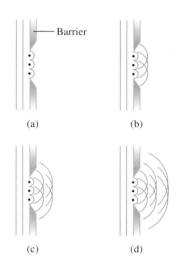

Figure 25.27 (a) A plane wave reaches a barrier. Points along the wavefront act as sources of spherical wavelets. (b) to (d) At later times, the initial wavelets are propagating outward as new ones form; the wavefront spreads around the edges of the barrier.

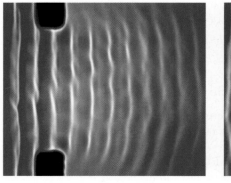

(a)

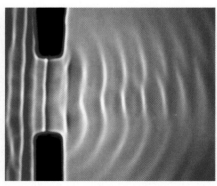

(b)

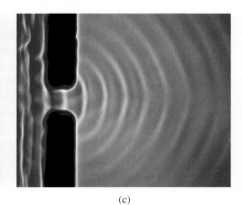

(c)

Figure 25.28 Water waves moving from left to right in a ripple tank pass through openings of different widths.

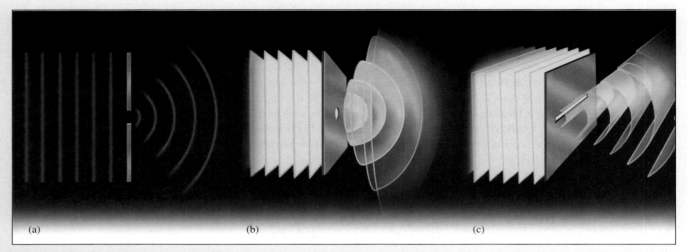

Figure 25.29 (a) Sketch of wavefronts that could represent either a small circular hole or a slit. (b) For a small circular hole, the emerging wavefronts are spherical. (c) For a slit, the emerging wavefronts are cylindrical.

Since EM waves are three-dimensional, we must be careful when interpreting two-dimensional sketches of Huygens wavelets. Figure 25.29a might represent light incident on a small circular hole or a long, thin slit. If it represents a hole, the light spreads in all directions, yielding spherically shaped wavefronts (Fig. 25.29b). If the opening represents a slit, we can think of the two directions in turn. The more narrowly restricted the wavefront, the more it spreads out. In the direction of the length of the slit, we get essentially a geometric shadow. In the direction of the width, the wavefront is restricted to a short distance, so the wave spreads out in that direction. The wavefronts past the slit are cylindrically shaped (Fig. 25.29c).

Conceptual Example 25.7

Diffraction and Photolithography

The CPU chip in a computer contains about 10^8 transistors, numerous other circuit elements, and the electrical connections between them, all in a very small package. One process used to fabricate such a chip is called photolithography. In photolithography, a silicon wafer is coated with a photosensitive material. The chip is then exposed to ultraviolet radiation through a mask that contains the desired pattern of material to be removed. The wafer is then etched. The areas of the wafer not exposed to UV are not susceptible to etching. In areas that were exposed to UV, the photosensitive material and part of the silicon underneath are removed. Why does this process work better with UV than it would with visible light? Why are researchers trying to develop x-ray lithography to replace UV lithography?

Strategy Without knowing details of the chemical processes involved, we think about the implications of different wavelengths. X-ray wavelengths are shorter than UV wavelengths, which are in turn shorter than visible wavelengths.

Solution and Discussion The photolithography process depends on the formation of a *sharp shadow* of the mask. To make smaller chips contain more and more circuit elements, the lines in the mask must be made as thin as possible. The danger is that if the lines are too thin, diffraction will spread out the light going through the mask. To minimize diffraction effects, the wavelength should be small compared to the openings in the mask. UV has smaller wavelengths than visible light, so the openings in the mask can be made smaller. X-ray lithography would permit even smaller openings.

Conceptual Practice Problem 25.7   Sunlight Through a Window

Sunlight streams through a rectangular window, illuminating a bright area on the floor. The edges of the illuminated area are fuzzy rather than sharp. Is the fuzziness due to diffraction? Explain. If not diffraction, what does blur the boundaries of the illuminated area?

PHYSICS AT HOME

Figure 25.30a shows the shadow of a razor blade illuminated by coherent laser light. Bright and dark fringes are formed by the diffraction of light. One of the counterintuitive predictions of the wave theory of light is that the shadow of a circular or spherical object in coherent light should have a *bright spot at the center* due to diffraction (Fig. 25.30b). Fresnel's prediction of this bright spot was considered by some eminent scientists of the nineteenth century (such as Poisson) to be ridiculous—until it was shown experimentally to exist. You can see the Poisson spot yourself. Use superglue to attach a ball bearing or small opaque marble to a glass microscope slide. View the shadow of the ball bearing by holding it near your eye so that it blocks a distant source of light. The source must be distant enough to act like a point source; there should be a minimal amount of light from other sources. Try a bright streetlight at night or a single lightbulb in an otherwise dark room. Remember that it is never safe to stare directly into a bright light.

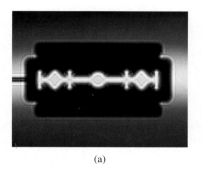
(a)

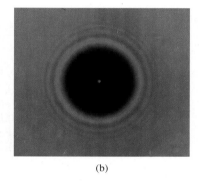
(b)

Figure 25.30 (a) Diffraction pattern formed when an old-fashioned razor blade is illuminated with laser light. (b) Diffraction pattern formed by a small sphere. Note the bright Poisson spot at the center.

PHYSICS AT HOME

Find a finely woven piece of cloth with a regular mesh pattern, such as a piece of silk, a nylon curtain, an umbrella, or a piece of lingerie. Look through the cloth at a distant, bright light source in an otherwise darkened room—or at a streetlight outside at night. Can you explain the origin of the pattern you see? Could it be simply a geometric shadow of the threads in the cloth? Observe the pattern as you rotate the cloth. Also try stretching the cloth slightly in one direction.

25.7 DIFFRACTION BY A SINGLE SLIT

In a more detailed treatment of diffraction, we must consider the *phases* of all the Huygens wavelets and apply the principle of superposition. Interference of the wavelets causes structure in the diffracted light. In the ripple tanks of Fig. 25.28, we saw structure in the diffraction pattern. In some directions, the wave amplitude was large; in other directions it was small. Figure 25.31 shows the diffraction pattern formed by light passing through a single slit. A wide central maximum contains most of the light energy. (*Central maximum* is the usual way to refer to the entire bright band in the center of the pattern, although the actual *maximum* is just at $\theta = 0$. A more accurate name is *central bright fringe*.) The intensity is brightest right at the center and falls off gradually until the first minimum on either side, where the screen is dark (intensity is zero). Continuing away from the center, maxima and minima alternate, with the intensity changing gradually between them. The lateral maxima are quite weak compared to the central maximum and they are not as wide.

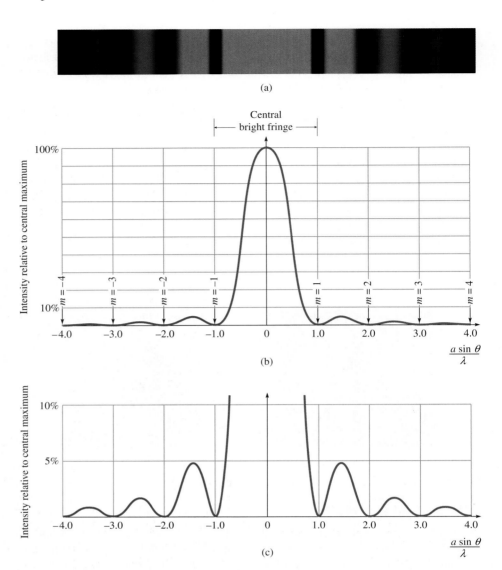

Figure 25.31 Single-slit diffraction. (a) Photo of the diffraction pattern as viewed on a screen. (b) Intensity (as a percentage of the intensity of the central maximum) as a function of the number of wavelengths difference in the path length from top and bottom rays [$(a \sin \theta)/\lambda$]. Minima occur at angles where $(a \sin \theta)/\lambda$ is an integer other than zero. (c) Close-up of the same graph. Intensities of the first three lateral maxima (as percentages) are 4.72%, 1.65%, and 0.834%. The first three lateral maxima occur when $a \sin \theta = 1.43\lambda$, 2.46λ, and 3.47λ.

According to Huygens's principle, the diffraction of the light is explained by considering every point along the slit as a source of wavelets (Fig. 25.32a). The light intensity at any point beyond the slit is the *superposition* of these wavelets. The wavelets start out in phase, but travel different distances to reach a given point on the screen. The structure in the diffraction pattern is a result of *the interference of the wavelets*. This is a much more complicated interference problem than any we have considered, because an *infinite* number of waves interfere—*every point* along the slit is a source of wavelets. Despite this complication, a clever insight—similar to one we used with the grating—lets us find out where the minima are without the need to resort to complicated math.

Figure 25.32b shows two rays that represent the propagation of two wavelets: one from the top edge of the slit and one from exactly halfway down. The rays are going off at the same angle θ to reach the same point on a *distant* screen. The lower one travels an extra distance $\frac{1}{2}a \sin \theta$ to reach the screen. If this extra distance is equal to $\frac{1}{2}\lambda$, then *these two wavelets* interfere destructively. Now let's look at two other wavelets, shifted down a distance Δx so that they are still separated by half the slit width ($\frac{1}{2}a$). The path difference between these two must also be $\frac{1}{2}\lambda$, so these two interfere destructively. *All the wavelets* can be paired off; since each pair interferes destructively, no light reaches the screen at that angle. Therefore, the first diffraction minimum occurs where

$$\frac{1}{2}a \sin \theta = \frac{1}{2}\lambda$$

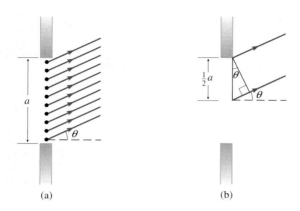

Figure 25.32 (a) Every point along a slit serves as a source of Huygens wavelets; (b) the ray from the center of the slit travels a greater distance to reach the screen than the ray from the top of the slit; the extra distance is $\frac{1}{2}a \sin \theta$.

or

$$a \sin \theta = \lambda$$

The other minima are found in a similar way, by pairing off wavelets separated by a distance of $\frac{1}{4}a, \frac{1}{6}a, \frac{1}{8}a, \ldots, \frac{1}{2m}a$, where m is any integer *other than zero*. The diffraction minima are given by

$$\frac{1}{2m} a \sin \theta = \frac{1}{2}\lambda \quad (m = \pm 1, \pm 2, \pm 3, \ldots)$$

Simplifying algebraically yields:

> **Single-slit diffraction *minima*:**
>
> $$a \sin \theta = m\lambda \quad (m = \pm 1, \pm 2, \pm 3, \ldots) \tag{25-12}$$

Be careful: Eq. (25-12) looks a lot like Eq. (25-10) for the interference maxima due to N slits, but it gives the locations of the diffraction *minima*. Also, $m = 0$ is excluded in Eq. (25-12); a maximum, not a minimum, occurs at $\theta = 0$.

What happens if the slit is made narrower? As a gets smaller, the angles θ for the minima get larger—the diffraction pattern spreads out. If the slit is made wider, then the diffraction pattern shrinks as the angles for the minima get smaller.

The angles at which the lateral maxima occur are much harder to find than the angles of the minima; there is no comparable simplification we can use. The central maximum is at $\theta = 0$, since the wavelets all travel the same distance to the screen and arrive in phase. The other maxima are *approximately* (not exactly) halfway between adjacent minima (see Fig. 25.31c).

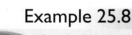

Example 25.8

Single-Slit Diffraction

The diffraction pattern from a single slit of width 0.020 mm is viewed on a screen. If the screen is 1.20 m from the slit and light of wavelength 430 nm is used, what is the width of the central maximum?

Strategy The central maximum extends from the $m = -1$ minimum to the $m = +1$ minimum. Since the pattern is symmetric, the width is twice the distance from the center to the $m = +1$ minimum. A sketch helps relate the angles and distances in the problem.

Solution The $m = 1$ minimum occurs at an angle θ satisfying

$$a \sin \theta = \lambda$$

Continued on next page

Example 25.8 Continued

We draw a sketch (Fig. 25.33) showing the angle θ for the $m = 1$ minimum, the distance x from the center of the diffraction pattern to the first minimum, and the distance D from the slit to the screen. The width of the central maximum is $2x$. From Fig. 25.33,

$$\tan \theta = \frac{x}{D}$$

Assuming that $x \ll D$, θ is a small angle. Therefore, $\sin \theta \approx \tan \theta$:

$$\frac{x}{D} = \frac{\lambda}{a}$$

$$x = \frac{\lambda D}{a} = \frac{430 \times 10^{-9} \text{ m} \times 1.20 \text{ m}}{0.020 \times 10^{-3} \text{ m}} = 0.026 \text{ m}$$

Comparing the values of x and D, our assumption that $x \ll D$ is justified. The width of the central maximum is $2x = 5.2$ cm.

Discussion   The width of the central maximum depends upon the angle θ for the first minimum and the distance D between the slit and the screen. The angle θ, in turn, depends on the wavelength of light and the slit width. For larger values of θ, which means either a longer wavelength or a smaller slit width, the diffraction pattern is more spread

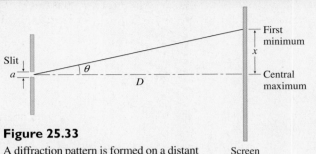

Figure 25.33

A diffraction pattern is formed on a distant screen by light of wavelength λ from a single slit of width a at a distance D from the screen.

out on the screen. For a given wavelength, narrowing the slit increases the diffraction. For a given slit width, the diffraction pattern is wider for longer wavelengths so the pattern for red light ($\lambda = 690$ nm) is more spread out than that for violet light ($\lambda = 410$ nm).

Practice Problem 25.8   Location of First Lateral Maximum

Approximately how far from the center of the diffraction pattern is the first lateral maximum?

Intensities of the Maxima in Double-Slit Interference

In a double-slit interference experiment, the bright fringes are equally spaced but are not equal in intensity (Fig. 25.18). Light diffracts from each slit; the light reaching the screen from either slit forms a diffraction pattern (Fig. 25.31). The two diffraction patterns have the same amplitude at any point on the screen, but different phases. Where the interference is constructive, the amplitude is twice what it would be at that point for a single slit (and therefore four times the intensity).

Figure 25.34 A graph of the intensity for double-slit interference where the spacing d between the two slits is five times the slit width a (that is, $d = 5a$). The first *diffraction* minimum occurs where $a \sin \theta = \lambda$; at that same angle, $5a \sin \theta = d \sin \theta = 5\lambda$. The fifth-order interference maximum is missing because it falls at the first diffraction minimum, where no light reaches the screen. The peak heights follow the intensity pattern for a single slit. At points of constructive interference, the amplitude is twice what it would be from one slit alone, so the intensity is *four* times what it would be from one slit.

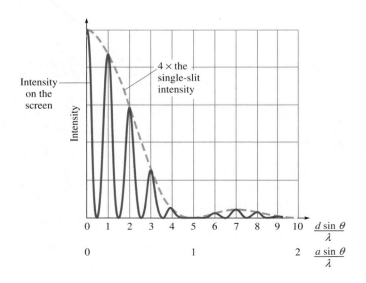

Figure 25.18 shows only interference maxima within the central diffraction maximum of each slit. If the light incident on the slits is bright enough, interference maxima beyond the first diffraction minimum can be observed (Fig. 25.34).

25.8   DIFFRACTION AND THE RESOLUTION OF OPTICAL INSTRUMENTS

Cameras, telescopes, binoculars, microscopes—practically all optical instruments, including the human eye—admit light through circular apertures. Thus, the diffraction of light through a circular aperture is of great importance. If an instrument is to resolve (distinguish) two objects as being separate entities, it must form separate images of the two. If diffraction spreads out the image of each object enough that they overlap, the instrument cannot resolve them.

When light passes through a circular aperture of diameter a, the light is restricted (the wavefronts are blocked) in *all* directions rather than being restricted primarily in a single direction (as for a slit). Thus, for a circular opening, light spreads out in all directions. The diffraction pattern due to a circular aperture (Fig. 25.35) reflects the circular symmetry of the aperture. The diffraction pattern has many similarities to that of a slit. It has a wide, bright central maximum, beyond which minima and weaker maxima alternate; but now the pattern consists of concentric circles reflecting the circular shape of the aperture.

Calculating the angles for the minima and maxima is a difficult problem. Of greatest interest to us is the location of the *first* minimum, which is given by

$$a \sin \theta = 1.22\lambda \qquad (25\text{-}13)$$

Deriving the factor of 1.22 is difficult, but we can make some sense of it. The width of the aperture along any particular direction varies between 0 and the diameter a; we can think of $a/1.22$ as an effective average aperture width. Then Eq. (25-13) becomes $a_{\text{eff}} \sin \theta = \lambda$.

The reason that the first minimum is of particular interest is that it tells us the diameter of the central maximum, which contains 84% of the intensity of the diffracted light. The size of the central maximum is what limits the resolution of an optical instrument.

When we look at a distant star through a telescope, the star is far enough to be considered a point source, but since the light passes through the circular aperture of the telescope, it spreads out into a circular diffraction pattern like Fig. 25.35. What if we look at two or more stars that appear close to each other? With the unaided eye, people with good vision can see two separate stars, Mizar and Alcor, in the handle of the Big Dipper (Fig. 25.36a). With a telescope, one can see that Mizar is actually *two* stars, called Mizar A and Mizar B (Fig. 25.36b); the eye cannot resolve (separate) the images of these two stars, but a telescope with its much wider aperture can. Spectroscopic observations reveal periodic Doppler shifts in the light coming from Mizar A and Mizar B, showing that each is a *binary star*—a pair of stars so close together that they rotate about their center of mass. The companion stars to Mizar A and Mizar B cannot be seen with even the best telescopes available. When light rays from these five stars pass through a circular aperture, diffraction spreads out the images, so that we see only three stars through a telescope or two stars when viewed directly.

Rayleigh's Criterion

Light from a single star (or other point source) forms a circular diffraction pattern after passing through a circular aperture. Two stars with a small angular separation form two overlapping diffraction patterns. Since the stars are incoherent sources, their diffraction patterns overlap without interfering with each other (Fig. 25.37). How far apart must the diffraction patterns be in order to resolve the stars?

A somewhat arbitrary but conventional criterion is due to Rayleigh, who said that the images must be separated by at least half the width of each of the diffraction patterns. In other words, **Rayleigh's criterion** says that two sources can just barely be resolved if the center of one diffraction pattern falls at the first minimum of the other one. Suppose light

Figure 25.35 Diffraction pattern from a circular aperture on a distant screen.

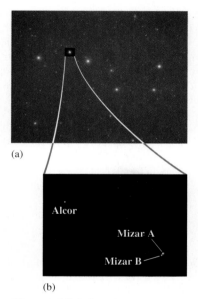

(a)

(b)

Figure 25.36 (a) The Big Dipper, a part of the constellation *Ursa Major*. (b) A telescope with a wide aperture reveals distinct images for Mizar A, Mizar B, and Alcor.

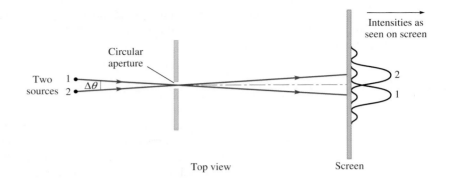

Figure 25.37 Two point sources with an angular separation $\Delta\theta$ form overlapping diffraction patterns when the light passes through a circular aperture. In this case, the images *can* be resolved according to Rayleigh's criterion.

from two sources travels through vacuum (or air) and enters a circular aperture of diameter a. If $\Delta\theta$ is the angular separation of the two sources as measured from the aperture and λ_0 is the wavelength of the light in vacuum (or air), then the sources can be resolved if

Rayleigh's criterion:

$$a \sin \Delta\theta \geq 1.22\lambda_0 \qquad (25\text{-}14)$$

Example 25.9

Resolution with a Laser Printer

A laser printer puts tiny dots of ink (toner) on the page. The dots should be sufficiently close together (and therefore small enough) that we don't see individual dots; rather, we see letters or graphics. Approximately how many dots per inch (dpi) ensure that you don't see individual dots when viewing a page 0.40 m from the eye in bright light? Use a pupil diameter of 2.5 mm.

Strategy If the angular separation of the dots exceeds Rayleigh's criterion, then you are able to resolve individual dots. Therefore, the angular separation of the dots must be *smaller* than that given by Rayleigh's criterion—we do *not* want to be able to resolve individual dots.

Solution Call the distance between the centers of two adjacent dots Δx, the diameter of the pupil a, and the angular separation of the dots $\Delta\theta$ (Fig. 25.38). The page is held a distance $D = 0.40$ m from the eye. Then, since $\Delta x \ll D$, the angular separation of the dots is

$$\Delta\theta \approx \frac{\Delta x}{D}$$

In order for the dots to merge, the angular separation $\Delta\theta$ must be *smaller* than the angle given by the Rayleigh criterion for resolution. The minimum $\Delta\theta$ for resolution is given by

$$a \sin \Delta\theta \approx a\,\Delta\theta = 1.22\lambda_0$$

Since we do *not* want the dots to be resolved, we want

$$a\,\Delta\theta < 1.22\lambda_0$$

Substituting for $\Delta\theta$,

$$a\frac{\Delta x}{D} < 1.22\lambda_0$$

To guarantee that Δx is small enough so that the dots blend together for *all* visible wavelengths, we take $\lambda_0 = 400.0$ nm, the smallest wavelength in the visible range. Now we solve for the distance between dots Δx:

$$\Delta x < \frac{1.22\lambda_0 D}{a} = \frac{1.22 \times 400.0 \text{ nm} \times 0.40 \text{ m}}{0.0025 \text{ m}}$$

$$= 7.81 \times 10^{-5} \text{ m} = 0.0781 \text{ mm}$$

To find the minimum number of dots per *inch*, first convert the dot separation Δx to inches.

$$\Delta x = 0.0781 \text{ mm} \div 25.4 \frac{\text{mm}}{\text{in}} = 0.00307 \text{ in}$$

$$\text{dots per inch} = \frac{1}{\text{inches per dot}}$$

$$\frac{1}{0.00307 \text{ inches/dot}} = 330 \text{ dpi}$$

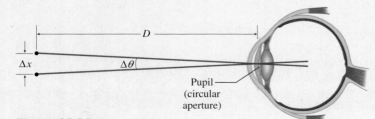

Figure 25.38
Angular separation $\Delta\theta$ of two adjacent dots.

Continued on next page

Example 25.9 Continued

Discussion Based on this estimate, we expect the printout from a 300-dpi printer to be slightly grainy, since we can just barely resolve individual dots. Output from a 600-dpi printer should look smooth.

You might wonder whether Eq. (25-14) applies to diffraction that occurs within the eye since it uses the wavelength in vacuum (λ_0). The wavelength in the vitreous fluid of the eye is $\lambda = \lambda_0/n$, where $n \approx 1.36$ is the index of refraction of the vitreous fluid. Equation (25-14) *does* apply in this situation because the factor of n in the wavelength is canceled by a factor of n due to refraction (see Problem 57).

Practice Problem 25.9   Pointillist Paintings

The Postimpressionist painter Georges Seurat perfected a technique known as *pointillism*, in which paintings are composed of closely spaced dots of different colors, each about 2 mm in diameter (Fig. 25.39). A close-up view reveals the individual dots; from farther away the dots blend together. Estimate the minimum distance away a viewer should be in order to see the dots blend into a smooth variation of colors. Assume a pupil diameter of 2.2 mm.

(a)

(b)

Figure 25.39   (a) *La grève du Bas Butin à Honfleur* by Georges Seurat (1859–1891). (b) A close-up view of the same painting.

Resolution of the Human Eye

In bright light, the pupil of the eye narrows to about 2 mm; diffraction caused by this small aperture limits the resolution of the human eye. In dim light, the pupil is much wider. Now the limit on the eye's resolution in dim light is not diffraction, but the spacing of the photoreceptor cells on the fovea (where they are most densely packed). For an *average* pupil diameter, the spacing of the cones is optimal (see Problem 54). If the cones were less densely packed, resolution would be lost; if they were more densely packed, there would be no gain in resolution due to diffraction.

Making the Connection:
resolution of the human eye

25.9   X-RAY DIFFRACTION

The interference and diffraction examples discussed so far have dealt mostly with visible light. However, the same effects occur for wavelengths longer and shorter than those visible to our eyes. Is it possible to do an experiment that shows interference or diffraction effects with x-rays? X-ray radiation has wavelengths much shorter than those of visible light, so to do such an experiment, the size and spacing of the slits in a grating (for example) would have to be much smaller than in a visible-light grating. Typical x-ray wavelengths range from about 10 nm to about 0.01 nm. There is no way to make a parallel-slit grating small enough to work for x-rays: the diameter of an atom is typically around 0.2 nm, so the slit spacing would be about the size of a single atom.

In 1912, Max von Laue (1879–1960) realized that the regular arrangement of atoms in a crystal makes a perfect grating for x-rays. The regular arrangement and spacing of the atoms is analogous to the regular spacing of the slits in a conventional grating, but a crystal is a *three-dimensional* grating (as opposed to the two-dimensional gratings we use for visible light).

Making the Connection:
x-ray diffraction

Figure 25.40 (a) Crystal structure of aluminum. The dots represent the positions of the aluminum atoms. (b) The x-ray diffraction pattern formed by polycrystalline aluminum (a large number of randomly-oriented aluminum crystals). The central spot, which is formed by x-rays that are not scattered by the sample, has been mostly blocked from reaching the film. Rings form at angles for which the scattered x-rays interfere constructively.

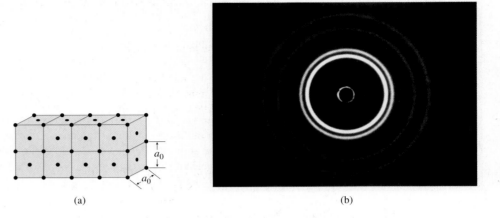

(a)   (b)

Figure 25.40a shows the atomic structure of aluminum. When a beam of x-rays passes through the crystal, the x-rays are scattered in all directions by the atoms. The x-rays scattered in a particular direction from different atoms interfere with each other. In certain directions they interfere constructively, giving maximum intensity in those directions. Photographic film records those directions as a collection of spots for a single crystal, or as a series of rings for a sample consisting of many randomly-oriented crystals (Fig. 25.40b).

Determining the directions for constructive interference is a difficult problem due to the three-dimensional structure of the grating. W. L. Bragg discovered a great simplification. He showed that we can think of the x-rays *as if they reflect from planes of atoms* (Fig. 25.41a). Constructive interference occurs if the path difference between x-rays reflecting from an adjacent pair of planes is an integral multiple of the wavelength. Figure 25.41b shows that the path difference is $2d \sin \theta$, where d is the distance between the planes and θ is the angle that the incident and reflected beams make with the plane (*not* with the normal). Then, constructive interference occurs at angles given by **Bragg's law**:

X-ray diffraction maxima:

$$2d \sin \theta = m\lambda \quad (m = 1, 2, 3, \ldots) \tag{25-15}$$

Although Bragg's law is a great simplification, x-ray diffraction is still complicated because there are many sets of parallel planes in a crystal, each with its own plane spacing. In practice, the largest plane spacings contain the largest number of scattering centers (atoms) per unit area, so they produce the strongest maxima.

X-ray diffraction has many uses:

- Just as a grating separates white light into the colors of the spectrum, a crystal is used to extract an x-ray beam with a narrow range of wavelengths from a beam with a continuous x-ray spectrum.
- If the structure of the crystal is known, then the angle of the emerging beam is used to determine the wavelength of the x-rays.

Figure 25.41 (a) Incident x-rays behave as if they reflect from parallel planes of atoms. (b) Geometry for finding the path difference for rays reflecting from two adjacent planes.

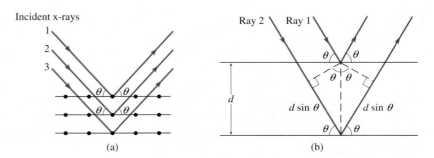

(a)   (b)

- The x-ray diffraction pattern can be used to determine the structure of a crystal. By measuring the angles θ at which strong beams emerge from the crystal, the plane spacings d are found and from them the crystal structure.
- X-ray diffraction patterns are used to determine the molecular structures of biological molecules such as proteins. X-ray diffraction studies by Rosalind Franklin were a key clue to James Watson and Francis Crick in their 1953 discovery of the double helix structure of DNA (Fig. 25.42). Intense beams of x-rays radiated by electrons in synchrotrons have even been used to study the structure of viruses.

25.10 HOLOGRAPHY

An ordinary photograph is a record of the intensity of light that falls on the film at each point. For incoherent light, the phases vary randomly, so it would not be useful to record phase information. A hologram is made by illuminating the subject with *coherent* light; the hologram is a record of the intensity *and the phase* of the light incident on the film. Holography was invented in 1948 by Dennis Gabor, but holograms were difficult to make until lasers became available in the 1960s.

Imagine using a laser, a beam splitter, and some mirrors to produce two coherent plane waves of light that overlap but travel in different directions (Fig. 25.43). Let the waves fall on a photographic plate. The exposure of the plate at any point depends on the intensity of the light falling on it. Since the two waves are coherent, a series of parallel fringes of constructive and destructive interference occur. The spacing between fringes depends on the angle θ_0 between the two waves; a smaller angle makes the spacing between fringes larger. In Problem 79, the spacing between fringes is found to be

$$d = \frac{\lambda}{\sin \theta_0}$$

When the plate is developed, the equally spaced fringes make a grating. If the plate is illuminated at normal incidence with coherent light at the same wavelength λ, the central ($m = 0$) maximum is straight ahead, while the $m = 1$ maximum is at an angle given by

$$\sin \theta = \frac{\lambda}{d} = \sin \theta_0$$

Thus, the $m = 0$ and $m = 1$ maxima re-create the original two waves.

Now imagine a plane wave with a point object (Fig. 25.44). The point object scatters light, producing spherical waves just as a point source does. The interference of the

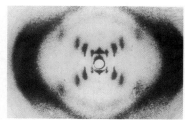

Figure 25.42 This x-ray diffraction pattern of DNA (deoxyribonucleic acid) was obtained by Rosalind Franklin in 1953. Some aspects of the structure of DNA can be deduced from the pattern of spots and bands. Franklin's data convinced James Watson and Francis Crick of DNA's helical structure, which is revealed by the cross of bands in the diffraction pattern.

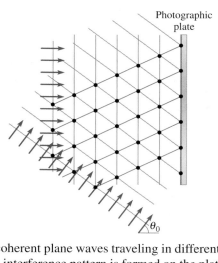

Figure 25.43 Two coherent plane waves traveling in different directions expose a photographic plate. An interference pattern is formed on the plate. The red lines indicate points of constructive interference between the two waves. Bright fringes occur where these lines intersect the photographic plate.

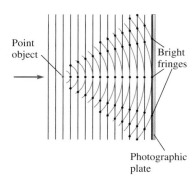

Figure 25.44 Coherent plane waves are scattered by a point object. The spherical waves scattered by the object interfere with the plane wave to form a set of circular interference fringes on a photographic plate.

 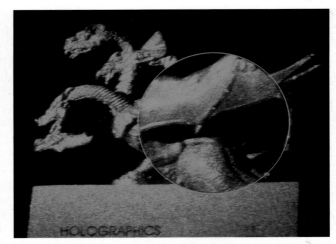

Figure 25.45 A holographic image of a dragon behind a lens. Notice that the part of the dragon that is magnified by the lens in the hologram depends on the viewing angle.

original plane wave with the scattered spherical wave gives a series of circular fringes. When this plate is developed and illuminated with laser light, both the plane and spherical waves are re-created. The spherical waves appear to come from a point behind the plate, which is a virtual image of the point object. The plate is a hologram of the point object.

With a more complicated object, each point on the surface of the object is a source of spherical waves. When the hologram is illuminated with coherent light, a virtual image of the object is created. This image can be seen from different perspectives (Fig. 25.45) since the hologram *re-creates wavefronts just as if they were coming from the object.*

MASTER THE CONCEPTS

- When two coherent waves are in phase, their superposition results in constructive interference:

  Phase difference $\Delta\phi = 2m\pi$ rad $(m = 0, \pm1, \pm2, \dots)$ (25-1)

  Amplitude $A = A_1 + A_2$ (25-2)

  Intensity $I = I_1 + I_2 + 2\sqrt{I_1 I_2}$ (25-3)

- When two coherent waves are 180° out of phase, their superposition results in destructive interference:

  Phase difference $\Delta\phi = (m + \frac{1}{2})\, 2\pi$ rad

  $(m = 0, \pm1, \pm2, \dots)$ (25-4)

  Amplitude $A = |A_1 - A_2|$ (25-5)

  Intensity $I = I_1 + I_2 - 2\sqrt{I_1 I_2}$ (25-6)

- A path length difference equal to λ causes a phase shift of 2π (360°). A path length difference of $\frac{1}{2}\lambda$ causes a phase shift of π (180°).

- When light reflects from a boundary with a slower medium (higher index of refraction), it is inverted (180° phase change); when light reflects from a faster medium (lower index of refraction), it is not inverted (no phase change).

- The angles at which the maxima and minima occur in a double-slit interference experiment are

  Maxima: $d \sin\theta = m\lambda$ $(m = 0, \pm1, \pm2, \dots)$ (25-10)
  Minima: $d \sin\theta = (m + \frac{1}{2})\lambda$ $(m = 0, \pm1, \pm2, \dots)$ (25-11)

  The distance between the slits is d. The absolute value of m is called the order.

- A grating with N slits produces maxima that are narrow (width $\propto 1/N$) and bright (intensity $\propto N^2$). The maxima occur at the same angles as for two slits.

- The minima in a single-slit diffraction pattern occur at angles given by

  $a \sin\theta = m\lambda$ $(m = \pm1, \pm2, \pm3, \dots)$ (25-12)

  A wide central maximum contains most of the light energy. The other maxima are approximately (not exactly) halfway between adjacent minima.

- The first minimum in the diffraction pattern due to a circular aperture is given by

  $a \sin\theta = 1.22\lambda$ (25-13)

MASTER THE CONCEPTS *continued*

- Rayleigh's criterion says that two sources can just barely be resolved if the center of one diffraction pattern falls at the first minimum of the other one. If $\Delta\theta$ is the angular separation of the two sources, then the sources can be resolved if

$$a \sin \Delta\theta \geq 1.22\lambda_0 \qquad (25\text{-}14)$$

- The regular arrangement of atoms in a crystal makes a grating for x-rays. We can think of the x-rays as if they reflect from planes of atoms. Constructive interference occurs if the path difference between x-rays reflecting from an adjacent pair of planes is an integral multiple of the wavelength.

- A hologram is made by illuminating the subject with coherent light; the hologram is a record of the intensity and the phase of the light incident on the film. The hologram re-creates wavefronts just as if they were coming from the object.

Conceptual Questions

1. Explain why two waves of significantly different frequencies cannot be coherent.

2. Why do eyeglasses, cameras lenses, and binoculars with antireflective coatings often look faintly purple?

3. Telescopes used in astronomy have large lenses (or mirrors). One reason is to let a lot of light in—important for seeing faint astronomical bodies. Can you think of another reason why it is an advantage to make these telescopes so large?

4. The Hubble telescope uses a mirror of radius 1.2 m. Is its resolution better when detecting visible light or UV? Explain.

5. Why can you easily hear sound around a corner due to diffraction, while you cannot see around the same corner?

6. Stereo speakers should be wired with the same polarity. If by mistake they are wired with opposite polarities, the bass (low frequencies) sound much weaker than if they are wired correctly. Why? Why is the bass (low frequencies) weakened more than the treble (high frequencies)?

7. Two antennas driven by the same electrical signal emit coherent radio waves. Is it possible for two antennas driven by *independent* signals to emit radio waves that are coherent with each other? If so, how? If not, why not?

8. A radio station wants to ensure good reception of its signal everywhere inside a city. Would it be a good idea to place several broadcasting antennas at roughly equal intervals around the perimeter of the city? Explain.

9. The size of an atom is about 0.1 nm. Can a light microscope make an image of an atom? Explain.

10. What are some of the advantages of a UV microscope over a visible light microscope? What are some of the disadvantages?

11. The *f-stop* of a camera lens is defined as the ratio of the focal length of lens to the diameter of the aperture. A large f-stop therefore means a small aperture. If diffraction is the only consideration, would you use the largest or the smallest f-stop to get the sharpest image?

12. In Section 25.3 we studied interference due to thin films. Why must the film be *thin*? Why don't we see interference effects when looking through a window or at a poster covered by a plate of glass—even if the glass is optically flat?

13. Describe what happens to a single-slit diffraction pattern as the width of the slit is slowly decreased.

14. Explain, using Huygens's principle, why the Poisson spot is expected.

15. What effect places a lower limit on the size of an object that can be clearly seen with the best optical microscope?

16. Make a sketch (similar to Fig. 25.16b) of the reflected rays from two adjacent steps of the *Morpho* butterfly wing for a large angle of incidence (around 45°). Refer to your sketch to explain why the wavelength at which constructive interference occurs depends on the viewing angle.

17. A lens ($n = 1.51$) has an antireflective coating of MgF_2 ($n = 1.38$). Which of the first two reflected rays has a phase shift of 180°? Suppose a different antireflective coating on a similar lens had $n = 1.62$. Now which of the first two reflected rays has a phase shift of 180°?

18. In the microwave experiment of Example 25.1 and in the Michelson interferometer, we ignored phase changes due to reflection from a metal surface. Microwaves and light *are* inverted when they reflect from metal. Why were we able to ignore the 180° phase shifts?

19. Why does a crystal act as a three-dimensional grating for x-rays but not for visible light?

Multiple-Choice Questions

1. If the figure shows the wavefronts for a double-slit interference experiment with light, at which of the labeled points is the intensity zero?

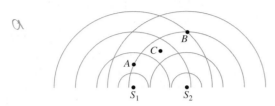

Multiple-Choice Questions 1 and 2. The wavefronts represent wave *crests* only (not crests and troughs).

(a) A only   (b) B only   (c) C only   (d) A and B
(e) B and C   (f) A and C   (g) A, B, and C

2. If the figure shows the surface water waves in a ripple tank with two coherent sources, at which of the labeled points would a bit of floating cork bob up and down with the greatest amplitude? (Same answer choices as Question 1.)

3. In a double-slit experiment, light rays from the two slits that reach the second maximum on one side of the central maximum travel distances that differ by
   (a) 2λ (b) λ (c) $\lambda/2$ (d) $\lambda/4$

4. A Michelson interferometer is set up for microwaves. Initially the reflectors are placed so that the detector reads a maximum. When one of the reflectors is moved 12 cm, the needle swings to minimum and back to maximum six times. What is the wavelength of the microwaves?
   (a) 0.5 cm   (b) 1 cm   (c) 2 cm   (d) 4 cm
   (e) Cannot be determined from the information given.

5. In a double-slit experiment with coherent light, the intensity of the light reaching the center of the screen from one slit alone is I_0 and the intensity of the light reaching the center from the other slit alone is $9I_0$. When both slits are open, what is the intensity of the light at the interference *minima* nearest the center? The slits are very narrow.
   (a) 0   (b) I_0 (c) $2I_0$
   (d) $3I_0$ (e) $4I_0$ (f) $8I_0$

6. Which of these actions will improve the resolution of a microscope?
   (a) increase the wavelength of the light
   (b) decrease the wavelength of the light
   (c) increase the diameter of the lenses
   (d) decrease the diameter of the lenses
   (e) both (b) and (c)   (f) both (b) and (d)
   (g) both (a) and (c)   (h) both (a) and (d)

7. Coherent light of a single frequency passes through a double slit, with slit separation d, to produce a pattern of maxima and minima on a screen a distance D from the slits. What would cause the separation between adjacent minima on the screen to decrease?
   (a) decrease the frequency of the incident light
   (b) increase of the screen distance D
   (c) decrease the separation d between the slits
   (d) increase the index of refraction of the medium in which the setup is immersed

8. Two narrow slits, of width a, separated by a distance, d, are illuminated by light with a wavelength of 660 nm. The resulting interference pattern is labeled (1) in the figure. The same light source is then used to illuminate another group of slits and produces pattern (2). The second slit arrangement is
   (a) many slits, spaced d apart.
   (b) many slits, spaced $2d$ apart.
   (c) two slits, each of width $2a$, spaced d apart.
   (d) two slits, each of width $a/2$, spaced d apart.

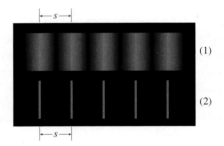

9. The figure shows the interference pattern obtained in a double-slit experiment. Which letter indicates a third-order maximum?

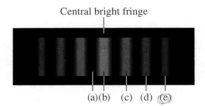

10. The intensity pattern in the diagram is due to
    (a) two slits.   (b) a single slit.
    (c) a grating.   (d) a circular aperture.

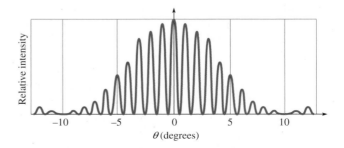

Problems

Ⓒ   Combination conceptual/quantitative problem

     Biological or medical application

No ✦   Easy to moderate difficulty level

✦   More challenging

✦✦   Most challenging

Blue #   Detailed solution in the Student Solutions Manual

| 1 | 2 | Problems paired by concept

25.1 Constructive and Destructive Interference

1. A 60-kHz radio transmitter sends an electromagnetic wave to a receiver 21 km away. The signal also travels to the receiver by another path where it reflects from a helicopter as shown. Assume that there is a 180° phase shift when the wave is reflected. (a) What is the wavelength of this EM wave? (b) Will this situation give constructive interference, destructive interference, or something in between?

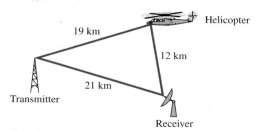

2. A steep cliff west of Lydia's home reflects a 1020-kHz radio signal from a station that is 74 km due east of her home. If there is destructive interference, what is the minimum distance of the cliff from her home? Assume there is a 180° phase shift when the wave reflects from the cliff.

3. Roger is in a ship offshore and listening to a baseball game on his radio. He notices that there is destructive interference when seaplanes from the nearby Coast Guard station are flying directly overhead at elevations of 780 m, 975 m, and 1170 m. The broadcast station is 102 km away. Assume there is a 180° phase shift when the EM waves reflect from the seaplanes. What is the frequency of the broadcast?

4. Sketch a sinusoidal wave with an amplitude of 2 cm and a wavelength of 6 cm. This wave represents the electric field portion of a visible EM wave traveling to the right with intensity I_0. (a) Sketch an identical wave beneath the first. What is the amplitude (in cm) of the sum of these waves? (b) What is the intensity of the new wave? (c) Sketch two more coherent waves beneath the others, one of amplitude 3 cm and one of amplitude 1 cm, so all four are in phase. What is the amplitude of the four waves added together? (d) What intensity results from adding the four waves?

5. Draw a sketch like that of Problem 4 but this time draw the third wave 180° out of phase with the others.

(a) What is the amplitude of the sum of these waves? (b) What is the intensity for the four waves together? (c) Consider the case for the first three waves in phase and the fourth wave 180° out of phase. What is the amplitude for the sum of these waves? (d) What is the intensity of the wave?

6. Two incoherent EM waves of intensities $9I_0$ and $16I_0$ travel in the same direction in the same region of space. What is the intensity of EM radiation in this region?

7. When Albert turns on his small desk lamp, the light falling on his book has intensity I_0. When this is not quite enough, he turns the small lamp off and turns on a high intensity lamp so that the light on his book has intensity $4I_0$. What is the intensity of light falling on the book when Albert turns both lamps on? If there is more than one possibility, give the range of intensity possibilities.

8. Coherent light from a laser is split into two beams with intensities I_0 and $4I_0$, respectively. What is the intensity of the light when the beams are recombined? If there is more than one possibility, give the range of possibilities.

9. A *simplified model* of the step structure of the wing of the *Morpho* butterfly is shown in the figure. Assume that the step height is $h = 223$ nm, which gives constructive interference for $\lambda = 446$ nm *at normal incidence*. Using this model, find the wavelength of reflected visible light that interferes constructively if the wing is viewed at an angle θ to the normal. Evaluate numerically for $\theta = 0$, 10.0°, and 20.0°. [*Hint:* The path length difference for reflection from each adjacent step is $2d - d'$.]

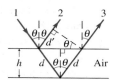

Problems 9 and 10

10. The feathers of the ruby-throated hummingbird have an iridescent green color due to interference. A simplified model of the step structure of the feather is shown in the figure with Problem 9. (a) If the strongest reflection for normal incidence is at $\lambda = 520$ nm, what is the step height h? Assume h has the smallest possible value. (b) At what wavelength is the strongest reflection for incidence at $\theta = 20.0°$?

11. An experiment similar to Example 25.1 is performed; the power at the receiver as a function of x is shown in the figure. (a) Approximately what is the wavelength of the microwaves? (b) What is the ratio of the *amplitudes* of the microwaves entering the detector for the two maxima shown?

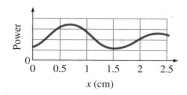

25.2 The Michelson Interferometer

12. A Michelson interferometer is adjusted so that a bright fringe appears on the screen. As one of the mirrors is moved 25.8 μm, 92 bright fringes are counted on the screen. What is the wavelength of the light used in the interferometer?

13. Suppose a transparent vessel 30.0 cm long is placed in one arm of a Michelson interferometer, as in Example 25.2. The vessel initially contains air at 0°C and 1.00 atm. With light of vacuum wavelength 633 nm, the mirrors are arranged so that a bright spot appears at the center of the screen. As air is slowly pumped out of the vessel, one of the mirrors is gradually moved to keep the center region of the screen bright. The distance the mirror moves is measured to determine the value of the index of refraction of air, n. Assume that, outside of the vessel, the light travels through vacuum. Calculate the distance that the mirror would be moved as the container is emptied of air.

14. A Michelson interferometer is set up using white light. The arms are adjusted so that a bright white spot appears on the screen (constructive interference for all wavelengths). A slab of glass ($n = 1.46$) is inserted into one of the arms. To return to the white spot, the mirror in the other arm is moved 6.73 cm. (a) Is the mirror moved in or out? Explain. (b) What is the thickness of the slab of glass?

25.3 Thin Films

15. At a science museum, Marlow looks down into a display case and sees two pieces of very flat glass lying on top of each other with light and dark regions on the glass. The exhibit states that monochromatic light with a wavelength of 550 nm is incident on the glass plates and that the plates are sitting in air. The glass has an index of refraction of 1.51. (a) What is the minimum distance between the two glass plates for one of the dark regions? (b) What is the minimum distance between the two glass plates for one of the light regions? (c) What is the next largest distance between the plates for a dark region? [*Hint:* Do not worry about the thickness of the glass plates; the *thin* film is the air between the plates.]

16. See Problem 15. This time the glass plates are immersed in clear oil with an index of refraction of 1.50. (a) What is the minimum distance between the two glass plates for one of the dark regions? (b) What is the minimum distance between the two glass plates for one of the light regions? (c) What is the next largest distance between the plates for a dark region?

17. A thin film of oil ($n = 1.50$) is spread over a puddle of water ($n = 1.33$). In a region where the film looks red from directly above ($\lambda = 630$ nm), what is the minimum possible thickness of the film?

18. A thin film of oil ($n = 1.50$) of thickness 0.40 μm is spread over a puddle of water ($n = 1.33$). For which

wavelength *in the visible spectrum* do you expect constructive interference for reflection at normal incidence?

19. A transparent film ($n = 1.3$) is deposited on a glass lens ($n = 1.5$) to form a nonreflective coating. What is the minimum thickness that would minimize reflection of light with wavelength 500.0 nm in air?

20. A camera lens ($n = 1.50$) is coated with a thin film of magnesium fluoride ($n = 1.38$) of thickness 90.0 nm. What wavelength in the visible spectrum is most strongly transmitted through the film?

21. A soap film has an index of refraction $n = 1.50$. The film is viewed in reflected light. (a) At a spot where the film thickness is 910.0 nm, which wavelengths are missing in the reflected light? (b) Which wavelengths are strongest in reflected light?

22. A soap film has an index of refraction $n = 1.50$. The film is viewed in *transmitted* light. (a) At a spot where the film thickness is 910.0 nm, which wavelengths are weakest in the transmitted light? (b) Which wavelengths are strongest in transmitted light?

23. Two optically flat plates of glass are separated at one end by a wire of diameter 0.200 mm; at the other end they touch. Thus, the air gap between the plates has a thickness ranging from 0 to 0.200 mm. The plates are 15.0 cm long and are illuminated from above with light of wavelength 600.0 nm. How many bright fringes are seen in the reflected light?

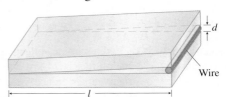

24. A lens is placed on a flat plate of glass to test whether its surface is spherical. (a) Show that the radius r_m of the mth dark ring should be

$$r_m = \sqrt{m\lambda R}$$

where R is the radius of curvature of the lens surface facing the plate and the wavelength of the light used is λ. Assume that $r_m \ll R$. [*Hint:* Start by finding the thickness t of the air gap at a radius $r = R \sin\theta \approx R\theta$. Use small angle approximations.] (b) Are the dark fringes equally spaced? If not, do they get closer together or farther apart as you move out from the center?

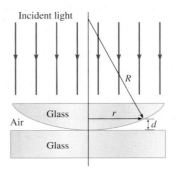

C 25. A thin film is viewed both in reflected and transmitted light at normal incidence. The figure shows the strongest two rays for each. Show that if rays 1 and 2 interfere constructively, then rays 3 and 4 must interfere destructively, and if rays 1 and 2 interfere destructively, then rays 3 and 4 interfere constructively. Consider all of the following possibilities: n is the largest of the three indices, n is the smallest of the three indices, or n is in between the other two indices.

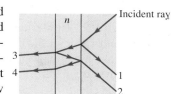

25.4 Young's Double-Slit Experiment

26. Light of 650 nm is incident on two slits. A maximum is seen at an angle of 4.10° and a minimum of 4.78°. What is the order m of the maximum and what is the distance d between the slits?

27. You are given a slide with two slits cut into it and asked how far apart the slits are. You shine white light on the slide and notice the first-order color spectrum that is created on a screen 3.40 m away. On the screen, the red light with a wavelength of 700 nm is separated from the violet light with a wavelength of 400 nm by 7.00 mm. What is the separation of the two slits?

28. Show that the interference fringes in a double-slit experiment are equally spaced on a distant screen near the center of the interference pattern. [*Hint:* Use the small angle approximation for θ.]

C 29. Use a compass to make an accurate drawing of the wavefronts in a double-slit interference experiment similar to Fig. 25.18c. Place the slits 2.0 cm apart and let the wavelength of the incident wave be 1.0 cm. Using a straightedge, draw lines of constructive interference (antinodes) and use them to find the locations of the $m = \pm 1$ maxima on a screen 12 cm from the slits. Measure the angles of the maxima with a protractor; do they agree with those given by Eq. (25-10)? Explain any discrepancy.

30. In a double-slit interference experiment, the wavelength is 475 nm, the slit separation is 0.120 mm, and the screen is 36.8 cm away from the slits. What is the linear distance between adjacent maxima on the screen? [*Hint:* Assume the small angle approximation is justified and then check the validity of your assumption once you know the value of the separation between adjacent maxima.]

31. Light incident on a pair of slits produces an interference pattern on a screen 2.50 m from the slits. If the slit separation is 0.0150 cm and the distance between adjacent bright fringes in the pattern is 0.760 cm, what is the wavelength of the light? [*Hint:* Is the small angle approximation justified?]

32. Ramon has a coherent light source with wavelength 547 nm. He wishes to send light through a double slit with slit separation of 1.50 mm to a screen 90.0 cm away. What is the minimum width of the screen if Ramon wants to display five interference maxima?

33. Light from a helium-neon laser (630 nm) is incident on a pair of slits. In the interference pattern on a screen 1.5 m from the slits, the bright fringes are separated by 1.35 cm. What is the slit separation? [*Hint:* Is the small angle approximation justified?]

34. Light of wavelength 589 nm incident on a pair of slits produces an interference pattern on a distant screen in which the separation between adjacent bright fringes at the center of the pattern is 0.530 cm. A second light source, when incident on the same pair of slits, produces an interference pattern on the same screen with a separation of 0.640 cm between adjacent bright fringes at the center of the pattern. What is the wavelength of the second source? [*Hint:* Is the small angle approximation justified?]

35. A double slit is illuminated with monochromatic light of wavelength 600.0 nm. The $m = 0$ and $m = 1$ bright fringes are separated by 3.0 mm on a screen 40.0 cm away from the slits. What is the separation between the slits? [*Hint:* Is the small angle approximation justified?]

25.5 Gratings

36. A grating has exactly 8000 slits uniformly spaced over 2.54 cm and is illuminated by light from a mercury vapor discharge lamp. What is the expected angle for the third-order maximum of the green line ($\lambda = 546$ nm)?

37. A red line (wavelength 630 nm) in the third order overlaps with a blue line in the fourth order for a particular grating. What is the wavelength of the blue line?

38. Red light of 650 nm can be seen in three orders in a particular grating. About how many slits per cm does this grating have?

39. A grating has 5000.0 slits per cm. How many orders of violet light of wavelength 412 nm can be observed with this grating?

40. A grating is made of exactly 8000 slits; the slit spacing is 1.50 μm. Light of wavelength 0.600 μm is incident normally on the grating. (a) How many maxima are seen in the pattern on the screen? (b) Sketch the pattern that would appear on a screen 3.0 m from the grating. Label distances from the central maximum to the other maxima.

C 41. A reflection grating spectrometer is used to view the spectrum of light from a helium discharge tube. The three brightest spectral lines seen are red, yellow, and blue in color. These lines appear at the positions labeled *A*, *B*, and *C* in the figure, though not necessarily in that order of color. In this spectrometer, the distance between the grating and slit is 30.0 cm and the slit spacing in the grating is 1870 nm. (a) Which is the red line? Which is the yellow line? Which is the blue line? (b) Calculate the wavelength (in nm) of spectral line *C*. (c) What is the highest order of spectral line *C* that it is possible to see using this grating?

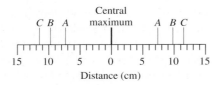

42. A spectrometer is used to analyze a light source. The screen-to-grating distance is 50.0 cm and the grating has 5000.0 slits/cm. Spectral lines are observed at the following angles: 12.98°, 19.0°, 26.7°, 40.6°, 42.4°, 63.9°, and 77.6°. (a) How many different wavelengths are present in the spectrum of this light source? Find each of the wavelengths. (b) If a different grating with 2000.0 slits/cm were used, how many spectral lines would be seen on the screen on one side of the central maximum? Explain.

43. White light containing wavelengths from 400 nm to 700 nm is shone through a grating. Assuming that at least part of the third-order spectrum is present, show that the second- and third-order spectra always overlap, regardless of the slit separation of the grating.

C 44. A grating 1.600 cm wide has exactly 12,000 slits. The grating is used to resolve two nearly equal wavelengths in a light source: $\lambda_a = 440.000$ nm and $\lambda_b = 440.936$ nm. (a) How many orders of the lines can be seen with the grating? (b) What is the angular separation $\theta_b - \theta_a$ between the lines in each order? (c) Which order best resolves the two lines? Explain.

45. A grating spectrometer is used to resolve wavelengths 660.0 nm and 661.4 nm in second order. (a) How many slits/cm must the grating have to produce both wavelengths in second order? (The answer is either a maximum or a minimum number of slits per cm.) (b) The minimum number of slits required to resolve two closely spaced lines is $N = \lambda/(m\Delta\lambda)$, where λ is the average of the two wavelengths, $\Delta\lambda$ is the difference between the two wavelengths, and m is the order. What minimum number of slits must this grating have to resolve the lines in second order?

25.7 Diffraction by a Single Slit

46. The central bright fringe in a single-slit diffraction pattern from light of wavelength 476 nm is 2.0 cm wide on a screen that is 1.05 m from the slit. (a) How wide is the slit? (b) How wide are the first two bright fringes on either side of the central bright fringe? (Define the width of a bright fringe as the linear distance from minimum to minimum.)

47. The first two dark fringes on one side of the central maximum in a single-slit diffraction pattern are 1.0 mm apart. The wavelength of the light is 610 nm and the screen is 1.0 m from the slit. What is the slit width?

48. Light of wavelength 630 nm is incident upon a single slit with width 0.40 mm. The figure shows the pattern observed on a screen positioned 2.0 m from the slit. Determine the distance from the center of the central bright fringe to the second minimum on one side.

49. Light from a red laser passes through a single slit to form a diffraction pattern on a distant screen. If the width of the slit is increased by a factor of two, what happens to the width of the central maximum on the screen?

C 50. The diffraction pattern from a single slit is viewed on a screen. Using blue light, the width of the central maximum is 2.0 cm. (a) Would the central maximum be narrower or wider if red light is used instead? (b) If the blue light has wavelength 0.43 μm and the red light has wavelength 0.70 μm, what is the width of the central maximum when red light is used?

51. Light of wavelength 490 nm is incident on a narrow slit. The diffraction pattern is viewed on a screen 3.20 m from the slit. The distance on the screen between the central maximum and the third minimum is 2.5 cm. What is the width of the slit?

25.8 Diffraction and the Resolution of Optical Instruments

52. The Hubble Space Telescope has excellent resolving power because there is no atmospheric distortion of the light. The Hubble deep field camera uses the 2.4-m-diameter mirror to collect light from distant galaxies that formed very early in the history of the universe. How far apart can two galaxies be from each other if they are 10 billion light-years away from Earth and are barely resolved by the Hubble Telescope using visible light with a wavelength of 400 nm?

53. A beam of yellow laser light (590 nm) passes through a circular aperture of diameter 7.0 mm. What is the angular width of the central diffraction maximum formed on a screen?

54. The photosensitive cells (rods and cones) in the retina are most densely packed in the fovea—the part of the retina used to see straight ahead. In the fovea, the cells are all cones spaced about 1 μm apart. Would our vision have much better resolution if they were closer together? To answer this question, assume two light sources are just far enough apart to be resolvable according to Rayleigh's criterion. Assume an average pupil diameter of 5 mm and an eye diameter of 25 mm. Also assume that the index of refraction of the vitreous fluid in the eye is 1; in other words, treat the pupil as a circular aperture with air on both sides. What is the spacing of the cones if the centers of the diffraction maxima fall on two nonadjacent cones with a single intervening cone? (There must be an intervening dark cone in order to resolve the two sources; if two *adjacent* cones are stimulated, the brain assumes a single source.)

Ⓒ 55. A pinhole camera doesn't have a lens; a small circular hole lets light into the camera, which then exposes the film. For the sharpest image, light from a distant point source makes as small a spot on the film as possible. What is the optimum size of the hole for a camera in which the film is 16.0 cm from the pinhole? A hole smaller than the optimum makes a larger spot since it diffracts the light more. A larger hole also makes a larger spot because the spot cannot be smaller than the hole itself (think in terms of geometrical optics). Let the wavelength be 560 nm.

56. The radio telescope at Arecibo, Puerto Rico, has a reflecting spherical bowl of 305 m (1000 ft) diameter. Radio signals can be received and emitted at various frequencies with appropriate antennae at the focal point of the reflecting bowl. At a frequency of 300 MHz, what is the angle between two stars that can barely be resolved?

57. To understand Rayleigh's criterion as applied to the pupil of the eye, notice that rays do *not* pass straight through the center of the lens system (cornea + lens) of the eye except at normal incidence because the indices of refraction on the two sides of the lens system are different. In a simplified model, suppose light from two point sources travels through air and passes through the pupil (diameter a). On the other side of the pupil, light travels through the vitreous fluid (index of refraction n). The figure shows two rays, one from each source, that pass through the center of the pupil. (a) What is the relationship between $\Delta\theta$, the angular separation of the two *sources*, and β, the angular separation of the two *images*? [*Hint:* Use Snell's law.] (b) The first diffraction minimum for light from

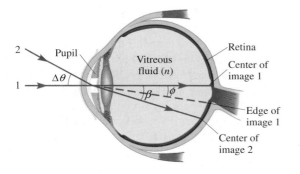

source 1 occurs at angle ϕ, where $a \sin \phi = 1.22\lambda$ [Eq. (25-13)]. Here, λ is the wavelength *in the vitreous fluid*. According to Rayleigh's criterion, the sources can be resolved if the center of image 2 occurs no closer than the first diffraction minimum for image 1; that is, if $\beta \geq \phi$ or, equivalently, $\sin \beta \geq \sin \phi$. Show that this is equivalent to Eq. (25-14), where λ_0 is the wavelength *in air*.

Comprehensive Problems

58. A beam of coherent light of wavelength 623 nm in air is incident on a rectangular block of glass with index of refraction 1.40. If, after emerging from the block, the wave that travels through the glass is 180° out of phase with the wave that travels through air, what are the possible lengths d of the glass in terms of a positive integer m?

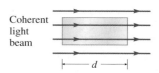

59. Light with a wavelength of 660 nm is incident on two slits and the pattern shown in the figure is viewed on a screen. Point A is directly opposite a point midway between the two slits. What is the path length difference of the light that passes through the two different slits for light that reaches the screen at points A, B, C, D, and E?

60. A thin layer of an oil ($n = 1.60$) floats on top of water ($n = 1.33$). One portion of this film appears green ($\lambda = 510$ nm) in reflected light. How thick is this portion of the film? Give the three smallest possibilities.

61. If diffraction were the only limitation, what would be the maximum distance at which the headlights of a car could be resolved (seen as two separate sources) by the naked human eye? The diameter of the pupil of the eye is about 7 mm when dark-adapted. Make reasonable estimates for the distance between the headlights and for the wavelength.

62. Find the height h of the pits on a CD (Fig. 25.6a). When the laser beam reflects partly from a pit and partly from land (the flat aluminum surface) on either side of the "pit", the two reflected beams interfere destructively; h is chosen to be the smallest possible height that causes destructive interference. The wavelength of the laser is 780 nm and the index of refraction of the polycarbonate plastic is $n = 1.55$.

63. The Very Large Array (VLA) is a set of 30 dish radio antennas located near Socorro, New Mexico. The dishes are spaced 1.0 km apart and form a Y-shaped pattern, as in the diagram. Radio pulses from a distant pulsar (a rapidly rotating neutron star) are detected by the dishes; the arrival time of each pulse is recorded using atomic clocks. If the pulsar is located 60.0° above the horizontal direction parallel to the right branch of the Y, how much time elapses between the arrival of the pulses at adjacent dishes in that branch of the VLA?

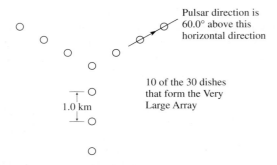

Pulsar direction is 60.0° above this horizontal direction

10 of the 30 dishes that form the Very Large Array

1.0 km

Problems 64 and 65: Two radio towers are a distance d apart as shown in the overhead view. Each antenna *by itself* would radiate equally in all directions in a horizontal plane. The radio waves have the same frequency and start out in phase. A detector is moved in a circle around the towers at a distance of 100 km.

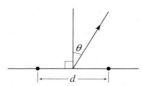

Problems 64 and 65

64. The power radiated in a horizontal plane by both antennas together is measured by the detector and is found to vary with angle. (a) Is the power detected at $\theta = 0$ a maximum or a minimum? Explain. (b) Sketch a graph of P versus θ to show qualitatively how the power varies with angle θ (from $-180°$ to $+180°$) if $d = \lambda$. Label your graph with values of θ at which the power is maximum or minimum. (c) Make a qualitative graph of how the power varies with angle for the case $d = \lambda/2$. Label your graph with values of θ at which the power is maximum or minimum.

65. The waves have frequency 3.0 MHz and the distance between antennas is $d = 0.30$ km. (a) What is the difference in the path lengths traveled by the waves that arrive at the detector at $\theta = 0°$? (b) What is the difference in the path lengths traveled by the waves that arrive at the detector at $\theta = 90°$? (c) At how many angles ($0 \leq \theta <$

360°) would you expect to detect a maximum intensity? Explain. (d) Find the angles (θ) of the maxima in the first quadrant ($0 \leq \theta \leq 90°$). (e) Which (if any) of your answers to parts (a) to (d) would change if the detector were instead only 1 km from the towers? Explain. (Don't calculate new values for the answers.)

66. Two narrow slits with a center-to-center distance of 0.48 mm are illuminated with coherent light at normal incidence. The intensity of the light falling on a screen 5.0 m away is shown in the figure, where x is the distance from the central maximum on the screen. (a) What would be the intensity of the light falling on the screen if only one slit were open? (b) Find the wavelength of the light.

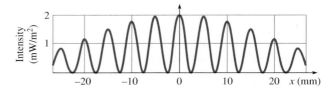

67. When a double slit is illuminated with light of wavelength 510 nm, the interference maxima on a screen 2.4 m away gradually decrease in intensity on either side of the 2.40-cm-wide central maximum and reach a minimum in a spot where the fifth-order maximum is expected. (a) What is the width of the slits? (b) How far apart are the slits?

68. Sonya is designing a diffraction experiment for her students. She has a laser that emits light of wavelength 627 nm and a grating with a distance of 2.40×10^{-3} mm between slits. She hopes to shine the light through the grating and display a total of nine interference maxima on a screen. She finds that no matter how she arranges her setup, she can see only seven maxima. Assuming that the intensity of the light is not the problem, why can Sonya not display the $m = 4$ interference maxima on either side?

69. A lens ($n = 1.52$) is coated with a magnesium fluoride film ($n = 1.38$). (a) If the coating is to cause destructive interference in reflected light for $\lambda = 560$ nm (the peak of the solar spectrum), what should its minimum thickness be? (b) At what two wavelengths closest to 560 nm does the coating cause *constructive* interference in reflected light? (c) Is any visible light reflected? Explain.

70. A thin soap film ($n = 1.35$) is suspended in air. The spectrum of light reflected from the film is missing two visible wavelengths of 500.0 nm and 600.0 nm, with no missing wavelengths between the two. (a) What is the thickness of the soap film? (b) Are there any other visible wavelengths missing from the reflected light? If so, what are they? (c) What wavelengths of light are strongest in the *transmitted* light?

71. Instead of an antireflective coating, suppose you wanted to coat a glass surface to *enhance* the reflection of visible light. Assuming that $1 < n_{coating} < n_{glass}$, what should the minimum thickness of the coating be to maximize the reflected intensity for wavelength λ?

72. If you shine a laser (wavelength 0.60 μm) with a small aperture at the Moon, diffraction makes the beam spread out and the spot on the Moon is large. Making the aperture smaller only makes the spot on the Moon *larger*. On the other hand, shining a wide searchlight at the Moon can't make a tiny spot—the spot on the Moon is at least as wide as the searchlight. What is the radius of the *smallest* possible spot you can make on the Moon by shining a light from Earth? Assume the light is perfectly parallel before passing through a circular aperture.

73. A mica sheet 1.00 μm thick is suspended in air. In reflected light, there are gaps in the visible spectrum at 450, 525, and 630 nm. Calculate the index of refraction of the mica sheet.

74. In bright light, the pupils of the eyes of a cat narrow to a vertical *slit* 0.30 mm across. Suppose that a cat is looking at two mice 18 m away. What is the smallest distance between the mice for which the cat can tell that there are two mice rather than one using light of 560 nm? Assume the resolution is limited by diffraction only.

75. Parallel light of wavelength λ strikes a slit of width a at normal incidence. The light is viewed on a screen that is 1.0 m past the slits. In each case that follows, sketch the intensity on the screen as a function of x, the distance from the center of the screen, for $0 \le x \le 10$ cm. (a) $\lambda = 10a$. (b) $10\lambda = a$. (c) $30\lambda = a$.

76. About how close to each other are two objects on the Moon that can just barely be resolved by the 5.08-m-(200-in.)-diameter Mount Palomar reflecting telescope? (Use a wavelength of 520 nm.)

77. A grating in a spectrometer is illuminated with red light ($\lambda = 690$ nm) and blue light ($\lambda = 460$ nm) simultaneously. The grating has 10,000.0 slits per cm. Sketch the pattern that would be seen on a screen 2.0 m from the grating. Label distances from the central maximum. Label which lines are red and which are blue.

78. Two slits separated by 20.0 μm are illuminated by light of wavelength 0.50 μm. If the screen is 8.0 m from the slits, what is the distance between the $m = 0$ and $m = 1$ bright fringes?

79. Two coherent plane waves travel at angle θ_0 toward a photographic plate. Show that the distance between fringes of constructive interference on the plate is given by $d = \lambda/\sin\theta_0$. See Fig. 25.43.

80. In a double-slit experiment, what is the linear distance on the screen between adjacent maxima if the wavelength is 546 nm, the slit separation is 0.100 mm, and the slit-screen separation is 20.0 cm?

Answers to Practice Problems

25.2 The mirror should be moved in (shorter path length). Since the number of wavelengths traveled in the arm with the vessel decreases, we must decrease the number of wavelengths traveled in the other arm.

25.3 560 nm and 458 nm

25.4 (a) 0, 0.020 rad, 0.040 rad; (b) 0.010 rad, 0.030 rad; (c) 4.0 cm

25.5 The intensity is maximum at the center ($\theta = 0$) and gradually decreases to either side but never reaches zero.

25.6 4760 slits/cm; fourth-order maxima are present for wavelengths up to 525 nm.

25.7 No; the window is large compared to the wavelength of light, so we expect diffraction to be negligible. The Sun is not distant enough to treat it as a point source; rays from different points on the Sun's surface travel in slightly different directions as they pass through the window.

25.8 3.9 cm

25.9 9 m

REVIEW AND SYNTHESIS: CHAPTERS 22–25

Review Exercises

1. You are watching a baseball game on television that is being broadcast from 4500 km away. The batter hits the ball with a loud "crack" of the bat. A microphone is located 22 m from the batter, and you are 2.0 m from the television set. On a day when sound travels 343 m/s in air, what is the minimum time it takes for you to hear the crack of the bat after the batter hit the ball?

2. Sketch a sinusoidal wave with an amplitude of 3 V/m and a wavelength of 600 nm. This represents the electric field portion of a visible EM wave traveling to the right with intensity I_0. Beneath the first wave, sketch another that is identical to the first in wavelength, but with an amplitude of 2 V/m and 180° out of phase. Beneath the second wave, sketch a third wave of the same wavelength with an amplitude of 0.5 V/m and in phase with the first wave. The three waves are coherent. What is the intensity of light when the three waves are added?

3. On a cold, autumn day, Tuan is staring out of the window watching the leaves blow in the wind. One bright yellow leaf is reflecting light that has a predominant wavelength of 580 nm. (a) What is the frequency of this light? (b) If the window glass has an index of refraction of 1.50, what are the speed, wavelength, and frequency of this light as it passes through the window?

4. You are standing 1.2 m from a 1500-W heat lamp. (a) Assuming that the energy of the heat lamp is radiated uniformly in a hemispherical pattern, what is the intensity of the light on your face? (b) If you stand in front of the heat lamp for 2.0 min, how much energy is incident on your face? Assume your face has a total area of 2.8×10^{-2} m². (c) What are the rms electric and magnetic fields?

5. Juanita is lying in a hammock in her garden and listening to music on her portable radio tuned to WMCB (1408 kHz), a station located 98 km from her home. A plane, about to land at the airport, flies directly overhead and causes destructive interference. Juanita estimates the plane to be at least 500 m over her head. Assume there is a 180° phase shift when the radio wave reflects from the airplane. (a) What is the closest possible distance between Juanita and the plane if her estimation is correct? (b) Find two other possible elevations, the next one lower and the next one higher, for the plane in case her estimation is off.

6. Consider the three polarizing filters shown in the figure. The angles listed indicate the direction of the transmission axis of each polarizer with respect to the vertical. (a) If unpolarized light of intensity I_0 is incident from the left, what is the intensity of the light that exits the last polarizer? (b) If vertically polarized light of intensity I_0 is incident from the left, what is the intensity of the light that exits the last polarizer? (c) Can you remove one polarizer from this series of filters so that light incident from the left is not transmitted at all if unpolarized light is incident as in part (a)? If so, which polarizer should you remove? Answer the same questions for vertically polarized incident light as in part (b). (d) If you can remove one polarizer to maximize the amount of light transmitted in part (a), which one should you remove? Answer the same question for part (b).

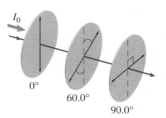

7. The projector in a movie theater has a lens with a focal length of 29.5 cm. It projects an image of the 70.0-mm-wide film onto a screen that is 38.0 m from the projector. (a) How wide is the image on the screen? (b) What kind of lens is used in the projector? (c) Is the image on the screen upright or inverted compared with the film?

8. A converging lens with a focal length of 5.500 cm is placed 8.00 cm to the left of a diverging lens with a radius of curvature of 8.40 cm. An object that is 1.0 cm tall is placed 9.000 cm to the left of the converging lens. (a) Where is the final image formed? (b) How tall is the final image? (c) Is the final image upright or inverted?

9. Why don't you see an interference pattern on your desk when you have light from two different lamps illuminating the surface?

10. A radio wave with a wavelength of 1200 m follows two paths to a receiver that is 25.0 km away. One path goes directly to the receiver and the other reflects from an airplane that is flying above the point that is exactly halfway between the transmitter and the receiver. Assume there is no phase change when the wave reflects off the airplane. If the receiver experiences destructive interference, what is the minimum possible distance that the reflected wave has traveled? For this distance, how high is the airplane?

11. A thin film of oil with index of refraction of 1.50 sits on top of a pool of water with index of refraction of 1.33. When light is incident on this film, a maximum is observed in reflected light at 480 nm and a minimum is observed in reflected light at 600 nm, with no maxima or minima for any wavelengths between these two. What is the thickness of the film?

12. A camera lens ($n = 1.50$) is coated with a thin layer of magnesium fluoride ($n = 1.38$). The purpose of the coating is to allow all the light to be transmitted by canceling out reflected light. What is the minimum thickness of the coating necessary to cancel out reflected visible light of wavelength 550 nm?

13. A grating made of 5550 slits/cm has red light of 0.680 μm incident on it. The light shines through the grating onto a screen that is 5.50 m away. (a) What is the distance between adjacent slits on the grating? (b) How far from the central bright spot is the first-order maximum on the screen? (c) How far from the central bright spot is the second-order maximum on the screen? (d) Can you assume in this problem that $\sin \theta = \tan \theta$? Why or why not?

14. When using a certain grating, third-order violet light of wavelength 420 nm falls at the same angle as second-order light of a different wavelength. What is that wavelength?

15. (a) In double-slit interference, how does the slit separation affect the distance between adjacent interference maxima? (b) How does the distance between the slits and screen affect that separation? (c) If you are trying to resolve two closely spaced maxima, how might you design your double-slit spectrometer?

16. The radio telescope at Arecibo, Puerto Rico, has a reflecting spherical bowl of 305 m (1000 ft) diameter. Radio signals can be received and emitted at various frequencies with the appropriate antennae at the focal point. If two Moon craters 499 km apart are to be resolved, what wavelength radio waves must be used?

17. Geraldine uses a 423-nm coherent light source and a double slit with a slit separation of 20.0 μm to display three interference maxima on a screen that is 20.0 cm wide. If she wants to spread the three maxima across the full width of the screen, from a minimum on one side to a minimum on the other side, how far from the screen should she place the double slit?

18. A convex mirror produces an image located 18.4 cm behind the mirror when an object is placed 32.0 cm in front of the mirror. What is the focal length of this mirror?

19. Simon wishes to display a double-slit experiment for his class. His coherent light source has a wavelength of 510 nm and the slit separation is $d = 0.032$ mm. He must set up the light on a desk 1.5 m away from the screen that is only 10 cm wide. How many interference maxima will Simon be able to display for his students?

20. Bruce is trying to remove an eyelash from the surface of his eye. He looks in a shaving mirror to locate the eyelash, which is 0.40 cm long. If the focal length of the mirror is 18 cm and he puts his eye at a distance of 11 cm from the mirror, how long is the image of his eyelash?

21. Coherent green light with a wavelength of 520 nm and coherent violet light with a wavelength of 412 nm are incident on a double slit with slit separation of 0.020 mm. The interference pattern is displayed on a screen 72.0 cm away. (a) Find the separation between the $m = 1$ interference maxima of the two colors. (b) What is the separation between the $m = 2$ maxima for the two beams?

22. When the NASA Rover *Spirit* successfully landed on Mars in January of 2004, Mars was 170.2×10^6 km from Earth. Twenty-one days later, when the Rover *Opportunity* landed on Mars, Mars was 198.7×10^6 km from Earth. (a) Once the Rover *Spirit* was operational, how long did it take for a one-way transmission to the scientists on Earth from the Rover on its landing day? (b) How long did it take for scientists to communicate with the Rover *Opportunity* on its first day? (c) What was the magnitude of the average velocity of Mars with respect to Earth during those 21 days?

MCAT Review

The section that follows includes MCAT exam material and is reprinted with permission of the Association of American Medical Colleges (AAMC).

1. An object is placed upright on the axis of a thin convex lens at a distance of three focal lengths ($3f$) from the center of the lens. An inverted image appears at a distance of $\frac{3}{2}f$ on the other side of the lens. What is the ratio of the height of the image to the height of the object?

   A. $\frac{1}{2}$

   B. $\frac{2}{3}$

   C. $\frac{3}{2}$

   D. $\frac{2}{1}$

2. A concave spherical mirror has a radius of curvature of 50 cm. At what distance from the surface of this mirror should an object be placed to form a real, inverted image the same size as the object?

   A. 25 cm

   B. 37.5 cm

   C. 50 cm

   D. 100 cm

Read the paragraph and then answer the following questions:

The Hubble telescope is the largest telescope ever placed into orbit. Its primary concave mirror has a diameter of 2.4 m and a focal length of approximately 13 m. In addition to having optical detectors, the telescope is equipped to detect ultraviolet light, which does not easily penetrate Earth's atmosphere.

3. When the Hubble telescope is focused on a very distant object, the image from its primary mirror is

A. real and upright.

B. real and inverted.

C. virtual and upright.

D. virtual and inverted.

4. The magnification of a telescope is determined by dividing the focal length of the primary mirror by the focal length of the eyepiece. If an eyepiece with a focal length of 2.5×10^{-2} m could be used with the primary mirror of the Hubble telescope, it would produce an image magnified by a factor of approximately

A. 10.

B. 96.

C. 520.

D. 960.

5. The image of a very distant object on the axis of a mirror such as that used in the Hubble telescope will be at what location in relationship to the mirror and focal point?

A. behind the mirror

B. between the mirror and the focal point

C. very close to the focal point

D. very close to twice the distance from the mirror to the focal point

6. Which of the following is the best explanation of why ultraviolet light does not penetrate Earth's atmosphere as easily as visible light does?

A. Ultraviolet light has a shorter wavelength and is more readily absorbed by the atmosphere.

B. Ultraviolet light has a lower frequency and is more readily absorbed by the atmosphere.

C. Ultraviolet light contains less energy and cannot travel as far through the atmosphere.

D. Ultraviolet light undergoes destructive interference as it travels through the atmosphere.

Appendix A

Mathematics Review

A.1 ALGEBRA

There are two basic kinds of algebraic manipulations.

- The same operation can always be performed on both sides of an equation.
- Substitution is always permissible (if $a = b$, then any occurrence of a in any equation can be replaced with b).

Products distribute over sums

$$a(b + c) = ab + ac \qquad \text{(A-1)}$$

The reverse—replacing $ab + ac$ with $a(b + c)$—is called *factoring*. Since dividing by c is the same as multiplying by $1/c$,

$$\frac{a + b}{c} = \frac{a}{c} + \frac{b}{c} \qquad \text{(A-2)}$$

Equation (A-2) is the basis of the procedure for adding fractions. To add fractions, they must be expressed with a *common denominator*.

$$\frac{a}{b} + \frac{c}{d} = \frac{a}{b} \times \frac{d}{d} + \frac{c}{d} \times \frac{b}{b} = \frac{ad}{bd} + \frac{bc}{bd}$$

Now applying Eq. (A-2), we end up with

$$\frac{a}{b} + \frac{c}{d} = \frac{ad + bc}{bd} \qquad \text{(A-3)}$$

To divide fractions, remember that dividing by c/d is the same as multiplying by d/c:

$$\frac{a}{b} \div \frac{c}{d} = \frac{\dfrac{a}{b}}{\dfrac{c}{d}} = \frac{a}{b} \times \frac{d}{c} = \frac{ad}{bc}$$

A product in a square root can be separated:

$$\sqrt{ab} = \sqrt{a} \times \sqrt{b} \qquad \text{(A-4)}$$

Pitfalls to Avoid

These are some of the most common *incorrect* algebraic substitutions. Don't fall into any of these traps!

$$\sqrt{a + b} \neq \sqrt{a} + \sqrt{b}$$
$$\frac{a}{b + c} \neq \frac{a}{b} + \frac{a}{c}$$
$$\frac{a}{b} + \frac{c}{d} \neq \frac{a + c}{b + d}$$
$$(a + b)^2 \neq a^2 + b^2$$

In the last one, the cross term is missing: $(a + b)^2 = a^2 + 2ab + b^2$.

Graphs of Linear Functions

If the graph of y as a function of x is a straight line, then y is a *linear function* of x. The relationship can be written in the standard form

$$y = mx + b \qquad \text{(A-5)}$$

where m is the *slope* and b is the *y-intercept*. The slope measures how steep the line is. It tells how much y changes for a given change in x:

$$m = \frac{\Delta y}{\Delta x} = \frac{y_2 - y_1}{x_2 - x_1} \tag{A-6}$$

The *y-intercept* is the value of y when $x = 0$. On the graph, the line crosses the *y*-axis at $y = b$.

Example A.1

What is the equation of the line graphed in Fig. A.1?

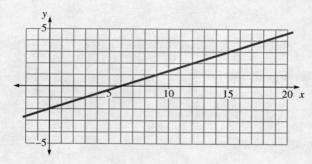

Figure A.1

Solution   The *y-intercept* is –2. To find the slope, we choose two points on the line and then divide the "rise" (Δy) by the "run" (Δx). Using the points $(0, -2)$ and $(18, 4)$,

$$m = \frac{\text{rise}}{\text{run}} = \frac{y_2 - y_1}{x_2 - x_1} = \frac{4 - (-2)}{18 - 0} = \frac{1}{3}$$

Then $y = mx + b = \frac{1}{3}x - 2$.

A.2   SOLVING EQUATIONS

Solving an equation means using algebraic operations to isolate one variable. Many students tend to substitute numerical values into an equation as soon as possible. In many cases, that's a mistake. Although at first it may seem easier to manipulate numerical quantities than to manipulate algebraic symbols, there are several advantages to working with symbols:

- Symbolic algebra is much easier to follow than a series of numerical calculations. Plugging in numbers tends to obscure the logic behind your solution. If you need to trace back through your work (to find an error or review for an exam), it'll be much clearer if you have worked through the problem symbolically. It will also help your instructor when grading your homework papers or exams. When your work is clear, your instructor is better able to help you understand your mistakes. You may also get more partial credit on exams!

- Symbolic algebra lets you draw conclusions about how one quantity depends on another. For instance, working symbolically you might see that the horizontal range of a projectile is proportional to the *square* of the initial speed. If you had substituted the numerical value of the initial speed, you wouldn't notice that. In particular, when an algebraic symbol cancels out of the equation, you know that the answer doesn't depend on that quantity.

- On the most practical level, it's easy to make arithmetic or calculation errors. The later on in your solution that numbers are substituted, the fewer number of steps you have to check for such errors.

When solving equations that contain square roots, be careful not to assume that a square root is positive. The equation $x^2 = a$ has *two* solutions for x, $x = \pm\sqrt{a}$. (The symbol $\pm$ means *either + or –*.)

Solving Quadratic Equations

An equation is quadratic in x if it contains terms with no powers of x other than a squared term (x^2), a linear term (x^1), and a constant (x^0). Any quadratic equation can be put into the standard form:

$$ax^2 + bx + c = 0 \qquad (\text{A-7})$$

The quadratic formula gives the solutions to any quadratic equation written in standard form:

$$x = \frac{-b \pm \sqrt{b^2 - 4ac}}{2a} \qquad (\text{A-8})$$

The symbol "$\pm$" (read "plus or minus") indicates that in general there are two solutions to a quadratic equation; that is, two values of x will satisfy the equation. One solution is found by taking the + sign and the other by taking the – sign in the quadratic formula. If $b^2 - 4ac = 0$, then there is only one solution (or, technically, the two solutions happen to be the same). If $b^2 - 4ac < 0$, then there is no solution to the equation (for x among the real numbers).

The quadratic formula still works if $b = 0$ and/or $c = 0$, although in such cases the equation can easily be solved without recourse to the quadratic formula.

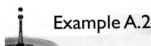

Example A.2

Solve the equation $5x(3 - x) = 6$.

Solution First put the equation in standard quadratic form:

$$15x - 5x^2 = 6$$
$$-5x^2 + 15x - 6 = 0$$

We identify $a = -5$, $b = 15$, $c = -6$. Then

$$x = \frac{-b \pm \sqrt{b^2 - 4ac}}{2a}$$

$$= \frac{-15 \pm \sqrt{15^2 - 4 \times (-5) \times (-6)}}{-10}$$

$$\approx \frac{-15 \pm 10.25}{-10} = 0.475 \text{ or } 2.525$$

Solving Simultaneous Equations

Simultaneous equations are a set of N equations with N unknown quantities. We wish to solve these equations *simultaneously* to find the values of all of the unknowns. We *must* have at least as many equations as unknowns. It pays to keep track of the number of unknown quantities and the number of equations in solving more challenging problems. If there are more unknowns than equations, then look for some other relationship between the quantities—perhaps some information given in the problem that has not been used.

One way to solve simultaneous equations is by *successive substitution*. Solve one of the equations for one unknown (in terms of the other unknowns). Substitute this expression into each of the other equations. That leaves $N - 1$ equations and $N - 1$ unknowns. Repeat until there is only one equation left with one unknown. Find the value of that unknown quantity, and then work backward to find all the others.

Example A.3

Solve the equations $2x - 4y = 3$ and $x + 3y = -5$ for x and y.

Solution   First solve the second equation for x in terms of y:

$$x = -5 - 3y$$

Substitute $-5 - 3y$ for x in the first equation:

$$2 \times (-5 - 3y) - 4y = 3$$

This can be solved for y:

$$-10 - 10y = 3$$
$$-10y = 13$$
$$y = \frac{13}{-10} = -1.3$$

Now that y is known, use it to find x:

$$x = -5 - 3y = -5 - 3 \times (-1.3) = -1.1$$

It's a good idea to check the results by substituting into the original equations.

A.3   EXPONENTS AND LOGARITHMS

These identities show how to manipulate exponents.

$$a^{-x} = \frac{1}{a^x} \tag{A-9}$$

$$(a^x) \times (a^y) = a^{x+y} \tag{A-10}$$

$$\frac{a^x}{a^y} = (a^x) \times (a^{-y}) = a^{x-y} \tag{A-11}$$

$$(a^x) \times (b^x) = (ab)^x \tag{A-12}$$

$$(a^x)^y = a^{xy} \tag{A-13}$$

$$a^{1/n} = \sqrt[n]{a} \tag{A-14}$$

$$a^0 = 1 \quad \text{(for any } a \neq 0) \tag{A-15}$$

$$0^a = 0 \quad \text{(for any } a \neq 0) \tag{A-16}$$

A common mistake to avoid: $(a^x) \times (a^y) \neq a^{xy}$ [see Eq. (A-10)].

Logarithms

Taking a logarithm is the inverse of exponentiation:

$$x = \log_b y \quad \text{means that} \quad y = b^x \tag{A-17}$$

Thus, one undoes the other:

$$\log_b b^x = x \tag{A-18}$$

$$b^{\log_b x} = x \tag{A-19}$$

The two commonly used bases b are 10 (the *common* logarithm) and $e = 2.71828 \ldots$ (the *natural* logarithm). The common logarithm is written "$\log_{10}$," or sometimes just "log" if base 10 is understood. The natural logarithm is usually written "ln" rather than "$\log_e$."

These identities are true for any base logarithm.

$$\log xy = \log x + \log y \tag{A-20}$$

$$\log \frac{x}{y} = \log x - \log y \tag{A-21}$$

$$\log x^a = a \log x \tag{A-22}$$

Here are some common mistakes to avoid:

$$\log (x + y) \neq \log x + \log y$$

$$\log (x + y) \neq \log x \times \log y$$

$$\log xy \neq \log x \times \log y$$

$$\log x^a \neq (\log x)^a$$

Semilog Graphs

A semilog graph uses a logarithmic scale on the vertical axis and a linear scale on the horizontal axis. Semilog graphs are useful when the data plotted is thought to be an exponential function. If

$$y = y_0 e^{ax}$$

then

$$\ln y = ax + \ln y_0$$

so a graph of $\ln y$ versus x will be a straight line with slope a and y-intercept $\ln y_0$.

Rather than calculating $\ln y$ for each data point and plotting on regular graph paper, it is convenient to use special semilog paper. The vertical axis is marked so that the values of y can be plotted directly, but the markings are spaced proportional to the log of y. (If you are using a plotting calculator or a computer to make the graph, log scale should be chosen for one axis from the menu of options.) The slope a on a semilog graph is *not* $\Delta y/\Delta x$ since the logarithm is actually being plotted. The correct way to find the slope is

$$a = \frac{\Delta(\ln y)}{\Delta x} = \frac{\ln y_2 - \ln y_1}{x_2 - x_1}$$

Note that there cannot be a zero on a logarithmic scale.

The two graphs of Figs. A.2 and A.3 are linear and semilog plots, respectively, of the function $y = 3e^{-2x}$.

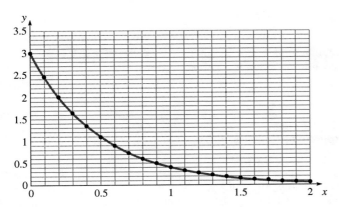

Figure A.2 Graph of the exponential function $y = 3e^{-2x}$ on linear graph paper.

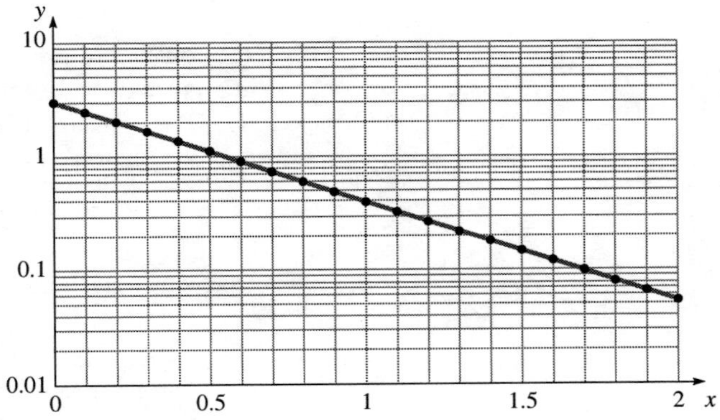

Figure A.3 Graph of the exponential function $y = 3e^{-2x}$ on semilog graph paper.

Log-Log Graphs

A log-log graph uses logarithmic scales for both axes. Log-log graphs are useful when the data plotted is thought to be a power function

$$y = Ax^n$$

For such a function,

$$\log y = n \log x + \log A$$

so a graph of $\log y$ versus $\log x$ will be a straight line with slope n and y-intercept $\log A$. The slope (n) on a log-log graph is found as

$$n = \frac{\Delta(\log y)}{\Delta(\log x)} = \frac{\log y_2 - \log y_1}{\log x_2 - \log x_1}$$

The graphs of Figs. A.4 and A.5 are linear and log-log plots, respectively, of the function $y = 130x^{3/2}$.

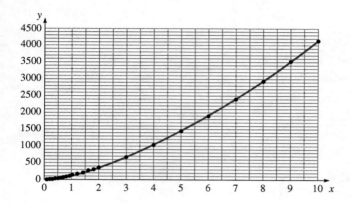

Figure A.4 Graph of the power function $y = 130x^{3/2}$ on linear graph paper.

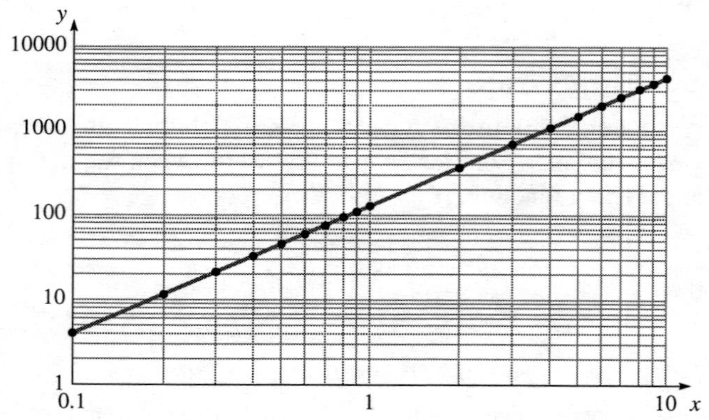

Figure A.5 Graph of the power function $y = 130x^{3/2}$ on log-log graph paper.

A.4   PROPORTIONS AND RATIOS

The notation

$$y \propto x$$

means that y is directly proportional to x. A proportionality can be written as an equation

$$y = kx$$

if the constant of proportionality k is written explicitly. Be careful: an equation can *look like* a proportionality without being one. For example, $V = IR$ means that $V \propto I$ *if and only if R* is constant. If R depends on I, then V is not proportional to I.

The notation

$$y \propto \frac{1}{x}$$

means that y is inversely proportional to x. The notation

$$y \propto x^n$$

means that y is proportional to the nth power of x.

Writing out proportions as ratios usually simplifies solutions when some common items in an equation are unknown but we do know the values of all but one of the proportional quantities. For example if $y \propto x^n$, we can write

$$\frac{y_1}{y_2} = \left(\frac{x_1}{x_2}\right)^n$$

Percentages

Percentages require careful attention. Look at these four examples:

"B is 30% of A" means $B = 0.30A$

"B is 30% larger than A" means $B = (1 + 0.30)A = 1.30A$

"B is 30% smaller than A" means $B = (1 - 0.30)A = 0.70A$

"A increases by 30%" means $\Delta A = +0.30A$

Example A.4

If $P \propto T^4$, and T increases by 10.0%, by what percentage does P increase?

Solution

$$\Delta T = +0.100 T_i$$

$$T_f = T_i + \Delta T = 1.100 T_i$$

$$\frac{P_f}{P_i} = \left(\frac{T_f}{T_i}\right)^4 = 1.100^4 \approx 1.464$$

Therefore, P increases by about 46.4%.

A.5   APPROXIMATIONS

Binomial Approximations

A binomial is the sum of two terms. The general rule for the nth power of an algebraic sum is given by the binomial expansion:

$$(a + b)^n = a^n + na^{n-1}b + \frac{n(n-1)}{1 \times 2} a^{n-2}b^2 + \frac{n(n-1)(n-2)}{1 \times 2 \times 3} a^{n-3}b^3 + \cdots$$

The binomial approximations are used when a binomial in which one term is much smaller than the other is raised to a power n. Only the first two terms of the binomial expansion are of significant value; the other terms are dropped. A common case for physics problems is that in which $a = 1$, or can be made equal to one by factoring. The basic approximation forms are then given by

$$(1 + x)^n \approx 1 + nx \quad \text{when } x \ll 1 \tag{A-23}$$

$$(1 - x)^n \approx 1 - nx \quad \text{when } x \ll 1 \tag{A-24}$$

The power n can be any real number, including negative as well as positive numbers. It does not have to be an integer. An *estimate* of the error—the difference between the approximation and the exact expression—is given by

$$\text{error} \approx \tfrac{1}{2}n(n-1)x^2 \tag{A-25}$$

Of course, the larger term in a binomial is not necessarily 1, but the larger term can be factored out and then Eq. (A-23) or Eq. (A-24) applied. For instance, if $A \gg b$, then

$$(A + b)^n = \left[A \times \left(1 + \frac{b}{A}\right)\right]^n = A^n \left(1 + \frac{b}{A}\right)^n$$

Another common expansion is

$$e^x = 1 + x + \frac{x^2}{2!} + \frac{x^3}{3!} + \cdots$$

where, for any integer n, $n! = n \times (n-1) \times (n-2) \times \cdots \times [n - (n-1)]$; for example, $3! = 3 \times 2 \times 1 = 6$.

Small-Angle Approximations

Approximations for small angles appear in Section A.7 on trigonometry.

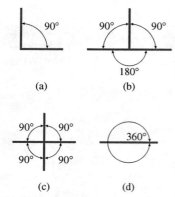

Figure A.6 (a) A right angle; (b) two adjacent right angles, or a straight line; (c) four adjacent right angles; (d) a full circle.

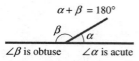

$$\alpha + \beta = 180°$$

$\angle\beta$ is obtuse $\angle\alpha$ is acute

Figure A.7 Acute and obtuse angles.

A.6   GEOMETRY

Geometric Shapes

Table A.1 lists the geometric shapes that commonly appear in physics problems. It is often necessary to determine the area or volume of one of these simple shapes to complete the solution of a problem. The formulae for the properties associated with each geometric form are listed in the column to the right.

Angular Measure

An angle between two straight lines that meet at a single point is specified in degrees. If the two lines are perpendicular to each other, as shown in Fig. A.6a, the angular separation is said to be a right angle or 90°. In Fig. A.6b two such 90° angles are placed side by side; they add to 180°, so a straight line represents an angular separation of 180°. When four right angles are grouped as shown in Fig. A.6c, the angles add to 360° and a full circle contains 360° as shown in Fig. A.6d. An angle that is less than 90° is called an **acute** angle; one greater than 90° is called an **obtuse** angle.

When two lines meet, as shown in Fig. A.7, there are two possible angles that might be specified; one is the acute angle α and the other is the obtuse angle β. The symbol used to indicate an angle is $\angle$. When two angles placed adjacent to each other form a straight line, they are called supplementary angles; angles α and β in Fig. A.7 are supplementary angles. When two angles placed adjacent to each other form a right angle, they are called complementary angles.

Table A.1

Properties of Common Geometric Shapes

Geometric Shape	Properties	Geometric Shape	Properties
Circle	Diameter $d = 2r$ Circumference $C = \pi d = 2\pi r$ Area $A = \pi r^2$	Sphere	Surface area $A = 4\pi r^2$ Volume $V = \frac{4}{3}\pi r^3$
Rectangle	Perimeter $P = 2b + 2h$ Area $A = bh$	Parallelepiped	Surface area $A = 2(ab + bc + ac)$ Volume $V = abc$
Right triangle	Perimeter $P = a + b + c$ Area $A = \frac{1}{2}\text{base} \times \text{height} = \frac{1}{2}ba$ Pythagorean theorem $c^2 = a^2 + b^2$ Hypotenuse $c = \sqrt{a^2 + b^2}$	Right circular cylinder	Surface area $A = 2\pi r^2 + 2\pi rh$ $\qquad = 2\pi r(r + h)$ Volume $V = \pi r^2 h$
Triangle	Area $A = \frac{1}{2}bh$		

Various triangles are shown in Fig. A.8. The sum of the interior angles of any triangle is 180°. An isosceles triangle has two sides of equal length; the angles opposite to the equal sides are equal angles. An equilateral triangle has all three sides of equal length; it is also equiangular. Right triangles have one right angle, 90°, and the sum of the other two angles is 90°, so those angles are acute angles. Commonly used right triangles have sides in the ratio of 3:4:5 and 5:12:13.

Triangles are similar when all three angles of one are equal to the three angles of the other. If two angles of one triangle are equal to two angles of the other, the third angles are necessarily equal and the triangles are similar. The ratio of corresponding sides of similar triangles are equal, as shown in Fig. A.9. Similar triangles of the same size are called congruent triangles.

Figure A.10 shows other useful relations among angles between intersecting lines. When two angles add to 180°, as $\angle\alpha + \angle\beta$ in one of the small figures, the angles are supplementary. Another small figure shows two angles, $\angle\alpha + \angle\beta$ adding to 90°, so in that case the angles are complementary.

For many physics problems it is convenient to use angles measured in radians rather than in degrees; the abbreviation for radians is rad. The arc length s measured along a circle is proportional to the angle between the two radii that define the arc, as shown in Fig. A.11. One radian is defined as the angle subtended when the arc length is equal to the length of the radius.

For θ measured in radians,

$$s = r\theta$$

When the angular displacement is all the way around the circle, 360°, the arc length is equal to the circumference of the circle:

$$s = 2\pi r = r\theta$$

The equivalent to 360° measured in radians is thus $\theta = 2\pi$ radians and the equivalence between radians and degrees is

$$1\text{ rad} = \frac{360°}{2\pi} \approx 57.3° \quad \text{or} \quad 1° = \frac{2\pi}{360°} \approx 0.01745\text{ rad}$$

Note that the radian has no physical dimensions; it is a ratio of two lengths so it is a pure number. We use the term *rad* to remind us of the angular units being used.

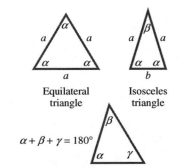

Equilateral triangle   Isosceles triangle

$\alpha + \beta + \gamma = 180°$

Figure A.8 Triangles.

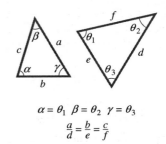

$\alpha = \theta_1 \ \ \beta = \theta_2 \ \ \gamma = \theta_3$
$$\frac{a}{d} = \frac{b}{e} = \frac{c}{f}$$

Figure A.9 Similar triangles.

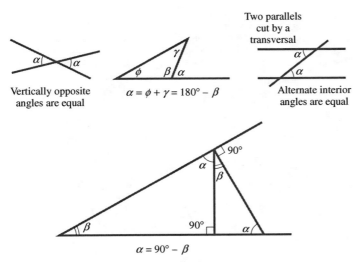

Vertically opposite angles are equal

$\alpha = \phi + \gamma = 180° - \beta$

Two parallels cut by a transversal

Alternate interior angles are equal

$\alpha = 90° - \beta$

Figure A.10 Angles formed by intersecting lines.

If $s = r$, $\theta = 1$ radian

Figure A.11 Radian measure.

A.7 TRIGONOMETRY

The basic trigonometric functions used in physics are shown in Fig. A.12. Note that in determining the function values, the units of length cancel, so the sine, cosine, and tangent functions are dimensionless.

The side opposite and the side adjacent to either of the acute angles in the right triangle are of lesser length than the hypotenuse, according to the Pythagorean theorem. Therefore, the absolute values of the sine and cosine cannot exceed 1. The absolute value of the tangent can exceed 1.

Figure A.13 shows the signs (positive or negative) associated with the trigonometric functions for an angle θ located in each of the four quadrants. The hypotenuse r is positive, so the sign for the sine or cosine is determined by the signs of x or y as measured along the positive or negative x- and y-axes. The sign of the tangent then depends on the signs of the sine and cosine. The angle θ is measured in a counterclockwise direction starting from the positive x-axis, which represents $0°$. Angles measured from the x-axis going in a clockwise direction (below the x-axis) are negative angles; an angle of $-60°$, which is located in the fourth quadrant, is the same as an angle of $+300°$. Figure A.14 shows graphs of $y = \sin \theta$ and $y = \cos \theta$ as functions of θ in radians. Also graphed are two functions that are useful approximations for the sine and cosine functions when $|\theta|$ is sufficiently small (see **Small-Angle Approximations**, p. A-12).

Table A.2 lists some of the most useful trigonometric identities.

Figure A.12 Trigonometric functions used in physics problems; angles θ and ϕ are complementary angles.

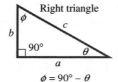

$$\sin \theta = \frac{\text{side opposite } \angle \theta}{\text{hypotenuse}} = \frac{b}{c} = \cos \phi$$

$$\cos \theta = \frac{\text{side adjacent } \angle \theta}{\text{hypotenuse}} = \frac{a}{c} = \sin \phi$$

$$\tan \theta = \frac{\text{side opposite } \angle \theta}{\text{side adjacent } \angle \theta} = \frac{b}{a} = \frac{\sin \theta}{\cos \theta} = \frac{1}{\tan \phi}$$

$\phi = 90° - \theta$

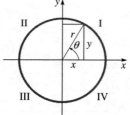

Quadrant I: $0 < \theta < 90°$
$\sin \theta = y/r$ is positive
$\cos \theta = x/r$ is positive
$\tan \theta = y/x$ is positive

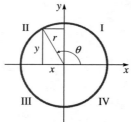

Quadrant II: $90° < \theta < 180°$
$\sin \theta = y/r$ is positive
$\cos \theta = x/r$ is negative
$\tan \theta = y/x$ is negative

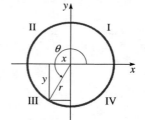

Quadrant III: $180° < \theta < 270°$
$\sin \theta = y/r$ is negative
$\cos \theta = x/r$ is negative
$\tan \theta = y/x$ is positive

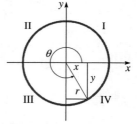

Quadrant IV: $270° < \theta < 360°$
$\sin \theta = y/r$ is negative
$\cos \theta = x/r$ is positive
$\tan \theta = y/x$ is negative

Figure A.13 Signs of trigonometric functions in various quadrants.

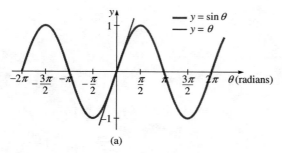

(a)

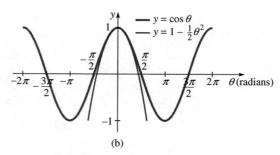

(b)

Figure A.14 (a) Graphs of $y = \sin \theta$ and $y = \theta$. Note that $\sin \theta \approx \theta$ for small θ. (b) Graphs of $y = \cos \theta$ and $y = 1 - \frac{1}{2}\theta^2$. Note that $\cos \theta \approx 1 - \frac{1}{2}\theta^2$ for small θ.

Table A.2

Useful Trigonometric Identities

$\sin^2\theta + \cos^2\theta = 1$

$\sin(-\theta) = -\sin\theta$

$\cos(-\theta) = \cos\theta$

$\tan(-\theta) = -\tan\theta$

$\sin(180° \pm \theta) = \mp\sin\theta$

$\cos(180° \pm \theta) = -\cos\theta$

$\tan(180° \pm \theta) = \pm\tan\theta$

$\sin(90° \pm \beta) = \cos\beta$

$\cos(90° \pm \beta) = \mp\sin\beta$

$\sin 2\theta = 2\sin\theta\cos\theta$

$\cos 2\theta = \cos^2\theta - \sin^2\theta$
$\qquad = 2\cos^2\theta - 1 = 1 - 2\sin^2\theta$

$\tan 2\theta = \dfrac{2\tan\theta}{1-\tan^2\theta}$

$\sin(\alpha \pm \beta) = \sin\alpha\cos\beta \pm \cos\alpha\sin\beta$

$\cos(\alpha \pm \beta) = \cos\alpha\cos\beta \mp \sin\alpha\sin\beta$

$\tan(\alpha \pm \beta) = \dfrac{\tan\alpha \pm \tan\beta}{1 \mp \tan\alpha\tan\beta}$

$\sin\alpha + \sin\beta = 2\sin\left[\frac{1}{2}(\alpha+\beta)\right]\cos\left[\frac{1}{2}(\alpha-\beta)\right]$

$\sin\alpha - \sin\beta = 2\cos\left[\frac{1}{2}(\alpha+\beta)\right]\sin\left[\frac{1}{2}(\alpha-\beta)\right]$

$\cos\alpha + \cos\beta = 2\cos\left[\frac{1}{2}(\alpha+\beta)\right]\cos\left[\frac{1}{2}(\alpha-\beta)\right]$

$\cos\alpha - \cos\beta = -2\sin\left[\frac{1}{2}(\alpha+\beta)\right]\sin\left[\frac{1}{2}(\alpha-\beta)\right]$

Inverse Trigonometric Functions

The inverse trigonometric functions can be written in either of two ways. To use the inverse cosine as an example: $\cos^{-1} x$ or arccos x. Both of these expressions mean *an angle whose cosine is equal to x.* A calculator returns only the *principal value* of an inverse trigonometric function (see Table A.3), which may or may not be the correct solution in a given problem.

Law of Sines and Law of Cosines

These two laws apply to any triangle labeled as shown in Fig. A.15:

Law of sines: $\dfrac{\sin\alpha}{a} = \dfrac{\sin\beta}{b} = \dfrac{\sin\gamma}{c}$

Law of cosines: $c^2 = a^2 + b^2 - 2ab\cos\gamma$ (where γ is the interior angle formed by the intersection of sides a and b)

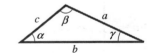

Figure A.15 A general triangle.

Table A.3

Inverse Trigonometric Functions

Function	Principal Value		To Find Value in a Different Quadrant
	Range	(Quadrants)	
$\sin^{-1}$	$-\dfrac{\pi}{2}$ to $\dfrac{\pi}{2}$	(I and IV)	Subtract principal value from π
$\cos^{-1}$	0 to π	(I and II)	Subtract principal value from 2π
$\tan^{-1}$	$-\dfrac{\pi}{2}$ to $\dfrac{\pi}{2}$	(I and IV)	Add principal value to π

Figure A.16 Illustration of the small angle approximations $\sin \theta \approx \theta$ and $\cos \theta \approx 1 - \frac{1}{2}\theta^2$ (for θ in radians) using a right triangle with $\theta \ll 1$ rad.

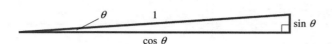

Small-Angle Approximations

These approximations are written for θ *in radians* and are valid when $\theta \ll 1$ rad.

$$\sin \theta \approx \theta \tag{A-26}$$

$$\cos \theta \approx 1 - \frac{1}{2}\theta^2 \tag{A-27}$$

$$\tan \theta \approx \theta \tag{A-28}$$

The sizes of the errors involved in using these approximations are roughly $\frac{1}{6}\theta^3$, $\frac{1}{24}\theta^4$, and $\frac{2}{3}\theta^3$, respectively. In *some* circumstances it may be all right to ignore the $\frac{1}{2}\theta^2$ term and write

$$\cos \theta \approx 1 \tag{A-29}$$

The origin of these approximations can be illustrated using a right triangle of hypotenuse 1 with one very small angle θ (Fig. A.16). If θ is very small, then the adjacent side ($\cos \theta$) will be nearly the same length as the hypotenuse (1). Then we can think of those two sides as radii of a circle that subtend an angle θ. The relationship between the arc length s and the angle subtended is

$$s = \theta r$$

Since $\sin \theta \approx s$ and $r = 1$, we have $\sin \theta \approx \theta$. To find an approximate form for $\cos \theta$ (but one more accurate than $\cos \theta \approx 1$), we can use the Pythagorean theorem:

$$\sin^2 \theta + \cos^2 \theta = 1$$
$$\cos \theta = \sqrt{1 - \sin^2 \theta} \approx \sqrt{1 - \theta^2}$$

Now, using a binomial approximation,

$$\cos \theta \approx (1 - \theta^2)^{1/2} \approx 1 - \frac{1}{2}\theta^2$$

A.8   VECTORS

The distinction between vectors and scalars is discussed in Section 2.1. Scalars have magnitude while vectors have magnitude and direction. A vector is represented graphically by an arrow of length proportional to the magnitude of the vector and aligned in a direction that corresponds to the vector direction.

In print, the symbol for a vector quantity is sometimes written in bold font, or in roman font with an arrow over it, or in bold font with an arrow over it (as done in this book). When writing by hand, a vector is designated by drawing an arrow over the symbol: $\vec{A}$. When we write just plain A, that stands for the *magnitude* of the vector. We also use absolute value bars to stand for the magnitude of a vector, so $A = |\vec{A}|$.

Addition and Subtraction of Vectors

When vectors are added or subtracted, the magnitudes and direction must be taken into account. Details on vector addition and subtraction are found in Sections 2.2 and 2.4. Here we provide a brief summary.

The graphical method for adding vectors involves placing the vectors tip to tail and then drawing from the tail of the first to the tip of the second, as shown in Fig. A.17. To

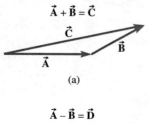

Figure A.17 Graphical (a) addition and (b) subtraction of two vectors.

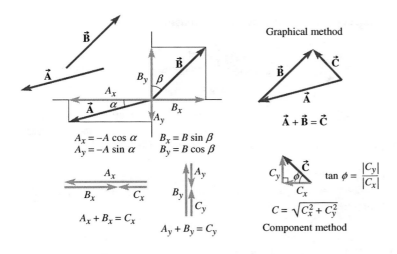

Figure A.18 Adding two arbitrary vectors by two different methods.

subtract a vector, add its opposite. In Fig. A.18, $-\vec{B}$ has the same magnitude as $\vec{B}$ but is opposite in direction. Then $\vec{A} + \vec{B} = \vec{A} - (-\vec{B})$.

Figure A.18 shows both the graphical and component methods of vector addition.

Product of a Vector and a Scalar

When a vector is multiplied by a scalar, the magnitude of the vector is multiplied by the absolute value of the scalar, as shown in Fig. A.19. The direction of the vector does not change unless the scalar factor is negative, in which case the direction is reversed.

Figure A.19 Multiplication of a vector by a scalar.

Scalar Product of Two Vectors

One type of product of two vectors is the *scalar product* (also called the *dot product*). The notation for it is

$$C = \vec{A} \cdot \vec{B}$$

As its name implies, the scalar product of two vectors is a scalar quantity; it can be positive, negative, or zero but has no direction.

The scalar product depends on the magnitudes of the two vectors and on the angle θ between them. To find the angle, draw the two vectors starting *at the same point* (Fig. A.20). Then the scalar product is defined by

$$\vec{A} \cdot \vec{B} = AB \cos \theta$$

Reversing the order of the two vectors does not change the scalar product: $\vec{B} \cdot \vec{A} = \vec{A} \cdot \vec{B}$. The scalar product can be written in terms of the components of the two vectors:

$$\vec{A} \cdot \vec{B} = A_x B_x + A_y B_y + A_z B_z$$

Figure A.20 Two vectors are drawn starting at the same point. The angle θ between the vectors is used to find the scalar product and the cross product of the vectors.

Cross Product of Two Vectors

Another type of product of two vectors is the *cross product* (also called the *vector product*), which is introduced in Chapter 19. It is denoted by

$$\vec{A} \times \vec{B} = \vec{C}$$

The cross product is a *vector* quantity; it has magnitude and direction. $\vec{\mathbf{A}} \times \vec{\mathbf{B}}$ is read as "$\vec{\mathbf{A}}$ cross $\vec{\mathbf{B}}$."

For two vectors, $\vec{\mathbf{A}}$ and $\vec{\mathbf{B}}$, separated by an angle θ (with θ chosen to be the *smaller* angle between the two as in Fig. A.20), the magnitude of the cross product $\vec{\mathbf{C}}$ is

$$|\vec{\mathbf{C}}| = |\vec{\mathbf{A}} \times \vec{\mathbf{B}}| = AB \sin \theta$$

The direction of the cross product $\vec{\mathbf{C}}$ is one of the two directions perpendicular to both $\vec{\mathbf{A}}$ and $\vec{\mathbf{B}}$. To choose the correct direction, use the right-hand rule explained in Section 19.2.

The cross product depends on the order of the multiplication.

$$\vec{\mathbf{A}} \times \vec{\mathbf{B}} = -\vec{\mathbf{B}} \times \vec{\mathbf{A}}$$

The magnitude is $AB \sin \theta$ in both cases, but the direction of one cross product is opposite to the direction of the other.

A.9   SELECTED MATHEMATICAL SYMBOLS

$\times$ or $\cdot$	multiplication
Δ	change in, small increment, or uncertainty in
$\approx$	is approximately equal to
$\neq$	is not equal to
$\leq$	is less than or equal to
$\geq$	is greater than or equal to
$\ll$	is much less than
$\gg$	is much greater than
$\propto$	is proportional to
$|Q|$	absolute value of Q
$|\vec{\mathbf{a}}|$	magnitude of vector $\vec{\mathbf{a}}$
$\perp$	perpendicular
$\parallel$	parallel
∞	infinity
$'$	prime (used to distinguish different values of the same variable)
$Q_{av}, \overline{Q},$ or $\langle Q \rangle$	average of Q
Σ	sum
Π	product
$\ln x$	the natural (base e) logarithm of x
$\pm$	plus or minus
$\mp$	minus or plus
$\cdots$	ellipsis (indicates continuation of a series or list)
$\angle$	angle
$\Rightarrow$	implies
$\therefore$	therefore

Appendix B

Table of Selected Nuclides

Atomic Number Z	Element	Symbol	Mass Number A	Mass of *neutral atom* (u)	Percentage Abundance (or Decay Mode)	Half-life (if Unstable)
0	(Neutron)	n	1	1.008 664 9	β^-	10.24 min
1	Hydrogen	H	1	1.007 825 0	99.985	
	(Deuterium)	(D)	2	2.014 101 8	0.015	
	(Tritium)	(T)	3	3.016 049 3	β^-	12.32 yr
2	Helium	He	3	3.016 029 3	0.000 137	
			4	4.002 603 2	99.999 863	
3	Lithium	Li	6	6.015 122 3	7.6	
			7	7.016 004 0	92.4	
4	Beryllium	Be	7	7.016 929 2	EC	53.22 d
			8	8.005 305 1	2α	6.8×10^{-17} s
			9	9.012 182 1	100	
5	Boron	B	10	10.012 937 0	19.8	
			11	11.009 305 5	80.2	
6	Carbon	C	11	11.011 433 8	EC	20.39 min
			12	12.000 000 0	98.89	
			13	13.003 354 8	1.11	
			14	14.003 242 0	β^-	5730 yr
			15	15.010 599 3	β^-	2.449 s
7	Nitrogen	N	12	12.018 613 2	EC	11.00 ms
			13	13.005 738 6	EC	9.965 min
			14	14.003 074 0	99.634	
			15	15.000 108 9	0.366	
8	Oxygen	O	15	15.003 065 4	EC	122.24 s
			16	15.994 914 6	99.762	
			17	16.999 131 5	0.038	
			18	17.999 160 4	0.200	
			19	19.003 578 7	β^-	26.88 s
9	Fluorine	F	19	18.998 403 2	100	
10	Neon	Ne	20	19.992 440 2	90.48	
			22	21.991 385 5	9.25	
11	Sodium	Na	22	21.994 436 8	EC	2.6019 yr
			23	22.989 769 7	100	
			24	23.990 963 3	β^-	14.9590 h
12	Magnesium	Mg	24	23.985 041 9	78.99	
13	Aluminum	Al	27	26.981 538 6	100	
14	Silicon	Si	28	27.976 926 5	92.230	
15	Phosphorus	P	31	30.973 761 5	100	
			32	31.973 907 2	β^-	14.262 d
16	Sulfur	S	32	31.972 070 7	95.02	
17	Chlorine	Cl	35	34.968 852 7	75.77	
18	Argon	Ar	40	39.962 383 1	99.6003	
19	Potassium	K	39	38.963 706 9	93.2581	
			40	39.963 998 7	0.0117; β^-	1.248×10^9 yr
20	Calcium	Ca	40	39.962 591 2	96.94	
24	Chromium	Cr	52	51.940 507 5	83.789	
25	Manganese	Mn	54	53.940 358 9	EC	312.0 d
			55	54.938 045 1	100	

Atomic Number Z	Element	Symbol	Mass Number A	Mass of neutral atom (u)	Percentage Abundance (or Decay Mode)	Half-life (if Unstable)
26	Iron	Fe	56	55.934 937 5	91.754	
27	Cobalt	Co	59	58.933 195 0	100	
			60	59.933 817 1	β^-	5.271 yr
28	Nickel	Ni	58	57.935 342 9	68.077	
			60	59.930 786 4	26.223	
29	Copper	Cu	63	62.929 597 5	69.17	
30	Zinc	Zn	64	63.929 142 2	48.63	
36	Krypton	Kr	84	83.911 506 6	57.0	
			86	85.910 610 3	17.3	
			92	91.926 152 8	β^-	1.840 s
37	Rubidium	Rb	85	84.911 789 3	72.165	
			93	92.922 032 8	β^-	5.84 s
38	Strontium	Sr	88	87.905 614 3	82.58	
			90	89.907 737 6	β^-	28.79 yr
39	Yttrium	Y	89	88.905 847 9	100	
			90	89.907 151 4	β^-	64.00 h
47	Silver	Ag	107	106.905 096 8	51.839	
50	Tin	Sn	120	119.902 194 7	32.58	
53	Iodine	I	131	130.906 124 6	β^-	8.0207 d
55	Cesium	Cs	133	132.905 446 9	100	
			141	140.920 044 0	β^-	24.84 s
56	Barium	Ba	138	137.905 247 2	71.698	
			141	140.914 406 4	β^-	18.27 min
60	Neodymium	Nd	143	142.909 814 3	12.2	
62	Samarium	Sm	147	146.914 897 9	14.99; α	1.06×10^{11} yr
79	Gold	Au	197	196.966 568 7	100	
82	Lead	Pb	204	203.973 043 6	1.4	$\geq 1.4 \times 10^{17}$ yr
			206	205.974 449 0	24.1	
			207	206.975 896 9	22.1	
			208	207.976 652 1	52.4	
			210	209.984 188 5	β^-	22.20 yr
			211	210.988 737 0	β^-	36.1 min
			212	211.991 897 5	β^-	10.64 h
			214	213.999 805 4	β^-	26.8 min
83	Bismuth	Bi	209	208.980 398 7	100	
			211	210.987 269 5	α	2.14 min
			214	213.998 698 7	β^-	19.9 min
84	Polonium	Po	210	209.982 857 4	α	138.376 d
			214	213.995 201 4	α	164.3 µs
			218	218.008 965 8	α	3.10 min
86	Radon	Rn	222	222.017 570 5	α	3.8235 d
88	Radium	Ra	226	226.025 402 6	α	1600 yr
			228	228.031 070 3	β^-	5.75 yr
90	Thorium	Th	228	228.028 741 1	α	1.91 yr
			232	232.038 050 4	100; α	1.405×10^{10} yr
			234	234.043 595 5	β^-	24.10 d
92	Uranium	U	235	235.043 923 1	0.7204; α	7.038×10^8 yr
			236	236.045 561 9	α	2.342×10^7 yr
			238	238.050 782 6	99.2742; α	4.468×10^9 yr
			239	239.054 287 8	β^-	23.45 min
93	Neptunium	Np	237	237.048 173 4	α	2.144×10^6 yr
94	Plutonium	Pu	239	239.052 163 4	α	24,110 yr
			242	242.058 742 6	α	3.75×10^5 yr
			244	244.064 203 9	α	8.00×10^7 yr

EC = electron capture.

Answers to Selected Questions and Problems

Chapter 1

Multiple-Choice Questions

1. (b) **2.** (a) **3.** (b) **4.** (c) **5.** (d) **6.** (b) **7.** (d) **8.** (b)
9. (d) **10.** (c)

Problems

1. 7.7% **3.** 6/s **5.** 2.5 m **7.** 56% **9.** (a) 1.29×10^8 kg
(b) 1.3×10^8 m/s **11.** (a) 3.63×10^7 g (b) 1.273×10^2 m
13. 1.7×10^{-10} m^3 **15.** 459 m/s **17.** 0.278 m/s
19. (a) 220 markers (b) 221 markers **21.** 13.6 g/cm^3
23. 1.7×10^{-10} kg^3 **25.** (a) 2.7×10^{-3} ft/s (b) 1.9×10^{-3} mi/h
27. kg·m^2·s^{-2}

29. $[T]^2 = \dfrac{[L]^3}{\frac{[L]^3}{[M][T]^2} \times [M]} = \dfrac{[L]^3}{[M]} \times \dfrac{[M][T]^2}{[L]^3} = [T]^2$ **31.** 30–40 cm

33. (a) 10 kg (b) 10 m **35.** Answers may vary. **37.** 100 m
39.

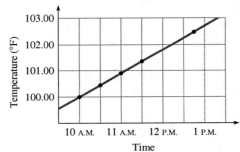

(a) 101.8°F (b) 0.9°F/h (c) No; the patient would die before
12 hours passed and the temperature reached 113°F.
41. 104.5°F **43.** (a) a (b) $+v_0$
45. (a)

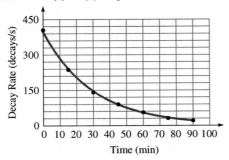

(b)

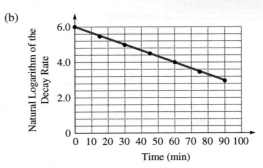

The presentation is useful because the graph is linear.
47. (a) 186.303 (b) 186.297 (c) 0.56 (d) 62,000
(e) Case (a): 0.0016%; Case (b): 0.0016%; For case (c), ignoring
0.0030 causes you to multiply by zero and get a zero result. For
case (d), ignoring 0.0030 causes you to divide by zero. (f) You
can neglect small values when they are added to or subtracted
from sufficiently large values. The term "sufficiently large" is
determined by the number of significant figures required.
49. 4.0 **51.** 434 m/s **53.** (a) 3; 5.74×10^{-3} kg (b) 1; 2 m
(c) 3; 4.50×10^{-3} m (d) 3; 4.50×10^1 kg (e) 4; 1.009×10^5 s
(f) 4; 9.500×10^3 mL **55.** (a) 6 Mm (b) 2 m (c) 1 μm
(d) 3 nm (e) 0.3 nm **57.** (a) 3.3×10^{-8} m (b) 3.3×10^{-2} μm
(c) 1.3×10^{-6} in **59.** 2.2×10^2 m^3 **61.** (a) $a = K\dfrac{v^2}{r}$, where K is

a dimensionless constant. (b) 21.0% **63.** 2.24 mi/h = 1 m/s;
For a quick, approximate conversion, multiply by 2.
65. 10^{11} gal

67. $\dfrac{\text{kg·m}}{\text{s}^2}$ **69.** \$41,000,000,000 **71.** (a) 2.4×10^5 km/h

(b) 10 min **73.** (a) $\sqrt{\dfrac{hG}{c^5}}$ (b) 1.3×10^{-43} s **75.** 0.46 s^{-1}

77. (a)

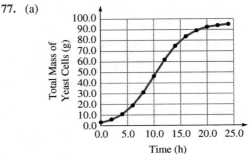

(b) about 100 g
(c) ; 0.30 s^{-1}

Chapter 2

Multiple-Choice Questions

1. (b)   **2.** (b)   **3.** (a)   **4.** (d)   **5.** (b)   **6.** (c)   **7.** (b)   **8.** (c)
9. (d)   **10.** (e)

Problems

1. the weight of the person   **3.** velocity   **5.** 778 N   **7.** 70 N at about 5° below the horizontal
9.

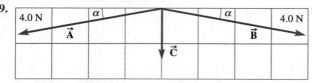

about 1.4 N
11. 14 N to the east   **13.** 806 N   **15.**

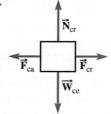

17. s = sailboat; e = Earth; w = wind; l = lake; m = mooring line

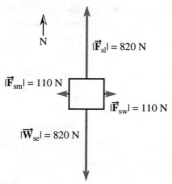

19. (a) 30 N to the right (b) 0 (c) 18 N downward   **21.** 2.5 N, opposite the direction of motion   **23.** 8.7 units   **25.** (a) 5.0 m/s² (b) 37° CCW from the +y-axis   **27.** (a) 9.4 cm at 32° CCW from the +y-axis   (b) 130 N at 27° CW from the +x-axis   (c) 16.3 m/s at 33° CCW from the –x-axis   (d) 2.3 m/s² at 1.6° CCW from the +x-axis   **29.** 1.1 kN forward (along the center line)   **31.** (a) and (b) are third-law pairs; (a) and (c) are equal and opposite due to the first law.   **33.** One force acting on the fish is an upward force on the fish by the line; its interaction partner is a downward force on the line by the fish. A second force acting on the fish is the downward gravitational force on the fish; its interaction partner is the upward gravitational force on the Earth by the fish.
35. (a) 543 N   (b) contact force of Margie's feet   (c) 588 N (d) contact force on the Earth due to the scale

37. (a) 50.0 N upward (total for both feet)   (b) 650.0 N upward (c) s = woman and chair system; e = Earth; f = floor

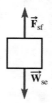

39. (a) The rock will fall toward the Moon's surface.
(b) 1.6 N toward the Moon   (c) 2.7 mN toward Earth
(d) 1.6 N toward the Moon   **41.** (a) 392 N   (b) 88.1 lb
43. 1.5×10^{-9} N   **45.** 640 N   (a) 240 N   (b) 580 N
(c) 100 N   **47.** 4 km   **49.** (a) 1.98×10^{20} N   (b) the same
51. 3.770   **53.** b = book; t = table; e = Earth; h = hand
(a)   (b)

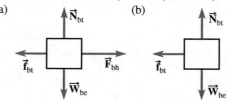

(c)

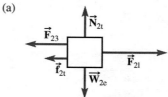   (d) (a) and (b)   (e) 2.0 N opposite the direction of motion   (f) The FBD would look just like the diagram for part (c). The book would not slow down because there is no net force on the book.

55.

	$\vec{\mathbf{N}}$	$\vec{\mathbf{f}}$
(a)	perpendicular to and away from	along the ramp upward
(b)	perpendicular to and away from	along the ramp downward
(c)	perpendicular to and away from	along the ramp upward

57. (a) zero   (b) $\dfrac{T}{mg}$ **59.** t = table; e = Earth; 1 = block 1; 2 = block 2; 3 = block 3; 4 = block 4; h = horizontal force; 1234 = system of blocks (The blocks are numbered from left to right.)
(a)

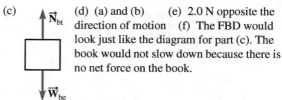

(b)

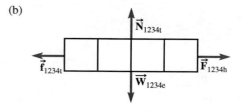

63. (a) 160 N up the slope   (b) 0.19
65. 400 N   **67.** $\dfrac{W}{2\sin\theta}$ **69.** Both scales read 120 N.
71. Scale B reads 120 N; scale A reads 120 N.   **73.** (a) $\sqrt{2}\,Mg$
(b) 45°   **75.** $T_{15} = 30$ N; $T_{25} = 18$ N   **77.** electromagnetic and
gravitational forces   **79.** the weak force   **81.** (a) 530 N
(b) 510 N   (c) no   **83.** 440 N   **85.** (a) zero   (b) 2.6×10^4 N
87. 90.0% of the Earth-Moon distance   **89.** (a) All 0
(b) $A > B > C$ (c) $A = 16.5$ N; $B = 11.0$ N; $C = 5.5$ N
91. (a) $\mu_s > 0.48$ (b) 0.60   (c) 0.48   **93.** (a) 110.0 N
(b) $T_A = 115.0$ N $= T_C$ and $T_B = 110.0$ N $= T_D$.
95. i = ice; e = Earth; s = stone; o = opponent's stone
(a)   (b)   (c)

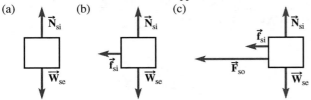

97. (a) c = computer; d = desk; e = Earth

(b) zero   (c) 52 N   **99.** (a) In both cases the two ropes pull on
the scale with forces of 550 N in opposite directions, so the scales
give the same reading.   (b) 550 N   **101.** (a) A = 137 N;
B = 39 N

(b) A = 147 N; B = 39 N   **103.** 0.49%   **105.** $\dfrac{mg}{\cos\theta}$

107. 1810 N; 5 times the force with which Yoojin pulls; the oak
tree supplies additional force.   **109.** (a) 2.60×10^8 m from Earth
(b) away from

Chapter 3

Multiple-Choice Questions

1. (e)   **2.** (d)   **3.** (a)   **4.** (b)   **5.** (e)   **6.** (d)   **7.** (a)   **8.** (b)
9. (a)   **10.** (a)   **11.** (c)   **12.** (a)   **13.** (a)   **14.** (d)   **15.** (c)
16. (a)   **17.** (**a**) (b)   (**b**) (a)   (**c**) (d)   (**d**) (c)   **18.** (a)
19. (c)   **20.** (**a**) increasing   (**b**) +x   (**c**) decreasing   (**d**) –x

Problems

1.

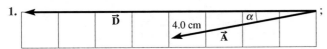

about 7.9 cm   **3.** (a) $B_x = 6.9$; $B_y = -1.7$ (b) 6.9 at 15° CW
from the –y-axis   (c) 10 at 30° CCW from the –x-axis
(d) x-comp: –8.7; y-comp: –5.0   **5.** 4.92 mi at 24.0° north of

east   **7.** 2.0 km at 20° east of south   **9.** 29 nautical miles at 17°
south of east   **11.** (a) 54 mi at 26° north of east   (b) 134 mi
13. 91.5 mph   **15.** 32 s
17. (a)

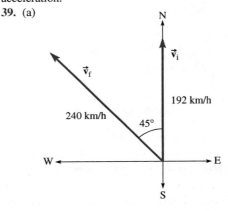

(b) 59.9 km at 85° north of east   (c) 80 km/h at 85° north of east
19. (a) 8 m   (b) $t = 10$ s to $t = 14$ s   **21.** 16.5 m   **23.** 1.0 m/s
25. 27 m/s west   **27.** 26 km/h at 31° north of east
29. (a) 102 km/h   (b) 90.8 km/h at 16.6° south of west
31. 7.0 m/s² in the direction opposite the car's velocity
33. (a) –10 m/s²   (b) 0   (c) 5.0 m   **35.** 2.5 m/s²
37. (a) 9.4 m/s at 45° north of east   (b) 15 m/s² at 45° south of
east   (c) Changing the direction of the velocity requires an
acceleration.
39. (a)

(b) 170 km/h at 7° south of west   (c) 57 km/h² at 7° south of
west   **41.** 44.7 m/s at 26.6° south of east   **43.** 28 m/s² toward
the paddle   **45.** 2.1 m/s² in the direction of motion
47. 22.7 kN upward   **49.** (a) 3.5 m/s² up   (b) 15 m/s up
51. (a) m_1: 2.5 m/s² up; m_2: 2.5 m/s² down   (b) 37 N
53. 1.8 m/s²; yes   **55.** (a) 3.0 kN upward   (b) 3.3 m/s²
downward   **57.** 23 N downward   **59.** 254 s   **61.** 0.42 km/h
63. (a) 39.0 m/s   (b) 7.4° south of west   **65.** 27° upstream
67. (a) 76.37° north of east   (b) 2.717 h   **69.** (a) 1.80 mi/h
(b) 48.0 min   (c) 0.800 mi upstream   (d) 32.2° upstream

71.

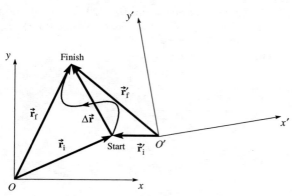

73. (a) 873 km   (b) 9.90° south of east   (c) 2.250 h
(d) 2.18 h   **75.** (a) $g(\sin \theta_2 - \cos \theta_2 \tan \theta_1)$ (b) 3.8 m/s²
77. (a) 16 N   (b) The block will accelerate.   (c) 1.3 m/s²
79. (a) zero   (b) 18 N in the forward direction   (c) 2.9 m/s²
81. (a) $mg \tan \theta$ (b) $mg \tan \theta$ (c) $mg \tan \theta + \dfrac{ma}{\cos \theta}$
83. (a) 68.5 km/h at 12.5° north of east   (b) 68.5 km/h at 12.5°
south of west   **85.** $\vec{\mathbf{a}} \neq \vec{\mathbf{a}}_{av}$, so the acceleration is not constant.
87. 2.0×10^5 N west   **89.** (a) 1.8 m/s² down   (b) 8.7 m/s
91. 39 s   **93.** $\dfrac{m_1}{m_1 + m_2}$ **95.** (a) 1.0 mm/s   (b) 20 ms
(c) 100 m/s   **97.** (a) t_3 and t_4 (b) $t_0, t_2, t_5,$ and t_7 (c) t_1 and t_6
(d) $t_0, t_3,$ and t_7 (e) t_6 **99.** (a) $1.10mg$ (b) $1.10mg$

Chapter 4

Multiple-Choice Questions

1. (c)   **2.** (c)   **3.** (e)   **4.** (c)   **5.** (a)   **6.** (d)   **7.** (d)   **8.** (a)
9. (b)   **10.** (d)   **11.** (e)   **12.** (b)   **13.** (a)   **14.** (b)

Problems

1. (a) 0.85 m/s²   (b) 0.087   **3.** (a) 23 m/s   (b) 0.19
5. (a) 224 m   (b) 0.99 m/s²   **7.** (a) 45.9 m   (b) 30.0 m/s² up
9. 52.1 m before you stop; the tractor is 1.5 m in front of you; you
won't hit the tractor.   **11.** (a) 0.34 m/s², where the watermelon
moves up and to the left   (b) 1.5 cm   (c) 6.8 cm/s
13. (a)

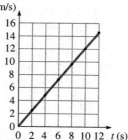

(b) 86.4 m   (c) 14.4 m/s
15. (a)

(b) 2.00 m/s² north   (c) 135 m   **17.** 5.0 m/s² in the
+x-direction   **19.** 0.365°;

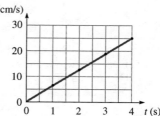

21. 0.50 m   **23.** (a) 1.6 s   (b) 48 m   **25.** 5.0 m/s
27. 30.0 m/s   **29.** 13 m   **31.** 1.22 s   **33.** (a) 55 m   (b) 7.5 s
35. (a) 5.9 m   (b) 17.0 m/s   **37.** (a) 202 m   (b) 51.1° below
the horizontal   **39.** 15.8 m
41. (a)

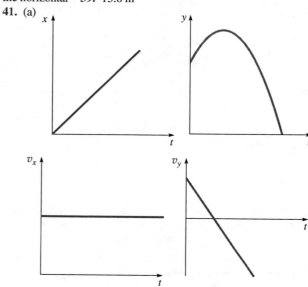

(b) 27.6 m/s at 25.0° above the horizontal   (c) 37.5 m
(d) 44.4 m above the ground   **43.** 37.1 m   **45.** (a) 37 m
(b) 170 m   (c) 32 m/s; –27 m/s   **47.** 200 km   **49.** (a) 127 m,
127 m   (b) 96.2 m, 96.2 m   (c) 134 m   (d) The ranges are the
same for each pair of complementary angles. The largest range
occurred for an angle of 45.0° above the horizontal.   **51.** 766 N
downward   **53.** 0.8 m/s² downward   **55.** (a) 567 N   (b) 629 N
57. 620 N   **59.** 0.5 s   **61.** (a) 570 N up   (b) 5.0 m/s²
downward   (c) 92 m/s   **63.** 13 m/s² up   **65.** (a) 4.5 s
(b) 81 m   **67.** step 4   **69.** (a) 5 m   (b) 1 km   **71.** (a) 0.30 s
(b) 0.05 s   (c) 0.45 m   (d) 10 m/s² down   (e) 120 m/s² up
73. 12 m east and 40 m north   **75.** (a) 88 N   (b) 2 s   (c) 70 N
(d) 10 kg   **77.** $2v$ **79.** 48 m   **81.** 3260 ft; 25.5 s
83. (a) 28.6 cm   (b) smaller   (c) larger   (d) $H = 21.3$ cm;
$R = 85.1$ cm   **85.** (a) 33.1 h   (b) 34.1 h   (c) 33.6 h
91. (a) $a = \dfrac{m_2 - \mu_k m_1}{m_1 + m_2} g; \ T = (1 + \mu_k)\dfrac{m_1 m_2}{m_1 + m_2} g$
(b) $m_1 \ll m_2$: $a \approx g$ and $T \approx (1 + \mu_k)m_1 g \ll m_2 g$, so the tension
is negligible compared to the weight of m_2; it's essentially in
free fall. $m_1 \gg m_2$: $a = 0$ and $T = m_2 g$. $m_1 = m_2 = m$: $a = (1 - \mu_k)g/2$ and $T = (1 + \mu_k)mg/2$.   (c) $a = 0$ only for $m_2 = 0$;
thus, there is no value at which the two masses slide with constant
velocity. For $m_2 = 0$, there is no tension in the cord.   **93.** No; the
flowerpot either fell from 133 m high or, if it came from a lower
location (such as the 24th floor), it was thrown downward. The
first witness is not credible.

Chapter 5

Multiple-Choice Questions

1. (b)   **2.** (a)   **3.** (f)   **4.** (b)   **5.** (a)   **6.** (b)   **7.** (b)   **8.** (a)
9. (e)   **10.** (c)   **11.** (b)

Problems

1. 17 m   **3.** 0.105 rad/s   **5.** 26 rad/s   **7.** (a) 3.49 rad/s
(b) 0.45 m/s   **9.** 3800 ft   **11.** 5.74 m/s   **13.** (a) 31 m/s
(b) 31 rad/s   **15.** 3.37 cm/s^2 **17.** (a) $\dfrac{mv^2}{L}$
(b) $T = \sqrt{\left(\dfrac{mv^2}{L}\right)^2 + (mg)^2}$; $\theta = \tan^{-1}\dfrac{gL}{v^2}$ **19.** (a) $\sqrt{\mu_s gR}$
(b) The static frictional force is not large enough to keep the car
in a circular path; the car skids toward the outside of the curve.
21. 7.9 m/s   **23.** 59°   **25.** (a) 2300 N   (b) 19 m/s
27. $\tan^{-1}\dfrac{v^2}{rg}$ **29.** 2.99×10^4 m/s   **31.** 130 h

33. $r_{\text{Io}} = 420{,}000$ km; $r_{\text{Europa}} = 670{,}000$ km   **35.** 2.04×10^7 m
37. 16 h   **39.** (a) 13 N   (b) The bob has an upward
acceleration, so the net F_y must be upward and greater than the
weight of the bob.   **41.** 23.2 m/s   **43.** $g \sin\theta$ **47.** 4.0 rad/s^2
49. 0.39 rad/s^2 **51.** (a) 17.7 m/s   (b) 6.28 m/s^2
(c) 6.59 m/s^2 at an angle of 17.7° east of south
53. (a) 1.3×10^6 s   (b) 5.0×10^{10} rev   **55.** (a) 0.034 m/s^2
(b) less   (c) 0.34% smaller   (d) at the poles   **57.** 7.0 rad/s
59. (a) $m(g - \omega^2 R)$ (b) $m(g + \omega^2 R)$ **61.** $16g$ **63.** (a) 400 N
(b) 180 N   **65.** 150 m/s   **67.** (a) 3.00 m/s east   (b) 3.00 m/s
west   **69.** 2.9 rotations for A; 5.7 rotations for B
71. (a) 38 m/s   (b) You would need 135 km of tape to record
one hour.   **73.** (a) $8.0\pi^2$ m/s^2 = 79 m/s^2 (b) $4.0\pi^2$ N = 39 N
75. smallest; 4.1 s   **77.** 0.40ω **79.** 8 cm   **81.** 120 km/h
83. (a) 90 g   (b) 7.9×10^{-11} N   (c) 4.4×10^{-18} N
(d) $5.0 \times 10^5 g$ **85.** 110 μm/s   **87.** (a) 90°   (b) $T = \dfrac{2\pi m}{k}$
(c) $r = \dfrac{m}{k}v$

Review and Synthesis: Chapters 1–5

Review Exercises

1. N/m = kg/s^2 **3.** (a) 1.74 m/s   (b) 0.332 m/s in his original
direction of motion   **5.** 17.5 m   **7.** (a) $W \tan 12°$
(b) $\dfrac{W}{\cos 12°}$ **9.** (a) 1 N   (b) 6 mN; Rapunzel will most
certainly not be made bald.   **11.** 4.2 m/s^2; 86 N   **13.** The
gravitational field is zero approximately one third (0.33) of the
distance between the stars as measured from the star with mass
M_1.   **15.** (a) 40 m/s^2 in the direction of motion   (b) $4W$ in the
direction of motion   (c) The trout pushes backward on the water.
17. (a) The rocks will have the same speed when they hit the
ground.   (b) 19.8 m/s   **19.** 2.40 s   **21.** 11.5 m/s   **23.** 2.02 s;
1.65 m to the left of B's initial position   **25.** 0.98 m/s directed
downward   **27.** (a) $R = \dfrac{2v_i^2 \sin\theta \cos\theta}{g}$ (b) 221 m
(c) 4 m   **29.** (a) 283 m   (b) 84.9 m

31. (a) a = air; w = water; s = sailboat

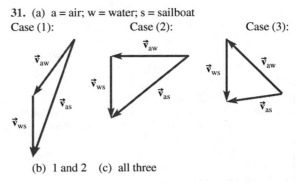

Case (1):   Case (2):   Case (3):

(b) 1 and 2   (c) all three

MCAT Review

1. D   **2.** C   **3.** D   **4.** C   **5.** C   **6.** D   **7.** A

Chapter 6

Multiple-Choice Questions

1. (c)   **2.** (b)   **3.** (b)   **4.** (a)   **5.** (c)   **6.** (c)   **7.** (c)   **8.** (c)
9. (b)   **10.** (b)   **11.** (f)

Problems

1. 75 J   **3.** No work is done.   **5.** 210 kJ   **7.** (a) 0   (b) 8.8 J
9. 1.3 m   **11.** 15.6 J   **13.** (a) 0.70 J   (b) 0.37 m/s   **15.** 0
17. −4.17 kJ   **19.** 5.8 MJ (meteoroid); 0.46 MJ (car); the meteoroid has more than 12 times the kinetic energy of the car.
21. (a) 0   (b) 3.4 kJ   (c) dissipated as heat   **23.** (a) 0
(b) −2.9 J   **25.** 2.5 kJ   **27.** $v_1 = 25$ m/s; $v_2 = 18$ m/s;
$v_3 = 21$ m/s   **29.** 1.9 m   **31.** 25 m   **33.** 2.9 m/s   **35.** 2.37 km/s
37. 22.4 km/s   **39.** 2   **41.** 60.0 km/s   **43.** 11.2 km/s   **45.** 8 J
47. (a) 3200 N/cm   (b) 4.0 J   **49.** (a) 6.0×10^{10} N/m
(b) 8.0 nm   (c) 1.9 μJ   **51.** (a) 1.5 J   (b) 1.1 J   **53.** 0.5 J
55. 0.35 m   **57.** 13 m   **59.** 8.7 cm   **61.** (a) 2.2 m/s
(b) 0.21 m   (c) 0.50 m   **65.** 150 W   **67.** (a) 20 N
(b) 6.7 m/s   **69.** 60 kW   **71.** 6.2 g; the other 90% of the energy
is dissipated as heat.   **73.** 930 kW   **75.** 4.8 m/s   **77.** 16 m/s
83. 27 N   **85.** 0.33 m   **87.** 1.6 m/s   **89.** (a) 10 kW   (b) 5.8°
91. (a) 2.62 kW   (b) 7.85 kW   **93.** (a) 2200 kcal/day
(b) more than 0.51 lb   **95.** (b) 4.9 m/s   (c) 1.24 m   **97.** $\frac{2}{3}R$
99. (a) $k = k_1 + k_2$ (b) 0.16 J   **101.** 1.3 cm; 32 J
103. (a) 26 cm   (b) 34 cm   **107.** No; because the kinetic
energy cannot be negative as would be the case in the region
3 cm < x < 8 cm. The particle must remain in the region x < 3 cm.

Chapter 7

Multiple-Choice Questions

1. (c)   **2.** (d)   **3.** (c)   **4.** (b)   **5.** (d)   **6.** (b)   **7.** (f)   **8.** (d)
9. (a)   **10.** (e)   **11.** (d)   **12.** (b)

Problems

1. 2.0 kg·m/s to the right   **3.** (a) 11 m/s   (b) 1300 N
5. 3 kg·m/s north   **7.** 20 kg·m/s in the −x-direction
9. 1.0×10^2 kg·m/s downward   **11.** 320 s   **13.** 6.0×10^3 N
opposite the car's direction of motion   **15.** (a) 750 kg·m/s upward
(b) 990 N·s downward   (c) 2500 N downward   **19.** (a) 33 m/s
(b) 0.94 N down   **21.** 2.6×10^5 m/s   **23.** 0.10 m/s   **25.** 0.30 m/s

27. (8.0 cm, 20 cm)   **29.** 4.0 cm in the positive x-direction
31. (0.900 m, –2.15 m)   **33.** 21 cm   **35.** (6 m/s, –4 m/s)
37. (a) (–0.13 m/s, –4.1 m/s)   (b) The center of mass of the
system remains at the origin after the explosion.   **39.** 5.0 m/s
41. (a) 0.20 m/s   (b) 0.25 m/s   **43.** 5.0 m/s   **45.** 0.20 kg
47. 43 m/s   **49.** 3.0 m/s   **51.** 0   **53.** 0.49 m   **55.** 270 m/s to
the right   **57.** 1.7 m/s at 30° below the x-axis
59. (a) $\Delta p_{1x} = -1.00 m_1 v_i$; $\Delta p_{1y} = 0.751 m_1 v_i$ (b) $\Delta p_{2x} = m_1 v_i$;
$\Delta p_{2y} = -0.751 m_1 v_i$; the momentum changes for each mass are
equal and opposite.   **61.** $1.73 v_{1f}$ **63.** 8.7 kg·m/s
65. 6.0 m/s at 21° south of east   **67.** 170 m/s   **69.** 20 m/s at
18° west of north   **71.** 5.0×10^9 kg·m/s   **73.** 34 N
75. (2.0, 0.75, 0.25) in   **77.** Inexperienced: 5000 N;
experienced: 500 N   **79.** 37 m/s in the $+x$-direction
81. 10.2 m/s   **83.** (a) 148.6° CCW from the electron's direction
(b) 9.60×10^{-19} kg·m/s in the direction found in (a)
85. The lighter car was speeding.   **87.** 10^{-18} N
89. $\frac{1}{9} h$ **91.** 10 m/s   **93.** (a) $\frac{111}{2}$ (b) 1   (c) $\frac{111}{2}$

Chapter 8

Multiple-Choice Questions

1. (b)   **2.** (d)   **3.** (a)   **4.** (c)   **5.** (e)   **6.** (b)   **7.** (a)   **8.** (f)
9. (e)   **10.** (c)

Problems

3. (a) 1.5 kg·m²   (b) 0.75 kg·m²   (c) 1.5 kg·m²
5. (a) reduced by a factor of 8   (b) reduced by a factor of 32
7. $\frac{2}{5} \frac{R_E^2}{R_o^2}$, where R_E is the Earth's radius and R_o is Earth's orbital

radius about the Sun.   **9.** (a) no   (b) 0.017   **11.** 4.0 N·m
13. (a) 58.5 N·m   (b) 39.9 N·m   (c) 0   **17.** 780 N·m
19. (a) 0   (b) 790 N·m   **21.** 1.2 cm toward the doorknob as
measured from the center of the door   **23.** (a) 3.14 m   (b) 15.7 J
(c) 2.50 N·m   (d) 6.28 rad   **25.** (a) 29 N·m   (b) 5.5 kJ
27. 17.0°   **29.** The center of mass = 0.8542 m < 0.8600 m; the
system balances.   **31.** 200 N   **33.** 180 N toward the wall
35. $(mg/2 + W)/\tan\theta$; For $\theta = 0$, $T \rightarrow \infty$, and for $\theta = 90°$, $T \rightarrow 0$.
37. 22.3°   **39.** palms: 390 N; feet: 270 N   **41.** 7.0 kN—too
much for a human, but maybe not for a cyborg   **43.** 130 N
45. 640 N   **49.** 0.0012 N·m   **51.** 0.88 N   **53.** 1.5 N·m
55. (a) 48 N·m   (b) 19 N   **57.** 0.09 N·m   **59.** 4.0 m/s²
61. solid sphere: $K = \frac{7}{10} mv^2$; solid cylinder: $K = \frac{3}{4} mv^2$; hollow
cylinder: $K = mv^2$ **63.** (a) 3.0 m/s   (b) 8.4 N   (c) 5.6 m/s²
down   **65.** (a) The drilled cylinder takes more time because its
rotational inertia is larger.   (b) 4% longer   **67.** $3r$
69. (a) 1.5 m/s   (b) 1.36 s   **71.** 7.0×10^{33} kg·m²/s
73. 16.9 Hz   **75.** 1.60 s   **77.** (a) 1   (b) 1.0×10^8
(c) 1.0×10^8 (d) 0.10 s   **79.** 15.6 rad/s   **81.** 3.15 rad/s
83. 2.10×10^6 N·m   **85.** $T_1 = 67$ kN; $T_2 = 250$ kN; $\vec{F}_p = 380$ kN
at 51° with the horizontal   **87.** (a) 6.53 m/s² down   (b) 4.2 N
89. 0.44 N·m   **91.** (a) 0.96 m from the right-hand edge
(b) 0.58 m from the left-hand edge   **93.** (a) 2.6×10^{29} J
(b) The length of the day would increase by 7 minutes.
(c) 2.6 million years   **95.** (a) 3.54 m   (b) 2.50 m
(c) 4.3×10^8 W   **97.** $\sqrt{3gL}$ **99.** 110 N
101. (a) 1.35×10^{-5} kg·m²   (b) 524 N   **103.** 0.19 kg·m²/s
105. (a) 9.4×10^{-4} kg·m²/s   (b) 1.2×10^{-6} kg·m²/s

107. 230 N   **109.** (a) $\dfrac{\omega_i}{1 + \dfrac{mr^2}{MR^2}}$ (b) The total angular

momentum does not change, since no external torques act on the
system.   (c) Yes; the kinetic energy changes.   **111.** (a) The
spool spins and moves down the incline with
$$a_{CM} = \frac{g \sin\theta}{1 + \dfrac{I}{mrR}}.$$ (b) $\dfrac{mg \sin\theta}{1 + \dfrac{R}{r}}$ up the incline   (c) $\dfrac{\tan\theta}{1 + \dfrac{R}{r}}$
113. (a) $\sqrt{2gL}$ (b) $\sqrt{3gL}$ (c) The roustabout should jump.
115. 1.5 kN
117. (a) $d = \left(\mu_s \dfrac{M + m}{M} \tan\theta - \dfrac{m}{2M} \right) L$ (c) 63°

Review and Synthesis: Chapters 6–8

Review Exercises

1. (a) 0.20 m   (b) 250 N/m   **3.** $2mg$ **5.** 53 kJ   **7.** 6.0 m/s
9. 3.7 m/s² down the ramp   **11.** 1.53 m   **13.** 1.53 m/s
15. 0.73 m   **17.** 10.3 J   **19.** $h_A = 0.57$ m; $h_B = 2.3$ m
21. 1.27 m   **23.** 2.0 m/s   **25.** 2.06 m/s at 41.6° south of east
27. (a) 0.267 m   (b) 12.1 m/s²   **29.** (a) 1.7 m/s
(b) 0.76 m/s²; 1.7 m/s

MCAT Review

1. D   **2.** D   **3.** B   **4.** B   **5.** D   **6.** C   **7.** B   **8.** B   **9.** D
10. A   **11.** B   **12.** D   **13.** B   **14.** C   **15.** A   **16.** D   **17.** C

Chapter 9

Multiple-Choice Questions

1. (b)   **2.** (b)   **3.** (d)   **4.** (a)   **5.** (a)   **6.** (b)   **7.** (a)   **8.** (a)
9. (d)   **10.** (c)

Problems

1. 49 atm   **3.** 22 kPa   **5.** The baby applies 2.0 times as much
pressure as the adult.   **7.** 4.0 kN southward   **9.** (a) 625 N
(b) 6.25 mm   (c) 16.0   **11.** (a) 30 N   (b) 5.8 N·m   **13.** 2.0 atm
15. (a) 343 kPa   (b) 410 Pa   **17.** 2.9 N   **19.** 4.65×10^{-5} m³;
$\dfrac{V_{Pt}}{V_{Al}} = 0.126$ **21.** (a) 2.2×10^5 Pa   (b) 1700 torr   (c) 2.2 atm
23. 114.0 cm Hg   **25.** (a) 5.6 cm   (b) 0.37 cm   **27.** (a) 91.7%
(b) 0.917   **29.** 250 kg/m³   **31.** (a) 8.8 N upward   (b) 9.6 N
upward   **33.** 100%   **35.** (a) 9.8 m/s² upward   (b) 3.3 m/s²
upward   (c) 68.6 m/s² upward   **37.** 0.78   **39.** yes   **41.** 50 m/s
43. (a) 39.1 cm/s   (b) 78.5 cm³/s   (c) 78.5 g/s   **45.** 1.12 ×
10^5 Pa   **47.** 1.9×10^5 N   **49.** (a) 78 W   (b) 392 kPa   (c) at
the bottom   **51.** 8.6 m   **55.** (a) 6850 Pa   (b) 0.685 N
57. 0.040 m³/s   **59.** (a) 50 Pa   (b) 1100 Pa
(c) approximately 13 kPa   **61.** (a) 1.3×10^{-10} N
(b) 2.6×10^{-14} W   **63.** 0.4 Pa·s   **65.** 2.9 cm/s   **67.** Since m/v_t
is constant, the drag force is primarily viscous.   **69.** 5 Pa
71. (a) $\gamma L \Delta s$ (b) $\Delta E = \gamma \Delta A$ **73.** (a) 1.54 N
(b) 1.54×10^4 N   (c) For a given depth the pressure is the same
everywhere, so the very tall, narrow column of water is as
effective as having a whole barrel of water filled to the same
height and pushing upward on the barrel top.   **75.** (a) 7.43%
(b) 1060 kg   **77.** (a) 5.94 m/s   (b) As long as we can assume
Bernoulli's equation applies, it doesn't matter what fluid is in the

vat.   (c) The speed would be reduced by a factor of 0.40.
79. 230 kg   **81.** 23.0 m   **83.** 110 m   **85.** (a) 1.4 N
(b) 0.43 N upward   (c) 6.8 m/s^2 downward   **87.** 1.1 cm

89. d is not a linear function of ρ: $d = \dfrac{m}{\pi \rho r^2}$.   **91.** 27 kPa

93. (a) 26 m/s   (b) 2.6 m/s   **95.** (a) 220%   (b) 0.68
97. 0.83 g/cm^3 **99.** (a) 5.2 kPa = 0.051 atm   (b) 11.8 Pa/m
(c) 8.61 km   (d) A decreasing air density means that the atmosphere extends to a higher altitude.   **101.** −110 kPa

Chapter 10

Multiple-Choice Questions

1. (c)   **2.** (b)   **3.** (b)   **4.** (a)   **5.** (a)   **6.** (a)   **7.** (c)   **8.** (b)
9. (c)   **10.** (a)   **11.** (f)   **12.** (e)   **13.** (e)   **14.** (f)   **15.** (f)
16. (e)   **17.** (c)   **18.** (c)   **19.** (j)   **20.** (k)

Problems

1. 0.097 mm   **3.** 2.2 cm   **5.** (a) 1.2×10^{-4} W
(b) 5.4×10^{-6} W; no   (c) 3.7×10^{-7} J   (d) 3.7×10^{-4} W; yes
7. 0.80 mm   **9.** tension: 1.5×10^{10} N/m^2; compression:
9.0×10^{9} N/m^2 **11.** 8.7×10^{-5} m   **13.** 630 N
15. (a) 2.8×10^{7} Pa   (b) 4.7×10^{-4} (c) 9.3×10^{-4} m
(d) 5.0×10^{5} N   **17.** human: 3 cm^2; horse: 7.1 cm^2
19. volume: 7.7×10^{-4}; radius: 2.6×10^{-4} **21.** The volume of
the steel sphere would decrease by 57×10^{-6} cm^3.   **23.** 7.5×10^{5} N
25. 0.30 N   **27.** 2.5 Hz   **29.** 7.9 m/s^2 **31.** 3.10 m/s; 8560 m/s^2
35. 5.0 rad/s   **37.** (a) high frequency   (b) 1.3×10^{-6} m/s;
1.6×10^{-4} m/s^2 (c) 0.0013 m/s; 160 m/s^2 **39.** (a) 1.7×10^{-4} m
(b) 0.13 m/s   (c) 510 N   **41.** (a) 1.4 kN   (b) 0.13 J
43. (a) 0.39 m   (b) 2.0 m/s   **45.** 0.70 s   **47.** 0.250 Hz

49. 2.0 mJ   **51.** (a) $\dfrac{2}{\pi}\omega A$ (b) ωA (c) $\dfrac{2}{\pi}$

(d)

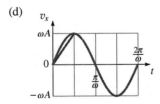

If the acceleration were constant so that the speed varied linearly, the average speed would be 1/2 of the maximum velocity. Since the actual speed is always larger than what it would be for constant acceleration, the average speed must be larger.

53. (a)

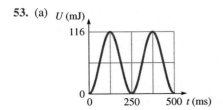

(b)

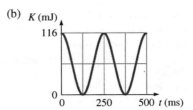

(c)

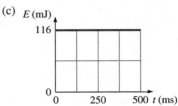

(d) U, K, and E would gradually be reduced to zero.

55. 4.0 s   **57.** 1.5 s

59. (a) $v_x = \omega A \cos \omega t$ (b) $\dfrac{1}{2} m \omega^2 A^2$

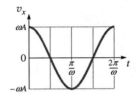

61. 1.11   **63.** (a) less   (b) 5.57 m/s^2 **65.** 1st method:
3.14 cm/s; 2nd method: 3.14 cm/s   **67.** (a) 6.1 mJ   (b) 1.1%
69. The energy has decayed by a factor of 400.   **71.** 2.5 s
73. 7.1×10^{7} N/m; 0.44 mm   **75.** (a) more   (b) 56 N
77. (a) The frequency and period don't vary with amplitude, they only vary with m and k. Since these two values remain constant, so do the frequency and period.   (b) The total energy for an amplitude of $2D$ is four times that for an amplitude of D.
(c) The frequency and period are still the same.   (d) The energy is greater when given an initial push, since it has an amplitude $> 2D$. The increase in energy is $\frac{1}{2}mv_i^2$.
79. (a) 42.2°   (b) 48 g   (c) 9.1 cm

81. (a) $2\pi \sqrt{\dfrac{L\left(\dfrac{m_1}{3} + m_2\right)}{g\left(\dfrac{m_1}{2} + m_2\right)}} = 2\pi \sqrt{\dfrac{2L(m_1 + 3m_2)}{3g(m_1 + 2m_2)}}$

(b) For $m_1 \gg m_2$, $T = 2\pi \sqrt{\dfrac{2L}{3g}}$, and for $m_1 \ll m_2$, $T = 2\pi \sqrt{\dfrac{L}{g}}$.

83. (a) $\sqrt{2gL}$ (b) $\dfrac{\pi}{2}\sqrt{gL}$; larger

87. $y = (1.6 \text{ cm}) \cos[(25 \text{ rad/s})t]$ **89.** (a) 0.395 m   (b) 1.11 m/s
(c) 0.960 m/s   **91.** 8.0×10^{8} Pa; it is just under the elastic limit.
93. 0.63 Hz   **95.** (a) $\rho g h$ (b) 7.6 km   (c) no   **97.** (a) 3.42 s
(b) no

Chapter 11

Multiple-Choice Questions

1. (b)   **2.** (c)   **3.** (d)   **4.** (f)   **5.** (a)   **6.** (b)   **7.** (d)   **8.** (a)
9. (b)   **10.** (d)

Problems

1. (a) 260 m   (b) 1.5×10^{-10} W/m^2 **3.** 170 mW/m^2
5. 4.0×10^{26} W   **7.** (a) 1.5 m/s   (b) 21 cm/s   **9.** 168 m/s
11. 16 ms   **13.** 0.375 m   **15.** (a) 340 Hz   (b) 3.0×10^8 Hz
17. 0.33 Hz   **19.** (a) 3.5 cm   (b) 6.0 cm   **21.** $y(x, t) =$
$(0.120$ m$)\sin [(134$ s$^{-1})t + (20.9$ m$^{-1})x]$ **23.** (a) 2.9 m/s
(b) 370 m/s^2 (c) 8.7 m/s   (d) The motion of the particles on
the string is not the same as the motion of the wave along the
string.   **25.** (a) to the left   (b) 2.0 mm; 1600 rad/s; 160 rad/m
(c) 1.0 ms, 5.0 ms, and 9.0 ms   **27.** (a) 2.6 cm   (b) 14 m
(c) 20 m/s   (d) 1.4 Hz   (e) 0.70 s

29.

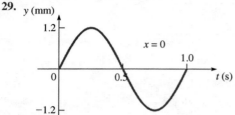

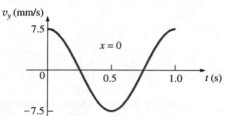

31.

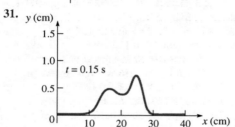

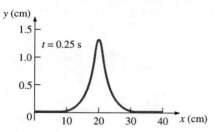

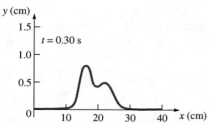

33. 96.0°

35. (a)   ; 6.9 cm

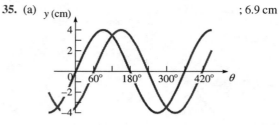

(b)   ; 5.7 cm

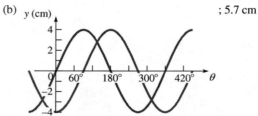

37. 4.8 m/s   **39.** 1.7 s   **41.** (a) 0°; 8.0 cm   (b) 180°; 2.0 cm
(c) 4:1   **43.** 79 mW/m^2 **45.** (a) 0.25 W/m^2 (b) 0.010 W/m^2
(c) 0.130 W/m^2 **47.** 7.8%   **49.** 0.050 kg   **51.** 0.016 m
53. (a) 33 Hz   (b) 300 N   **55.** 4.5×10^{-4} kg/m   **57.** (a) 260 Hz
(b) 2.8 g   **59.** 190 m   **61.** 3.3 m   **63.** (a) $y(x, t) =$
$(0.020$ m$) \sin[(1.6$ rad/s$)t + (0.0016$ rad/m$)x]$ (b) 0.031 m/s
(c) 1.0 km/s   **65.** $v \propto \sqrt{\lambda g}$ **67.** (a) left   (b) 7.00 cm
(c) 10.0 Hz   (d) 0.333 cm   (e) 3.33 cm/s   (f) The particle
oscillates sinusoidally along the y-axis about $y = 0$ with an
amplitude of 7.00 cm.   (g) transverse   **69.** 80 km

71.

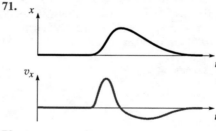

73.

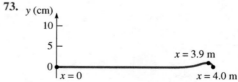

75. (a) 600.0 Hz, 900.0 Hz, 1.200 kHz   (b) 600.0 Hz,
1.200 kHz, 1.800 kHz, 2.400 kHz   (c) 600.0 Hz, 1.200 kHz,
1.800 kHz, 2.400 kHz   **77.** 1.4 kHz

79. (a)

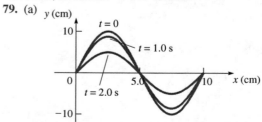

(b) No; this is a standing wave.

Chapter 12

Multiple-Choice Questions

1. (c)   **2.** (a)   **3.** (b)   **4.** (c)   **5.** (b)   **6.** (c)   **7.** (b)   **8.** (c)   **9.** (b)   **10.** (d)

Problems

1. 3.4 mm   **3.** 173 ms   **7.** 1.4 km/s   **9.** $4.7 \text{ s} \approx 5 \text{ s}$ **11.** 1.1 µJ   **13.** 95 dB; this is not much different than with only one machine running.   **15.** (a) 28.7 N/m^2 (b) 1.58 mN **19.** 8.58 mm   **21.** (a) 65.6 cm   (b) 252.4 Hz   **23.** 43.3 cm **25.** 34°C   **27.** (a) There is a displacement node (pressure antinode) at the center of the rod and displacement antinodes (pressure nodes) at the ends.   (b) 5100 m/s   (c) 13.1 cm   (d) The ends move in opposite directions and, thus, they are out of phase. **29.** (a) 1.20 m   (b) 90.0 cm   (c) 338 m/s   **31.** (a) 290.0 Hz (b) 1.4%   **33.** (a) 85.6 N   (b) 432 m/s   (c) 335 Hz (d) 0.256 m   **35.** 580 Hz   **37.** 6.35 Hz   **39.** (a) 1.5 kHz (b) 500 Hz   **41.** (a) 3.0 kHz   (b) 330 Hz   (c) 1.0 kHz **47.** 403 m   **49.** 83.6 kHz   **51.** 640 Hz   **53.** (a) 670 m (b) 2.8 s   **55.** (a) 319 Hz   (b) 319 Hz; 1.1 m   **57.** 17.9 Hz; 53.6 Hz; 89.3 Hz; 125 Hz   **59.** 1280 N   **61.** (b) First object: 110%; second object: 46%   **63.** 2.3 kHz   **65.** 196 Hz **67.** 2.0 km   **69.** (a) 6.7×10^{-8} m/s   (b) 1×10^{-19} J   (c) The ear is about as sensitive as it can be.   **71.** 29.0 dB   **73.** 0.019

Review and Synthesis: Chapters 9–12

Review Exercises

1. (a) Aluminum, since it is less dense it occupies more volume. (b) Wood, since it displaces more water than the steel. (c) Lead: 0.87 N; aluminum: 3.6 N; steel: 1.2 N; wood: 9.8 N **3.** 0.116 m/s   **5.** 0.88 m/s   **7.** (a) Eq. I; 1.50 cm/s   (b) Eq. II; 2.09 cm   (c) Eq. II; 13.5 cm/s   (d) Eq. II   **9.** (a) 58 N (b) 49 cm   **11.** 21.4 cm   **13.** 1500 Hz; 22.9 cm   **15.** about 1 min   **17.** 346 Hz   **19.** (a) 41.7 cm/s; 118 kPa   (b) 5.98 cm

MCAT Review

1. A   **2.** A   **3.** D   **4.** C   **5.** C   **6.** B   **7.** D   **8.** B   **9.** B **10.** A   **11.** B   **12.** D   **13.** C   **14.** C

Chapter 13

Multiple-Choice Questions

1. (e)   **2.** (d)   **3.** (b)   **4.** (c)   **5.** (b)   **6.** (d)   **7.** (a)   **8.** (c) **9.** (c)   **10.** (e)

Problems

1. (a) 29°C   (b) 302 K   **3.** (a) −40   (b) 575 **5.** $T_J = (0.750°\text{J}/°\text{C})T_C + 85.5°\text{J}$ **7.** 2.0 mm   **9.** (a) 3.6 mm (b) 10.8 mm   **11.** $3.8 \times 10^{-4} \text{ mm}^2$ **13.** (b) 2.4×10^{-3} **15.** 1.67 mL   **17.** 75°C   **19.** 1.3 m   **23.** 150°C   **25.** 24.98 cm **29.** 7.31×10^{-26} kg   **31.** 1.7×10^{27} **33.** 10^{18} atoms **35.** 2.650×10^{25} atoms   **37.** 8.9985 mol   **39.** 2.5×10^{19} molecules   **41.** 400°C   **45.** 135 kPa   **47.** (a) 1.3 kg/m^3 (b) 1.2 kg/m^3 **49.** 2.1 mm   **51.** 1.3×10^3 m^3 **53.** 1.50

55. (a) 28 min   (b) 11 min   **57.** 1.3×10^{26} **59.** (b) $3410 \times 10^{-6} \text{ K}^{-1}$ **61.** 152 J   **65.** 3.4 kJ   **67.** $\dfrac{1}{\sqrt{2}}$ **69.** (a) 493 m/s   (b) 461 m/s   (c) 393 m/s   **71.** yes **73.** 2220 K   **77.** 0.14°C   **79.** (a) 100 nm   (b) 200 nm (c) 1 m   **81.** 2.5×10^4 s   **83.** 140 atm   **85.** 165°C **87.** 3.05 mm   **89.** (a) The number of moles decreases by 25%. (b) −48°C   **91.** (b) 0.7 m   **93.** (a) 0.400 mm Hg/°C (b) 3.21×10^{-3} mol   **95.** 4 nm   **97.** (a) 5.2×10^{24} m^{-3} (b) 1.9%   **99.** 630°C   **101.** HNO_3 **103.** (a) 6.42×10^{-21} J (b) 0.25%   **105.** 1.9×10^{14} molecules   **107.** 25 m/s **109.** 7.4×10^3 N/m

Chapter 14

Multiple-Choice Questions

1. (a)   **2.** (b)   **3.** (d)   **4.** (d)   **5.** (c)   **6.** (b)   **7.** (c)   **8.** (d) **9.** (d)   **10.** (b)   **11.** (c)   **12.** (c)

Problems

1. (a) 34 J   (b) Yes; the increase in internal energy causes a slight temperature increase.   **3.** 4.90 kJ   **5.** (a) 250 J   (b) all three **7.** 5.4 J   **9.** 2.78×10^{-4} kW·h   **11.** 6.40×10^{-4} kJ/K **13.** 0.50 MJ   **15.** 700 m   **17.** (a) 2430 kJ/K   (b) 3500 kJ/K **19.** 742 kJ   **21.** 0.13 kJ/(kg·K)   **23.** 0.090 J   **25.** 27.5 kJ **27.** 57 kJ   **29.** 58°C   **31.** (a) B to C, solid to liquid; D to E, liquid to gas   (b) B   (c) D   **33.** 80 cal/g   **35.** 461 g   **37.** The ice will melt completely; 32°C   **39.** 157 g   **41.** 242 g; 35% **43.** 22.8 kJ/kg   **45.** 46.3 g   **47.** 2 g   **49.** 250 W **51.** (a) 2.0 cm   (b) 29 m   **53.** (a) 0.12 K/W (b) 2.5×10^{-4} K/W   (c) 5.0×10^{-5} K/W   **55.** 6.67 W/m^2 **57.** (a) 0.32 W   (b) 800 K/m   (c) 0.16 W   (d) 0.64 W (e) 64°C   **59.** −37°C   **61.** 112.0°C   **63.** 160 W   **65.** 420 W/m^2 **67.** 1.76 µm   **69.** 0.60   **71.** 150 W   **73.** Coffeepot: 4.5 W; teapot: 24 W   **75.** 390 W   **77.** (a) 39°C   (b) 182 W/m^2 **79.** 1.38 kW   **81.** 342 kJ   **83.** 330 m/s   **85.** 0.84 kJ/(kg·K) **87.** 0°C   **89.** 0.010°C   **91.** 10.4 W   **93.** (a) 9.9 kJ (b) 360 g   **95.** 5400 kcal/h   **97.** 480 g   **99.** 4.0 times higher **101.** (a) 190 W   (b) 31°C   (c) Wearing clothing slows heat loss by radiation because air layers trapped between clothing layers act as insulation.   **103.** 15.2 kJ/mol   **105.** $d_b = 1.3d_s$ **107.** 35°C   **109.** 2 days

Chapter 15

Multiple-Choice Questions

1. (d)   **2.** (d)   **3.** (c)   **4.** (c)   **5.** (d)   **6.** (c)   **7.** (a)   **8.** (c) **9.** (d)   **10.** (d)   **11.** (e)   **12.** (b)   **13.** (d)

Problems

1. 2.9 J   **3.** 100 J of heat flows out of the system.   **5.** 202.6 J **7.** (a) 98.0 kPa; 1180 K   (b) −200 J   (c) 66 J   (d) $\Delta U = 0$ because $\Delta T = 0$ in a cycle.   **9.** (a) −1372 J   (b) $\Delta U = 1216$ J; $Q = 2588$ J   **11.** −5.00 kJ; the heat flows out of the gas and into the reservoir.   **13.** 0.628   **15.** (a) 3.00 kJ   (b) 2.00 kJ **17.** 2.6×10^5 W; 1.9×10^5 W   **19.** 2.5×10^7 m^2 or 25 km^2 **21.** 1770 J   **23.** \$2.40   **25.** (a) 0.34   (b) 0.640   **27.** 0.0481

29. 4.5 GW   **31.** 14 W   **33.** The coal-fired plant and the nuclear plant exhaust 0.43 MJ and 0.60 MJ of heat, respectively.
35. (a) 443 K   (b) 233 J   **37.** 4.2%   **39.** 12 kJ   **41.** 0.0174
45. +250 W   **47.** (b), (a), (c), (d)   **49.** 0.12 J/K
51. +6.05 kJ/K   **53.** (a) 3.4×10^{-3} J/K   (b) -2.8×10^{-3} J/K
(c) 6.2×10^{-3} J/K   **55.** 0.102 J/(K·s)
57.

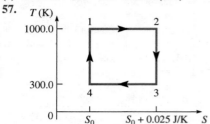

59. (a)

First Choice	Second Choice
1	2
1	3
1	4
2	1
3	1
4	1

(b) six
(c)

First Choice	Second Choice
2	3
2	4
3	2
3	4
4	2
4	3

(d) six   (e) No; the two are equally likely.   **61.** 1.79k
63. (a) $N_1 N_2$ (b) 36   (c) 11   (d) 7   (e) 1/6   (f) 1/36
65. $e^{8.9 \times 10^{22}}$ **67.** (a) 16   (b) 5   (c) two marbles in each box
(d) 2.47×10^{-23} J/K   (e) The two cases where four marbles are in one box and none are in the other.   (f) 0   **69.** (a) 304 kJ
(b) 2350 K   (c) 13.0 mol   **71.** The engine will not work.
73. 15 kJ   **75.** (a) 15.9°C   (b) −0.03 J/K   (c) The entropy of the universe never decreases.   **77.** -5.867×10^{-23} J/K; the entropy required to flip the coins is greater than the decrease in entropy of the coins.   **79.** 0.079 J   **81.** 24°C   **83.** 62.8 kW
85. (a) 22.0 J/K   (b) 0.777 J/K
87.

89. 87.1 kJ
91. (a)

Stage	W (J)	Q (J)	ΔU (J)
A	692	692	0
B	0	−2080	−2080
C	−506	−506	0
D	0	2080	2080

(b) 0.0670   (c) 0.268; $e_r = 4.00e$ **93.** (a) 0.051   (b) 31 m^3
(c) yes

Review and Synthesis: Chapters 13–15

Review Exercises

1. 108 kJ   **3.** (a) 74 g   (b) 11°C   **5.** 467 mol   **7.** (a) 320 W
(b) 18 kW   **9.** (a) 8.87 kPa; 1200 K   (b) 23 kJ   (c) 20.0 kJ
(d) 0   **11.** 10.9°C   **13.** 136 g/h   **15.** 60 Hz   **17.** (a) 39.6%
(b) 4.98×10^8 W   **19.** 0.168 m

MCAT Review

1. C   **2.** B   **3.** C   **4.** B   **5.** A   **6.** D   **7.** A   **8.** C   **9.** B
10. A   **11.** A

Chapter 16

Multiple-Choice Questions

1. (j)   **2.** (d)   **3.** (e)   **4.** (a)   **5.** (c)   **6.** (b)   **7.** (d)   **8.** (c)
9. (b)   **10.** (b)

Problems

1. 9.6×10^5 C   **3.** (a) added   (b) 3.7×10^9 **5.** (a) negative charge   (b) an equal magnitude of positive charge   **7.** $Q/4$; 0
9. 30 km   **11.** 6.21 μC and 1.29 μC   **13.** 2.268×10^{39}
15. 1.2 N at 28° below the negative x-axis   **17.** (a) 6.0×10^{-5} N toward the −3.0-nC charge   (b) 6.0×10^{-5} N toward the 2.0-nC charge   **19.** 8.617×10^{-11} C/kg   **21.** 2.8×10^{-12} N toward the Cl$^-$ ion   **23.** 6.8 mN   **25.** 1.61 N in the $+x$-direction
27. The charge should be placed on a line that makes an angle of 75.4° above the negative x-axis at a distance of 0.254 m along that line from point A. Thus, the charge is above and to the left of A.
29. (a) into the cell   (b) 1.6×10^{-12} N
31.

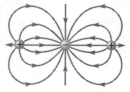

33. 3.2×10^{12} m/s^2 up   **35.** $\dfrac{kq}{2d^2}$ in the $+x$-direction

37. 400 N/C   **39.** $-0.43q$
41.

43. (a) 8.010×10^{-17} N down   (b) 2.40×10^{-19} J   **45.** (a) The gravitational force is about 1/3 of the electrical force, so the gravitational force can't be neglected.   (b) 1.78 m   **47.** 1.3×10^5 N/C
49. (a) vertically downward   (b) 2600 N/C   (c) 4.3×10^{-17} m
51. (a) 6.8×10^6 N/C   (b) 0   (c) 2.3×10^6 N/C
53. (a) $-6\,\mu$C   (b) $12\,\mu$C   **55.** (a) -6.8×10^5 C; -1.3 nC/m^2
(b) 1×10^{-12} C/m^3 **57.** 1.68×10^4 N·m^2/C   **59.** $0.866EA$
61. (a)

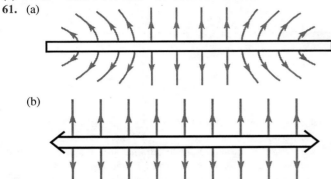

(b)

(c) The field strength is independent of the distance from the sheet.   (d) yes
63. (a)

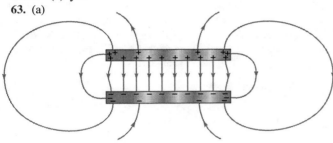

The fields due to each plate have the same direction (adding fields) between the plates and opposite directions (canceling fields) outside. Thus, the field is much stronger between the plates.   (c) The result agrees.

65. (a) $E(r \geq R) = \dfrac{kq}{r^2}$ (b) $E(r \leq R) = \dfrac{kq}{R^3}r$

(c)

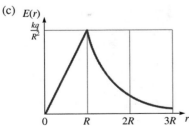

67. $6\,\mu$C/m   **69.** $E_x = 2.89 \times 10^5$ N/C; $E_y = 2.77 \times 10^6$ N/C
71. 1.3 m
73.

75. (a) 8.4×10^7 m/s   (b) 6.6 ns   **77.** $x = 33$ cm
79. 2.2×10^6 m/s   **81.** (a) $|Q_S| = 1.712 \times 10^{20}$ C and $|Q_E| = 5.148 \times 10^{14}$ C   (b) No, the force would be repulsive.

83. (a) $\dfrac{kqd}{x^3}$ (b) negative y-direction for all x **85.** -1.5 nC

87. 0.80   **89.** (a) 2 mN   (b) Coulomb's law is only valid for point charges or when the sizes of the charge distributions are much smaller than their separation.   (c) smaller

Chapter 17

Multiple-Choice Questions

1. (a)   **2.** (f)   **3.** (c)   **4.** (e)   **5.** (d)   **6.** (b)   **7.** (f)   **8.** (e)
9. (b)   **10.** (b)   **11.** (b)   **12.** (d)

Problems

1. -18 mJ   **3.** 8.4 J   **5.** -3.0 J   **7.** 2.8 mJ   **9.** $\vec{E} = 0$;
$V = 2.3 \times 10^7$ V   **11.** (a) -1.5 kV   (b) -900 V   (c) 600 V;
increase   (d) -6.0×10^{-7} J; decrease   (e) 6.0×10^{-7} J
13. (a) positive   (b) 10.0 cm
15. (a)   (b) 36 kV

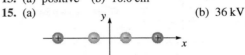

17. 9.0 V   **19.** (a) $V_a = 300$ V; $V_b = 0$ (b) 0   **23.** (a) Y
(b) 5.0 V   **25.**   ; spheres

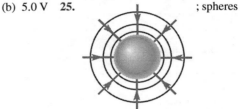

27. (a) 3.6 kW   (b) 5.4 J   **29.** $2e$ **31.** 9.612×10^{-14} J
33. (a) to a lower potential   (b) -188 V   **35.** 0
37. (a) upward   (b) $\dfrac{v_y md}{e\,\Delta V}$ (c) decreases   **39.** $612\,\mu$C
41. (a) stays the same   (b) increases   **43.** (a) 0.347 pF
(b) 0.463 pF   **45.** 8.0 pF   **47.** 4.51×10^6 m/s
49. (a) 3.3×10^3 V/m   (b) 6.0×10^2 V/m   **51.** (a) 1.1×10^5 V/m
toward the hind legs   (b) Cow A   **53.** 0.30 mm   **55.** 89 nF
57. (a) $7.1\,\mu$F   (b) 1.1×10^4 V   **59.** The energy increases by 50%.   **61.** (a) $0.18\,\mu$F   (b) 8.9×10^8 J   **63.** (a) 18 nC
(b) $1.3\,\mu$J   **65.** (a) 630 V   (b) 0.063 C   **67.** 0.27 mJ
69. (a) 0.14 C   (b) 0.30 MW   **71.** (a) 10.0 GJ   (b) 443 kg
(c) 0.694 month   **73.** (a) $U_a = -6.3\,\mu$J; $U_b = U_c = 0$ (b) $-6.3\,\mu$J
75. 450 kV   **77.** (a)

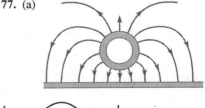

(b)

79. 4.85×10^{-14} m   **81.** 9×10^6 V/m   **83.** 51
85. 8.29×10^6 **87.** 3.44 mK   **89.** 5×10^{-14} F
91. (a) 2.5×10^{-12} J   (b) 3.4×10^8 ions   **93.** 6.0×10^{-15} J
95. 3.2×10^{-17} J   **97.** $3.0U_0$ **99.** (a) 3.2×10^{-7} F/m   (b) the outside of the membrane; 8.8×10^{-4} C/m^2

Chapter 18

Multiple-Choice Questions

1. (a)   **2.** (d)   **3.** (f)   **4.** (d)   **5.** (c)   **6.** (b)   **7.** (b)   **8.** (d)
9. (d)   **10.** (b)

Problems

1. 4.3×10^4 C   **3.** (a) from the anode to the filament
(b) 0.96 μA   **5.** 2.0×10^{15} electrons/s   **7.** 22.1 mA
9. 810 J   **11.** (a) 264 C   (b) 3.17 kJ   **13.** $v_1 = 4v_2$
15. 17.8 min   **17.** 81 μm   **19.** 0.11 mm/s   **21.** 1.3 A
23. 0.794   **25.** (a) 50 V   (b) to avoid becoming part of the
circuit   **27.** 2.5 mm   **29.** 1750°C   **31.** 4.0 V; 4.0 A
33. $E = \rho \dfrac{I}{A}$, where ρ is the resistivity.   **35.** The electric field
stays the same, the resistivity decreases, and the drift speed
increases.   **37.** (a) 7.0 V   (b) 18 Ω   **39.** (a) 23.0 μF
(b) 368 μC   (c) 48 μC   **41.** (a) 5.0 Ω   (b) 2.0 A
43. (a) 1.5 μF   (b) 37 μC   **45.** (a) 0.50 A   (b) 1.0 A
(c) 2.0 A   **47.** (a) $R/8$ (b) 0   (c) 16 A   **49.** (a) 8.0 μF
(b) 17 V   (c) 1.0×10^{-4} C   **51.** (a) 2.00 Ω   (b) 3.00 A
(c) 0.375 A

53.

Branch	I (A)	Direction
AB	0.20	right to left
FC	0.12	left to right
ED	0.076	left to right

55. 75 V; 8.1 Ω   **57.** 4.0 W   **59.** 0.50 A   **61.** yes; 600 W
63. 80.0 J   **65.** (a)

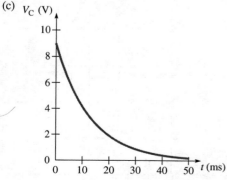

(b) 1.1 A   (c) 41 V
(d) upper branch: 0.68 A;
lower branch: 0.45 A
(e) $P_{50} = 64$ W; $P_{70} = 14$ W;
$P_{40} = 18$ W

67. (a) 36.5 Ω   (b) 0.657 A   (c) 7.58 V   (d) 0.505 A
(e) 3.83 W   **69.** (a) 6.5 Ω   (b) 18 A   (c) 0.86 mm   (d) 21 A
71. (a) 5.28 V   (b) 6.34 W   **73.** (a) in parallel; 120 Ω
(b) The meter readings should be multiplied by 1.20 to get the correct current values.   **75.** 833 kΩ   **77.** (a) 25 kΩ   (b) 250 kΩ
79. (a) 6.27 mA   (b) 5.37 mA   **81.** 2.77 s   **83.** (a) 140 μF;
90 Ω; 5.8 mJ   (b) 4.4 ms
(c)

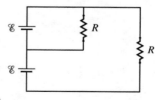

85. (a) 632 V   (b) 63.2 mC   (c) 6.7 Ω
87. (a)

(b) 1.2×10^{-4} C; 0   (c) 1.2 ms
(d) 8.0×10^{-4} s

89. (a) $I_1 = I_2 = 0.30$ mA; $V_1 = V_2 = 12$ V   (b) $I_1 = I_2 = 0.18$ mA;
$V_1 = 12$ V; $V_2 = 7.3$ V   (c) $I_1 = I_2 = 25$ μA; $V_1 = 12$ V; $V_2 = 0.99$ V
91. (a)

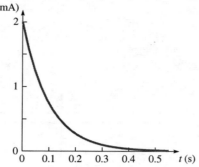

(b) 20 mW   (c) 1 mJ
93. (a) 4.2 mC   (b) 470 μF   (c) 130 Ω   (d) 74 ms
95. 50 mA   **97.** (a) The microwave is not grounded.   (b) The
wires are too small to handle the current.   (c) If a fuse blows out,
too much current is drawn, and the appliance has a short circuit.
(d) An electrical fire breaking out inside the kitchen wall is likely
the result of poor household wiring.   **99.** –8 V   **101.** (a) 2.00 A
(b) 1.00 A   **103.** (a) 9.6 Ω   (b) 13 A   (c) 1.3 cents
(d) 6.0 kW   (e) 25 A   **105.** (a) 0.090 F   (b) 2.5 TJ
(c) 29 kΩ; 260 A   (d) 200 min   **107.** 31 μA   **109.** 9.3 A
111. (a) The positive ions move down and the negative ions move
up.   (b) down   (c) 0.014 m/s   (d) 1.3 kA   **113.** (a) 250 MΩ
(b) 640 kΩ   (c) 0.50 mm   **115.** 7.21 V
117. (a)

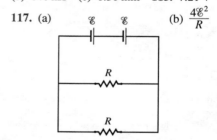

 (b) $\dfrac{4\mathcal{E}^2}{R}$

(c) The bulb on the right is brighter.

119. $\dfrac{\mathcal{E}^2}{2R}$ **121.** (a) 16%   (b) smaller   **123.** (a) 30 μA
(b) A: 3.0 V; B and C: 0.86 V   **125.** (a) 9.9 nC
(b) (c) 50 nJ

127. 350 Ω

Review and Synthesis: Chapters 16–18

Review Exercises

1. 12.0 µC   3. 6.24 N at 16.1° below the +x-axis
5. (a) –238 nC   (b) 0.889 N   7. 4.4 mm   9. (a) 35.0 Ω
(b) 0.686 A   (c) 16.5 W   (d) 6.9 V   (e) 0.34 A   (f) 2.4 W
11. 3.01×10^{-12} m   13. (a) 0.44 A   (b) 5.3 V   15. The
charge on the plates increases by a factor of 310.   17. 66.7 Ω
19. (a) 200 nC   (b) 5.6 µC   21. (a) 710 µF   (b) 9.8
(c) 8.0 kW   (d) 64 J

23. (a) $\sqrt{\dfrac{9\eta v_{t}}{2(\rho_{oil}-\rho_{air})g}}$ (b) $\dfrac{4\pi R^{3}\,(\rho_{oil}-\rho_{air})g}{3E}$

MCAT Review

1. D   2. C   3. C   4. B   5. A   6. D   7. A   8. C
9. D   10. C   11. C   12. C   13. C

Chapter 19

Multiple-Choice Questions

1. (g)   2. (f)   3. (e)   4. (e)   5. (c)   6. (b)   7. (c)   8. (g)
9. (b)   10. (b)   11. (d)   12. (d)

Problems

1. (a) F (b) A; highest density of field lines at point A and
lowest density at point F
3.

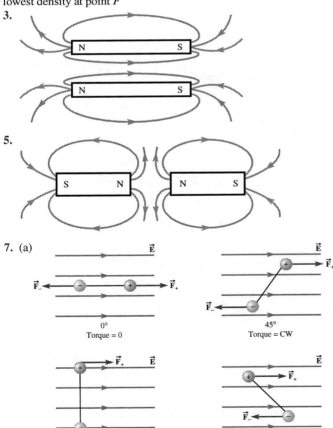

5.

7. (a)

(b) parallel to the electric field lines

9. 7.4×10^{-12} N east   11. (a) 3.0×10^{7} m/s   (b) 4.2×10^{18} m/s²
(c) 3.0×10^{7} m/s   (d) 2.4×10^{7} V/m   (e) Since the force due
to the magnetic field is always perpendicular to the velocity of the
electrons, it does not increase the electrons' speed but only
changes their direction.   13. 12 cm into the page   15. There are
two possibilities: 56° N of W and 56° N of E.   17. 2.1×10^{-16} N
to the west   19. particle 1: negative; particle 2: positive
21. 2.6×10^{-25} kg   23. 0.17 T   25. (a) 39 u   (b) potassium
27. 4.22×10^{6} m/s   29. (a), (b)

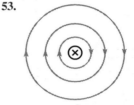

31. 8.4×10^{28} m⁻³   33. (a) upward   (b) 0.20 mm/s
35. (a) 0.35 m/s   (b) 4.4×10^{-6} m³/s   (c) the east lead
37. (a) 2.2 N   (b) Only the maximum possible force can be
calculated since only the magnitudes, and not the directions,
of $\vec{B}$ and $\vec{L}$ are given.   39. 0.072 N north   41. 0.33 A to the
left   43. (a) $\vec{F}_{top} = 0$; $\vec{F}_{bottom} = 0$; $\vec{F}_{left} = 0.50$ N out of the page;
$\vec{F}_{right} = 0.50$ N into the page   (b) 0   45. (a) 0.21 T
(b) clockwise   49. 4.9°
53.

55. (a) 9×10^{-8} T out of the page   (b) 1.6×10^{-5} T out of the
page   57. 3.2×10^{-16} N parallel to the current   59. B, D, C, A
61. 750 A into the page   63. $\dfrac{4}{\pi} B_{loop} \approx 1.27\, B_{loop}$ 65. (a) $5I$
out of the page   (b) $2I$ into the page   69. (c) S and (d) N
71. (a) 1.1 mA   (b) 9.3×10^{-24} A·m²   (c) The orbital and
intrinsic dipole moments are the same.   73. (a) graph a;
(b) graph c   75. 21 cm   77. (a) 1.7×10^{-8} N   (b) up
79. 8.94×10^{-5} T at 26.6° south of east   81. $\dfrac{2\pi m}{qB}$
83. (a) 1.1 mm/s   (b) 17 µV   (c) left side   85. (a) positive
(b) west   (c) north   (d) $\Delta V_1 = 1.6$ kV; $\Delta V_2 = 320$ V   (e) ΔV_1
= 1.4 kV; $\Delta V_2 = 280$ V   87. (a) $\vec{F}_{top} = 0.65$ N into the page;
$\vec{F}_{bottom} = 0.65$ N out of the page; $\vec{F}_{right} = 0.25$ N out of the page;
$\vec{F}_{left} = 0.25$ N into the page   (b) 0   89. (a) to the right
(b) 80 µT   91. (a)

Side	Current direction	Field direction	Force direction
top	right	out of the page	attracted to long wire
bottom	left	out of the page	repelled by long wire
left	up	out of the page	right
right	down	out of the page	left

(b) 1.0×10^{-8} N away from the long wire   93. into the page
95. (a) 9.5 A   (b) CCW   97. (a) 20 MHz   (b) 3.3×10^{-13} J
(c) 2.1 MV   (d) 100 rev   99. 52.4 cm

Chapter 20

Multiple-Choice Questions

1. (c)   **2.** (c)   **3.** (d)   **4.** (b)   **5.** (d)   **6.** (e)   **7.** (e)   **8.** (b)
9. (b)   **10.** (c)

Problems

1. (a) $\dfrac{vBL}{R}$ (b) CCW   (c) left   (d) $\dfrac{vB^2L^2}{R}$ **3.** (a) $\dfrac{vB^2L^2}{R}$
(b) $\dfrac{v^2B^2L^2}{R}$ (c) $\dfrac{v^2B^2L^2}{R}$ (d) Energy is conserved since the rate
at which the external force does work is equal to the power
dissipated in the resistor.   **5.** (a) 3.44 m/s   (b) The magnitude
of the change in gravitational potential energy per second and the
power dissipated in the resistor are the same, 0.505 W.
7. (a) into the page   (b) no   (c) no   (d) $\vec{\mathbf{F}}$ is out of the page;
no, electrons are pushed perpendicular to the length of the wire;
there is no induced emf. The situation for side 1 is identical to that
of side 3.   **9.** (a) positive   (b) $\frac{1}{2}\omega BR^2$ **11.** (a) 0.090 Wb
(b) 0.16 Wb   (c) $-z$-direction   **13.** (a) CW   (b) away from
the long straight wire   (c) 2.0 Wb/s   **17.** (a) to the right
(b) to the left
(c)

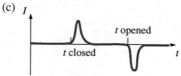

19. (a) $v_x(t) = -\omega x_m \sin \omega t$ (b) $\omega \Phi_0$ **21.** (a) 7.5 A   (b) 3.0 A
(c) 56 V   **23.** (a) 6.0 A   (b) 0.50 A   (c) 11 V   **25.** 0.10 A
27. 64 V   **29.** 1300   **31.** (a) 14   (b) 29 mA
33.

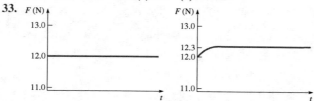

35. 1.8×10^{-7} Wb   **37.** The inductance is increased to 2.0 times
its initial value.   **39.** $U_E = 10^{-6}U_B$ **41.** 1.6 mV

43. $L_{eq} = \dfrac{L_1 L_2}{L_1 + L_2}$ **45.** (a) $V_{5.0} = 2.0$ V; $V_{10.0} = 4.0$ V
(b) $V_{5.0} = 6.0$ V; $V_{10.0} = 0$ (c) 1.2 A   **47.** (a) 38 mJ
(b) -7.5 W   (c) -38 mW   (d) 69 ms   **49.** (a) $I_1 = 1.7$ mA;
$I_2 = 0$; $V_{3.0} = 0$; $V_{27} = 45$ V; $P = 75$ mW; $V_L = 45$ V
(b) $I_1 = 1.7$ mA; $I_2 = 15$ mA; $V_{3.0} = V_{27} = 45$ V; $P = 0.75$ W;
$V_L = 0$ **51.** (a) 180 mA   (b) 2.5 mJ   (c) 1.1 W   (d) 0
53. (a) 5.7×10^{-6} s   (b) 1.1×10^{-5} J   (c) 8.8×10^{-6} s; This is
more than in part (a) because the energy stored in the inductor is
proportional to the current squared. It takes longer for the *square*
of the current to be 67% of the maximum *square* of the current
than for the current itself to be 67% of the maximum current.
55. (a) 0.27 W   (b) 0.27 W   (c) 0.55 W   **57.** (a) no   (b) no
59. (a) $2\pi r^2 NB$ (b) $\dfrac{2\pi r^2 NB}{\Delta t}$ (c) $\dfrac{2\pi r^2 NB}{R\,\Delta t}$ (d) $\dfrac{2\pi r^2 NB}{R}$

61.

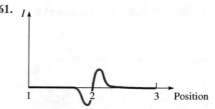

63. (a) CW   (b) 8.0 V   (c) yes; upward   (d) R decreases;
I increases; the magnetic force increases   **65.** $\dfrac{\mu_0 N^2 a^2}{2\pi R}$
67. (a) $\dfrac{\mu_0 N_1 N_2 \pi r^2}{L}$ (b) $\dfrac{\mu_0 N_1 N_2 \pi r^2 I_m \sin \omega t}{L}$
(c) $\dfrac{\mu_0 N_1 N_2 \pi r^2 \omega I_m \cos \omega t}{L}$ **69.** 250 rad/s   **71.** 68 nWb
73. (a) 3.1 V   (b) the northernmost wingtip
75. (a) 0.64 GJ/m^3 (b) 1.2×10^{10} V/m   **77.** 85
79. (a) $\dfrac{\mu_0 N_1 N_2 \pi r^2}{L}$ (b) $\dfrac{\mu_0 N_1 N_2 \pi r^2}{L} \dfrac{\Delta I_1}{\Delta t}$ **81.** (a) No; for dc
the magnetic field is constant so no emf is induced.   (b) No; the
currents flow in opposite directions.

Chapter 21

Multiple-Choice Questions

1. (i)   **2.** (b)   **3.** (a)   **4.** (d)   **5.** (a)   **6.** (d)   **7.** (c)   **8.** (c)
9. (c)   **10.** (b)

Problems

1. 120 times per second   **3.** 18 A   **5.** 6000 W; the heating element of the hair dryer will burn out because it is not designed for
this amount of power.   **7.** (a) 35 A   (b) 3.2 kW   **9.** -5.7 V and
5.7 V   **13.** The current is increased by a factor of 6.0.
15. (a) 60.0 Hz   (b) 13.3 kΩ **17.** 53 nF   **19.** (a) 8.0×10^5 Ω
(b) 3.3
21. (a)   (b) 0.48 A

C (μF)	V (V)
2.0	6.0
3.0	4.0
6.0	2.0

23. The current is reduced by a factor of 1/6.0.   **25.** 27 Ω
27. 7.33 kHz   **29.** (a) 180°   (b) 4.0 V
31.

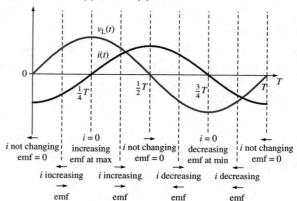

33. 470 Hz   **35.** (a) 384 Ω   (b) 236 Ω   (c) 1.48 kW
37. (a) $V_L = 919$ V; $V_R = 771$ V   (b) no; $\mathcal{E}_m = \sqrt{V_L^2 + V_R^2}$
(c)

39. 500 Ω

41. (a) 24 Hz   (b) $\dfrac{V_R}{\mathcal{E}_m} = \dfrac{V_C}{\mathcal{E}_m} = \dfrac{1}{\sqrt{2}}$ (c) I leads $\mathcal{E}$ by $\dfrac{\pi}{4}$ rad
$= 45°$.   (d) 4.7 kΩ   **43.** (a) 0.800   (b) $P_{av,C} = P_{av,L} = 0$;
$P_{av,R} = 8.0 \times 10^{-5}$ W   **45.** 0.33 W   **47.** 8.0×10^{-7} F; 310 Ω
49. (a) $V_2 \sin \phi_2 = V \sin \phi$; the result indicates that the
y-component of V_2 is equal to the y-component of V.
(b) $V_1 + V_2 \cos \phi_2 = V \cos \phi$; the result indicates that the sum of
the x-components of V_1 and V_2 is equal to the x-component of V.
51. 0.724 pF to 1.1 pF
53. (a) 0°   (b)

(c) 98.7 Hz

55. (a) 745 rad/s   (b) 790 Ω   (c) $V_R = \mathcal{E}_m = 440$ V;
$V_C = V_L = 125$ V   **57.** $\omega_0 = 22.4$ rad/s or $f_0 = 3.56$ Hz.
59. (a) 10 kHz   (b) 840 Hz   (c) Low-pass filter; for low
frequencies, $X_C \gg R$, so V_C (= output voltage) is approximately
equal to the input voltage.   **61.** 650 μF   **63.** (a) 27.3 Ω
(b) 8.74 V   **65.** 120 times per second   **67.** (a) a capacitor
(b) 0.396 A   (c) 37 μF   **69.** (a) 570   (b) 34 A   (c) 14 kW
71. (a) 92.8 mH   (b) 28 mH   **73.** 49 μF   **75.** (a) 69.8 Ω
(b) 185 mH   **77.** (a) 20 A   (b) 26 A   **79.** (a) $X_C = 20$ Ω;
$X_L = 35$ Ω   (b) 25 Ω   (c) 4.0 A   (d) 5.7 A   (e) 37°
(f) $V_{R\,rms} = 80$ V; $V_{L\,rms} = 140$ V; $V_{C\,rms} = 80$ V   (g) The current
lags the voltage.   (h)

81. (a) 13 Ω   (b) 18 A   (c) 27°   (d) The current leads the
voltage.   (e) $V_{R\,rms} = 210$ V; $V_{L\,rms} = 4.3$ kV; $V_{C\,rms} = 4.4$ kV;
83. (a) 0.75; ±41°   (b) No; V_L and V_C cannot be determined.
85. (a) 48 A   (b) 56 A   (c) The power lost in transmission is
greater.   **87.** (a) 0.3 H   (b) Yes; an inductor reduces the output
with little energy loss and, therefore, it is a much better choice for
a dimmer.

Review and Synthesis: Chapters 19–21

Review Exercises

1. 1.2 N·m; when the plane of the loop is parallel to the axis of
the solenoid.   **3.** (a) 1.66×10^{-4} T along the $+x$-axis   (b) out of
the page   (c) 8.84 A   **5.** 1.8×10^{-17} N out of the plane of the
paper in the side view (or to the right in the end on view)
7. (a) 6.7×10^3 A   (b) 530 MW; all of the power is dissipated,
since 530 MW is greater than the total power output of the power
plant.   (c) 17 A   (d) 3.3 kW; 0.42%   (e) 25
9. (a) A counterclockwise current is induced because the flux
through the loop is increasing as it nears the wire; the net force on
the loop is away from the wire.   (b) No current is induced
because there is no change in flux through the loop; there is no
magnetic force acting on the loop.   (c) A clockwise current is
induced because the flux through the loop is decreasing as it
moves away from the wire; the net force on the loop is toward the
wire.   **11.** (a) to the right   (b) 13.6 m/s   (c) The applied emf
has to increase because of the increased resistance in the longer
rail lengths in the circuit and because of the increasingly large
induced emf as the rod moves faster ($\mathcal{E} = vBL$).   **13.** (a) The
power is cut in half.   (b) The power is 4/5 of its original value.
15. (a) 445 Hz   (b) current   (c) −67°   (d) 0.51 A   (e) 67 W
(f) $V_R = 180$ V; $V_L = 150$ V; $V_C = 590$ V   **17.** 1.73×10^{-7} T

MCAT Review

1. A   **2.** D   **3.** D   **4.** B   **5.** B   **6.** C   **7.** A   **8.** D

Chapter 22

Multiple-Choice Questions

1. (d)   **2.** (f)   **3.** (b)   **4.** (f)   **5.** (d)   **6.** (b)   **7.** (b)   **8.** (c)
9. (d)   **10.** (d)

Problems

1. $\dfrac{\mu_0 I}{2\pi r}$ **3.** $\dfrac{\mu_0 I r}{2\pi R^2}$ **5.** east-west   **9.** 3.3 m   **11.** (a) $5.00 \times$
10^6 m   (b) The radius of the Earth is 6.4×10^6 m, which is close
in value to the wavelength.   (c) radio waves   **13.** (a) about one
octave   (b) approximately 8 octaves   **15.** 5000 km; This means
that in one oscillation, 1/60th of a second, the EM wave created
from household current has traveled the entire length of the U.S.
17. 1.62   **19.** 1.67 ns   **21.** (a) 455 nm   (b) 4.34×10^{14} Hz
25. (a) 7.5 mV/m; 3.0 MHz   (b) 4.5 mV/m; in the $+x$-direction
27. (a) $+y$-direction   (b) $B_x = \dfrac{E_m}{c} \sin(ky - \omega t + \pi/6)$, $B_y = B_z = 0$
29. (a) 4.7×10^{-6} J/m³   (b) 730 V/m; 2.4×10^{-6} T   **31.** 6.8 h
33. 49 kW   **35.** (a) 4.0×10^{26} W   (b) 9400 W/m²
39. (a) 7.3×10^{-22} W   (b) 1.3×10^{-12} W
(c) 1.9×10^{-12} V/m; 6.5×10^{-21} T   **41.** (a) $\frac{1}{4} I_0 \sin^2 2\theta$ (b) 45°
43. 21.1%   **45.** (a) (a)   (b) (c)   (c) $0.750 I_1$ **47.** 45.0 m/s
49. farther apart; 1.80×10^8 m/s   **51.** (a) 5.0×10^{12} Hz
(b) 3.3×10^6 Hz   (c) 23.5 Hz   (d) 2.00×10^{-3} Hz   **53.** 2.56 s
55. 1.58   **57.** (a) infrared   (b) 6.00 mm   (c) 4.51 mm
(d) 5660   (e) 1.20 pJ   **61.** 2.2×10^4 rad/s, 4.4×10^4 rad/s,
6.6×10^4 rad/s   **63.** 4.53×10^{-15} J/m³; 1.36×10^{-6} W/m²
65. (a) 8.0×10^5 W/m²   (b) 1.8×10^{-9} W/m²   **67.** (a) 4.3 min
(b) 8.7 min

Chapter 23

Multiple-Choice Questions

1. (b)   **2.** (d)   **3.** (f)   **4.** (c)   **5.** (d)   **6.** (c)   **7.** (b)   **8.** (d)
9. (a)   **10.** (d)

Problems

1.

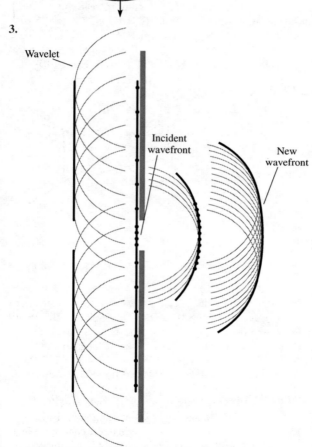

3.

incident side: two planar waves;
transmitted side: one hemispherical wave

5.

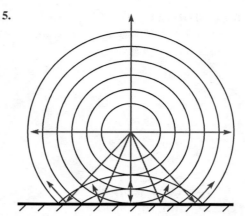

7. 100°   **11.** 63.1°   **13.** 11 m/s   **15.** 44.6°   **17.** 2.1 cm
19. $\delta = \beta(n-1)$ **21.** 44.1° ≤ θ ≤ 45.9°   **23.** (a) 24.42°
(b) 33.44°   (c) Under water, the larger critical angle means that
fewer light rays are totally reflected at the bottom surfaces of the
diamond. Thus, less light is reflected back toward the viewer.
25. (a) 1.556   (b) No; for $0 \le \theta_i \le \theta_c, 0 \le \theta_t \le 90°$.   **27.** The
minimum index of refraction is 1.41.   **29.** no   **31.** (a) the left
lens   (b) 53° (c) 1.3   **33.** (a) 37.38°   (b) perpendicular to
the plane of incidence   (c) 52.62°   **35.** 4.8 mm   **37.** 12.1 cm
39. 0.91 m;

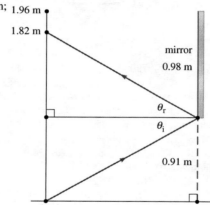

41. 2 m   **43.** He sees 7 images total.
47. 6.67 cm in front of the mirror

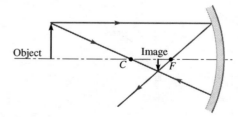

49. 18.8 cm in front of the mirror;

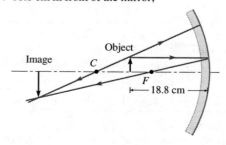

51. –210 cm   **57.** (a) 11.7 cm;

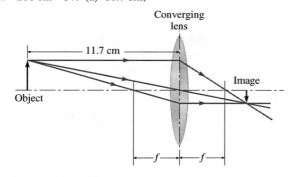

(b) real   (c) –0.429

59.

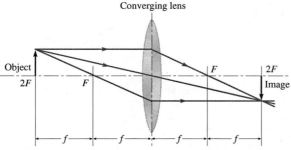

61.

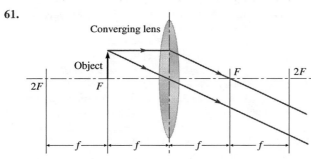

63.

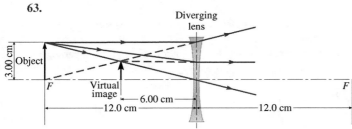

The image is located 6.00 cm from the lens on the same side as the object and has a height of 1.50 cm.

65. (a)

p (cm)	q (cm)	m	Real or virtual	Orientation	Relative size
5.00	–13.3	2.67	virtual	upright	enlarged
14.0	18.7	–1.33	real	inverted	enlarged
16.0	16.0	–1.00	real	inverted	same
20.0	13.3	–0.667	real	inverted	diminished

(b) $h' = 10.7$ cm; $h' = -2.67$ cm   **67.** (a) converging
(b) diverging   (c) converging   (d) diverging   **69.** (a) 3.24 m

(b) closer   **71.** (a) concave   (b) inside the focal length
(c) 144 cm   **73.** (a) 9.1 cm   (b) convex   (c) $f = -7.1$ cm;
$R = 14$ cm   **75.** 82.2 m   **77.** 2.79 mm   **79.** (a) 1.42
(b) 2.11×10^8 m/s   (c) 44.6°   **81.** (a) total internal reflection at
75°   (b) reflection at 25° and transmission at 34°   **83.** 8.0 km/h
85. pin-image distance = 40.0 cm; pin-mirror distance = 10.0 cm;

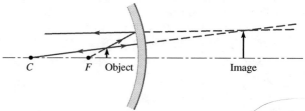

87.

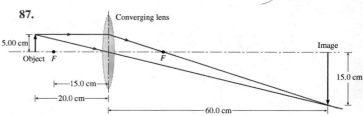

15.0 cm; 60.0 cm behind the lens   **89.** 15.0 cm; converging
95. red and yellow.   **97.** 32 cm in front of the mirror
99.

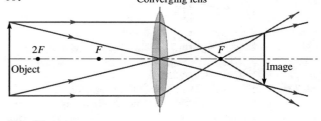

101. 50 cm

Chapter 24

Multiple-Choice Questions

1. (d)   **2.** (b)   **3.** (b)   **4.** (a)   **5.** (f)   **6.** (b)   **7.** (b)   **8.** (b)
9. (d)   **10.** (c)

Problems

1. (a) 2.5 cm past the 4.0-cm lens; real   (b) –0.27
3. (a) 11.8 cm   (b) 0.0793   **5.** 15.6 cm to the left of the
diverging lens   **7.** $q_1 = 12.0$ cm; $q_2 = -4.0$ cm; $h'_1 = -4.00$ mm;
$h'_2 = 4.0$ mm   **9.** (a) 4.05 cm   (b) converging   (c) 1.31
(d) 15.8 cm   **11.** (a) 12.0 cm to the right of the converging lens
(b) 3.3 cm to the right of the diverging lens   **13.** minimum:
20.00 cm; maximum: 22.2 cm   **15.** (a) inverted   (b) –0.42
(c) The cone of light rays, diverging from each point on the
object, is larger, so the eye can detect that the rays do not converge
to a single point.   (d) converging   (e) 2.0 m   **17.** (a) 224 mm
(b) 2.67 mm   (c) 16.7 m   **19.** 20 mm   **21.** 98 cm by 150 cm
23. (a) farsighted   (b) 70 cm to infinity   **25.** –0.50 D
27. (a) –0.51 D   (b) Without his glasses, his near point is
22 cm. With his glasses, his near point is 25 cm.   **29.** 1.4
31. (a) 4.2 cm   (b) 6.0   **33.** (a) 0.56 mm in diameter

(b) $4.4 \times 10^3 \, \text{kW/m}^2$ **35.** (a) $\dfrac{Nf}{N+f}$ (c) $M = \dfrac{N}{f} + 1 = M_\infty + 1$

37. (a) −250   (b) 0.720 cm   **39.** 50   **41.** 1.63 cm
43. (a) 19.0 cm   (b) −318   (c) 5.16 mm   **45.** (a) There
would be no magnification, so you can't really make a telescope.
(b) Using a lens from each pair of glasses, the telescope would be
1.05 m long and have an angular magnification of −2.7.
47. $f_o = 43.5$ cm; $f_e = 1.45$ cm   **49.** (a) 2.56 m   (b) 2.17 cm
(c) −15   **51.** (a) 5.10 cm to the right of the lens combination
(b) real   **53.** (a) diverging   (b) −3.0 cm
(c)

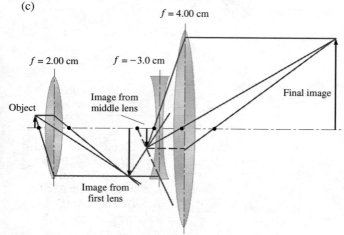

f = 2.00 cm   f = −3.0 cm   f = 4.00 cm

55. (a) Lens 1 is the objective and lens 2 is the eyepiece.
(b) 30.0 cm   **57.** 8.67 cm   **59.** (a) 5.25 cm to the right of the
lens   (b) real and inverted   (c) −0.750   (d) 1.54 cm to the
right of the mirror   (e) virtual and inverted with respect to the
original object   (f) 0.229   (g) −0.171   **61.** (a) real and
upright   (b) 30 cm to the left of the mirror   (c) 6.0
63. (a) 30 cm   (b) 3.3 D   **65.** (a) The intermediate image is
1.9 cm to the left of the first lens and the final image is 9.07 cm to
the left of the second lens.   (b) 0.42   (c) 0.84 mm   **67.** 1.7 mm
69. (a) 6.1 cm   (b) −29   **71.** (a) 1.85 cm   (b) 3.59 cm
(c) −68.2   **73.** −0.0068   **75.** (a) 1.6 m   (b) −0.63 D
(c) −0.63 D and 3.3 D

Chapter 25

Multiple-Choice Questions

1. (a)   **2.** (e)   **3.** (a)   **4.** (d)   **5.** (e)   **6.** (e)   **7.** (d)   **8.** (a)
9. (e)   **10.** (a)

Problems

1. (a) 5.0 km   (b) Destructive interference occurs, since the
path difference is 10 km and there is a $\lambda/2$ phase shift.

3. 1530 kHz   **5.**

(a) 2 cm   (b) I_0 (c) 6 cm   (d) $9I_0$ **7.** $5I_0$ **9.** 0°: 446 nm;
10.0°: 439 nm; 20.0°: 419 nm   **11.** (a) 3.2 cm   (b) 1.1
13. 86.7 μm   **15.** (a) touching; zero distance   (b) 140 nm
(c) 280 nm   **17.** 105 nm   **19.** 96 nm   **21.** (a) 683 nm, 546 nm,
and 455 nm   (b) 607 nm, 496 nm, and 420 nm   **23.** 667
27. 0.15 mm   **29.** maxima: ±6.9 cm from the central maximum;
±30°; yes, they agree.   **31.** 456 nm   **33.** 7.0×10^{-5} m
35. 8.0×10^{-5} m   **37.** 470 nm   **39.** four   **41.** (a) A is the blue
line, B is the yellow line, and C is the red line.   (b) 669 nm
(c) 2   **45.** (a) 7560 slits/cm   (b) 240   **47.** 0.61 mm
49. The new width is half the old width.   **51.** 0.19 mm
53. 0.012°   **55.** 0.47 mm   **57.** (a) $\sin \Delta \theta = n \sin \beta$
59. 0, 330 nm, 660 nm, 990 nm, and 1.3 μm, respectively
61. 20 km   **63.** 1.7 μs   **65.** (a) 0   (b) 0.30 km   (c) There
will be 12 maxima total.   (d) 0; 19°; 42°; 90°   (e) The answers
in parts (a), (b), and (c) would be unchanged. The angles calcu-
lated in part (d) for θ_0 and θ_3 would be unchanged, but θ_1 and θ_2
would be different than before.   **67.** (a) 0.10 mm   (b) 0.5 mm
69. (a) 100 nm   (b) 280 nm; 140 nm   (c) Yes; although
perfectly constructive interference does not occur for any visible
wavelength, some visible light is reflected at all visible
wavelengths except 560 nm (the only wavelength with perfectly
destructive interference).   **71.** $t = \dfrac{\lambda}{2n_{\text{coating}}}$ **73.** 1.6

75. (a)

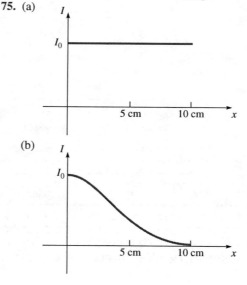

(b)

(c)

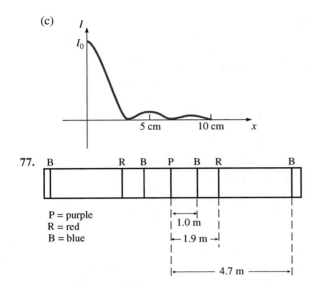

77.

P = purple
R = red
B = blue

1.0 m
1.9 m
4.7 m

Review and Synthesis: Chapters 22–25

Review Exercises

1. 85 ms   **3.** (a) 5.2×10^{14} Hz   (b) 2.00×10^8 m/s; 390 nm; 5.2×10^{14} Hz   **5.** (a) The plane must be at least $3\lambda = 638.8$ m over Juanita's head.   (b) 425.9 m and 851.7 m   **7.** (a) 8.95 m   (b) converging lens   (c) inverted   **9.** The lamps are not emitting coherent light.   **11.** 400 nm   **13.** (a) 1.80×10^{-6} m   (b) 2.24 m   (c) 6.33 m   (d) The assumption that $\sin \theta = \tan \theta$ is not valid because the angles are not small.   **15.** (a) The distance between adjacent maxima is inversely proportional to the slit separation.   (b) The distance between adjacent maxima increases linearly as the distance between the slit and the screen increases.   (c) You would want a large distance to the screen or a small slit separation or both.   **17.** 3.15 m   **19.** five   **21.** (a) 3.9 mm   (b) 7.8 mm

MCAT Review

1. A   **2.** C   **3.** B   **4.** C   **5.** C   **6.** A

Chapter 26

Multiple-Choice Questions

1. (e)   **2.** (d)   **3.** (a)   **4.** (a)   **5.** (c)   **6.** (a)   **7.** (b)   **8.** (a)
9. (b)

Problems

1. 2.2 µs   **3.** (a) 0.87c (b) c **5.** 8.9 h   **7.** 0.001c
9. (a) 30 years old   (b) 3420   **11.** 7.7 ns   **13.** (a) 2 m
(b) 0.50 m   **15.** (a) 79 m   (b) 610 ns   (c) 530 ns   **17.** 13 m
19. (a) 1.0 m   (b) 0.92 m   **21.** (a) 7.5 µs   (b) 13 µs
23. 6.0 km   **25.** (a) c (b) 0.802c **27.** 0.946c **29.** $\frac{1}{5}c$
31. $\frac{5}{13}c$ **33.** 1.0×10^{-18} kg·m/s   **35.** 4×10^{-8} %
37. (a) 1.8×10^7 N   (b) 8200 m/s²; this is much larger than any human could survive.   **39.** increased by 1.00×10^{-14} kg
41. 2.0×10^{47} J   **43.** 5.58 MeV   **45.** 0.595c **47.** 2.7×10^{15} J
49. 1 MeV/$c = 5.344 \times 10^{-22}$ kg·m/s   **51.** 4.9mc **53.** 6.5 MeV/c
59. (a) The electrons are relativistic.   (b) 0.63c **61.** 19.2 min
63. 33.9 MeV   **65.** (a) 1.2×10^{13} m   (b) 5.0×10^4 s   **67.** 92 yr

69. 1.326 GeV   **71.** 0.966c **75.** (a) 18.0 ly   (b) 22.5 yr
77. (a) 409 MeV/c (b) 147 MeV   (c) 495 MeV/c^2
79. (a) 32 J   (b) 3.3 m   (c) $\approx (1 - 1.1 \times 10^{-23})c =$
$0.999\,999\,999\,999\,999\,999\,999\,989c$ **83.** (a) $\dfrac{\gamma}{f_s}$ (b) $\dfrac{\gamma}{f_s}\left(1 + \dfrac{v}{c}\right)$

85. neutron: 5.7 MeV; pion: 35.4 MeV

Chapter 27

Multiple-Choice Questions

1. (e)   **2.** (c)   **3.** (d)   **4.** (a)   **5.** (a)   **6.** (c)   **7.** (e)   **8.** (b)
9. (e)   **10.** (f)

Problems

1. (a) ultraviolet   (b) infrared: 9.9×10^{-20} J; ultraviolet: 2.8×10^{-18} J   (c) infrared: 2.0×10^{21} photons/s; ultraviolet: 7.0×10^{19} photons/s   **3.** (a) 400 nm   (b) 7.5×10^{14} Hz
5. (a) 0.84 eV   (b) 574 nm   **7.** 477 nm   **9.** 4.5 eV
11. (a) No; violet light   (b) 2.56 eV   **13.** (a) 6.66×10^{-34} J·s
(b) 1.82 eV   **15.** 2.7 kV   **17.** 1.1×10^{19} Hz   **19.** 62.0 pm
21. (a) 2.50×10^{-12} m   (b) 55.6 keV   **23.** (a) 2.00 pm
(b) 152 pm   **25.** 2.4×10^{19} Hz   **27.** 4.45×10^6 m/s at 62.6°
south of east   **29.** 2.4×10^4 eV   **31.** 0.476 nm   **33.** (a) 1.59×10^{-10} m   (b) 1.06×10^{-8} m; the orbital separations are much larger for larger n values.   **35.** 122 eV   **37.** $n = 3$
39. 13.6 eV   **41.** 10.2 eV   **43.** (a) $\dfrac{ke^2}{r^2}$ **47.** 2.19×10^6 m/s
49. 2.11 eV   **51.** (a) one   (b) four   **53.** 370 nm   **55.** $n = 4$
57. 1.46 MeV   **59.** 2.43 pm   **61.** (a) conservation of momentum   (b) 511 keV
63. (a)

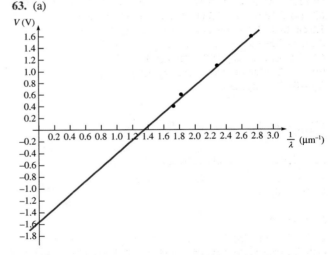

(b) 1.57 eV; 741 nm   (c) 1160 V·nm   **65.** 73 photons/s
67. 0.850 eV   **69.** $r_H/r_{He} = 1/2$; for levels of equal energy, the ratio of orbital radii appears to equal the ratio of atomic numbers.
71. (a) 1.9 eV; 9.9×10^{-28} kg·m/s   (b) 3×10^{15} photons/s
(c) 3×10^{-12} N   **73.** (a) 97.3 nm and 103 nm   (b) 4.07 m/s for the 97.3-nm photon; 3.86 m/s for the 103-nm photon   (c) two ways when the 103-nm wavelength is absorbed and four ways when the 97.3-nm wavelength is absorbed   **75.** (a) 2.426 pm
(b) 7.278 pm   (c) no change   **77.** The energies of the characteristic x-rays remain the same because they are characteristic of the target material's energy transitions.   **79.** (a) −54.4 eV

(b) −122 eV   (c) −13.6 eV   **81.** (a) 4.1 m/s   (b) 4 ways emitting 6 different photons

(c)

Transition	λ (nm)	Class
$4 \to 3$	1875	IR
$4 \to 2$	486	visible
$4 \to 1$	97	UV
$3 \to 2$	656	visible
$3 \to 1$	103	UV
$2 \to 1$	122	UV

83. 92.4 keV
85. 0.62 nm
87. 0.01541
89. (a) 97.3 nm
   (b) 102.6 nm; 656.3 nm
   (c) $\lambda \le 91.2$ nm

Chapter 28

Multiple-Choice Questions

1. (a)   **2.** (f)   **3.** (d)   **4.** (a)   **5.** (d)   **6.** (a)   **7.** (a)   **8.** (c)
9. (a)   **10.** (d)

Problems

1. 1.3×10^{-34} m; the wavelength is much smaller than the diameter of the hoop—a factor of 10^{-34} smaller!   **3.** (a) 1.0×10^{-35} m/s
(b) 3.8×10^{26} yr   **5.** 101   **7.** 3.23 pm   **9.** 250 eV
11. 391 eV   **13.** (a) 12.4 keV   (b) 150 eV   (c) 150 V
15. (a) 0.060 eV   (b) 0.060 V   (c) 5 nm is an x-ray
wavelength.   **17.** 1×10^{-29} m   **19.** (a) 1.3×10^{-32} m
(b) 1.1×10^{-6} m   **21.** 352 nm   **23.** (a) 4×10^{-32} m
(b) 0.5 mm   (c) The uncertainty principle can be neglected in the macroscopic world, but not on the atomic scale.
25. 3×10^{-4} eV   **27.** 380 GeV   **29.** (a) 6×10^{28}
(b) The energy difference between levels is too small to observe.
31. (a) 10.3 nm   (b) one fourth as much
33. (a)

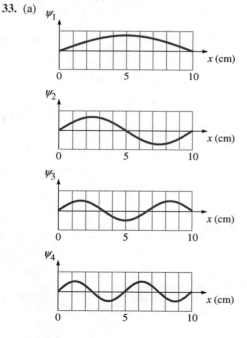

(b) 1.1×10^{-16} eV   **35.** $1s^2 2s^2 2p^6 3s^2 3p^6$ **37.** $-2\hbar, -\hbar, 0, \hbar,$
and $2\hbar$ **39.** (b) The kinetic energy of an electron at $r = 2a_0$ is zero, so there is no available energy to move the electron past this point.

41. For $\ell = 0, 1, 2, 3, 4, 5,$ and 6, there are 2, 6, 10, 14, 18, 22, and 26 electron states, respectively; the total is 98.
43. $1s^2 2s^2 2p^6 3s^2 3p^6 4s^2 3d^{10} 4p^5$ **45.** (a) Li: $1s^2 2s^1$;
Na: $1s^2 2s^2 2p^6 3s^1$; K: $1s^2 2s^2 2p^6 3s^2 3p^6 4s^1$ (b) s^1 subshell
47. (a) $1s^2 2s^2 2p^2$
(b)

n	ℓ	m_ℓ	m_s
1	0	0	$\pm\frac{1}{2}$
2	0	0	$\pm\frac{1}{2}$
2	1	−1	$\pm\frac{1}{2}$
2	1	0	$\pm\frac{1}{2}$
2	1	1	$\pm\frac{1}{2}$

49. 1.9 eV   **51.** 544 nm; green   **53.** (a) 0.0097°   (b) 130 km in diameter   **55.** −25%   **57.** 3.0 nm   **59.** (a) 2.21×10^{-34} m
(b) about 10^{-19} smaller   (c) No; the wavelength is so much smaller than any aperture that diffraction is negligible.
61. (a) 167 pm   (b) 66.5°   (c) yes   **63.** (a) 1.26 km/s
(b) 314 pm   (c) 303–324 pm
65. (a)

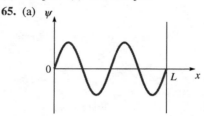

(b) $\frac{2h^2}{mL^2}$ (c)

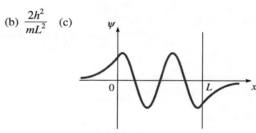

(d) less than   (e) $\frac{2L}{h}\sqrt{2mU_0}$ **67.** 1.7 kV
69. 3.9×10^{-6} eV   **71.** (a) 0.067 eV   (b) 0.20 eV, 0.33 eV, 0.47 eV, 0.53 eV, 0.80 eV, and 1.0 eV
(c) ψ (d) smaller since $E \propto 1/L^2$

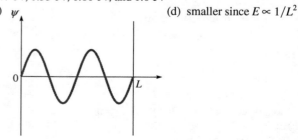

73. $\frac{1}{4}$ **75.** (a) 15,000 MeV   (b) The nucleus would be unstable because the helium-4 nucleus would emit an electron.
(c) 8.2 MeV; this energy is less than the binding energy of the helium-4 nucleus, so the proton-neutron theory is viable, but the electron-proton theory is not.   **77.** $\Delta m = 6.5 \times 10^{-55}$ kg; $\Delta m/m = 3.9 \times 10^{-28}$

Chapter 29

Multiple-Choice Questions

1. (b) **2.** (d) **3.** (a) **4.** (g) **5.** (d) **6.** (c) **7.** (f) **8.** (c)
9. (d) **10.** (e)

Problems

1. 4.5×10^{28} **3.** 13 km **5.** $^{40}_{19}K$ **7.** 54 **9.** 5.7 fm;
7.7×10^{-43} m^3 **11.** 2.225 MeV **13.** 8.595 28 MeV
15. 8.481 16 MeV/nucleon **17.** 0.112 355 3 u
19. (a) 1.46×10^{-8} u (b) no **21.** $^{40}_{20}Ca$
23. $^{22}_{11}Na + ^{0}_{-1}e \rightarrow ^{22}_{10}Ne + ^{0}_{0}\nu$; $^{22}_{10}Ne$ **25.** 4.8707 MeV
27. β^-; n/p = 1.2 **29.** 1.3111 MeV **31.** 1.820 MeV
33. (a) 10,000 s^{-1} (b) 2.308×10^7 (c) 3.466×10^{-3} s^{-1}
35. 1.2×10^7 Bq **37.** 270 yr **39.** 11,500 yr **41.** 2.4 min
45. 3×10^5 molecules **47.** 10^{-8} Ci **49.** (a) $^{7}_{3}Li$; $^{8}_{3}Li$; $^{8}_{4}Be$
(b) Yes; the emission of an electron (beta-minus decay) is
accompanied by the emission of one antineutrino.
51. $^{27}_{13}Al + ^{4}_{2}He \rightarrow ^{31}_{15}P \rightarrow ^{30}_{15}P + ^{1}_{0}n$ **53.** (a) 2 (b) 200 MeV
(c) 179.947 MeV (d) ≈ 0.000 822 **55.** 200 MeV
57. (a) $^{3}_{2}He$ (b) 5.6 MeV (c) At room temperature, the
kinetic energies of the proton and the deuteron are much too small
to overcome their Coulomb repulsion. **59.** 0.44 MeV
61. (a) 3.34×10^{25} molecules (b) 4.4×10^{-15}
63. 8.111 50 MeV **65.** 3.60×10^{-16} kg **67.** (a) 230 fm
(b) no (c) 26 MeV **69.** 7.67×10^9 yr **71.** 6.050 MeV, 5.763
MeV, 5.618 MeV, 5.598 MeV **73.** 3.25 mol **75.** 1300 A.D.
77. (b) 4.8 fm (c) $\dfrac{14ke^2}{d}$ (d) 1.1917 MeV
79. (a) 136 neutrons; 86 protons (b) 20 alpha particles per second **81.** (a) 1.42×10^7 m/s (b) 4.3×10^6 V/m (c) 98 cm
(d) Both m and q affect the radius of the trajectory.
83. 760 kW·h

Chapter 30

Multiple-Choice Questions

1. (b) **2.** (d) **3.** (a) **4.** (b) **5.** (d) **6.** (b) **7.** (c) **8.** (a)
9. (a) **10.** (b)

Problems

1. 34 MeV **3.** 52.7 MeV **5.** 0.80 GeV **7.** $\pi^+ \rightarrow \mu^+ + \nu_\mu$ and
$\pi^+ \rightarrow e^+ + \nu_e$ **9.** 1.1×10^{-18} m; which is approximately the same
as 1×10^{-17} m in Table 30.3. **11.** $\bar{u}\bar{u}\bar{d}$ **13.** (a) weak
(b) electromagnetic (c) weak **15.** (a) $u\bar{s}$ (b) uss (c) $\bar{s}\bar{s}\bar{s}$
(d) $\bar{u}d$ **17.** 1.2×10^{-18} m **19.** 6 pairs **21.** 4×10^5 revolutions; 2.5×10^6 km **23.** 10^{-12} s

Review and Synthesis: Chapters 26–30

Review Exercises

1. 3.91 m **3.** (a) 4.03×10^8 m/s (b) The disturbance that
moves across the Moon's surface is not an object that has mass,
so there is no violation. **5.** $0.895c = 2.68 \times 10^8$ m/s
7. (a) 9.8×10^5 m/s (b) No electrons are ejected.
(c) Doubling the intensity has no effect on the electron speed,
nor does it cause electrons to be ejected if none were ejected
prior to the doubling of the intensity. **9.** 9.8 cm
11. (a) $^{90}_{38}Sr \rightarrow ^{90}_{39}Y + ^{0}_{-1}e + ^{0}_{0}\bar{\nu}$ (b) 1.0×10^{16} Bq
(c) 3.6×10^5 Bq **13.** proton: 5.5 MeV; pion: 33 MeV
15. (a) 4.7 eV (b) maximum **17.** (a) 1.25×10^9 Bq
(b) an electron and an antineutrino **19.** 0.966c
21. 10^{-4} eV·s/m **23.** six **25.** 4:1 **27.** 0.527 eV

MCAT Review

1. C **2.** A **3.** D **4.** D **5.** C **6.** B **7.** A **8.** D **9.** C
10. B **11.** D **12.** C **13.** A

Credits

Photographs

About the Authors

Photo courtesy of Phil Krasicky, Department of Physics, Cornell University.

Chapter 1

Opener: NASA/JPL/Cornell; p. 2: Royalty-Free/CORBIS; 1.1 (atoms): © Science VU/Visuals Unlimited; 1.1 (child): Photo by Jennifer Merlis; 1.1 (earth): © Vol. 86/PhotoDisc RF; 1.1 (galaxy): © Vol. 56/CORBIS RF; 1.1 (HIV): © Hans Gelderblom/Getty Images; 1.1 (cathedral): © Jonathan Blair/CORBIS; 1.1 (sun): © Vol. 56/CORBIS RF; p. 11: © Vol. 86/PhotoDisc RF; 1.3: © Dr. Don W. Fawcett/Visuals Unlimited.

Chapter 2

Opener: NASA; p. 25: © Franck Seguin/CORBIS; p. 30: Vol. 125/PhotoDisc RF; p. 39: Felicia Martinez/PhotoEdit, Inc.; p. 65: © Vol. 85/CORBIS RF.

Chapter 3

Opener: NHPA Limited; p. 72(top): © Cosmo Condina/Getty Images; p. 72(bottom): Stone/Getty Images; p. 83: © Eye Wire/R-F Website.

Chapter 4

Opener: Courtesy Durango Soaring Club, Inc.; 4.25: © Loren M. Winters/Visuals Unlimited; 4.34: © 1995 Richard Megna, Fundamental Photographs, NYC; p. 141: Stouffer Productions/Animals Animals.

Chapter 5

Opener: AFP/Getty Images; p. 147: © Vol. 29/PhotoDisc RF; 5.14: © Chris Sattlberger/Getty Images; p. 165: © Corbis R-F Website; 5.23: Supplied by Globe Photos; p. 171(left): © Richard T. Nowitz; p. 171 (right): © Matthew Stockman/Allsport/Getty; p. 173: © Angelo Hornak/CORBIS.

Chapter 6

Opener: © Mark Newman/PictureQuest; 6.1: © Owaki-Kulla/CORBIS; 6.2: AP/Wide World Photo; 6.24: USA Archery;

6.32a-c: Dwight Kuhn; p. 210: Brand X Pictures/Getty RF; p. 211: Courtesy Pileco, Inc.; p. 212: U.S. Navy Photo; p. 216: © Free Agents Limited/CORBIS.

Chapter 7

Opener: 911 Pictures; p. 226: © Erica Lansner/Globe Photos; 7.8: © Vol. 56/Corbis RF; 7.11c: © Michael Steele/Allsport/Getty; 7.18: © Loren Winters/Visuals Unlimited; p. 246: Stone/Getty Images.

Chapter 8

Opener: © R.W. Jones/CORBIS; 8.5: AP/Wide World Photos; 8.20: © The Frank Lloyd Wright Foundation; 8.27: © Mike Powell/Allsport/Getty; 8.33: © Michael Newman/PhotoEdit; p. 280: © Kevin Fleming/CORBIS; 8.37a-b: Photography by Leah; p. 292: © Doug Pensinger/Allsport/Getty; p. 301a: © Tony Duffy/Allsport/Getty; p. 301b: © Jonathan Daniel/Allsport/Getty; p. 302: © Michel Hans, Agence Vandystadt, Paris-France/Allsport/Getty.

Chapter 9

Opener: © Corbis RF Website; 9.14: © Susan Van Etten/PhotoEdit; 9.17: © PhotoDisc RF Website; p. 323 (bottom): © Corbis R-F Website; 9.18: Ames Research Center; 9.21: Photo courtesy of Kohler Co.; 9.29: Gary S. Settles/Photo Researchers, Inc.; 9.30: © Dennis Drenner/Visuals Unlimited.

Chapter 10

Opener: © Hubert Stadler/CORBIS; 10.1: © Amoz Eckerson/Visuals Unlimited; 10.5: Brian Hall; p. 355(top): Greater Houston Convention and Visitors Bureau; p. 355(bottom): © John Springer/CORBIS; 10.9a: © Doug Pensinger/Getty Images; 10.9b: © SIU/Visuals Unlimited; 10.16: © Vol. 54/PhotoDisc RF; 10.28a-b: © Bettmann/CORBIS; p. 375: © Ray Malace Photo; p. 376: © Wolfgang Kaehler/CORBIS.

Chapter 11

Opener: AP/Wide World Photo; p 386: © David Young-Wolff/PhotoEdit;

11.6a-b: © Loren M. Winters/Visuals Unlimited.

Chapter 12

Opener: Alan Giambattista; p. 420: © Brian E. Small/www.briansmallphoto.com; p. 424: U.S. Navy photo by Ensign John Gay; 12.4: Image courtesy of Berghaus Organ Company; 12.6(both): © PhotoDisc/Getty RF; p. 428(top): © Loren M. Winters/Visuals Unlimited; p. 428(bottom): Stephen Dalton/Photo Researchers, Inc.; 12.19: AP/Wide World Photos; p. 430: (Alex James of blur), photo by author R. C. Richardson.

Chapter 13

Opener: Stone/Getty Images; 13.5: © John Sohlden/Visuals Unlimited; p. 465: Geoff Tompkinson/Photo Researchers, Inc.; 13.15a: © Joe McDonald/CORBIS; 13.15b: © Craig Lovell/CORBIS; 13.15c: © Ken Kaminesky/CORBIS.

Chapter 14

Opener: AP/Wide World Photos; 14.6: Photo by author R. C. Richardson; 14.18: © Montrose/Custom Medical Stock.

Chapter 15

Opener: © David Davis/Index Stock Imagery/PictureQuest.

Chapter 16

Opener: Image courtesy Massashi Kawasaki, University of Virginia; 16.2: © The McGraw-Hill Companies, Inc./Joe Franek, photographer; 16.3: © Tony Freeman/PhotoEdit; 16.34: Paul McMahn.

Chapter 17

Opener: © Lester Lefkowitz/CORBIS; 17.13: © Roger Ressmeyer/CORBIS; 17.15: © Melanie Brown/Photo Edit; 17.22: © Loren M. Winters/Visuals Unlimited; 17.24: © Tom Pantages; 17.30: © Dan Robinson, WVlighting.com; 17.34: Adam Hart-Davis/Photo Researchers, Inc.

Chapter 18

Opener: © Chuck Swartzell/Visuals Unlimited; 18.4: © Tom McHugh/Photo

Researchers, Inc.; 18.6: © Richard Megna/Fundamental Photographs, NYC; 18.7a: © The McGraw-Hill Companies, Inc./Joe Franek, photographer; 18.11: Photo courtesy of IBM Corporation; 18.12: © Tony Freeman/Photo Edit, Inc.; 18.39: © Tom Pantages.

Chapter 19

Opener: Image courtesy Hjatollah Vali, McGill University; p. 688: Photo by Stan Sherer; 19.1: Cordelia Molloy/Photo Researchers, Inc.; 19.2: © The McGraw-Hill Companies, Inc./Joe Franek, photographer; 19.15a: © CERN Geneva; 19.18: IBA Proton Therapy Cyclotron; 19.34a: © Richard Megna/Fundamental Photographs, NYC; 19.34b: © Loren Winters/Visuals Unlimited; 19.39a: © The McGraw-Hill Companies, Inc./Joe Franek, photographer; 19.44: © Tom Pantages; p. 732: Richard Paselk, Robert A. Paselk Scientific Instrument Museum.

Chapter 20

Opener: © The Picture Source/Terry Oakley; p. 737: U.S. Army Corps of Engineers; 20.16: Dr. Scriba/SPL/Custom Medical Stock; 20.24: © Mark Antman/The Image Works; 20.25: © Tom Pantages; 20.30: © The Image Works Archives.

Chapter 21

Opener: Alan Giambattista; 21.15: © Loren Winters/Visuals Unlimited; 21.17b: © The Image Works Archives.

Chapter 22

Opener: © George D. Lepp/CORBIS; 22.9a: © Dan McCoy/DoctorStock.com; 22.9b: © Richard Lowenberg/Photo Researchers, Inc.; 22.10a-b: © Charles Mazel; 22.14: © Anglo-Australian Observatory. Photograph by David Malin; 22.15: © D. Parker/Photo Researchers, Inc.; 22.17: © Inga Spence/Visuals Unlimited; 22.28a-b: Timothy Edberg; 22.29: Digital Image © 1996 CORBIS; 22.32: Image courtesy Lewis Ling, Carleton University.

Chapter 23

Opener: © Bettmann/CORBIS; 23.1: © 1998 Jeff J. Daly/Fundamental

Photographs; 23.3: © Thinkstock/Getty RF; 23.12a-b: © The Picture Source/Terry Oakley; 23.13a: © Peter Turner/Getty Images; 23.14a: © Pekka Parviainen/Polar Image; 23.22b: © Yoav Levy/Phototake; 23.29: © Tom Pantages; 23.33: © Paul A. Souders/CORBIS; 23.36a: © Felicia Martinez/PhotoEdit, Inc.; p. 864: © RDF/Visuals Unlimited.

Chapter 24

Opener: NASA; 24.6b: © Bettmann/CORBIS; 24.18: © Roger Ressmeyer/CORBIS; 24.20a-c: NASA, H. Ford (JHU), G. Illingworth (USCS/LO), M. Clampin (STScI), G. Hartig (STScI), the ACS Science Team, and ESA; 24.21: Courtesy of NAIC, Cornell University.

Chapter 25

Opener: © Kevin Schafer/Getty Images; 25.8: © The Picture Source/Terry Oakley; 25.13a-b: © The Picture Source/Terry Oakley; 25.14c: Tom Pantages; 25.15: © The Picture Source/Terry Oakley; 25.18a: © The Picture Source/Terry Oakley; 25.20: © 1986 Richard Megna/Fundamental Photographs; 25.23b: Alan Giambattista; 25.26: © Tom Pantages; 25.28a-c: © The Picture Source/Terry Oakley; 25.30a: © 1987 Ken Kay/Fundamental Photographs, NYC; 25.30b: © The Picture Source/Terry Oakley; 25.31a, 25.35: © Tom Pantages; 25.36a: David Malin; 25.36b: Dirk Panczyk; 25.39a-b: Erich Lessing/Art Resource, NY; 25.40b: © Education Development Center, Inc.; 25.42: Science Source/Photo Researchers, Inc.; 25.45(both): © Holographics North Inc.

Chapter 26

Opener: Map of the core and jet of the radio galaxy NGC6251 at 1.4GHz made by P.N. Werner, M. Birkinshaw & D.M. Worrall using the NRAO Very Large Array; p. 957: © Hulton-Deutsch Collection/CORBIS.

Chapter 27

Opener: © Spender Grant/PhotoEdit; 27.7: © Richard T. Nowitz/CORBIS; 27.12b:

© W. Cody/CORBIS; 27.13a-d: Don Klipstein; 27.22a-b: © Charles Mazel.

Chapter 28

Opener: © CNRI/Phototake; 28.4a-b: Education Development Center, Inc.; 28.6b: © Dennis Kunkel/Phototake; 28.6c: © Dennis Kunkel/Phototake; 28.14: Courtesy IBM Research, Almaden Research Center. Unauthorized use not permitted; 28.26: © Yoav Levy/Phototake.

Chapter 29

Opener: © Geoffrey Clements/CORBIS; 29.10b: Vesper V. Grantham & Lindsay Huckabaa, University of Oklahoma Health Sciences Center; 29.11b: Image courtesy Elekta Instruments, Inc.; 29.17: Reuters/Getty Images.

Chapter 30

Opener: © CERN Geneva; p. 1091: Kamioka Observatory, ICRR (Institute for Cosmic Ray Research), The University of Tokyo.

Text

Some examples and problems adapted from Alan H. Cromer, *Physics for the Life Sciences.* Copyright © 1977 by the McGraw-Hill Companies, Inc., New York. All rights reserved. Reprinted by permission of Alan H. Cromer.

Some examples and problems adapted from Alan H. Cromer, Study Guide for *Physics for the Life Sciences.* Copyright © 1977 by the McGraw-Hill Companies, Inc., New York. All rights reserved. Reprinted by permission of Alan H. Cromer.

Some examples and problems adapted from Alan H. Cromer, *Physics for the Life Sciences,* 2d. ed. Copyright © 1994 by the McGraw-Hill Companies, Inc. Primis Custom Publishing, Dubuque, Iowa. All rights reserved. Reprinted by permission of Alan H. Cromer.

Chapter 28, p. 1016: Quote by Richard Feynman from Richard Phillips Feynman, *The Character of Physical Law*; introduction by James Gleick. Copyright © 1994 by Modern Library, New York. All rights reserved. Reprinted by permission of MIT Press.

Index

UNIT CONVERSIONS

Length

1 in = 2.540 cm

1 cm = 0.3937 in

1 ft = 30.48 cm

1 m = 39.37 in = 3.281 ft

1 mi = 5280 ft = 1.609 km

1 km = 0.6214 mi

1 light-year (ly) = 9.461×10^{15} m

Time

1 y = 365.24 d = 3.156×10^7 s

1 d = 24 h = 1440 min = 8.640×10^4 s

Speed

1 mi/h = 1.467 ft/s

       = 1.609 km/h = 0.4470 m/s

1 km/h = 0.2778 m/s

       = 0.6214 mi/h = 0.9113 ft/s

1 ft/s = 0.3048 m/s = 0.6818 mi/h

1 m/s = 3.281 ft/s = 3.600 km/h = 2.237 mi/h

Volume

1 liter (L) = 1000 cm^3 = 10^{-3} m^3

1 cm^3 = 0.06102 in^3 = 1 mL = 1×10^{-6} m^3

1 m^3 = 1×10^6 cm^3 = 35.31 ft^3

1 gal = 3.785 L

Mass

1 kg = 1000 g

1 mass unit (u) = 1.6605×10^{-27} kg

    [1 kg weighs 2.20 lb where g = 9.80 m/s^2]

Force

1 N = 0.2248 lb

1 lb = 4.448 N

Energy

1 J = 0.7376 ft·lb = 6.242×10^{18} eV

1 ft·lb = 1.356 J

1 cal = 4.186 J

1 Btu = 1055 J

1 kW·h = 3.600 MJ

1 eV = 1.602×10^{-19} J

Mass-Energy Equivalents

1 u = 931.494 MeV/c^2

     = 1.492×10^{-10} J/c^2

Power

1 W = 1 J/s

1 hp = 550 ft·lb/s = 745.7 W

1 Btu/h = 0.2931 W

Pressure

1 Pa = 1 N/m^2 = 1.450×10^{-4} lb/in^2

1 atm = 0.1013 MPa = 14.70 lb/in^2

1 lb/in^2 = 6.895×10^3 Pa

1 mm Hg = 1.333×10^2 Pa

1 in Hg = 3.386×10^3 Pa

Angle

1 rad = 57.30°

1° = 0.01745 rad

360° = 2π rad

1 rad/s = 9.549 rpm

1 rpm = 0.1047 rad/s

SI PREFIXES

Power	Prefix	Symbol
10^{12}	tera	T
10^9	giga	G
10^6	mega	M
10^3	kilo	k
10^{-1}	deci	d
10^{-2}	centi	c
10^{-3}	milli	m
10^{-6}	micro	μ
10^{-9}	nano	n
10^{-12}	pico	p
10^{-15}	femto	f

SI DERIVED UNITS

Quantity	Units		Equivalents	
Force	newton	N	J/m	$kg·m/s^2$
Energy	joule	J	N·m	$kg·m^2/s^2$
Power	watt	W	J/s	$kg·m^2/s^3$
Pressure	pascal	Pa	N/m^2	$kg/(m·s^2)$
Frequency	hertz	Hz	cycle/s	s^{-1}
Electric charge	coulomb	C		A·s
Electric potential	volt	V	J/C	$kg·m^2/(A·s^3)$
Electric resistance	ohm	Ω	V/A	$kg·m^2/(A^2·s^3)$
Capacitance	farad	F	C/V	$A^2·s^4/(kg·m^2)$
Magnetic field	tesla	T	N·s/(C·m)	$kg/(A·s^2)$
Magnetic flux	weber	Wb	$T·m^2$	$kg·m^2/(A·s^2)$
Inductance	henry	H	V·s/A	$kg·m^2/(A^2·s^2)$

PHYSICAL CONSTANTS

Quantity	Symbol	Value
Universal gravitational constant	G	6.674×10^{-11} m^3/(kg·s^2)
Speed of light in vacuum	c	2.998×10^8 m/s
Elementary charge	e	1.602×10^{-19} C
Planck's constant	h	6.626×10^{-34} J·s
		4.136×10^{-15} eV·s
	$\hbar = h/(2\pi)$	1.055×10^{-34} J·s
		6.582×10^{-16} eV·s
Universal gas constant	R	8.314 J/(mol·K)
Avogadro's number	N_A	6.022×10^{23} mol^{-1}
Boltzmann constant	k_B	1.381×10^{-23} J/K
		8.617×10^{-5} eV/K
Coulomb force constant	$k = 1/(4\pi\epsilon_0)$	8.988×10^9 N·m^2/C^2
Permittivity of free space (electric constant)	ϵ_0	8.854×10^{-12} C^2/(N·m^2)
Permeability of free space (magnetic constant)	μ_0	$4\pi \times 10^{-7}$ T·m/A
Electron mass	m_e	9.109×10^{-31} kg
		$0.000\ 548\ 580$ u
Electron rest energy	$m_e c^2$	0.5110 MeV
Proton mass	m_p	1.673×10^{-27} kg
		$1.007\ 276\ 5$ u
Proton rest energy	$m_p c^2$	938.272 MeV
Neutron mass	m_n	1.675×10^{-27} kg
		$1.008\ 664\ 9$ u
Neutron rest energy	$m_n c^2$	939.565 MeV
Compton wavelength of electron	λ_C	2.426×10^{-12} m
Stefan-Boltzmann constant	σ	5.670×10^{-8} W/(m^2·K^4)
Rydberg constant	R	1.097×10^7 m^{-1}
Bohr radius of hydrogen atom	a_0	5.292×10^{-11} m
Ionization energy of hydrogen atom	$-E_1$	13.61 eV

USEFUL PHYSICAL DATA

Standard temperature (*T* of STP)		0°C = 273.15 K
Standard pressure (*P* of STP)		1 atm = 101.325 kPa
Water		
Density (4°C)	ρ_w	1.000×10^3 kg/m³
Heat of fusion	L_f	333.7 kJ/kg
Heat of vaporization	L_v	2256 kJ/kg
Specific heat capacity	*c*	4.186 kJ/(kg·K)
Index of refraction	n_w	1.33
Speed of sound in air (20°C, 1 atm)		343 m/s
Speed of sound in air (at STP)		331 m/s
Density of dry air (at STP)		1.29 kg/m³
Molar mass of air		28.98 g/mol
Molar volume of ideal gas (at STP)		2.241×10^{-2} m³/mol

THE GREEK ALPHABET

Alpha	A	α	Nu	N	ν
Beta	B	β	Xi	Ξ	ξ
Gamma	Γ	γ	Omicron	O	o
Delta	Δ	δ	Pi	Π	π
Epsilon	E	ϵ	Rho	P	ρ
Zeta	Z	ζ	Sigma	Σ	σ
Eta	H	η	Tau	T	τ
Theta	Θ	θ	Upsilon	Y	υ
Iota	I	ι	Phi	Φ	ϕ
Kappa	K	κ	Chi	X	χ
Lambda	Λ	λ	Psi	Ψ	ψ
Mu	M	μ	Omega	Ω	ω

ASTROPHYSICAL DATA

	Earth	Moon	Sun
Mass	5.974×10^{24} kg	7.349×10^{22} kg	1.987×10^{30} kg
Mean radius	6.371×10^6 m	1.737×10^6 m	6.96×10^8 m
Mean density	5.515×10^3 kg/m³	3.350×10^3 kg/m³	1.41×10^3 kg/m³
Orbital period	365.24 d	27.3 d	
Period of rotation	23.9345 h	27.3 d	about 26 d
Surface temperature	288 K	125 K – 375 K	5800 K
Surface gravitational field	9.80 N/kg	1.62 N/kg	274 N/kg
Mean distance from Earth		3.845×10^8 m	1.50×10^{11} m

MATHEMATICAL REVIEW

Area of a circle of radius *r*	$A = \pi r^2$
Circumference of a circle	$C = 2\pi r$
Surface area of a sphere	$A = 4\pi r^2$
Volume of a sphere	$V = \frac{4}{3}\pi r^3$
Area of a triangle	$A = \frac{1}{2}bh$

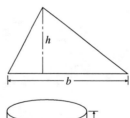

Surface area of right circular cylinder of radius *r* and height *h*	$A = 2\pi rh + 2\pi r^2$
Volume of the same cylinder	$V = \pi r^2 h$

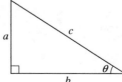

Pythagorean theorem	$c^2 = a^2 + b^2$
Trigonometric relations	$\sin\theta = a/c$
	$\cos\theta = b/c$
	$\tan\theta = \dfrac{a}{b} = \dfrac{\sin\theta}{\cos\theta}$

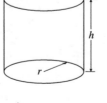

Quadratic equation

If $ax^2 + bx + c = 0$, $x = \dfrac{-b \pm \sqrt{b^2 - 4ac}}{2a}$

Need more help with your math? Go to www.aleks.com for individualized, specific math help on just those math areas you need to get through your physics course!

MAIN-GROUP ELEMENTS

MAIN-GROUP ELEMENTS

TRANSITION ELEMENTS

INNER TRANSITION ELEMENTS

Period

Key:
1 — Atomic number
H — Symbol
1.00794 — Atomic mass

Numbers in parentheses ( ) are for longest lived isotopes of elements without stable isotopes.

Legend:
- Metals (main-group)
- Metals (transition)
- Metals (inner transition)
- Metalloids
- Nonmetals

Period	1A (1)	2A (2)	3B (3)	4B (4)	5B (5)	6B (6)	7B (7)	8B (8)	8B (9)	8B (10)	1B (11)	2B (12)	3A (13)	4A (14)	5A (15)	6A (16)	7A (17)	8A (18)
1	1 H 1.00794																	2 He 4.00260
2	3 Li 6.941	4 Be 9.01218											5 B 10.811	6 C 12.011	7 N 14.00674	8 O 15.9994	9 F 18.99840	10 Ne 20.1797
3	11 Na 22.98977	12 Mg 24.3050											13 Al 26.98154	14 Si 28.0855	15 P 30.97276	16 S 32.066	17 Cl 35.4527	18 Ar 39.948
4	19 K 39.0983	20 Ca 40.078	21 Sc 44.95591	22 Ti 47.867	23 V 50.9415	24 Cr 51.9961	25 Mn 54.93805	26 Fe 55.845	27 Co 58.93320	28 Ni 58.6934	29 Cu 63.546	30 Zn 65.409	31 Ga 69.723	32 Ge 72.61	33 As 74.92159	34 Se 78.96	35 Br 79.904	36 Kr 83.798
5	37 Rb 85.4678	38 Sr 87.62	39 Y 88.90585	40 Zr 91.224	41 Nb 92.90638	42 Mo 95.94	43 Tc (98)	44 Ru 101.07	45 Rh 102.90550	46 Pd 106.42	47 Ag 107.8682	48 Cd 112.411	49 In 114.8	50 Sn 118.710	51 Sb 121.75	52 Te 127.60	53 I 126.90447	54 Xe 131.29
6	55 Cs 132.90543	56 Ba 137.327	57 La 138.9055	72 Hf 178.49	73 Ta 180.9479	74 W 183.84	75 Re 186.207	76 Os 190.23	77 Ir 192.217	78 Pt 195.08	79 Au 196.96654	80 Hg 200.59	81 Tl 204.3833	82 Pb 207.2	83 Bi 208.98037	84 Po (209)	85 At (210)	86 Rn (222)
7	87 Fr (223)	88 Ra (226)	89 Ac 227.0278	104 Rf (261)	105 Db (262)	106 Sg (266)	107 Bh (264)	108 Hs (277)	109 Mt (268)	110 Ds (269)	111 Rg (272)	112 (285)	114 (289)					

Rare Earths (Lanthanides), Period 6:

58 Ce 140.116	59 Pr 140.90765	60 Nd 144.24	61 Pm (147)	62 Sm 150.36	63 Eu 151.965	64 Gd 157.25	65 Tb 158.92534	66 Dy 162.50	67 Ho 164.93032	68 Er 167.26	69 Tm 168.93421	70 Yb 173.04	71 Lu 174.967

Actinides, Period 7:

90 Th 232.0381	91 Pa 231.035	92 U 238.0289	93 Np (237)	94 Pu (244)	95 Am (243)	96 Cm (247)	97 Bk (247)	98 Cf (251)	99 Es (252)	100 Fm (257)	101 Md (258)	102 No (259)	103 Lr (262)